THE TECHNICAL ARTS AND SCIENCES OF THE ANCIENTS

THE TECHNICAL ARTS AND SCIENCES OF THE ANCIENTS

BY

ALBERT NEUBURGER

TRANSLATED BY

HENRY L. BROSE
M.A., D.Phil. (Oxon.), F.Inst.P.

WITH 676 ILLUSTRATIONS

BARNES & NOBLE, Inc.
New York

METHUEN & CO. Ltd
London

Originally published in German under the title
"Die Technik des Altertums"

This Translation first published in 1930

Reprinted, 1969
by
Barnes & Noble, Inc., New York
and
Methuen & Co. Ltd, London

Printed in the United States of America

TRANSLATOR'S PREFACE

THE author of the present work, Dr. Albert Neuburger, was occupied for over twenty years in collecting and sifting the facts which he considered necessary for an adequate survey of the manifold technical activities of the ancients. His lively interest in antiquity and his scientific training qualified him admirably for this exacting and painstaking task. The welcome with which the book was received in its original German edition is a sufficient indication of the success which has rewarded his labours.

The translator has endeavoured to interpret the sense of the German original as closely as possible without sacrificing freedom of expression. Many of the technical terms that occur have not yet found their way into German-English dictionaries, and so the help of colleagues has been enlisted, wherever possible, to find the nearest equivalents. It is hoped that there will be but few errors in this respect.

It has not been considered necessary to follow the German edition by adding at the end of each section a detailed list of the literature dealing with the particular subject under consideration, as most of these references are to German books or periodicals. Those readers who wish to pursue the facts to their sources are referred to the German edition, which contains a very extensive bibliography.

The title of the German original is *Die Technik des Altertums*. In view of the wide range of subjects under review it seemed impossible to express this in English otherwise than by *The Technical Arts and Sciences of the Ancients*. Our word 'science' seems less open to objection, as applied to the present volume, than the German word 'Wissenschaft,' which etymologically signifies 'formed' knowledge (*gestaltetes Wissen*); the knowledge of the ancients consisted largely of disconnected facts which had not been amalgamated by theory. The high standard reached by the ancients in at least some technical branches is shown strikingly by the fact that only a short while ago it was admitted at a meeting of the Iron and Steel Institute at Birmingham that in spite of modern scientific progress the metal of the 1600-year-old pillar at Delhi (Kutub) was still superior to anything we could produce to-day; it was freer from inclusions even than Swedish charcoal iron. The recent discovery of elastic glass by two Viennese professors was regarded as a triumph of research, yet a similar substance seems to have been known many centuries ago. But although isolated facts of this kind come to the notice of the scientist or layman from time to time, few people realize the immense field that has been explored by the ancients. Books dealing with special subjects have appeared at intervals, for example *Manufacturing Arts in Ancient Times* (with special reference to Bible History) by James Napier (Paisley, 1879), but no complete treatise has appeared. It is therefore felt that the present volume will supply a much-felt want and will also be of use to those who are no longer compelled or have no longer the opportunity to study the ancient classical languages as a compulsory subject. It will be a positive gain if the achievements recorded in these pages will lead to a true appreciation of the genius of the ancients which no training in the elements of Latin and Greek seems to have been able to inculcate.

The work of Vitruvius shows what an amount of varied knowledge, ingeniously applied, was at the command of students of the mechanical arts in his day (the beginning of the Christian era). His style of writing is often obscure and has caused translators and commentators great difficulty. His ten books on architecture (*De Architectura Libri Decem*) deal with many subjects and are dedicated to the Emperor Augustus, whose sister Octavia procured for him a pension in his old age. These books were lost for a long time, but came to light again at St. Gall in the fifteenth century. During the time of the revival of classical learning Vitruvius' treatise was regarded as the most valuable work of reference for architects ; through Michael Angelo and others his ideas ultimately exerted an influence on the architecture of most European countries.

A great drawback to forming a true estimate of the actual knowledge acquired by the ancients is that in all probability the most important of the technical writers of antiquity have not come down to us at all. Ernst Mach (in the introduction to his *Mechanik*) quotes a passage from Vitruvius (v, 3, 6) in which he indicates in rough outline and by analogy a wave-theory of sound. This leads Mach to suggest that these remarks of Vitruvius are rather those of a popular writer on a subject which has perhaps been more carefully expounded in works now no longer in existence, and he points out that if the popular writings of the present day were the only source of information of our activities to generations a thousand years hence, our state of knowledge would present an aspect no less strange and misleading. Other writers of less technical ability than Vitruvius have given far more inaccurate and uncritical reports of discoveries. The chief and most notorious offender in this respect is Pliny, who, moreover, was not above pirating the writings of others. There are actually passages in Pliny that tally almost word for word with Vitruvius, but nowhere is an acknowledgment of the source to be found. Fanciful reports of discoveries in those days are, as Mach comments, no worse than the picturesque tales of Newton's apple or Watts' kettle.

Up till recently there was a popular delusion that the Greeks, in particular, had neglected experiment entirely. Evidence to the contrary is given by Pythagoras' use of the sonometer with its movable bridge for detecting the ratio of the lengths of similar vibrating strings when in harmony ; also by Ptolemy's systematic experiments on the refraction of light and Aristotle's observations bearing on the explanation of the rainbow. The real lack in ancient technical knowledge, apart from astronomy, appears to have been the absence of mathematical treatment. Calculation alone could lead to systematic development and could weave the isolated facts into the fabric of a science. Indeed, recent advances in physics seem to be bringing us back from the opposite direction, as it were, to a form of the ancient theory, due chiefly to Pythagoras, that number is the essence of reality. The German physicist, Planck, defines real quantities as only those which are measurable ; this same definition is at the basis of Einstein's theory of relativity. The most recent theory of the atom (founded on Schrödinger's wave-mechanics) seems to push this abstraction even a stage further.

Unless otherwise stated the translations of the passages quoted from Vitruvius are from the English edition by Morgan (Harvard University Press, 1914). I am indebted to Professor F. S. Granger, Vice-Principal of University College, Nottingham, for many useful suggestions. A new translation of Vitruvius' treatise on architecture is being prepared by Professor Granger for the Loeb Classical Library, to other volumes of which frequent acknowledgments are made in the present book.

I also wish to express my thanks to one of my colleagues, Dr. W. Schweizer, for assisting me in finding the equivalents of many technical terms and for collaborating in the translation of the second and third quarters of this book.

HENRY L. BROSE.

July, 1929.
UNIVERSITY COLLEGE,
NOTTINGHAM.

FROM THE AUTHOR'S PREFACE

ALTHOUGH the study of antiquity has been pursued with great intensity and devotion since the time of the Renaissance and the great Humanists, one of its most important branches, the technical arts and sciences, has received rather scant attention. It is only fairly recently that the beginnings of this field of human activity have been studied with increasing care. This has caused a world of wonders in the truest sense of the word to be revealed to us and has given us deep glimpses of the advanced knowledge and extraordinary technique of bygone peoples.

The reason for this long delay in investigating and appreciating their achievements in this direction was due to diverse circumstances. When the great Humanists of the fifteenth century directed the attention of people anew to antiquity, and in particular to that epoch of time which is nowadays briefly called ' classical antiquity ', it was first of all the beauty of language and the beauty of works of art which gripped the imagination. The glimpses of technical ability which presented themselves in passing exerted no attraction. The ' technical age ' had not yet dawned, the mental sciences alone held sway. But even at that time it was the great technical inventors of the Renaissance Period who first became aware of the remarkable technical accomplishments of the ancients and who eagerly studied them and sought to apply them to their own purposes. In particular, architects found many suggestions in the books of Vitruvius. Werner [1] has tried to prove that the technical science of Leonardo da Vinci, the greatest inventor of the Renaissance, was founded on an exhaustive study of the works of learned Arabian and other ancient writers.

But there was another circumstance that contributed to the delay in making ancient technical science generally accessible. Those who were occupied with this task were often insufficiently versed in languages or had no opportunity of penetrating deeply into the philological side of ancient technical expressions. The philologists, on the other hand, who possessed this equipment, had no adequate technical training for treating this great field of knowledge competently. And so the meanings of many technical expressions (for example ' aes,' ' nitrum,' ' byssos ') have only recently been made fully clear. There are, of course, exceptions among these two groups of researchers ; we need refer only to scientists like Diergart, and to philologists like Blümner and Reber, but

[1] Werner, *Zur Physik da Vincis.* Berlin.

their meritorious labours were far from sufficient to cover the whole field thoroughly.

Only in the last few years, owing to the combined efforts of many scholars and to the fact that scientists had at last acquired a taste for historical research in their subjects, has it become possible to gain a comprehensive and detailed survey of what had been achieved by the ancients in this field. But the works of these writers are scattered far and wide through journals and have been published at different times. Whereas one investigator, for example Le Chatelier, has chiefly occupied himself with ancient ceramic art, another, Kassner, has dealt with ancient inks, whereas a third, Berger, has specialized in ancient painting in wax, and so forth. This circumstance alone made it appear desirable to gather together these scattered facts so that as wide a perspective as possible would be obtained of the whole range of ancient technical knowledge. . . . .

The author hopes that he may have been successful in building up out of his own reading and experience a work which will serve as a foundation for further investigations on the part of scholars and scientists. At the same time he trusts that it will inspire in the general reader a thirst for further knowledge of these great achievements, characterized by such beauty in their details. . . .

In general we take as the beginning of antiquity a time not definitely specified, which differs for different peoples and denotes roughly the time at which these peoples appear in history up to about the last part of the fifth century A.D., when the downfall of the Western Roman Empire was being accompanied by great changes of religion and civilization; this period was characterized chiefly by the founding of Christian States and the stormy events due to the migration of races. This rough definition of antiquity applies equally well to the age of technical discovery among the ancients. . . .

The author expresses his warm thanks to all those who either as individuals, whether scientists or archaeologists, or as committees of museums, or as owners of private collections lent their kind assistance during the long years when the present work was being prepared.

ALBERT NEUBURGER.

BERLIN.

CONTENTS

LIST OF ILLUSTRATIONS

BOOKS OF WHICH FREQUENT USE HAS BEEN MADE

Baumeister : *Denkmäler des klassischen Altertums zum Erläuterung des hebens der Griechen und Römer in Religion.* Kunst und Sitte. Munich and Leipzig, 1885–1888.

Blümner : *Technologie und Terminologie der Gewerbe und Künste bei Griechen und Römern.* Berlin and Leipzig, 1912.

Curtius : *Griechische Geschichte.* Berlin, 1857–1861.

Davemberg and Saglio : *Dictionnaire des antiquitées Grecques et Romaines.* Paris, 1877–1917.

Forrer : *Reallexikon der prähistorischen, klassischen und frühchristlichen Altertümer.* Berlin and Stuttgart, 1908.

Friedländer : *Darstellungen aus dar Sittengeschichte Roms.* Leipzig, 1888–1890.

Herodotus : *Histories.* Translation by Lange. Leipzig.

Hero of Alexandria : Greek and German edition of his works, edited by Wilhelm Schmidt. Leipzig, 1899.

Hoops : *Reallexikon der germanischen Altertums kunde.* Strassburg. From 1911 onwards.

Mommsen : *Römische Geschichte.* Berlin, 1903.

Pauly-Wissowa : *Realenzyklopädie der klassischen Altertums-wissenschaften.* Stuttgart, from 1894 onwards.

Pliny : *Natural History.* Translated and commented on by Ph. C. Külb. Stuttgart, 1840.

Tacitus : *Die Germania des Cornelius Tacitus.* Translated from the Latin with an Introduction and explanatory notes by Max Oberbreyer. Leipzig.

Vitruvius : *Des Vitruvius zehn Büchen über die Architektur.* Stuttgart, 1865.

INTRODUCTION

THE present has often been called the age of technical science. This statement unintentionally suggests that it has been reserved for our times to create the technical sciences and to develop them to a high standard, and that they did not exist in the remoter past. This idea is entirely erroneous. In reality technical science has existed throughout the ages from the very beginnings of the human race. That of the present differs from that of the past chiefly in making use of certain natural forces, above all steam-power and electricity, to an extent never before thought possible, with the result that some branches of our civilization have assumed entirely new forms. This is most strikingly exemplified in our means of locomotion.

It is therefore wrong to speak of a particular 'Age of Technical Science.' We must rather regard technical science as an expression of the human mind, that has its root in the nature of things and has from time immemorial been inspired by Man's very existence. Like all expressions of the human spirit, however, technical science, which may be defined as the unceasing struggle of man with matter, has its periods of ebb and flow. These periods exhibit immense differences. If we review them in succession we observe two great flood-tides: the present time and antiquity.

The technical science of antiquity differs from that of the present chiefly in having, by methods much simpler than those which would now be available, achieved results which are in some ways so remarkable that they have not since been surpassed. In making full use of steam and electricity and of the other sources of power which have become known to us in the course of time our technical science has developed more broadly, whereas on the other hand that of the ancients certainly penetrated more deeply. The much more limited knowledge of that time was exploited to the utmost. Simple means were used for hundreds or even thousands of years without in many cases being essentially improved, but so ingeniously and efficiently as often to astonish us.

Compared, however, with the technical science of later periods, and in particular of that of the Middle Ages, the technical science of antiquity differs widely in several respects. Throughout the Middle Ages and for some centuries subsequently, it commonly suffered stagnation in consequence of being restricted within the narrow limits and regulations imposed by the system of guilds which rigorously prescribed the hours of work; the number of qualified workmen, the types of raw material to be used, as well as the shape and size of all the means involved. All free development, all attempts to overstep these bounds, were vigorously suppressed and heavily punished. The efforts of the Middle Ages produced good results, but these results were always achieved by generation after generation working unwaveringly along perfectly definite lines within close limits, freedom of artistic expression alone being permitted. In antiquity the conditions were different. In this case, too, there were guilds and for long periods of time the same purpose was pursued with the same means, but otherwise no obstacles were placed in the way of free development. Genius was given a fre^ rein. It received intelligent encouragement on all sides, in particular from the state authorities—a condition of things which was not repeated until the end of the Middle Ages and then only in isolated instances and at a time, namely the Renaissance, which was characterized by having its roots in antiquity. But even in this case the complete freedom of former times was never fully attained. For whoever dared to advance too far, whose spirit even in the realm of technical science soared too far beyond the traditional limits, could not always be shielded by the most powerful of patrons from being led before the tribunal of the Inquisition and from having to submit to whatever consequences ensued.

We thus see in ancient technical science a period of development which is definitely characterized by great results achieved with comparatively simple means, and by unrestrained growth in almost every direction. These simple means refer not only to the machines used, but above all to the scientific basis on which technical life was founded. What has been accomplished technically by the ancients is in many instances so surprising and extraordinary that one often hears the opinion that the ancients must have possessed knowledge that has since become lost to us ; they must have been familiar with properties, particularly of a physical nature, of which we have not the faintest idea. In some cases this opinion is not to be entirely ignored, but no cogent proof of its correctness have ever been adduced. As has already been mentioned, the technical science of antiquity excels in depth of penetration rather than in extensiveness. The astronomical, mathematical and physical knowledge then available was exploited to the fullest extent. It was applied practically in every way possible at that time. It may be that the knowledge of some particular substance or plant which the ancients used for a special technical purpose, such as for painting or embalming, has not been handed down to posterity ; nevertheless we are fairly well informed generally about the extent and details of their knowledge. It is not then this knowledge itself that excites our admiration so much as the systematic and deliberate manner in which they applied it ; with a comparatively meagre equipment they often accomplished as much as—indeed, sometimes even more than—we who have at our disposal such wide knowledge in the most diverse fields. Among the factors utilized to the utmost was human labour and the time-element, to which little value was attached at that period. We shall refer to these two points frequently in the sequel.

In antiquity, just as in modern times, it was left to a few pre-eminent minds to open up new avenues in technical science, apart from the high-road of gradually accumulated knowledge. The names of these pioneers have mostly sunk into oblivion; only a few have survived the passage of time. But one fact emerges from what has been passed down to us: the technical worker of antiquity had a much higher prestige than in later times until quite recently, notwithstanding our pride in this so-called technical age and its wonderful achievements. If the technical scientist nowadays occupies the position to which his general education, knowledge and achievements entitle him, we must not forget that it has been won only after a hard and prolonged struggle, and that even now there are representatives of other branches of knowledge who deny him full standing. In antiquity, however, the technical expert was a much sought after person who enjoyed the greatest respect. It may even be conjectured that among some races there were certain relationships between such experts and the priests, who held supreme rank. The form of some ancient constructions still bears witness to the high honour in which the technical worker was held in antiquity. In the ancient Roman Empire, indeed, there was hardly a bridge that was not crowned by a sort of triumphal arch in honour of the builder. The mightiest rulers of the world drew the technical scientist into their service and in some cases gave him a particularly high position. Very often, too, provision was made for the special training of expert workers. Technical officials were appointed for the State as well as for the towns, and some armies had even a special corps for engineers.

The influence of technical science in the State was far-reaching in antiquity, and there are numerous indications that the ancients were fully aware of its importance. The State's existence could be maintained only with the help of the arts and crafts; they alone could assure the prosperity that was the basis of its existence. In almost all the ancient empires technical experts checked the overflowing of the rivers and in this way rescued large tracts of land from destruction. In many cases they knew how to drain marshy country and convert it into fruitful land, and to convert sandy deserts into flourishing cornfields by a well-built system of irrigation. It was they who created the network of roads which made it possible to send the army quickly to the most distant frontiers of the empire, so that they could not only be protected from hostile attacks but could be continually extended. It was the technical worker who built strong walls that defied the onslaught of the enemy, and it was he who had to construct the machines by which the enemy was finally vanquished. It was he who built and unceasingly improved the various means of communication and so encouraged trade, this most important factor of prosperity. Between the existence of the State and ancient technical science many links were thus forged which in turn exerted their influence on the life of the individual. Technical science created prosperity and, reciprocally, prosperity presented technical science with new problems. Improved conditions called for development in Art; again it was the technical worker who furnished the artist with the many requirements of his work. Streets and houses increased in dimensions. It was the business of the technical worker to introduce hygienic measures in the form of drains, aqueducts and so forth, the need of which in every moderately sized community was recognized even in antiquity. The wonderful remnants of these achievements still extant are an imperishable testimony to the difficulty of the problems that presented themselves and to the masterly way in which they were solved.

We see, then, that technical science exerted a strong influence over the whole of civic and public life in antiquity. It may be said that then, just as nowadays, the State which had at its disposal the best technical scientists and the best technical equipment had the most favourable prospects for the future. Many things prove that the ancients were by no means blind to this fact. A knowledge of ancient technical science is indispensable to anyone who wishes to comprehend fully the mind of antiquity.

THE TECHNICAL ARTS AND SCIENCES OF THE ANCIENTS

MINING

NO technical science is possible without mining. This was equally true in ancient times, for no technical development would have been possible if man had not known how to wrest from the earth the treasures which it held concealed. Comparatively little could be done with what it offered voluntarily. Wood and other parts of plants, loose stones, bones of dead animals and fish, satisfied the needs of primitive man and savages. At the moment, however, when that many-sided development of human activity commenced, which we summarize as 'civilization', it was necessary to look round for other means. Tools were required for working the materials necessary to build houses. Agricultural implements as well as improved weapons were needed, and domestic life made demands which could be satisfied only by making new substances available. The major part of these could, however, be obtained only by means of mining.

It may therefore be said that the beginning of civilization among the individual peoples coincided with that of mining. It is true that the date when the technical science of mining commenced in the case of any one race cannot be determined even approximately. Probably individual peoples of the East, following the instinct for development, started quite of themselves to probe the earth for treasure. They found, sometimes here, sometimes there, a stone or a precious metal which was of use. The desire of possessing more drove them to continue digging. In this way, perhaps, the science of mining gradually evolved. When trade and commerce later became factors in life, this science was transmitted to other peoples. For example, a Greek legend relates that Kadmos, who was probably of Phoenician extraction, had opened up gold and silver mines at Mount Pangaeus in Thrace. These mines may justifiably be regarded as the oldest in Europe. In the same way mines were started by the Phoenicians on several islands in the Mediterranean and on the coast of Spain. Similarly commerce was responsible for the introduction of mining into other countries. For example, when the Emperor Hadrian arrived in Britain with the Sixth Legion in the year A.D. 120, he immediately started mines, which were worked and improved till the year 409. He, of course, applied the methods usual in Roman mines.

Mining was at different stages of advancement among the various ancient peoples. It was particularly developed among the Egyptians, who probably opened up copper mines on the peninsula of Sinai as early as the third millennium B.C. Besides these the vast quarries of Turra near Cairo have also been preserved; they prove to us that at that very early date open working had been given up in favour of shafts. The ancient Egyptians were thus not satisfied with merely removing the stones in the hill from the outside, but penetrated far into the interior. Wells of the same period, for example, Joseph's well at Cairo, descend up to 300 ft. vertically into the earth. In view of the fact that these shafts were constructed about 2500 B.C., it can hardly be doubted that similar ones were also dug out for mining purposes in some cases.

The high standard of mining construction attained by the Egyptians is rivalled by the Indians and the Chinese, who likewise sank pits about 5,000 years ago. These mines are mostly choked up nowadays and investigators have given them scant attention. Nevertheless, there are other indications that men knew even at that early time how to distinguish the mineral ore from the sterile stone. These were separated and, just as nowadays, the dross was collected into great heaps. The pit-heaps of our modern mines are an inexhaustible source of information for the mineralogist, the geologist, the mining engineer and the representatives of several other branches of research. In the same way the pit-heaps of ancient mines bear striking testimony to the standard reached in a lost science. They enable us to recognize the metals of which the production was at that time promoted and give us clues to the means adopted for that purpose. The metals themselves and the art of working in metal are dealt with in other sections of this book. Here, where we wish to discuss the question of mining, we are primarily concerned only with the construction and working of ancient mines.

Before going into details we must preface our remarks by mentioning that almost all ancient peoples sank and worked their mines according to the same principles. It has already been remarked that in consequence of the growth of trade and commerce technical science was communicated from people to people. We thus find in the Indian and Chinese mines very much the same conditions as later in the Phoenician and Egyptian mines, and still later in those of the Greeks, Romans, Celts, Gauls, Britons and others. The treasures that were being sought and the ores that were being separated out differ more or less in the various countries, but the manner of their extraction was much the same in all.

The miner of ancient times was nearly always either a slave or a criminal. This explains why the means used remained almost unchanged for thousands of years. The purpose of machines is to economize labour or time. It was not considered necessary to make the work easier for the slave, whose hard lot inspired no sympathy, although it kept him to the end of his days buried in the gloomy depths of the earth, suffering all sorts of torments and privations. There was mostly a superabundance of slaves. After campaigns there were usually so many that great numbers of them were massacred. So there was no dearth of labour. Time was as yet but little valued. And so it happened that in almost all the mines of the ancients only the simplest means were adopted. In the copper mines of Rio Tinto and Tharsis in the Spanish province of Huelva, which were worked by the Romans and the Carthaginians, the method of working was so simple that the slaves in the mines had to scratch off with their fingers the clay which covered the ore. The clay which is found nowadays in ancient mines still bears the impress of thousands of fingers; if we examine them we make a curious observation, viz., that on account of the nature of the work the thumb is very highly developed, as in the case of certain artisans even at the present time. Usually, however, the ancients used hammers and wedges, and probably also bones and horns. A familiar emblem of mining consists of two crossed hammer-shaped tools, the mallet and the wedge, the former serving as a hammer, while the edge of the latter was forced into the stone. The tools of the ancient miner exhibit the same form. No matter whether they are of horn, bone, stone or metal we always find the 'iron', that is, the wedge, which was held against the stone and which was struck by means of a mallet. It is significant that among the miners in Germany the mallet is still called 'Fäustel'[1] (miner's hammer), a name which is immediately explained by the discovery—in ancient mines or their pit-heaps—of stones whose form indicates that they were used as hammers, being grasped in the fist. In a choked-up tunnel of the ancient Roman mine mentioned above (in the Spanish province of Huelva), fifteen skeletons were found of which several were still holding the 'Fäustel' in their hands at the time of the discovery. But the 'Fäustel' was often provided with a handle and thus converted into a proper hammer, and similarly a handle was stuck through or tied on to the wedge.

FIGS. 1 and 2.—Representation of the method of working in ancient Mines, according to the Corinthian Pinakes

We also find such tools represented on ancient votive tablets that probably date from the seventh or sixth century B.C., and are the only remaining pictorial representations of the working of ancient mines. These votive tablets, the so-called Corinthian pinakes, are made of painted clay. Most of them are preserved in the Berlin Antiquarium. They show that on account of the heat the miners usually went about their work naked or simply wore an apron. The form of the hammer and the length of the handle as in the case of the other tools were adapted to the nature of the mineral and to the type of work, which was done

[1] The German word 'Faust' signifies fist.—H. L. B.

sometimes in a standing, sometimes in a sitting, sometimes in a lying posture. We see from the tablets that the mines were illuminated by amphorae suspended from the roof, although the more usual method of lighting was by lamps placed in small stone cavities. Further, boys collected the mineral in baskets provided with a handle, which were then tied up and passed up to other boys, who likewise passed them on or else carried them away (see Figs. 1 and 2). The left side of Fig. 2 leads us to surmise that in order to descend into the mines either steps were hewn out of the stone (perhaps ladders were used) or wooden blocks were let into the stone.

The tunnels constructed in the rock by these simple means are often of astonishing length. It has been computed and confirmed by observing the marks of wedges that in even relatively soft stone the progress made amounted to about half an inch in twenty-four hours: in hard stone it was not more than 25 or 30 ft. per year. This low efficiency was compensated to some extent by making the tunnels very low, by working only along the seams of the ore and by avoiding as far as possible the removal of unnecessary stone. Consequently, the galleries and tunnels were so narrow that a slave could squeeze himself through only with great difficulty. In many mines, in particular in those of the Egyptians, Greeks and Romans, children were employed, so that as little stone as possible would have to be removed. Although the slaves must have become weakened by their sojourn in the mines and by the unhealthy posture during work, as well as through sickness—in lead mines particularly through lead-poisoning—they must often have used very heavy tools. Hammers have been found which weighed between 20 and 26 lbs.

At the same time there were no precautions against accidents. The galleries were not propped up and therefore often collapsed, burying workmen beneath them. In ancient mines many skeletons have been found of slaves who had lost their lives in this way while at work. Nor were attempts made to replenish the supply of air or to take other steps for preserving health. When the air in the mines became so hot and foul that breathing was rendered impossible the place was abandoned and an attack was made at some other point. These conditions must have become still more trying wherever, in addition to the mallet and chisel, the only other means of detaching the stone was applied, namely fire. The mineral-bearing stone was heated and water was then poured over it. There was no outlet for the resulting smoke and vapours. This method of constructing tunnels and galleries is described by Pliny somewhat as follows: 'Tunnels are bored into the mountains and are carefully explored. These tunnels are called "arrugiae," little ways or little streets. They often collapse and bury many workers. When hard minerals occur one seeks to blast them with fire and vinegar.[1] As the resulting steam and smoke often fill the tunnels, the workmen prefer to split the rock into pieces of 150 lbs. or more, and for this purpose they use iron wedges and hammers.[2] These pieces are removed

[1] Concerning the 'vinegar' used for blasting rock, see p. 461.
[2] The exact sense of the Latin is doubtful.—*Trans.*

from the galleries that have been hewn out, so that an open cavern is formed. So many of these caverns or hollows are made adjacent to each other in the mountain that finally they collapse with a loud noise, and so the mineral in the interior becomes exposed. Often the eagerly sought gold vein fails to appear, and the long sustained and arduous work which had often cost many human lives has been in vain.'

It is surprising what depths were reached by these simple means.

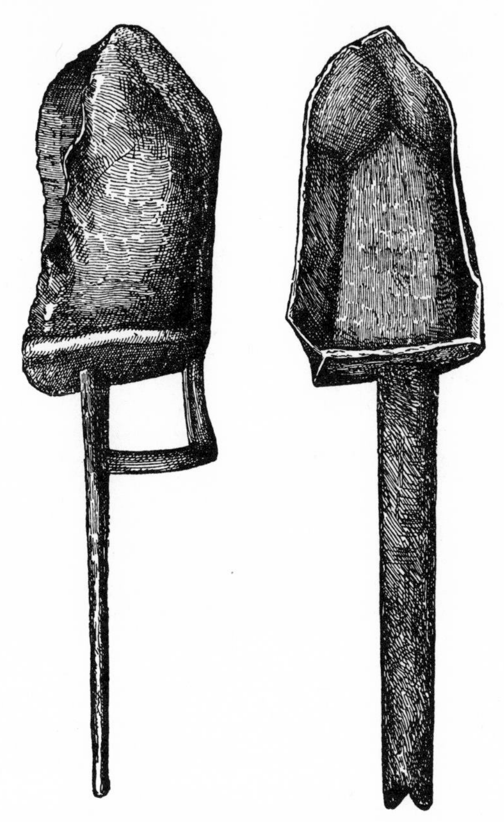

FIGS. 3 and 4.—Spoon-shaped Miners' Lamps of Lead
Found at Villefranche

When Diodorus relates that the Romans had mine-pits which were 'some stadia deep,' he is certainly not exaggerating.[1] For example, a copper tablet with an ancient Roman inscription has been found in a Spanish mine at a depth of 650 ft.

That part of mining which we nowadays call 'transport' was no less simply effected. The ore was filled into sacks or chests which were dragged out by children, as only they were able to make progress in the narrow galleries with their burden. If a cavity was reached in the interior on the way out, the ore was probably picked there and then;

[1] See p. 501. It is sufficiently accurate to take 1 stadium = 202 yards.—H. L. B.

otherwise the sorting was done above by daylight. From the size of the bags and the specific weight of the ores it has been calculated that the burden carried by such a child often amounted to as much as 45 lbs. It is distressing to think how many of these children must have broken down under their heavy burdens and the whips of the overseers. Many of the tunnels in ancient mines were so steep that ropes must have been used for effecting transportation, just as in the case of vertical shafts. Such ropes have, however, not been discovered.

The farther one penetrated into the interior the greater was the chance of water channels being encountered, and hence of the mines becoming flooded. No precautionary measures were taken against this danger such as we should consider adequate. The water was scooped

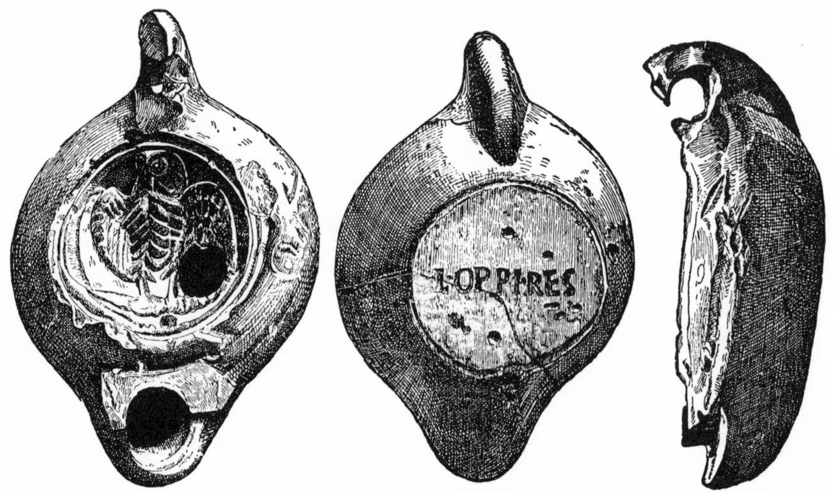

Figs. 5, 6 and 7.—Miners' Earthenware Lamps
Found in Villefranche

out by means of vessels or leather skins which were passed from hand to hand. The Egyptians hauled up these bags by ropes, which were wound up on a windlass. This very ancient method of transporting water is still used nowadays to draw water from wells. When the water could no longer be drawn off in this way, the mines had to be allowed to become flooded; this often meant that the labour of many decades and, indeed, sometimes of centuries, was lost.

The illumination of ancient mines was no less simple than all the other arrangements. In many cases light was provided by pieces of wood soaked in resin or fat and attached to the walls by means of lumps of clay. Bundles of twigs were also sometimes ignited. In several ancient Roman mines as, for example, at Villefranche, spoon-shaped miners' lamps of lead have also been found (Figs. 3 and 4). The hollow of the spoon was filled with oil into which a wick was immersed and then lit. The lamp was held by a straight stem. In the same mines there have also been found earthenware lamps which resemble in form and appearance those that were used for domestic purposes (Figs. 5, 6, 7). A lamp mentioned by Treptow and found in Tunis consisted of a double layer of sheet-lead, which proves that these lamps were also sometimes made of lead—probably because those of earthenware were too easily broken during mining operations. The expense incurred in this way was of little account at that time, but it was probably very unpleasant to have lamps broken as the mines would be left in darkness. They were therefore often made of more lasting material.

The art of mining appears to have made almost no technical progress during the whole of antiquity, that is, from the date of the earliest traces recorded to the fall of the Roman Empire. This can but increase our wonder at the prodigious results achieved in this branch of work, both as regards the depth of the shafts and the quantity of ore raised, results that can be accounted for only by the very great number of human beings sacrificed in the cause of gain.

METALS AND THEIR EXTRACTION (METALLURGY)

THE Greek poet Hesiod, who lived round about the year 770 B.C., relates the well-known story of the four different ages of the human race: the Gold, the Silver, the Bronze, and the Iron Age. For a long time this fable was believed, and it was assumed that man had become acquainted first with gold, then with silver, which was followed by bronze, and finally with iron. Recent investigations have proved that this assumption is untenable. They show that there can be no question, among the peoples of antiquity, of any age having been characterized by the chief use of one particular metal. In the first place it cannot be determined which metal first became known to man. Further, the same conditions do not hold among all peoples. Thus a Bronze Age in the sense of Hesiod is an impossibility, for the simple reason that there were many races among the Ancients who entirely lacked the substances necessary for making bronze. They could therefore have become acquainted with bronze only if trade relationships had existed between them and other peoples who were in possession of these substances. But if they had already had trade relationships with other peoples who were familiar with the extraction of iron, the Bronze Age must, of course, have been preceded by an Iron Age in their case. On the other hand, gold is certainly among the oldest of known metals. For wherever it had been precipitated in the form of small particles in streams its shimmering brightness must readily have attracted attention. But gold in this particular form is not to be discovered everywhere, and so not a few peoples must have known and used other metals long before gold first met their gaze.

GOLD

In general it may be asserted that most peoples at the beginning of their history were acquainted with gold, silver, copper, iron, lead, and, in many cases, also tin. It has been definitely established that the Egyptians, when they first entered the realm of history, that is, about 3000 B.C., were familiar with gold, copper, silver, lead, and iron. Gold, which they called ' nub,' was alleged to have been discovered by Osiris and was supplied by Nubia, the Land of Gold. As the Nubians did not voluntarily deliver up their treasures of gold, the Egyptians were continually making warlike incursions into their country. The wealth of

Egypt or, rather, Ethiopia, was supposed to have been so great that, according to Herodotus' narrative, even the prisoners were bound with chains of gold—a fact which excited the astonishment of the ambassadors of the Persian King Cambyses (Herodotus III, 22, 23). The stories of Herodotus are, however, a mixture of fact and fable. As no such golden slave-chains have ever been discovered, this tale is best consigned to the region of fancy. Nevertheless, the riches that the Egyptians derived from the Nubian gold mines were stupendous. Diodorus reports that the annual yield of the Nubian gold mines at the time of Ramses II (1300–1230 B.C.) appoached 32 million minae, that is, about £132,000,000.

A detailed description of the technical extraction of gold as practised by the ancient Egyptians has been handed down to us by Diodorus.

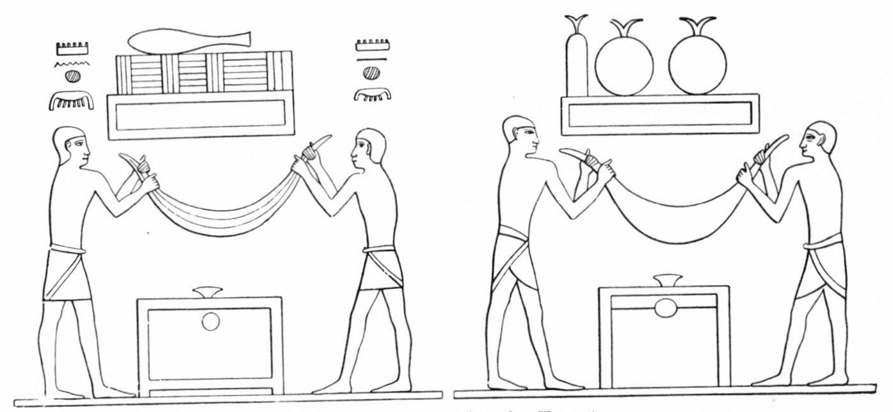

FIG. 8.—Gold-washing in Egypt

Two workmen treat the gold with water in a sack which they swing to and fro in order to remove the lighter particles of sand. The sacks probably contain sponges in which the fine particles of gold remain suspended. The tables below seem to the author to be formed like chests or cisterns into which the water used for the washing flows by way of the funnels indicated at the top. The water is thus collected in the chests, so that any gold still contained in it can be extracted by repeating the operation. Painting from Beni Hasan, 16th century B.C.

Nubian gold was present in quartz in the form of veins. Slaves and convicts worked at it in the manner already described in the section on 'Mining' by cutting passages with the help of hammers and sharp wedges along the direction of the gold veins. Youths under seventeen years carried away the fractured stone, which was then further broken up in stone mortars with the aid of iron pestles. The raw material containing the gold was first reduced to the size of a pea. These small pieces were next ground down to a powder in stone mills. The powder was placed on wooden tables and washed gently with water, sponges being used to which the free grains of gold adhered. The washing swept away the light sand while the sand which was heavier on account of the contained gold was left behind. This residue was then melted up with lead in order to separate the gold from the stone. Another smelting process followed, during which fresh lead and common salt were added. This stage lasted for five days. The impurities in the gold, the compounds formed by it and the added ingredients, as well as the excess of the latter, was partly sublimated and partly formed a slag with the silver chloride, which was produced by the silver present with the gold in the ore, and with the substance composing the smelting-pot. Pure gold was left as a residue in the pot. Bellows were used in the smelting furnaces; they were expanded by pulling up cords and compressed by treading with the feet.

The extraction of gold by the peoples of the East was probably carried out in an analogous way. Among all of them gold is to be found, partly derived from their own sources and partly imported from Africa. Certain countries, such as, for example, the mythical land of gold, Ophir, which was probably situated in South Africa and from which King Solomon procured the gold necessary to build his temple, are famous for the wealth of gold they contained. But the technical extraction of gold had not everywhere reached the high standard attained by the ancient Egyptians, who, as we have seen, applied chemical and metallurgical processes. Wherever gold was discovered as a secondary deposit, that is, already washed out of the weather-worn stone, simpler means were used to extract it. Strabo (XI, 2, 19) describes this method of extraction as follows: 'It is related also that mountain streams carry gold down into the valleys and that the barbarians catch it in troughs, which are pierced with holes, and on fleeces; hence, they say, comes the legend of the Golden Fleece'. This method of extraction is confirmed by Appian (*Bellum Mithridaticum*, 103): 'Many springs conduct gold out of the Caucausus in the form of invisible bodies, and the inhabitants place sheepskins with thick fleeces in the stream. They then collect from the skins the fine particles that are held fast in them. The golden fleece of Aeetes was perhaps something of this sort.' Actually, the Argonautic Expedition (about 1350 B.C.), which the Greeks undertook to Colchis,[1] the land of gold, was an ordinary raiding adventure; they probably pursued no other purpose than of securing golden fleeces as their booty, that is, the rams' skins placed in the water to arrest the golden grains. From this aspect the old Greek story of the Argonauts gives us a remarkable insight into an old method of extracting gold, which, moreover, up till a few decades ago was practised in a similar way in Africa and California. The Romans used similar processes when they plundered the Spanish gold deposits. In this case the gold existed in the interior of mountains. The problem was first to get it into the daylight. To achieve this a singular procedure was adopted, according to the information of Pliny. By boring shafts one reached the interior of the mountain, where a cave was hollowed out, whose ceiling was supported by props. These props were afterwards made to collapse, and in consequence the cave fell in. The rubble was then washed by means of currents of water which were introduced into the interior of the mountain by specially constructed leads (*corrugi*). The issuing waters were distributed among numerous trenches (*agogae*), along which it gently flowed. Foliage and twigs were inserted in these ditches, playing

[1] Now called Mingrelia, situated in Georgia. The explanation of the Golden Fleece is fantastic.—H. L. B.

the part of the fleece. The gold collected in them and was then melted together. According to calculations by Breidenbach, the Romans treated (chiefly in the Spanish gold mines) about 500 million tons of rock in this way in order to extract the contained gold.

SILVER

Silver, also called white gold, came into use among the Egyptians later than gold. It was probably introduced into Egypt by the Phoenicians. An alloy of gold and silver called 'asem' was regarded in olden times as an independent metal. This alloy, which, according to recent analysis, contains 80 to 75 per cent. of gold and 20 to 25 per cent.

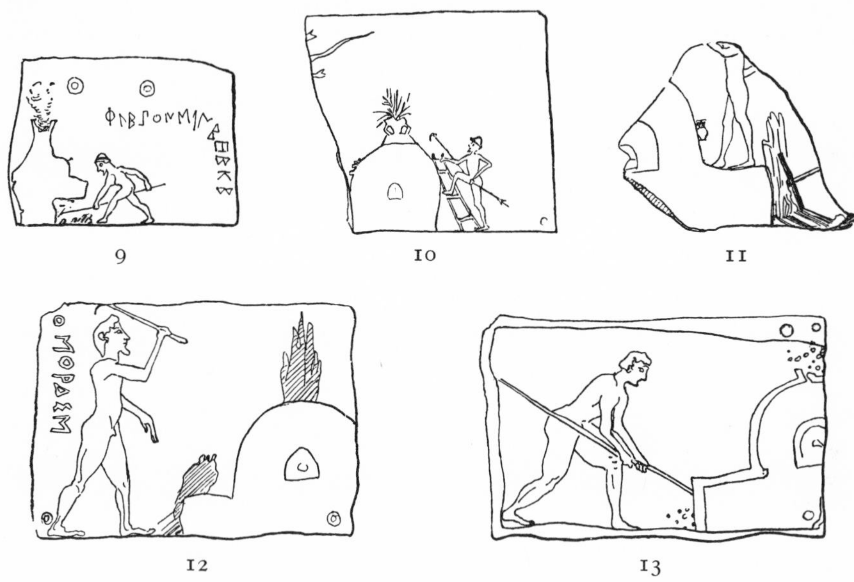

FIGS. 9–13.—Representations of old Smelting Furnaces on the Corinthian Pinakes

of silver, was called 'electrum'[1] by Pliny, and represents a combination which can be obtained directly from Nature or can be prepared artificially. In contrast with the Egyptians the Romans, who produced it artificially, had already recognized that 'asem' or 'electrum' was no independent metal. On the other hand, native silver was unknown to Pliny. This is the more surprising as a considerable portion of the silver used by the ancients was presumably found in the metallic state. At the beginning of the Persian wars (490–449 B.C.) the silver mines of Attica yielded over £100,000 worth of silver. That silver was used in Greece very long ago may be gathered from the fact that Homer speaks of its uses in various connections. He relates, for example, that the sword of

[1] In the opinion of Rhousopoulos, the name (which had already been used in ancient Greece) was due to the fact that the colour of the alloy resembled that of amber (*ἤλεκτρον*).

Achilles had a silver 'haft' or hilt (*Iliad*, I, 219), and that his shield had a silver handle (*Iliad*, XVIII, 480), and so forth. It is fairly safe to assert that silver was much more widely circulated than gold among all peoples of antiquity. Germania [1] was poorly supplied with this metal. In the time of Tacitus there was only one solitary silver mine.

When the silver was not found in its elementary metallic state it was obtained from argentiferous ores by metallurgical processes. No trustworthy information is, however, available about the form of these processes. They are, indeed, mentioned by ancient writers but are never accurately or minutely described ; almost the only detailed account that has been preserved, that of Pliny,[2] is so obscure and confused that no proper idea of the method of extracting silver can be formed from it. Pliny himself probably understood very little of it, and wrote down vaguely only what he had heard. From his statements as well as from those of Strabo (IV, 399, 400) it is at any rate clear that galena (lead sulphide) containing silver was treated metallurgically, or that silver ore was smelted with lead.

In both cases the smelting process produced lead containing silver (workable lead). The lead was then removed by heating the mixture on an open hearth with access of air, thus transforming the lead into one of its oxides, red lead or litharge (*λιθάργυρος*). The pure silver remains behind. In this process there was also formed a slag (*σκωρία*, *ἕλκυσμα*) containing probably about 24 per cent. of lead and spodium (*σποδός*). Analysis shows that spodium is zinc oxide, which forms as a deposit on the upper parts of the furnace.

The purity of the silver was tested by heating. Pure silver may be glowed in air without changing its colour. If it turns a brownish-red when heated on an iron plate, it is, according to the view of the ancients, not quite pure ; and if it turns black, it is impure. This observation is quite correct, for we know that the alloys of silver with other metals, in particular lead and copper, change colour in the manner described, when heated in air. Nevertheless, the other metals that occur in silver ores, as well as in lead ores containing silver, must sometimes have caused considerable trouble. It is to be assumed that arsenic and zinc raised difficulties which were perhaps overcome, particularly in Greece, by the construction of special furnaces, in which they could vaporize. Various circumstances point to this conclusion, above all, the fact that the earthen votive tablets, already mentioned on page 3, the Corinthian pinakes, also exhibit line-drawings of furnaces. Moreover, in various localities remains of these furnaces have been discovered. So far as can be recognized from the Corinthian pinakes, the furnaces were fired from below and had an opening at the top which allowed the smoke to escape and through which the flames probably leaped forth at times. Some (Fig. 9) seem to have been fed with fuel from below, others (Figs. 11 and 12) from above. This view is supported by the raised ledge on the side and

[1] In ancient geography Germania refers to the region included between the North Sea, Baltic, Vistula, Danube and Rhine.—H. L. B.

[2] *Hist. nat.*, in particular XXXIII, 6, 31, 35, 44 ; and XXXIV, 16, 47.

the man shown in the act of stepping up. The furnaces have an opening in the centre which seems to pass right through and which probably represents a muffle or a refining-hearth. Where there is no step a ladder is used to mount the hearth. On one votive tablet (Fig. 13) a furnace is to be seen which is apparently burnt out ; the slag is being removed through the hollow step. In many parts, above all in Greece, the silver was specially again purified before being worked into ornaments, coins, and so forth. The process of refinement adopted is not known. The slag left over from this process (at this stage called ἀργυρῖτις κέγχρος = silver millet) was again treated by a process, also unknown, which allowed the silver still contained in it to be extracted.

COPPER

Copper was no less widely distributed than silver. When it first became known cannot be determined. But it is probable that many ancient peoples knew copper long before iron. The reverse is true of the Germanic races. They became acquainted with copper long after they had used iron, and it is to be assumed that they never prepared it themselves but acquired it by trading. With this exception, however, we find copper among all other ancient peoples, and in some cases, indeed, in very considerable quantity, both as pure copper and also combined with tin in its most important and much used alloy, bronze. It is impossible to count up all the old sources of copper, as their number is legion. The oldest copper mines of Egypt are situated on Mount Sinai and, according to Berthelot, were started into action about 5000 B.C. This figure is probably too high. The fact remains, however, that the old copper mines of Sinai were still being worked in the reign of the Egyptian king, Thothmes III (1515–1461 B.C.). The ores of these mines contained chiefly the green carbonate and the acid silicate of copper (malachite and chrysocolla). The percentage of ore in the sandstone was not large, so that to extract the copper very elaborate preparations were necessary at the beginning. To smelt the ore furnaces of sandstone were used, into which crucibles composed of a mixture of quartz, sand and clay were placed. As Mount Sinai was not wooded at that time the firewood or fuel necessary for the furnace must have been brought from far away. Slags discovered in 1896, which are partly heavy and dark, partly light in both colour and weight, as well as solidified glass bubbles of very varied composition, prove that the action of the furnace was irregular and imperfect, and that the process of extracting the copper was not always carried out in a uniform way. No indications of the use of bellows have been found at Mount Sinai. According to Hesiod, however, crucibles were later used by the Greeks, which were provided with lateral apertures through which wind could be blown by a bellows. Whereas sulphurous ores were often used elsewhere, only oxides were treated metallurgically at Mount Sinai.

Ores containing sulphur were, however, worked to extract the copper by all manner of ancient peoples. These ores, called pyrites, were transformed into oxides, by being first subjected to a process of roasting.

Dioscorides has left us extensive information about this stage, which reveals that the roasting or burning was carried out exactly after the model of lime-burning. Furnaces or kilns were made of the material itself and, after having been supplied with fuel, were filled with the ore to be roasted. The fuel was then ignited and the work of the burner was devoted only to keeping up the supply of fuel. The pyrites roasted themselves; the end of the process was recognized, according to Dioscorides, by the ore having become red. The proper smelting-furnaces for copper, such as were particularly used on the island of Cyprus, which exported great quantities of copper to all parts of the ancient world from the earliest times, were high cupolas fed through a furnace-mouth from above. Into this mouth alternate layers of copper-ore and charcoal were introduced. The whole mass was then again smelted, air being blown through from below by means of bellows. This construction is thus in its essentials similar to that of the smelting-furnaces of the large foundries of our own times. For the rest, smelting-pots or crucibles were also used; indeed, in the extraction of copper very different types of furnaces seem to have been utilized in the different countries.

In the metallurgical process of extraction a mixture of copper, slag dross (at the mouth), spongy impurities, and a regulus of copper was obtained. As the copper was still impure it had to be re-smelted. Pliny relates that this was repeated again and again until the copper was of the required purity. The re-smelting took place in furnaces of various shapes, from which the copper was probably drawn off and solidified by cooling with water. For trade purposes copper was prepared not only in the form of plates but also as blocks. Like many other metallurgical processes of the ancients, however, the effective yield of copper from this process was rather unsatisfactory. Whereas only about 15 to 25 per cent. of the copper contained in the ores was extracted, the slag sometimes contained not less than 50 per cent.

TIN

Tin, like copper, played an important part in antiquity. Without doubt it is one of the oldest metals known at that time. The date of its discovery is not yet definitely established. The weight of tin-ore probably suggested that it contained a metal; and this metal was perhaps accidentally discovered while the ore was being smelted with wood or charcoal. Tin is already mentioned in the Old Testament. All peoples of the East were familiar with it. It was known even in countries where no tin-ore existed, and this leads us to infer that a great amount of tin-ore must have been imported into these countries at that time. The fact that Herodotus makes special mention of the Tin Islands, the Cassiterides,[1] points to the same conclusion. It has not been possible to determine their position, and, indeed, it is not certain whether the term *κασσίτερος* actually denoted tin in Homer's time. The first unmistakable use of this expression for tin occurs in the first century A.D. Moreover, besides *κασσίτερος* other terms were also used for tin, in particular

[1] Identified by some authorities as the Scilly Islands.—H. L. B.

μολυβδος. The Romans called it *plumbum candidum* or *album*. The word *stannum*, which was originally written *stagnum*, denoted crude lead. In fact, tin and lead were often confused in antiquity; this is easy to understand seeing that analysis in our sense was unknown at that early date and that metals often were distinguished only by their outward appearance. Later on, however, lead and tin could be clearly distinguished, and Pliny states explicitly that the lead plates used by the Romans for water-pipes were soldered by means of an alloy consisting of two parts of lead and one part of tin. He also writes about the plating of copper vessels by tin, incidentally mentioning that the weight of the copper did not increase in the process, so that only a very thin layer of tin could have been applied.

Tin was extracted by the ancients exclusively from stannic ores, which were probably for the greater part derived from Britain, which is by some regarded as the ‘ Islands of Tin ’, while others identify them with India, an opinion which is based on the fact that the Sanskrit name for tin is *kastira*. The Phoenicians, at any rate, obtained their tin from India. Later, the Spanish tin mines were exploited and, after the conquest of Britain by the Romans, particularly those in what is now Cornwall. No direct accounts have been passed down to us of the method by which tin was extracted by the ancients. From remains of furnaces, however, it is clear that the method was a simple process of reducing and smelting. It was carried out by heating the ore over a wood fire, by which the contained tin oxide was reduced; the metallic tin thus obtained was simply smelted out.

Whether bellows were later used appears doubtful. Apertures at the bottom of some furnaces may be regarded as wind-holes through which air was forced in order to intensify the glow of the fire. But they may also have served merely as a more convenient means of drawing off the metal. Their purpose seems not yet to have been definitely established.

BRONZE

Far more important than copper and tin in themselves in ancient times was the bronze alloy composed of both. It may very well be said, indeed, that bronze was the characteristic feature of that epoch. Bronze —at that time called ‘ brass ’ and undistinguished in name from copper— seems at first chiefly to have served the purpose of imbuing the copper with greater hardness and firmness. This does not, however, always appear to have been successful. For example, in ancient Thebes a chisel has been found which is one of the earliest specimens of Egyptian bronze, and which is so soft that, when pressed against a stone, it simply bends back. It is composed of 94 parts of copper, 5·9 parts of tin, and 0·1 parts of iron. Later, harder bronzes were made, which were called *chomt* in Egypt, and are in general of fairly uniform composition. On the average they contain 80 to 85 parts of copper and 20 to 15 parts of tin. It is not certain who discovered bronze. There are indications that it was perhaps first made in the valley of the Euphrates, where it was already known about the year 2000 B.C. The Jews may have been acquainted with a copper alloy still earlier, for the Bible speaks of Tubal-Cain, 'an instructor of every artificer in brass and iron,' but it appears doubtful whether the term[1] for brass in this quotation (from Genesis iv. 22) really signifies bronze. The Greeks and Romans also made very extensive use of bronzes, which were, indeed, an important factor of civilization in ancient times. On account of its low melting point, which lies between 786° and 900° Centigrade, and its beautiful colour, as well as the ease with which its properties could be modified by altering the proportion of the contained tin, it enjoyed wide popularity. Concerning the technical properties of ancient bronzes it is to be remarked that when they contained less than 5 per cent. of tin, they could be shaped while cold. Bronzes containing 10 parts of tin were chiefly used for making tools, and those containing more than 15 parts could be used only for casting purposes, on account of their hard and brittle quality.

The melting-points of various ancient bronzes are as follows:

Bronze containing	8 parts of tin	900° C.
,, ,,	13 ,, ,, ...	835° C.
,, ,,	25 ,, ,, ...	786° C.

Detailed analyses of ancient bronzes have been carried out by Berthelot, Andrée, Rhousopoulos and others. They show that ancient bronzes contained not only copper and tin, but also other very different metals, although only in small proportions. These admixtures were due to the imperfect development of metallurgical processes at that time. In the following table we give some analyses of antique bronzes which exhibit their varying composition and indicate the manifold variety of admixed metals.

We first give analyses of Assyrian bronzes now in the British Museum (according to Fellenberg):

Name of Object.	Copper.	Tin.	Lead.	Iron.	Antimony.	Arsenic.	Nickel.
1. Thick grey rod	88·03	0·11	3·28	4·06	3·92	0·60	—
2. Bent rod	88·84	12·70	0·28	a trace	—	—	0·18
3. Ornament on a domestic utensil	86·99	12·33	0·38	,,	—	—	0·30
4. Round pieces from a bowl .	80·84	18·37	0·43	0·16	—	—	0·20

These analyses are of particular importance because, in addition to the metals arsenic, antimony, iron and nickel contained presumably as impurities in one of the bronzes (No. 1), there is so high a percentage of lead that we must conclude that it was intentionally added as an ingredient. According to von Bibra, no lead occurs in the bronzes of the true bronze period. This comparatively large proportion of lead leads

[1] The German Bible uses the word 'Erz', which may stand for ore, metal, brass or bronze.—H. L. B.

him to conclude that these bronzes were made after the true bronze period, indicating that a higher degree of civilization had already been reached. Later Assyrian bronzes have a proportion of lead which varies between 7 per cent. and 9 per cent.

The following table gives further analyses of different ancient bronzes (according to Ledebur) :

Object.	Copper.	Tin.	Zinc.	Lead.	Iron.	Nickel.	Silver.	Phosphorus.
Dagger (old Egyptian) [1]	85·0	14·0	—	—	1·10	—	—	—
Arrow head (old Egyptian)	76·6	22·2	—	—	—	—	—	—
Bronze bowl from Nineveh	80·8	18·4	—	0·4	0·2	0·4	—	—
Handle of a vessel from Mycenae	89·7	10·1	—	—	—	—	—	—
Coin (old Attic)	88·46	10·04	—	1·50	—	—	—	—
Coin (Athenian)	76·41	7·05	—	16·54	—	—	—	—
Statue of Victory (Brescia)	80·8	19·4	1·9	7·7	—	—	—	—
Coin (of Titus Claudius)	81·4	8·6	—	—	—	—	—	—
Coin (of Nero)	81·1	1·1	17·8	—	—	—	—	—
Coin (of Diocletian)	95·8	2·2	—	1·9	—	—	—	—

[1] There is a remarkable coincidence between the chemical composition of this old Egyptian dagger and that of the bronzes contained in a prehistoric musical wind-instrument discovered at Daberkow in the district of Demmin, Hither Pomerania. The analysis of the latter was given by Rathgen as : copper, 85·03 per cent. ; tin, 13·96 per cent. ; other metals (lead, iron, cobalt), 1·1 per cent.

In general, silver does not occur in ancient bronzes. In later Roman times there occur, however, bronzes containing silver, which were used for making 'silver' coins, but which contained so little silver that, to be correct, we must class them among bronze coins. In fact, the analyses of Roman silver coins, which were carried out by Klaproth, Thomson, and others, present an excellent picture of the decline of the Roman Empire. As its power waned, so the content of the copper in its coins increased. Towards the end they were made of a bronze containing silver, and finally (under the Emperor Gallienus) they were made only of copper and plated with tin. It has already been pointed out above that Pliny mentions the art of tin-plating as practised in Rome.

As is evident from the last table above, ancient bronzes were found to contain no zinc at all except in a few very rare cases, as for example in an ancient Egyptian statue which is at present in the Germanisches Museum at Nuremberg. More sensible quantities of zinc do not occur in regular proportions in old bronzes until the time of the Romans. This leads to the conclusion that zinc was not added intentionally to the alloy before this comparatively late date. These alloys owe their origin to the fact that to obtain different tints of bronze the mineral calamine [1] derived from Spanish mines was added to the raw material used in making the bronze.

[1] Latin *cadmia*, from Greek *kadmia* (gē) = cadmean (earth).

ZINC

Pure zinc was altogether unknown to the ancients. The Romans did, indeed, use the natural zinc-ore (the carbonate) in the form of calamine (see above) for manifold purposes, but they did not know how to extract the metallic element from it. Besides using calamine for preparing certain bronzes in which zinc was to be an ingredient, they used it to extract zinc oxide (' cadmia ') and chiefly to manufacture brass. But ' cadmia ' was also used to denote an ore whose exact composition has not yet been determined. It is probable that brass owes its discovery to the accidental smelting of copper-ore with calamine, the result of which was the beautiful yellow alloy. According to pseudo-Aristotle (*de mirab. aus.*, lxxii/63), the Mossynoikoi who inhabited the shores of the Black Sea are the discoverers of brass. Some hold the opinion that the word ' Messing ' (German for brass) is due to these Mossynoikoi, but its derivation from the Latin *massa*, that is mass, seems more likely to be correct. All that has been definitely established is that brass was known at the time of the Roman Empire. It is mentioned by Pliny, Vergil, Strabo, Horace, Cicero and Plautus. Whether the alloys mentioned by Homer, Plato, and so forth were actually brass is uncertain.

The aurichalcum (ὀρείχαλκος) of the ancients was probably nothing other than brass. The identity of the substance which this term signifies has long been a subject of discussion. In the opinion of the author there are two facts that speak in favour of the interpretation ' brass.' In the first place the grammarian Sextus Pomponius Festus (probably of the second century A.D.) describes the preparation of ' aurichalcum.' He states that it was prepared by throwing cadmia on to copper. Concerning cadmia it is to be remarked that it is an ' earth.' It is important to note this, as it precludes the notion of cadmia being an ore in the sense of the ancients. So the reference is to zinc oxide ; this naturally produces brass when smelted with copper. A second proof that ' aurichalcum ' stands for brass is furnished by Blümner, who refers to a metal plate found between Bâle and Augst [1] and bearing the actual inscription ' aurichalcum.' Its analysis, according to Fellenberg, showed that it contained a high percentage of zinc. The fact that ' aurichalcum ' was sometimes also used to denote other alloys is very well explained by Percy, who points out that even nowadays the terms brass and bronze are continually confused by the technical worker as well as by the layman. This is particularly so in the case of metal ornaments.

Certain circumstances make it probable that the Romans were also acquainted with an alloy of zinc and iron, ' hard zinc ' (Diergart).

LEAD

In contrast with zinc, lead played an extremely important part over the whole period of ancient history. It was known even to the early Egyptians, Indians and Jews. The first Pharaohs who gained victories

[1] In Switzerland on the left bank of the Rhine.—H. L. B.

in Asia, had some of their tribute paid in the form of lead by the conquered peoples. Thothmes III brought home lead as a spoil of victory; this lead was apparently partly used as roofing, as seems to be borne out by a picture in the temple of Ramses III, in which long plates with rounded corners are depicted and on which is written the word *taht* (lead), in hieroglyphics. According to a calculation by Lepsius these plates have a surface 10 by $5\frac{1}{2}$ sq. in., a thickness of about $\frac{1}{10}$-in., and a weight of about 4 pounds each. In India, too, lead was used for a variety of purposes, sometimes medicinally, sometimes for keeping the threads taut in weaving, sometimes for preparing cosmetics, and so forth. The Romans exploited the lead works of Spain. At the time of Titus no less than 40,000 slaves were occupied in working them. In the Greek lead mines there were also as many as 20,000 slaves at certain times. Among the Greeks and the Romans lead was used for a great variety of purposes. It served to fix clamps into stones, for making water-pipes, as an ingredient of alloys used to make coins, for medical purposes, to prepare lids for medical boxes, to cast small statues and children's toys,[1] to prepare plummets (sounding-lines for ships), for sling-bullets (*glans missilis*, lit. an acorn that is to be hurled) for purposes of war, and, indeed, even for making false dice. Furthermore, it was used for making numerous implements—incidentally, a dangerous practice, particularly when it was applied to making domestic utensils and vessels. The physiologist Kobert has proved that lead-poisoning was already widely prevalent among the ancients, and, indeed, that the many childless marriages of the Romans at the time of the Empire are largely to be traced back to the action of foods and drinks which had become tainted with lead owing to their having been preserved in leaden vessels. This produced chronic lead-poisoning and consequently sterility.

Fig. 14.—Relief Decorations in head on a Roman Coffin. Provincial Museum, Trèves

The extraction of lead in ancient times was effected by processes of which no account has been transmitted to us. But it is immediately clear to anyone who is at all conversant with the metallurgy of lead that the processes must have been practically the same as that described above for the extraction of silver from galena (lead sulphide). The galena was roasted and then reduced by smelting in furnaces, for which purpose

[1] Lead soldiers were used by the Spartans as early as in the sixth century before Christ; they were made of pure lead, according to Rhousopoulos.

green wood or charcoal (or both) was used. Green wood was used because it developed large quantities of smoke and gases, which were thought to exert a favourable influence. Probably bellows were used to produce stronger currents of air. The slag and the lead were drawn off and separated mechanically. The crude lead obtained was again smelted. The slag still contained a fair percentage of lead, a fact of which the ancients became aware later and which led to its being collected from the dumps at Laurion, as reported by Strabo, and subjected to smelting over again. It is probable that lead-ores free from silver also served for the extraction of lead. The process of roasting was not always necessary; it could be dispensed with, for example, when the galena contained oxides of lead. Whether this was actually recognized or whether the ores were always roasted remains uncertain. An ancient Roman lead furnace which has been discovered was found to be sunk right into the ground. It was about 11 ft. deep and 8½ ft. wide at the top. The walls, which were made of a fire-proof mixture of brick-dust and clay, were 5½ in. thick. The crude lead flowed out of a drain situated at the bottom into a large shallow recipient, from which the slag was scooped off, while the lead was run off into smaller crucibles to be re-smelted or separated from the contained silver.

IRON

The importance of iron in ancient times was somewhat overshadowed among many peoples by that of other metals, such as copper and lead. Although iron may be fairly easily prepared, as it is only necessary to produce the comparatively low temperature of 700° C., the most ancient iron implements were probably meteorites. It has been doubted whether the hardness of meteoric iron did not prevent its being worked; it is not at all necessary to imagine that a need for proper chisels or similar tools was felt, for a meteoric stone manipulated by hand constitutes a good hammer. Moreover, it can be sharpened on a stone, and so forth. Various ancient terms, such as the ancient Egyptian name *baaenepe*, 'gift of heaven,' and the Greek term *σίδηρος*, lend support to the view that meteoric iron once had a certain importance. At any rate, it is certain that in the form of meteoric stones it was known to the ancients; meteoric iron has been found in prehistoric tombs. There are even indications that the ancient Egyptians made use of such iron. In May, 1837, J. R. Hill discovered in a stone rabbet of the great pyramid of Gizeh a piece of iron which must have been placed there during the fourth dynasty, that is, a little after the year 2700 B.C. This piece of iron contains nickel, a circumstance which would favour the view that it is meteoric iron, were it not that it also contains carbon in chemical combination. This find at least proves that iron was known to the Egyptians at that time. This is corroborated by a later discovery at Abydos by Flinders Petrie.

We have definite information about the length of time iron was known to the ancient Indians. An iron industry existed in India probably in the year 2500 B.C. and certainly in 1500 B.C. The very fact that the Sanskrit word *ajas* is undoubtedly related to the old Gothic *ais*, which later led to the German *Eisen*, justifies the assumption that the Indo-Germanic races must have been familiar with iron before they separated (1500 B.C.). C. R. von Schwarz has found in the Province of Rewah in Central India great heaps of cinder and slag covering many square miles, testifying to the very flourishing state to which the iron industry must once have attained in ancient India. At the same time specimens of worked iron have been discovered of enormous dimensions; this is the more wonderful as even nowadays, in the age of the steam-hammer, pieces of this size can be produced only in the largest workshops.

Such colossal pieces of iron could never be worked in the small furnaces in use in India at the present time. The greatest relic of ancient Indian iron work still left to us is the Kutub column near Delhi. It weighs more than 17 tons and is composed of almost chemically pure iron, as has been shown by analysis. Its height is 23 ft. above the ground, and it is probably formed of very many blocks that have been forged together. Nevertheless it nowhere exhibits a seam which would betray welding. An inscription which has been cut into the column indicates that it was completed in the ninth century B.C.

It is very remarkable that, in spite of the long time that the column has been standing, it has up to the present exhibited no sign of rust. This was formerly ascribed to a layer of fat which was supposed to have been smeared over the whole length of the column, which is estimated at 52 feet, for it is sunk far into the ground. This view is unlikely, as such a layer of fat would certainly have been washed off in the course of centuries. Others ascribe the absence of rust to the dryness of the air. It is much more probable, however, that it is due to the extraordinary purity of the iron. Analysis, such as that of Percy, has proved its high degree of purity. In 1891 the present author, in conjunction with Professor von Klobukow, prepared a sample of chemically pure iron by electrolysis in the Electrochemical Laboratory of the Technical High School at Munich. All efforts to make this sample rust failed. Chemically pure iron does not, then, possess the property of rusting; this has since been confirmed by others. The fact that the ancients knew how to manufacture iron that has not rusted up to the present time receives further support from finds made in a quite different locality. In Oseberg an old Viking ship was found, whose wooden parts were fastened together by iron nails which are still bright and beautifully preserved. This ship, which is now preserved in the National Museum in Oslo, was examined by Gustafson, who could not, however, ascertain the reason for the absence of rust. This was found—by a special commission, appointed later for the purpose—to be due to the purity of the iron. For the rest, it must be remarked that means of preventing rust were also known to the ancients. Discoveries made at the Roman fort of Saalburg, near Bad Homburg and Frankfort-on-the-Main, prove that in the time of the Romans vivianite (a mineral containing iron phosphate) was used as a protection against rust, and Pliny mentions a whole series of similar substances, such as minium (red lead), white lead, gypsum, bitumen and liquid tar.

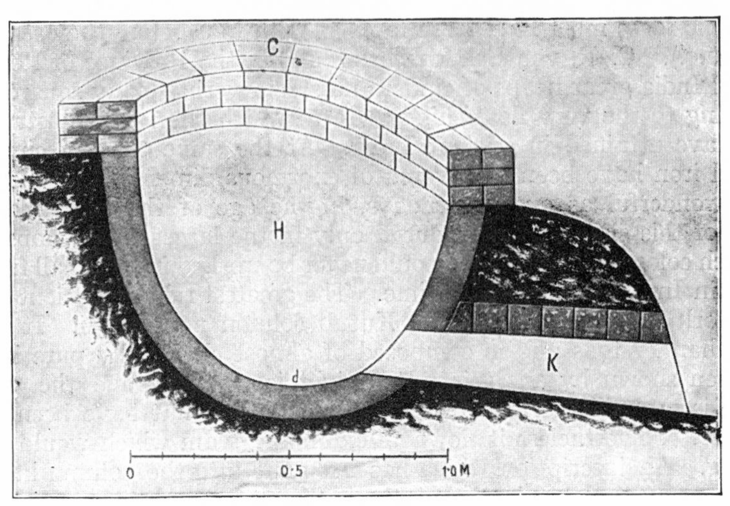

FIG. 15.—Prehistoric Blast-furnace (Belgium)

H is the interior, lined with clay, in which the smelting is effected, and into which the wind blows through the canal lined with stones. A bellows was not used. The stone brim C keeps the flames convergent

Besides wrought-iron, cast-iron was also known in India 3,000 years ago. Tombs of about the time 1400 B.C. contain objects (tools and so forth) made of cast-iron.

Iron was known very long ago to other peoples of the East besides the Indians, and was used for making articles of the most varied kind. The Egyptian king Thothmes III brought back from his campaigns great quantities of iron spears and other weapons, etc. But these are not the only proofs of the high standard reached by the iron industry in Asia. A more powerful indication is given by the fact that iron was exported in great quantities to other countries. Once again it was the enterprising Phoenicians who had chief control of the iron trade.

FIG. 16.—Prehistoric Pit Furnace (Épernay, Marne)

The furnace has been dug out of the base of a hill, lined with clay, and after having been filled with the ore, covered with loam or mud. Ignition was effected through the holes punctured in the clay, which also caused a draught of air

It is also very probable that the earliest iron in Germania was imported from Asia. The appearance and the composition of iron of the

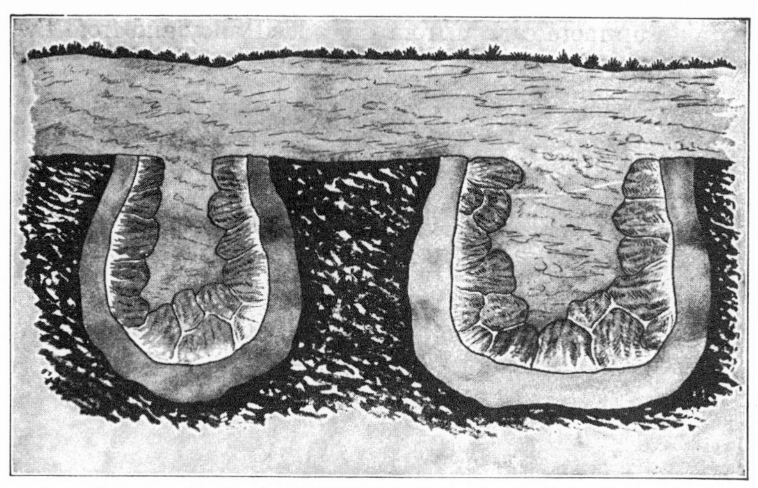

FIG. 17.—An ancient Bloomery (Waltendorf in Carniola)

year 900 B.C. leads to this conclusion. Later on, iron production was introduced into Germania itself and was by no means uncommon. In the same way, the Greeks and the Romans probably became acquainted with iron as an article of commerce before they began to prepare it themselves.

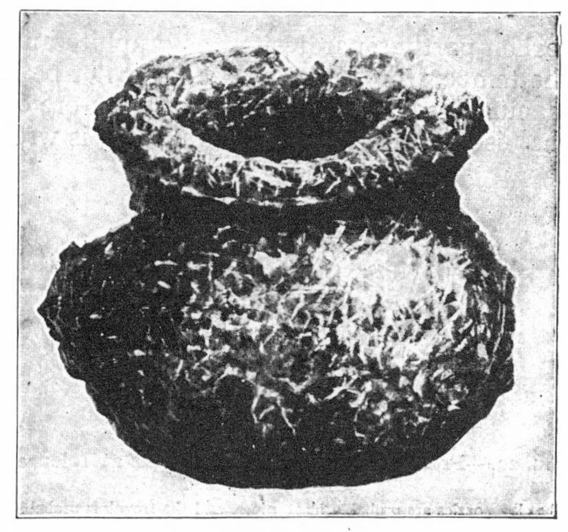

FIG. 18.—Bloomery Pot from Lower Lusatia

Consisting of a hole made in the earth, into which slag was melted; this formed the wall of the pot, an aperture for blowing being left at the top and another for drawing off the molten product at the bottom

A very characteristic feature of the extraction of iron in ancient times is that pig-iron was not known at all. Every specimen of ancient iron, no matter by which people it was prepared, belongs to the types that we nowadays call wrought-iron and steel. If we trace the causes of this phenomenon we find that they arise from the following circumstances. It has already been shown above what an important position was occupied by copper during the whole of antiquity. To reduce copper-ores a temperature of 1,100° C. is necessary. This is probably the highest temperature attained by the ancients in their metallurgical processes. The construction of all the furnaces that are known to be of that time leads us to infer that, in spite of the general use of bellows later, no higher temperatures were reached. Now, pig-iron is produced where iron which has been reduced and is poor in carbon takes up more carbon from the added alloy and from the gases present in the furnace at a temperature of 1,225° C. On cooling, this

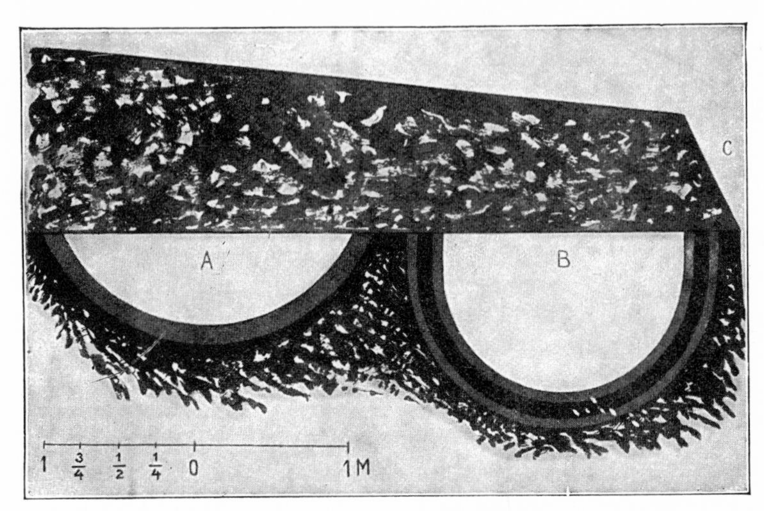

Fig. 19.—Roman Bloomeries from Hüttenberg in Carinthia
The less deep pit probably served for roasting the ore, the deeper one, lined with clay, for the actual bloomery process

carbon partly separates out as graphite and partly forms a carbide. As the temperature of 1,225° C. could not be reached, no pig-iron could be manufactured. The reduction of iron-ore occurs at 700° C. The product that is obtained at this temperature is wrought-iron or steel. Whether the one or the other was formed probably depended in the main on chance. At any rate the use of the same ores and the same fuel in the same furnaces would probably have led to a product of uniform composition. A proof of the correctness of this view is again given by the column of Kutub. It is hardly possible that masses of iron greater than 55 lbs. were smelted at one and the same time in the ancient Indian furnaces used to supply the iron for the column. As the latter weighs about 17 tons it must be formed of a great number of smaller pieces welded together. Nevertheless, it exhibits a uniform composition throughout, which has suggested to some investigators, for example, C. R. von Schwarz, the opinion that it must have been formed

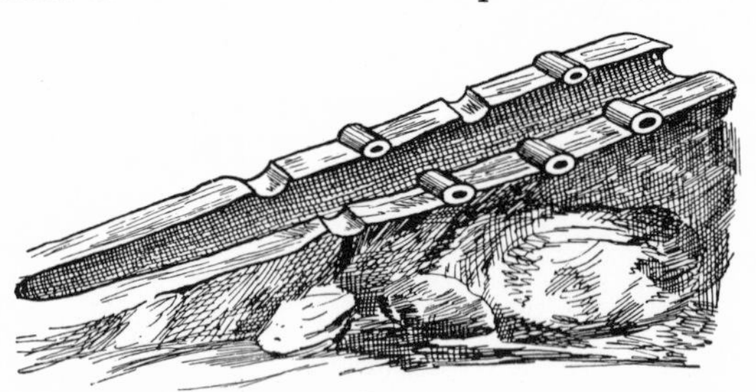

Fig. 20.—Prehistoric Iron Smelting Works at Iolenze in Carniola
The clay nozzles are probably blast pipes, and the trough is probably inclined so as to allow the slag to flow away more easily

of a single block. But nowhere have traces been found of constructions which would make the preparation of so vast a piece of iron in a single process in one furnace seem probable.

In ancient times the smelting of iron from its ores was carried out by the process which we usually call direct extraction (Catalan method) nowadays. We still find among savage races of the present day examples of the primitive method, for they use the same furnaces as were employed in the earliest times (Figs. 15–18). A primitive furnace was used which often consisted of only a pit sunk into the ground, which was lined with fire-proof material such as clay or bricks or a mixture of both. The furnace was then fed with ore and fuel, the latter probably consisting almost entirely of charcoal. A wood-fire was probably used to start the fuel burning. The iron was in these cases left in the furnaces and removed when cold. More often, however, it was run off through a sloping groove at the bottom of the furnace. Later, the walls were made higher and bellows were added (Figs. 20–23). The bellows that were used at the time of Thothmes III are known from the discoveries in Theban tombs. There is a picture of a sort of bloomery which is kept in action by two bellows devices (Fig. 24). The ores lie in a pit; over it is a mound with holes from which the flames shoot forth. We must therefore imagine ore and charcoal to be added to

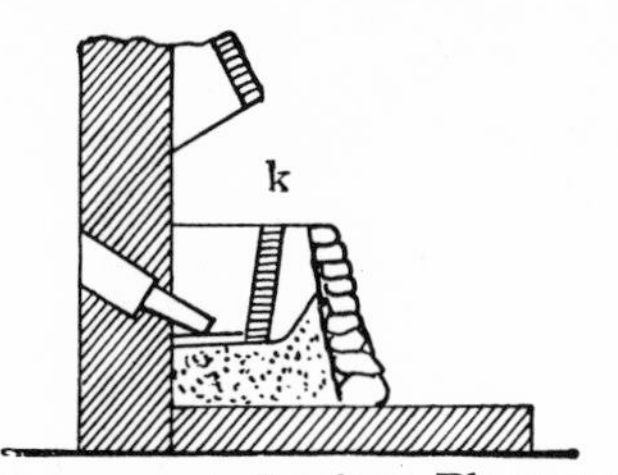

FIG. 21.—A Corsican Bloomery

FIG. 22.—A Catalan Bloomery

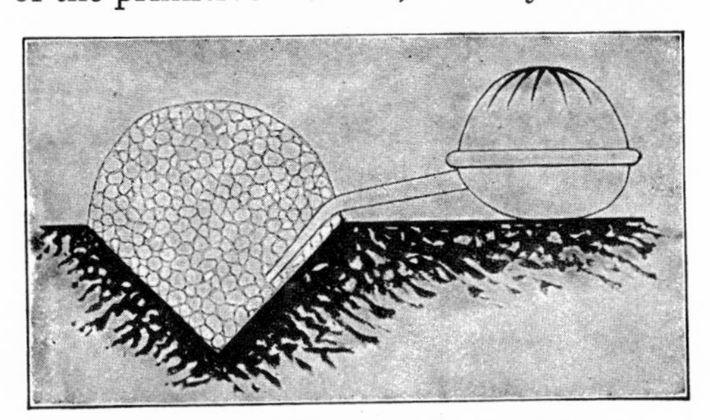

FIG. 23.—A Bloomery in Kordofan

FIG. 24.—A supposed Bloomery in ancient Egypt

the top of the pile and to sink in gradually as the metal (in this case, gold) melted out. The bellows are leather skins, which are fastened to a frame to hold them in position. They are compressed by treading and are expanded by cords which are pulled upwards. A draught of air is introduced into the furnace by means of clay pipes. The picture also displays in the background a basket filled with wood-charcoal (Fig. 24).

Generally, the iron flows out, as already mentioned, through the exit channel and collects in the form of 'bloom' on the floor of the receiving pit. The lumps of bloom, of which many are still found in deserted smelting works of the ancients, weigh from 15 to 55 lbs. (Figs. 25 and 26). They were covered by slag, which flowed out simultaneously and which was either scooped off or knocked off when cold. The process of making iron and steel was always effected in one stage. According to Aristotle it is only in India that fused iron was first prepared and afterwards subjected to a fresh treatment.

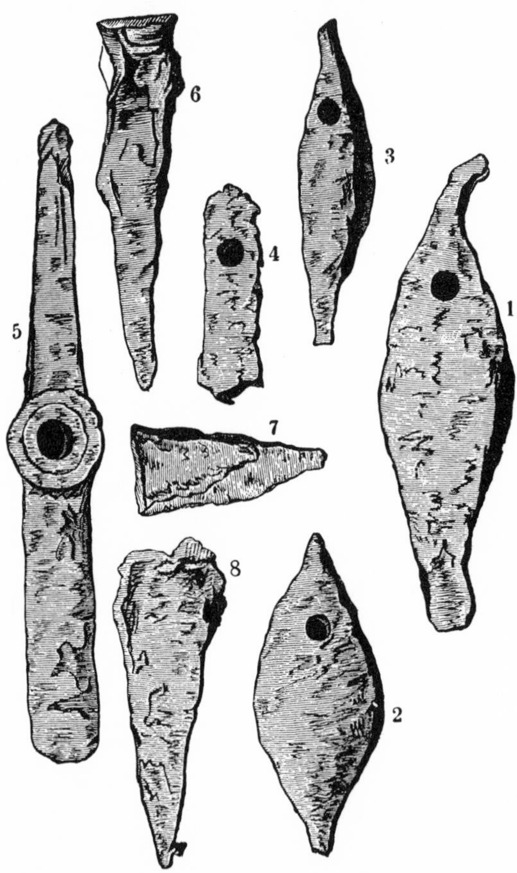

FIG. 25.—Crude Bloom (1, 2, 3) and Worked Bloom from the Excavations of Khorsabad

The holes in these lumps of crude bloom were to enable them to be strung up on ropes so as to be transportable by animals or men

In general the extraction of iron seems not to have been improved upon in the course of time, if we disregard the increase of size and height of the furnaces, which gradually attained greater and greater dimensions, so that eventually, instead of the original simple hearths, there were proper cupolas or blast-furnaces. From these our huge smelting-furnaces of the present day evolved (Fig. 27). In isolated instances coke or lignite (brown coal) was used instead of charcoal to fire the furnaces, as, for example, among the Chinese. Theophrastus also (fourth century B.C.) mentions that the metallurgists in Elis and Liguria made copious use of a coal which occurred there naturally. The masses of bloom extracted passed from the iron works into the hands of traders and were transformed only at their destination into weapons, tools, and so forth, by being re-smelted and re-forged. Certain kinds of iron were particularly popular among some peoples; for example, the Romans had a special liking for iron from Elba and later for iron from the Noric provinces, after they had been conquered. The number of ancient iron works and iron relics discovered is extraordinarily great. In the burial-ground of Hallstatt several thousand specimens of iron have been found, and in the Jura Mountains alone over 230 iron pits have been discovered.

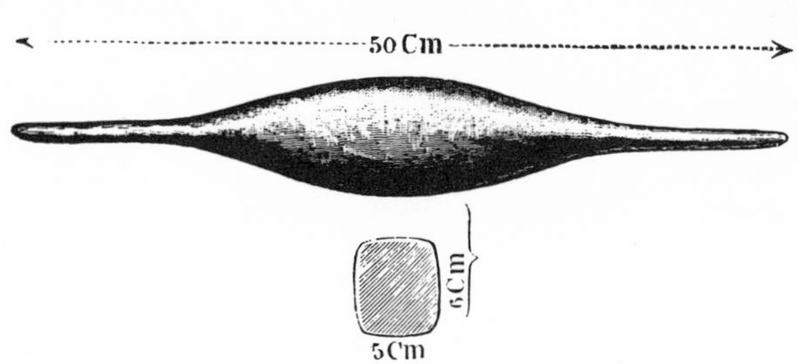

Fig. 26.—Re-forged Bloom in the Romano-Germanic Museum at Mainz

OTHER METALS

The other metals known to the ancients were of considerably less importance to them than those already discussed. Mercury was known to them, but was probably used only very little in the pure state. It was chiefly employed in the form of the sulphide, cinnabar, which served as a red pigment. It is also probable that it was applied in Spain to extract gold by making it form an amalgam with it. For both mercury and gold occur in Spain, and, further, Vitruvius relates that the gold from the garments which had been interwoven with gold thread could be recovered by reducing the garments to ash in a crucible and treating the ash with mercury, which took all the gold. When this amalgam was pressed through the pores of a cloth bag the gold remained behind. Like mercury, antimony and arsenic were probably also known only in their sulphur compounds. Whether plati-

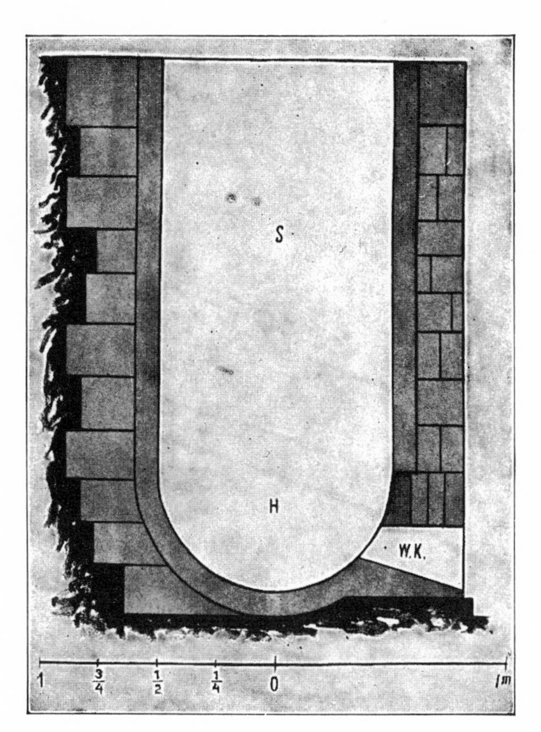

Fig. 27.—An Isolated Ancient Blast Furnace from Ore Deposits in Carinthia

H = hearth. S = pit. WK = wind-canal (draught hole).

num as such was known to the ancients appears doubtful. It is disputed by von Lippmann. It may have been mistaken for silver in isolated instances and have been worked as such. Berthelot investigated a box, of Egyptian origin, ornamented with inscribed hieroglyphics, which belonged to Queen Shaperapit, the daughter of Psammetichus I in the seventh century B.C. He found that the inscription was made of platinum containing a fair percentage of iridium. As platinum was not known to occur in Africa, the metal was probably introduced from elsewhere. Berthelot assumes that it was washed out of Nile sand together with gold.

METAL-WORKING

NO use could be made of the metals in the state in which they were found in Nature or in which they were obtained metallurgically from their ores. They had therefore to be subjected to particular methods of treatment before jewellery, tools, household utensils and other articles of the most varied kind could be made from them. This treatment was sometimes mechanical, sometimes chemical. Whereas the mechanical process served the purpose of bringing the metal into a suitable form, the chemical treatment was applied to effect a change in appearance, particularly of the surface, or to join pieces of metal, as in the case of soldering, which depends on the formation of alloys.

In both these methods of treatment, the mechanical and the chemical, the peoples of even the most remote antiquity possessed an extraordinary technique. They knew how to make use of the property of extensibility, especially of the precious metals, not only by increasing their surfaces through hammering and embossing, but also by forcing them to assume particular forms by the same means. The use of casting for producing new forms probably originated later. The oldest images, such as the statues of gods and so forth, were modelled in clay or carved in wood and then covered with thin gold foil. To make the pieces of foil adhere to the model and also to make them join up riveting and probably also welding was applied. Moreover, the gold foil was sometimes hammered into the model with the help of artificially made corners and edges—a method which has been found to occur among nearly all the most ancient races.

METAL LEAF AND EMBOSSING

Among metals gold possesses the property of ductility to a particularly marked degree. It is therefore not surprising that this property was early recognized and exploited. Gold-leaf, that is, gold which has been beaten out into thin sheets by continued hammering, occurs almost everywhere in prehistoric times. Such gold was used to make magnificent goldsmith's work even in the year 3500 B.C., as is proved by an ancient Egyptian necklace at present in the Berlin Museum. About the same time objects of the most diverse description were covered with gold foil, and as early as 2600 B.C. proper gilding with the help of gold-leaf occurs in the Egyptian kingdom ; that is, the gold is no longer attached by riveting or welding, but use is made of its property of adhesion. For example, wood is covered with wax, on which the gold-leaf is laid and to which it then simply adheres. In the case of objects of other material a layer of stucco is first applied. This is painted and the gold-leaf is then superposed on it, as in our modern method of gilding ceilings. The property of adhesion is also the basis of making gold-fillings in teeth; gold-leaf is pressed or hammered into the tooth. It has been proved that this was practised by the ancients, and was universally adopted later. It is remarkable that this method of filling teeth was also prevalent

FIG. 28.—The Workshop of a Goldsmith
On the left is a gold-beater—Picture taken from a grave in Saqqarah (= Saccara)

among the original Aztecs in Ecuador, where Saville, in pursuing researches under the auspices of Columbia University, discovered skulls, in some of which the teeth were filled with cement and in others with gold. The ancient Egyptians were able to beat out gold to leaf as thin

FIG. 29.—Representation of a Gold-beater (in the centre) from the Tomb of Rekhmara

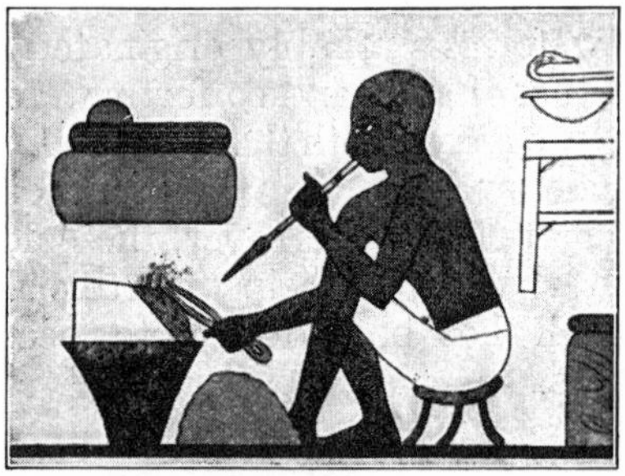

FIG. 30.—Melting Metal in Egypt by means of a Blowpipe
In the left top corner are implements which, according to Theobald, must be interpreted as the anvil, form and hammering stone of a goldsmith. (Notice the frame, which consists of alternate layers of parchment and gold)

as that made in the eighteenth century of our era. Berthelot found from measurements that such gold leaves of the twelfth and thirteenth dynasties (about 2000–1800 B.C.) were only ·001 mm. thick (about $\frac{4}{100000}$ of an inch). Silver, like gold, was also hammered out to thin sheets (·001 to ·0025 mm.).

What method was used by the ancient Egyptians and other ancient peoples to make such thin gold leaves? Pictures from a grave at Saqqarah (Fig. 28), which date back to about 2500 B.C., and others from the tomb of the Egyptian dignitary Rekhmara (about 1450 B.C.) (Fig. 29), must be interpreted, according to Theobald, as representing the goldsmith's art (see also Fig. 30). On a stone, which also serves as anvil, the so-called 'form,' in this case a pile consisting of alternate layers of gold-leaf and pieces of skin, is placed. The gold-beater holds this form with his left hand and manipulates with his right the heavy stone with which he strikes the form. The method is thus identical with that still used in the goldsmith's workshop, except that the stone is now replaced by a hammer; and whereas nowadays the pile of gold-leaf and skins which constitute the form is made fairly high, it was at that time kept low and consisted only of a few layers. We do not know what kinds of skins were used. It is hardly likely that the ancients used the same skin as the modern

FIG. 31.—Colossal Bronze Statue of Hercules which has been entirely gilt by being covered with gold-leaf. Roman work

(Rome, Museum of the Vatican)

FIG. 32.—Roman Gold-beater, probably preparing an Ingot

(Museum of the Vatican)

gold-beater, namely, that prepared from a bullock's cæcum. Maspero holds the opinion that parchment was used, that is, asses' skin. This view is shared by Wilkinson.[1]

The preparation of the gold-foil to be hammered into leaf is nowadays carried out by casting the gold into ingots, that is, into oblong masses, which are then rolled out into long narrow thin plates. The metal was probably prepared in a similar way by the ancient Egyptians. Concerning the casting and the apparatus involved there are still preserved pictures which we shall discuss in detail later when we come to the section on 'Casting in Metal', p. 54.

[1] *The Manners and Customs of the Ancient Egyptians*. London, 1878, Vol. II, p. 243.

As we find either relics of gold-leaf or reports of its use among all peoples of antiquity, those of the Near East, the Jews, the Indians and so forth, it must be assumed that it was prepared in the same way as by the Egyptians, owing to the trade relationships of that time and to the fact that many technical arts were thus disseminated from race to race. Many peoples that used gold-leaf may also have drawn their supplies from foreign countries. The Chinese, whose civilization is largely based on the applications of paper, probably used thin sheets of black paper in place of parchment.

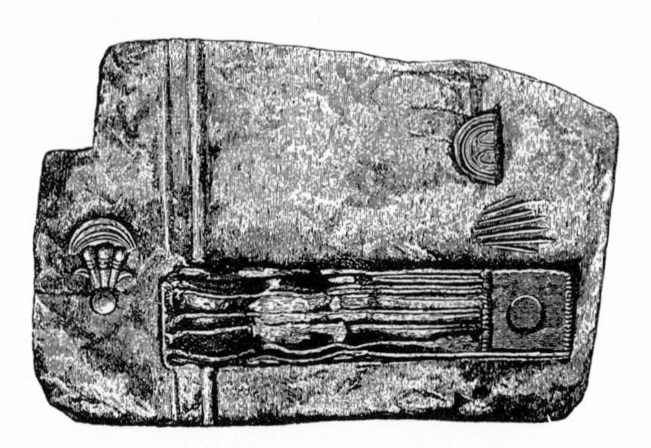

FIGS. 33 and 34.—Two Sides of a Granite Form used to emboss various Pieces of Jewellery

Schliemann's assumption that they are moulds for casting is certainly wrong, for the counterpart pieces are missing, as also the funnel, and the canals, air-pipes, etc. Moreover, the form resembles those used for embossing up till recent times, and the objects depicted in these forms were always produced by embossing. The picture is two-thirds of the true size

Gold-leaf was very widely distributed among the Greeks and the Romans. The former used it even in the age of Homer, that is, probably about 850–800 B.C. The 'form' was not composed of gold leaves and skin, but probably of alternate layers of gold sheets and copper foil. For about A.D. 75 Dioscorides writes (V, 91) that to prepare copper vitriol it was also possible to use the filings from the copper leaves between which gold-leaf was beaten (*λεπίδων αἷς περιεχόμενα τὰ χρυσᾶ πέταλα ἐλαύνεται*). Both the Greeks and the Romans had various terms for gold plates and gold-leaves. The Romans used different names, according to the thickness of the gold-leaf. Pliny relates (XXXIII, 61) that from one ounce (30·59 grams) of gold it was possible to beat 750 and more leaves having a length of side equal to the width of four fingers (1 digitus = ·0185 metres, i.e. about ·73 in.). Clarac (see below) assumes a value that differs only inappreciably from this. Thus the thinnest leaves were about $\frac{1}{300}$ mm. thick, or $\frac{13}{1000000}$ in.; so that they were about thirty times as thick as the best gold leaves made nowadays (which are less than $\frac{1}{9000}$ mm. thick). From experiments which Clarac had made to test Pliny's statements, he arrived at the following remarkable table, giving a comparison between the goldsmith's art in ancient Roman and in modern times. It must be remarked that the leaves of ·00018 mm. thickness represent a particularly good result not commonly achieved.

No. of Roman leaves from one Roman ounce.	No. of Paris leaves from one Roman ounce.	Length of side (in Roman fingers).	Area in sq. cms.	Total surface of the leaves in square metres.	Weight of leaf in grms.	Thickness of leaf in mm.
750	750,000	4·00	54·3904	4·04185	·0363	·0003
750	427,733	6·72	153·9351	6·58303	·6374	·00018

The hammer used by the Romans to beat the gold probably resembled the modern goldsmith's hammer, although it is not definitely established whether the only preserved picture of a gold-beater (*aurifex brattearius*) on a relief in the Vatican (in which the second word is spelt *brattiarius*) represents the actual beating-out of the form (see Fig. 32, p. 31). It may represent the preliminary stage of preparing long narrow gold bands, the so-called ingots. As the modern gold-beater stands while hammering the gold and is probably only able in this position to strike the strong but elastic blow, which alone prevents the thin gold leaves from tearing, it seems most improbable to the author that the ancient goldsmiths, who also produced very fine leaves, performed this work while seated. In this posture the strength and elasticity of the blows would be considerably reduced. Nor is the hammer in this picture being used to deliver an elastic blow such as comes out quite clearly in the ancient Egyptian sketches, in which the goldsmith is shown kneeling.[1]

Fig. 35.—Fragment of Limestone on which is a drawing representing Coppersmiths embossing a Vessel

Found at Dêr el-Medîna. Width 11 cms. Berlin Museum, Egyptian Department

Besides gold and silver, other metals were also made into thin leaves by hammering, and at the same time often brought into a definite shape or embossed.[2] Plates were made, also useful articles and objects of art. For making plates an anvil was used, on which the metal was hammered

[1] Concerning the use of the scraps left over from the hammering of gold and silver for the production of colours, see p. 195.

[2] Gk. *τορεύματα* from *τορεύειν*, to bore; according to O. Müller, *Handbuch der Archäologie*, it was a Greek invention. Lat. *caelatura*.

out to the desired thinness. For embossing, forms or moulds of wood or stone (Figs. 33, 34 and 39) were used, over which the sheet of metal was superposed or into which it was laid and then hammered by a metal

FIG. 36.—Attic Phiale representing the Process of Embossing in Bronze.
Note the form of the hammer with its rounded and thickened ends. Berlin, Altes Museum, Antiquarium

or wooden hammer, depending on the metal composing the sheet, until it had acquired the form of the mould. The hammer often had rounded

FIG. 37.—Embossing large Vessels
In the centre a large piece is apparently being embossed over a form. The author is of the opinion that the shape of the hammer (round corners) shows that embossing is being performed. On the right the embossed articles are probably being polished

or thickened edges, as is also usual nowadays, in order that the metal may not be damaged by sharp edges (see Figs. 36 and 37). Difficulties were at first encountered in embossing large objects. Separate parts were therefore embossed and afterwards riveted together. Later, however, the ancients learned how to emboss whole vessels, pitchers, goblets and so forth, in one piece. A further advance in the art of metal-working was made by embossing metal by freehand, in which the form or mould was no longer used and which required a highly developed technique. A drawing was made, according to which the expert worker modelled the object by shaping the reverse side by means of hammers and other tools. The parts which have been embossed were then protected from injury

FIG. 38.—The Sword of Tiberius

An excellent example of Roman embossing. It was found on August 10, 1848, in Mainz. Length = 16 inches. Width = 2·8 inches

during the further course of the work by being filled with pitch or, as Rhousopoulos has shown by analysis, wax. Faults in embossing, such as parts that have been hammered out too far, were corrected by using punches on which the too prominent or too deep parts could be hammered back. To prevent tearing in this process and to soften the blow the interior was in this case also filled with pitch. By this process the ancients produced vessels, fastenings, tripods, goblets, plates, statuettes and so forth, some of which were entirely made by embossing, whereas others

FIG. 39.—Ancient Egyptian Embossing Mould

(Rome, Museum of the Vatican)

For figures made of gold plate. Hard yellowish stone 1·9 × 1·7 inch. Berlin Museum, Egyptian Department

FIG. 40.—Egyptian Embossing in Gold

Winged figure in gold-leaf; human-headed 'soul-giver'. Height = 1·3 inch; breadth = 3 inches. Abusir el Meleq. Common Tomb of the Priests of Ansaphes. Berlin Museum, Egyptian Department

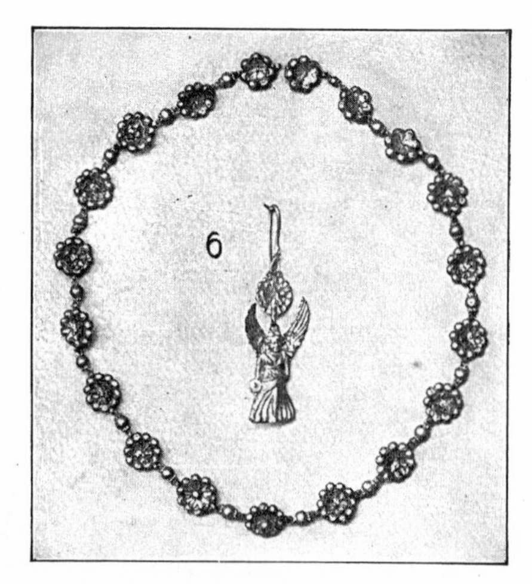

FIG. 41.—Specimens of Roman Embossing in Gold

(Bangle and Ear-ring.) Berlin, Altes Museum, Antiquarium

FIG. 42.—Embossed Diadem from Mycenæ. About 1600 B.C.

Alloy (Electrum) of 75 per cent. gold and 24·9 per cent. silver. Athens Museum (Catalogue No. 37)

were ornamented only with relief-work. The metal most used besides the precious metals was copper and its derivative bronze. The bronzes of Siris in the British Museum show that in embossing this metal the

FIG. 43.—An Embossed Gold Vase from Mycenæ (about 1600 B.C.)
Analysis revealed the presence of wax in the inner parts. Athens Museum (Catalogue No. 351)

ancients succeeded in hammering it out to the thinness of paper. Embossing was also performed on lead plates and sheets; the latter were then used for various technical purposes, for example, for water-pipes, for sieves in drains, and so forth.

WIRES

The ancients had many uses for wire, especially for that made from the precious metals, which they formed into ornaments and used even to fasten loose teeth (according to Saville). Ancient Egyptian finds of about 3500 B.C. include copper wire, and there are many traces that indicate the use of wire in later times. There are still preserved wires from the sixth century A.D. as much as 5 feet long (Germanisches Museum, Nuremberg). At the time of the destruction of Pompeii (A.D. 79) wire cables were already in use. One of these found in Pompeii is 15 feet long and 1 inch in circumference. It consists of bronze wire in which three cables, each composed of 15 strands, are twisted round each other. Thus all sorts of metals were formed into wire, but only very little is known about how they were made. One method is described in the Bible

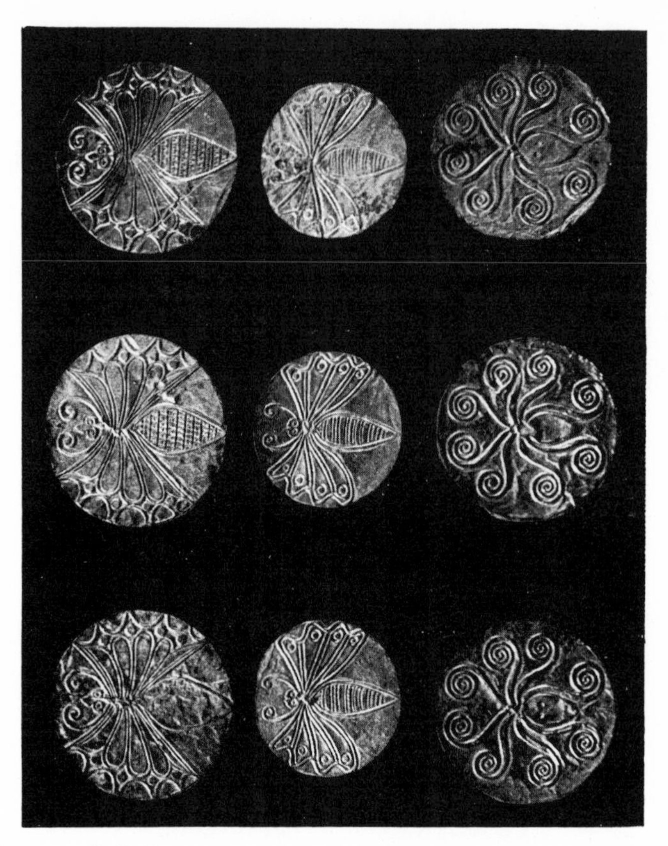

FIG. 44.—Gold Rosettes. Embossed Work (from a grave in Mycenae)
About 1600 B.C. Athens Museum (Catalogue No. 590)

(Exodus xxxix, 3), in which the passage occurs: 'and they did beat the gold into thin plates, and cut it into wires, to work it . . . in the fine linen.' Wire was further produced by hammering out metals and also by forging them. According to Schliemann (*Ilion, Stadt und Land der Trojaner*, p. 509) drawn wire was known even in the age of Homer, and it has also been found in various localities (among them Mycenae) in which valuable finds of ancient objects have been made. No word has been

FIG. 45.—Embossed Metal Vessels being sold in the street
The size may be estimated by comparison with the accompanying human figures. Wall-painting in Herculaneum

passed down to us as to how this drawn wire was prepared, but we may assume that long pieces of wire, such as were used as long ago as

FIG. 46.—Examples of Roman goldsmith's work in gold wire and gold foil

1. Bracelet made of gold-foil. 2 and 4. Chains composed of beads made from gold-foil. 3. Chain woven from very fine gold wire no thicker than a hair. Berlin. Altes Museum, Antiquarium

2900 B.C. at Saqqarah, were made by welding together various forged pieces.

STAMPING

Another form of metal-working that was much practised in antiquity was that of stamping, by which metallic sheets were not only given a definite form, but were also decorated by raising or lowering the surface according to design. Whether little pieces were also stamped out of the sheets has not been proved, although the punch was already known in Mycenaean times and was used for producing ornamentation. Round metal discs were probably cut out with scissors or knives. Ornamentations were stamped into caskets, into pieces of metal which were then sewn on to garments, and so forth ; this was carried out by placing the metal sheet on a lead anvil. The stamp-mould, which was made of

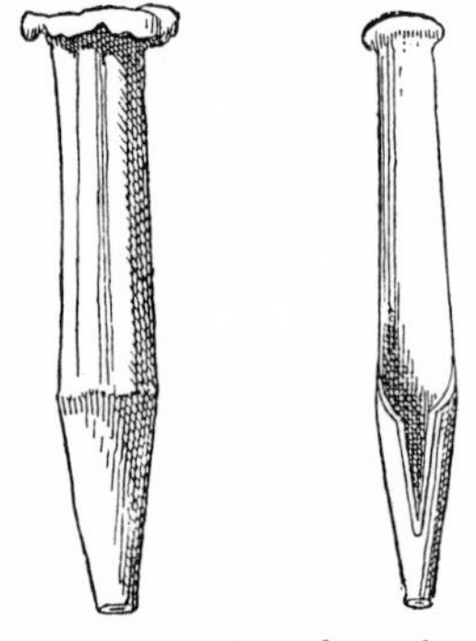

FIG. 47.—Punches for punching ornamentations in sheet-metal

harder metal, that is, of bronze or even iron, was then placed on top. This die carried the ornamental pattern, which had usually been engraved in it, but had in some cases perhaps been cut out by means of a grinding wheel. By a vigorous blow of the hammer the pattern on the die was impressed upon the metal sheet. Sometimes this sheet was perhaps placed on the stamp, the engraved face of which was then upwards, and driven by hammering to follow the pattern of the die. Designs which were often repeated, such as ornaments on bowls, rims on goblets, and so forth, were mostly produced by using the same die in succession.

COINING, CHASING AND ENGRAVING

Closely related to the stamping of sheet-metal was the stamping of solid metal, which was extensively used for coining money. Coins were very often, however,—particularly in Roman times—made by casting. We shall return to this method later, when dealing with metal-casting generally. Here we shall first discuss coinage, which owed its origin to a peculiar set of circumstances. Metal was originally not the only thing used for money. Very different objects were used, and in China as early as the year 2697 B.C. paper money is supposed to have been issued, which was prepared from the fibre of the mulberry-tree and was inscribed with the maxim: 'All that thou doest, do with caution.' When metal began to be used as money, it was treated like merchandise, that is, it was weighed out for payment. This was done by the Jews before the Babylonian Captivity. In Egypt the money, which was in the form of rings made of precious metal, was weighed by means of scales of very appropriate design (see Figs. 48 and 49). Nor did the Greeks and Romans use coined money at the outset. As weighing wasted

FIG. 48.—Weighing of Money Rings

The man is observing whether the balance is equipoised. There is equilibrium when the three threads by which the little weight is suspended from the middle of the beam are all taut at once. If one thread is slack the scales are not balanced. 18th Dynasty (about 1550 B.C.). From the tombs Abd el Guma, Thebes

time the process was simplified by giving the precious metal the already mentioned form of rings or else of bars, which were designed to have a definite weight. On the basis of the money coined by so simple a process an extensive system of finance arose, as, for example, in Babylon. There was no guarantee, however, that the rings were made from metal of the correct degree of purity. A ring might have the correct weight and yet not contain the proper amount of gold. It occurred relatively late to the ancients to guarantee the weight and purity of content by stamping the rings or the bars (ingots). In Babylon and Egypt this method of marking had not come into use. The art of striking coins seems to have arisen about the year 700 B.C., and according to recent research (H. Halke) Herodotus was probably right in asserting that 'they (the Lydians) were, so far as we know, the first to stamp and use gold and silver coins' (Herodotus I, 94). The coins were egg-shaped and exhibited on one side a number of parallel stripes; on the other there were irregular dents. They were made of 'electrum', the alloy of gold and silver which has been mentioned above (p. 11), and which in this case contained these metals in the proportion 3 : 1. It was only later that pictures were stamped on the coins (heads of animals, figures of gods, and finally of the rulers of the country in question).

FIG. 49.—Another Egyptian Balance, of different construction

Attached to the beam is a pointer directed vertically downwards and carrying a plummet that is evidently to coincide with a point marked on the support

Coins were struck by a sort of improved process of stamping. A die was used in which the design to be impressed was engraved. The dies were made of hardened bronze, but very often also of iron. They do not seem to have been very durable, since from one and the same mint in the course of a very short time, often only a year, coins were sent out with constantly changing designs owing to the use of new dies. There must have been an enormous variety of types in antiquity. Of all these dies, however, only two Greek and a number of Roman examples have come down to us. Moreover, numismatists do not regard the latter dies as genuine. They are considered to be dies used by forgers for making counterfeit coins. A further die, only recently found in Egypt (Fig. 50) dates back to the time 430–322 B.C., that is, to the time of the Persian kings, and shows that coins were then already being struck in Egypt.

This die is made of bronze, being over 2 in. high and weighing about $\frac{1}{3}$ lb.; it has the form of two truncated pyramids of unequal height, placed base to base. The lower pyramid, which carries the design, is the one of less altitude. An investigation by Zenghelis disclosed that the die was of the same hardness and colour throughout. Apparent thickenings are due to the action of a hammer and the resistance of what was below it. Analysis of the metal contained in this die showed that the original composition of the alloy was 75 parts by weight of copper and 25 parts by weight of tin. The usual tin-copper alloy contains 90 parts of copper to 10 parts of tin. Among the hundreds of analyses carried out by Zenghelis only one other case of this unusually high percentage of tin (nearly twice as much as usual) was discovered; this was an Egyptian spear-point, that is, an object which likewise demanded great hardness together with considerable density. But the die had also to be sufficiently soft to allow the picture which was to be stamped on the coin, the owl of the Athenian tetradrachm,[1] to be engraved in it. The fact that this particular alloy was chosen as having all these properties simultaneously and that it contains no trace of any foreign metal that might have affected these properties shows how clearly the influence of chemical composition on physical properties was recognized even at that time.

FIG. 50.—Greek Dies for Coins

Found in Tel el Ahrib in Egypt (about 430–322 B.C.). Height = 6 cms. (about 2·4 in.). Weight, 164·12 grms. (about $\frac{1}{3}$ lb.)

The coins of Greece and Rome—in particular those of the earlier times—are technically very imperfect. The greatest importance appears always to have been attached to giving as artistic a reproduction as possible of the picture in the die. Famous engravers of dies, such as the Greek Euainetos, inscribed their names on the dies of their own making. The metal for the die was not carved in the form of round discs out of ingots, as is usual with us, but rather each piece was cast separately and forms were used which could be opened out, like those nowadays used in mints to prepare metallic bars. As the stamping caused the coin to flatten or hollow out in the middle, and as the reliefs of some of the dies were rather prominent, the piece of metal to be stamped was often cast in the form of a lens slightly convex on each side. The edge of this piece of metal, which was usually not milled, in some cases still exhibits traces of the seam due to casting and the orifice for admitting the molten metal. The oldest serrated coins, the *serrata*, which had toothed edges like a saw, first occurred about 190 B.C. and were very popular among

[1] The tetradrachm (4 drachmae) was the famous Athenian stater or standard piece. See pp. 17 and 18 of the second edition of *A Guide to the Exhibition illustrating Greek and Roman Life*, issued by the British Museum, which contains excellent examples of the coins mentioned in the text. A perusal of this Guide is much to be recommended.—H. L. B.

FIG. 51.—Ancient Coins bearing Traces of the Process of Coining
Collection belonging to Dr. Cahn, Frankfort-on-the-Main. See Key at the foot of the following page

the Germanic tribes (Tacitus). In order to keep the coin in position whilst being stamped (this was at first done only on one side) a square serrated block was fixed on the anvil so that the blow of the hammer on the die forced the coin to be gripped firmly by the edges of the block and so to be marked by it. On old Greek coins one can still see the marks of this block, that projected from the anvil. Later on, the ancients made a virtue of necessity and gave the block any convenient form. As shown in the accompanying Fig. 51 this form was very often that of a square, either simple or marked with lines (*quadratum incusum*). This fulfilled technical requirements best. It effectively counteracted any pressure due to displacement, no matter in what direction it was exerted. When marked with lines, this block held the coin in a particularly firm grip, as any unsteady tendency was then checked at various points simultaneously.

FIG. 52.—Chasing a Helmet (left bottom corner) in the Workshop of Hephaistos (wall painting in Pompeii)

Letters were also cut into the block so that it served as a sort of counter-die or mould (*matrix*). From it there later developed the proper counterpart piece. Coins were prob-

Key to Fig. 51, p. 43.

1. Archaic Tetradrachm from Acanthus in Macedonia with a simple *quadratum incusum*; sixth century B.C.
2. Drachma from Aegina with Tortoise and simple lined ' quadratum incusum '; fifth century.
3. Archaic Stater from Corinth with the head of Athena in the *quadratum incusum*; fifth century.
4. Archaic Didrachm from Caulonia in South Italy, about 550 B.C., on which the picture on the obverse side is repeated on the reverse side. Of great technical interest.
5. Tetradrachm of Queen Philistis of Syracuse, 275 B.C.; the golden age of making dies for coins; high relief.
6. Tetradrachm of the Province of Macedonia while under Roman rule after 148 B.C. Example of late Greek die-cutting.
7. Early Romano-Campanian double denarius, about 250 B.C., bearing the legend ' Roma ' indented.
8. Didrachm from Hyria in Campania stamped with a faulty die.
9. Denarius of Julius Caesar, in which the impress overlaps the edge, owing to the die not having been centrally placed.
10. Denarius of the *Gens Pomponia,* about 100 B.C., with crenated (notched) edge (so-called ' Serratus ').
11. Didrachm from Metapontum (Lucania), impressed on too small a piece.
12. Cast Roman Triens ($= \frac{1}{3}$ As $= 4$ Unciae), with the hole of the casting form left as an excrescence; from the heavy copper coins issued by the city of Rome, fourth century B.C.
13. Ovally cast Sextans ($= \frac{1}{6}$ As $= 6$ Unciae) from the series of heavy Umbrian copper coins. The excrescences due to the casting holes have been clipped off.

ably always struck from the cold metal, although it has often been assumed that it was placed hot on the anvil and held with tongs. Several powerful blows on the die executed presumably by means of a heavy hammer constituted the actual process of coining. The relief mostly appears quite prominent, but, even as late as in Imperial Roman times, the impress is very often not in the middle. It is displaced towards the edge, sometimes it is indistinct, showing clearly that the die had not been accurately in position or had not been firmly fixed or that the coin itself had shifted, or else that in order to improve a bad impress a second had been attempted on top of the first. It is not improbable that large coins were first cast in a form or mould, which already contained the relief; the latter was made by taking a lead cast of the die and impressing this cast on the form. This relief, obtained by casting in the latter mould, was then placed in contact with the die and the somewhat blurred cast relief was brought out more distinctly by hammering.

Fig. 51 shows a number of other ancient coins in which characteristic features of the art of coining are recognizable.

Even before coins were struck, medals appear to have been made by the same process. In the Berlin Museum there is a gold medal which is probably of the time of the legendary Queen Semiramis, the daughter-in-law of Shalmanassar III (860–826 B.C.). Although the execution of this medal is primitive, it is of high artistic merit.

Besides the above processes of working metals mechanically, chasing was also practised (see Fig. 52, p. 44). As in the case of engraving, it was performed with instruments that are essentially similar to those nowadays in use.

RIVETING, SOLDERING, WELDING, CEMENTING

The joining up of several pieces of metal to form a single large piece was effected, as already mentioned above, by riveting or by using clamps. It is not known when these methods were supplanted by the more intimate union obtained by soldering. Glaucus of Chios is regarded by some as the inventor of soldering, or at any rate he was apparently so considered by the ancients. Actually, however, the arts of soldering and welding were both known before the time of Glaucus, who lived around the year 700 B.C. 'Soldering' we take as meaning the union of two pieces of the same or different metal by means of fire and the use of a third metal, the so-called 'solder'. 'Welding' is likewise effected by fire, but without the use of a third metal. Welded pieces which date back to the year 1490 B.C. were found among the excavations at Thebes (Wilkinson,[1] II, 258). Further, there is in the British Museum an Egyptian rattle of Pharaonic date, which is soldered with lead. Its exact date could not be ascertained, but it is at any rate older than the objects reputed to have been constructed by Glaucus. Moreover, Schliemann has excavated gold vessels which have also been soldered, but in this case with gold solder. From these and various other finds it is quite clear that soldering and

[1] See reference on p. 31.

welding are very ancient arts. It has emerged from investigation, particularly of the silver objects found at Hildesheim, which are of the time of the Julian Emperors, that hard soldering and soft soldering were already both in use. Soft solder consists of tin or a tin-alloy and is easily fusible. Hard solder is a copper alloy, mostly of the composition of bronze or brass. To what extent these two kinds of solder were used in Pliny's time cannot be discerned from his writings as (according to Blümner) he gives only a vague account of the art of soldering (XXXIII, 94). He says: 'For gold, "chrysocolla" is used; for iron, alumina; for large pieces of copper, calamine; for copper sheets, alum; for lead with marble, resin, with which also lead is joined to tin; for tin with tin, oil; and the same for the union of crude lead with bronze or crude lead with silver.' It is impossible to follow Pliny's meaning, as he jumbles up the solders with the other agents used to exclude the air from the joint during soldering in order to prevent oxidation of the metal surfaces. All that we can gather is that among such agents, according to Pliny, there were alumina, alum, and oil. Lead cannot be soldered with marble at all. Resin probably served both as a protective agent, in the above sense, for lead solderings as well as for filling up holes made in marble by pouring in lead. The latter process was often used to fasten bronze or iron clamps in marble. 'Chrysocolla' is malachite, that is, a basic copper carbonate, having the formula $CuCO_3.Cu(OH)_2$, which was probably not used directly as a solder but indirectly as a constituent of gold solder, the preparation of which is described in detail by both Dioscorides (v. 92) and Pliny. Verdigris is mixed with a boy's urine in a copper mortar. Soda is then added. Probably malachite, that is, chrysocolla, which has a composition resembling that of verdigris, could be used in place of the latter.

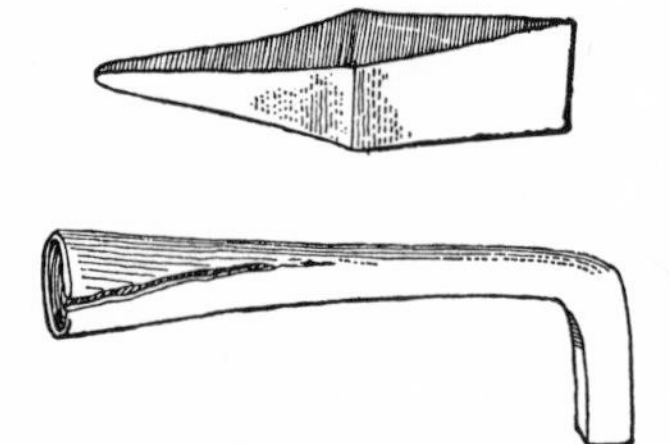

FIGS. 53 and 54.—Roman Blow-pipe and Soldering Iron. Found at Châtelet in France

Verdigris is a basic copper acetate having the composition $Cu(C_2H_3O_2)_2.2Cu(OH)_2$; it decomposes under the influence of heat in the same way as malachite, so that pure molten copper is finally produced, which effects the join. Thus, in both cases carbon dioxide or carbon monoxide is given off among other gases or vapours, and they protect the surfaces from oxidation.

The use of calamine as a solder, as alleged by Pliny, is perhaps explained by the fact that in a coal fire this compound of zinc and carbonic acid is reduced to pure zinc, which formed brass with the copper that was to be soldered, and so a hard solder was produced. A favourite and much used solder was lead, and also its alloy with tin. Pure tin was further used to solder the precious metals (as in the silver objects discovered at Hildesheim).

The actual process of soldering probably hardly differed at all from the modern method. The blow-pipe which served to concentrate the flame was probably already known to the ancient Egyptians. It is certain that the Roman goldsmiths used it and also the soldering iron (Figs. 53 and 54). For combining metals with other materials, there were used (apart from the process involving lead and resin above mentioned), cements whose composition is not yet wholly explained. Thus, in a tomb at Mycenae Rhousopoulus found rosettes of gold which had been fastened to the wooden cover of the coffin by means of a cement containing manganese. Other cements, also containing manganese, have been found elsewhere, so that there are grounds for believing that some manganese ore, probably pyrolusite, was a common constituent of such cements in ancient Greece.

FORGING METALS. THE SMITHY

In ancient times, just as nowadays, the forging of metals occupied a prominent position among the metallic arts. For even in antiquity the smith furnished a great portion of the implements necessary for agriculture, technical work, and for the household as well as for purposes connected with transport and war. The metal most used for forging at that time was bronze; pure copper was also used. Father Scheil discovered in Susa a smith's bill for bronze weapons, which was inscribed on terra-cotta and dated back to the thirtieth century B.C. Later, iron formed the basis of the smith's art. Whether and to what extent bronze and copper were actually forged in the true sense, that is, were worked after they had been softened by being heated in a fire, must remain an open question. The methods of working metals when cold and forging them when hot were probably both used at the same period; at any rate the following passage in the eighteenth book of the *Iliad* which deals with the making of Achilles' armour by Hephaistos, allows us to infer that bronze was in this case worked in both the hot and the cold state and was provided with external ornaments or artistically stamped:

'This said, he left her there, and forth did to his bellows go,
Apposed them to the fire again, commanding them to blow.
Through twenty holes made to his hearth at once blew twenty pair,
That fired his coals, sometimes with soft, sometimes with vehement air.
As he will'd, and his work requir'd. Amidst the flame he cast
Tin, silver, precious gold, and brass; and in the stock he plac'd
A mighty anvil; his right hand a weighty hammer held,
His left his tongs. And first he forged a strong and spacious shield
Adorn'd with twenty several hues, about whose verge he beat
A ring, three-fold and radiant; and on the back he set
A silver handle; five-fold were the equal lines he drew
About the whole circumference: in which his hand did shew,
Directed with a knowing mind, a rare variety, . . .' [1]

---

[1] Chapman's translation.—H. L. B.

This description by Homer gives us important information about the art of forging in far-distant antiquity, and shows above all that, at that early time, in the main the tools used were the same as nowadays, namely the bellows, the anvil, the hammer and the tongs. Actually the bellows appears to have been one of the earliest contrivances used to work metals when hot, for it is represented in the paintings on the ancient Egyptian temple at Karnak (sixteenth century B.C.) and is also mentioned in the Bible, in which we read in Jeremiah vi. 29: 'The bellows is burned.' The Romans also often refer to it, as for example Vergil, *Georgics* iv, 170 foll.,

> So the Cyclopes, when in haste they forge
> Jove's thunderbolts, to melt the stubborn mass
> Some with their bellows of tough ox's hide
> Drive in and out the blast; the hissing bronze
> Others in water plunge, till Aetna groans
> Beneath their anvils' weight.

Similarly Cicero, *de natura deorum*, i, 54, speaks of 'anvils and bellows'.

What was the appearance of the ancient bellows? Old Egyptian pictures represent them as bags made of skin, probably from an ox, fastened into a frame to hold them fixed in position, and provided in front with a wind-channel, probably made of bamboo, which stretched nearly to the hearth. To prevent the bamboo from getting ignited a nozzle was placed over the end. The man who worked the bellows stood on two such bags, one foot on each, and held in each hand a cord with which to pull it up and so distend it. While he pressed down on one bag he released his foot from the other and pulled it up by means of the corresponding cord. (See Fig. 55, and Fig. 24 on p. 25.) The forerunner of the bellows was probably the common fan, which was used to make the fire glow more brightly. Further, in ancient Egypt, the fire was also stimulated by means of tubes blown by mouth (Fig. 28, p. 30). In later times, too, the bellows were made of animal skins sewn together into bags. Horace in his Satires (i, 4, 19) mentions that goatskins (*folles hircini*) were used. For larger bellows tanned oxenskins (*folles taurini*) were used. The smaller bellows looked exactly like those we nowadays use in the home and work by hand. They were furnished with a valve, and the frame was made from beechwood, but probably also from other kinds of wood (Ausonius, *Mosella*, 268). Larger bellows were worked by means of a lever.

The anvil which, like the hammer and tongs, is supposed, according to Pliny (VII, 195), to have been invented by Kinyras of Cyprus, appears in very different forms, as is shown by pictures that have been preserved and by actual finds. It consists either of one block, or of three blocks superposed on one another, or of a wooden base on which the iron anvil proper rests. In the latter case the anvil is fastened deep into the base by means of a long point. Further, the anvil was either square or circular in cross-section, either hollowed out conically, or made in the shape of a long horn, and in this case, it must be assumed that it was used to weld tubes, that is, as a so-called 'core'. An anvil of this kind was found on the Saalburg, together with smaller ones intended for finer work. The effective part of the anvil always consisted of iron. The surface, the so-called 'face', was hardened by tempering (Pliny, XXXIV, 41). There is not much to be said about the hammers and the tongs. They exactly resembled the modern forge-hammers and tongs and were of very varied form according to the purposes which they were to serve. In Fig. 56 and the following figures a number of such hammers and tongs are shown.

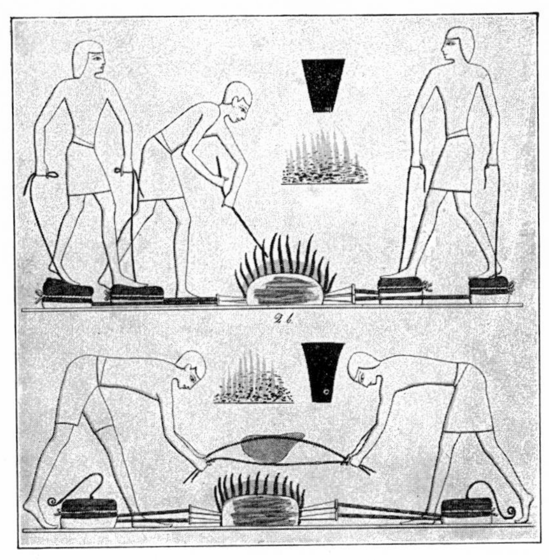

FIG. 55.—Egyptian Bellows

Forging itself, which consists in heating and working metal with the hammer, was carried out in the same way as nowadays. To us it seems curious that the smith (who is represented on the ancient Roman pictures

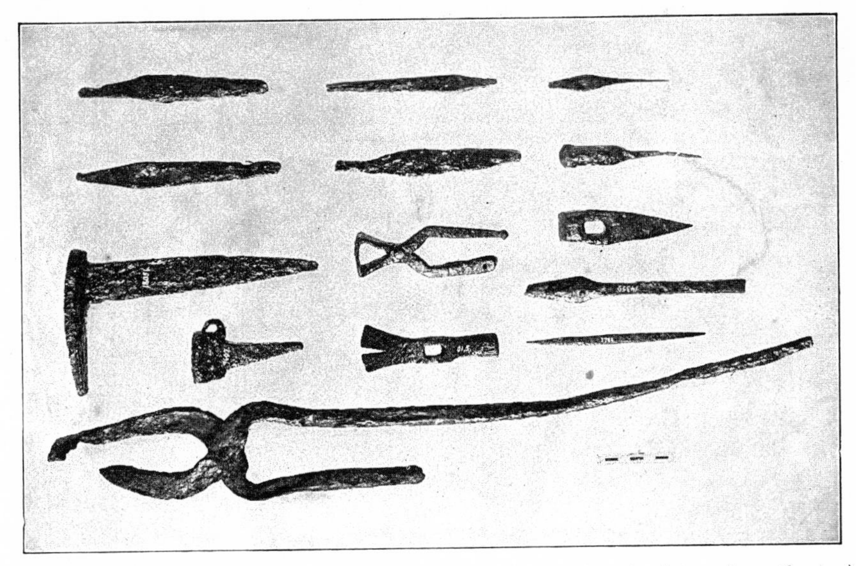

FIG. 56.—Smith's Tongs, two Anvils (on the left, third and fourth picture from the top), Hammers, Files, Punches and other Tools of the Roman Smith. Provincial Museum of Trèves

that are still preserved as always wearing a beard, whereas his assistants are clean-shaven) appears to have done much of his work in a sitting posture. At any rate the representations just mentioned show him in many cases sitting in front of the fire manipulating the hammer. In other pictures the smith proper is standing while his assistant (Eros), who holds the piece to be worked, is seated. These sketches thus give us reasonable grounds for concluding that the forging of smaller objects which required no particular effort was carried out in the sitting posture, whereas larger pieces of metal were worked in the standing posture. The tempering of the glowing iron, that is, plunging it suddenly into cold water to harden it, is mentioned very early, even by Homer (*Odyssey*, IX, 391): 'And as when a smith dips an axe or adze in chill water with a great hissing, when he would temper it—for hereby anon comes the strength of iron . . .'[1]

FIG. 57.—Greek Smithy depicted on an Attic Vase dating from the sixth century B.C., found in Orvieto

On the left is the hearth; above are forged objects and tools, a pitcher and a sword. Boston, Fine Arts Museum

Actually, the hardening that was produced by plunging the hot iron into water was ascribed to mysterious agencies. Moreover, some water was regarded as better suited to tempering than other, a view that may have been based on the fact of the different temperature of the waters. Water drawn from a very cold stream and used immediately for tempering would produce harder and more brittle steel than water from a warmer source, such as a stagnant pool. But it could hardly have escaped notice that the colder water, when left unused in the smithy for a time, so that it gradually acquired a higher temperature, produced the different grades of tempering just mentioned. Besides water, various other liquids were used for tempering, such as the blood of he-goats (Pliny, XXVIII, 148); boys' urine, that of red-headed boys being particularly valued, and so forth. Their action may be attributed to the presence of carbon, for they all yield charcoal on being heated. This becomes

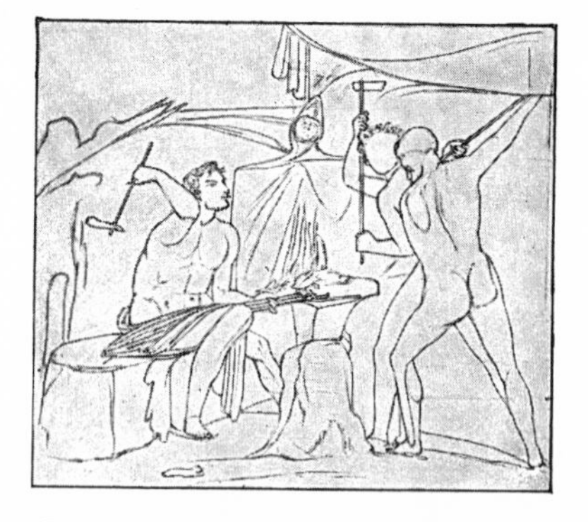

FIG. 58.—Smiths in action in the Workshop of Hephaistos. Wall-painting in Pompeii

[1] Butcher and Lang, English Prose Translation, Macmillan & Co.. London.

dissolved in the iron and acts as so-called tempering carbon. Oil was also used, as nowadays, for tempering finer tools and the like. Since oil gives only a mild hardness and since Hippocrates and others specifically mention that tempering in oil was to serve the purpose of avoiding fissures and

FIG. 59.—A Cutler

This and Fig. 60 are taken from a tombstone of the Galeria lapidaria in the Vatican

FIG. 60.—A Cutler's Shop, which allows us to recognize the various forms of knives obtained by forging processes

fractures, this clearly refers to tempering for the purpose of covering the surface of a hard piece of steel with a very thin but somewhat softer layer which is less brittle and so prevents the metal from cracking and breaking. Treating steel by heating it with colouring matters, which has assumed such importance latterly, does not seem to have been

FIG. 61.—A Common Smith

FIG. 62.—Roman Smiths

On the left a bellows is apparently being worked; an assistant is seated on the handle. Tombstone in the Lateran Museum

known to the ancients. On the other hand, the ancients knew how to weld steel points and steel blades on to weapons and tools made of wrought-iron.

For the further treatment of forged metal the smithy was equipped with all the appliances that we still meet with in modern workshops, such as grindstones, which were probably not different from those of the present day and like them were set in rotation by means of a treadle. The stones used came from Crete and Laconia. Oil was used with them, whereas other grindstones (possibly emery from Naxos) were moistened with water. Files were used, but relatively less than nowadays. A pointed four-edged file of ancient Roman origin has been dug up in Aliso. To smooth the pieces of forged metal Samian earth and he-goat's blood was chiefly used, besides the less common file.

Like the process of forging itself, the objects obtained by it in many ways resembled our own—so closely, in fact, that very often only the locality has made it possible to decide whether a horseshoe was of recent

FIG. 63.—Roman Regimental Smith with anvil, hammer, tongs and piece of metal

Tombstone in the Museum of Sens

FIG. 64.—Cupids at work in the Smithy

From a Roman sarcophagus. On the left a piece of bloom is being worked

FIG. 65.—A Grindstone (authenticity not established)

or of ancient Roman make. The existence of ancient horseshoes is, indeed, disputed by some authorities (Schlieben) on grounds that carry a certain amount of conviction, whereas others (for example, Schaaf-hausen) support the opposite view. To the author the presence of great quantities of such horseshoes in certain ancient Roman settlements seems conclusive evidence that they were actually used, and were indeed made by mass-production in some parts (see below). The horseshoe was developed from the *solea ferrea*, the so-called ' hippo-sandal ', which was also forged from iron, but it is not yet certain whether it did not serve as a protection for horses with afflicted hoofs. From the finds made at Saalburg, Jacobi distinguishes three kinds, of which the oldest are rather roughly made and lie in the lowest layers. The strength of the horseshoes was improved in the course of time, but it is difficult to derive

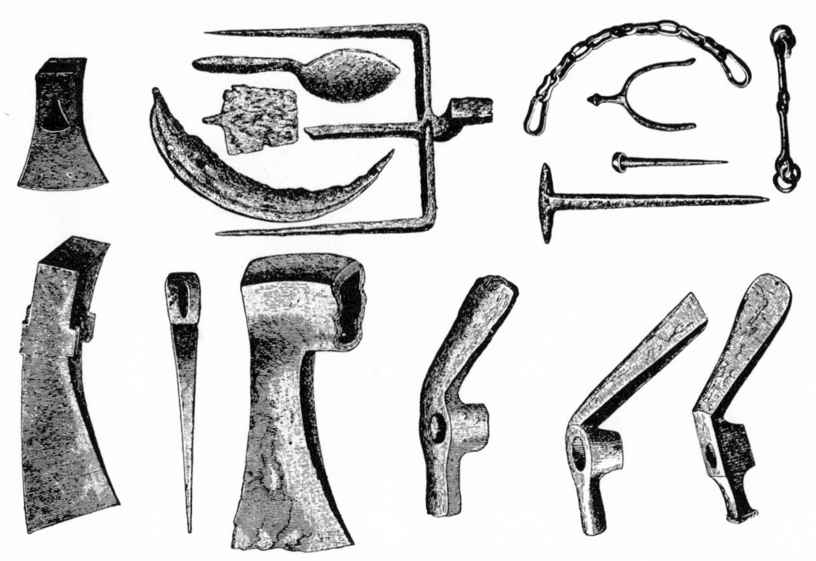

FIG. 66.—Various pieces of ancient Roman Forged Metal

accurate information on account of the wear to which they have been subjected. The horseshoe in our illustration belongs to the latest kind and gives the most developed form. This type of horseshoe is strongly made, 4 to 4½ in. wide and 5 to 5½ in. long. They contain six to eight holes for nails (nowadays seven, three on one arm and four on the other), which lie in a groove. In the front there is a thickened excrescence, the 'grip'; this was probably first introduced because the horses in climbing mountains wore off this part of the shoe soonest. Further, we also see 'sponges', that is, the two ends are bent back. The weight of the shoes varies within wide limits. The lightest that have been discovered weigh about a quarter of a pound, the heaviest nearly a pound. The various marks found on many of them suggest that they were manufactured in factories.

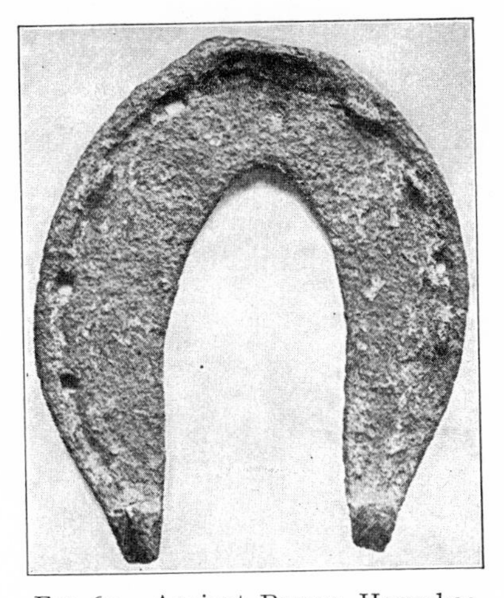

FIG. 67.—Ancient Roman Horseshoe

CASTING IN METAL

The zenith of metal-working in antiquity was reached in *casting*, which was carried out with various metals such as lead, probably also tin, copper and certainly bronze. It has been affirmed on various sides that cast-iron was in use, but this has not been proved. The most perfect works of art were done in bronze-casting, the beginning of which is lost in the grey dawn of time. Some features indicate that it may have originated in India, where, as we know, the art of working metals was highly developed at a very early period. It is clear that, at first, only solid casts were made, in which the cast is composed throughout of metal and is consequently not only heavy but requires a considerable quantity of metal. How solid casting was practised in Egypt is shown in an old

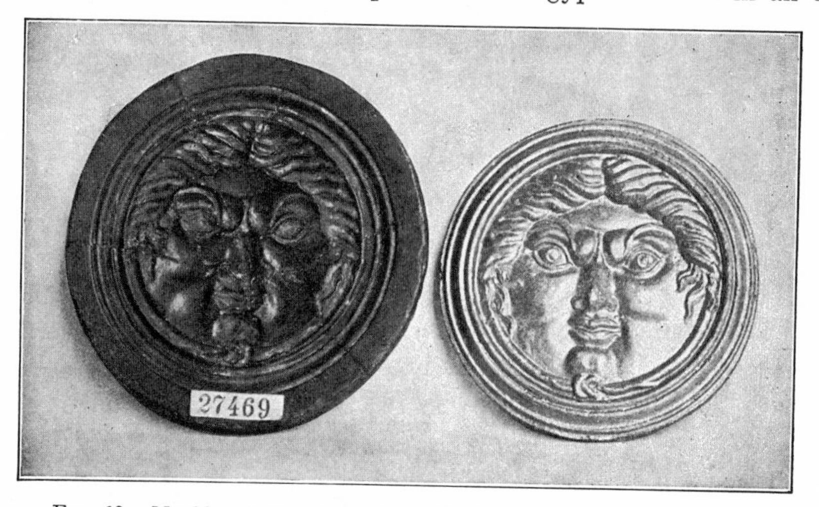

Fig. 68.—Mould and Counterpart (or Cast) as used in casting a Relief

Deutsches Museum, Munich

picture of 1600 B.C., which came from a temple at Karnak and depicts the casting of a bronze door of a temple. The mould rests on the ground and consists of two open boxes that are filled with sand (presumably wet). Slaves carry on their shoulders bags containing this sand and empty it into the foundry. The model, previously prepared, possibly of wood, is pressed into the sand, one half into that of one box and the other half into that of the other box. The sand is then allowed to dry in the air and the two boxes are placed together to form a closed compartment, which is provided at the top with numerous apertures into which funnel-shaped head pieces are inserted. These serve to allow the molten metal to be run in and also the air to escape when it is displaced from the hollow mould during the filling. The metal is melted in casting crucibles which are held fast between two rods and thus brought to the mouths of the funnels (see Fig. 55 and Fig. 69). Tongs such as are nowadays used to grip the crucibles appear not to have been known. The arrangement of rods resembles the frame carrier which is nowadays employed in transporting casting crucibles. By inclining the crucible the metal is poured out as a glowing stream into the funnel so as to fill the mould, where it is left to cool. The halves of the casting-box are then separated and the finished cast is disclosed to view. The two temple doors (perhaps also their models) are represented at the top of Fig. 69. We also clearly discern, above and below, the hinges on which they are to turn. The workmen beside them, to judge from the tongs and blow pipes they are carrying, appear to have the duty of attending to the fire under the casting crucibles.

Solid casting was later superseded by hollow casting which, however, like the former appears not to have been known to the Greeks of mytho-

FIG. 69.—Casting a Temple-door in ancient Egypt

logical times and of the immediately succeeding epochs; for when Homer describes how the equipment of his heroes was made, he mentions only forged work, never casts. It seems that implements, weapons and similar articles, which were later made by forging, were in very early times made by some other process. To cite only one example, in making excavations at the acropolis of Susa, the old capital of the Persian kings, Morgan found a javelin which had been made not by casting but by tightly twisting up a bronze plate, about an eighth of an inch thick, which had been previously prepared by being hammered. The direction of the cracks in it proved beyond doubt that it had been made in this way. It is probable that the two Samians, Rhoikos and Theodoros,[1] did not, as the Greeks assert, actually invent bronze-casting, but introduced it about 650 B.C. from Asia Minor into Greece. Little moulds made of stone and of an early date have, indeed, been found—for example, by Schliemann in his Mycenaean excavations—and have been regarded as casting-moulds, but probably they are only forms that were used for embossing. Neverthe-less, stone moulds have actually been used for making solid casts, as is

[1] Cf. Seyffert, *Dictionary of Classical Antiquities* (Sonnenschein).

proved by various prehistoric finds (Fig. 73). Such moulds possessed the advantage that they did not have to be broken after the cast had solidified but could be used over and over again. Rhoikos and Theodoros, even at that early period, produced works of large dimensions; they applied the process known as *cire perdue*, a method of casting which predominated subsequently. Even in very old Egyptian bronze work there is unmistakable evidence of the use of this method. For when the patina layer, often very thick, is removed from them it is found that the cast was a reproduction of a model prepared from some soft substance, and that the finer details had not been added to the cast later. Traces of finishing off with a chisel or a file are to be found only at the points at which the metal was run in and at points where

FIG. 70.—Egyptian Hand-Mirror of bronze, cast in two pieces

The two pieces (handle and mirror) were drilled after casting, and were riveted together. The mirror itself is gilt. On the reverse side papyrus umbels are engraved. Length 12 in. Berlin Museum, Egyptian Section

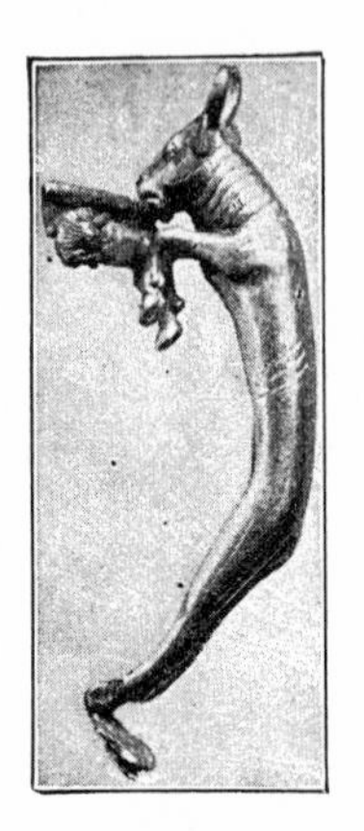

FIG. 71.—Solid Egyptian Cast, of precious metal; gold handle in the form of a wild ox (fixed to a silver vessel)

The folds in the neck are cast, those on the body are engraved. Length 4¼ in. Berlin Museum, Egyptian Section

FIG. 72.—Egyptian Hollow Cast. Bronze figure of Buto, with a lion's head, and the sun's disc, sitting on a throne. Eyes of gold. Marked with engravings

Height 30 in. From Sais. Berlin Museum, Egyptian Section

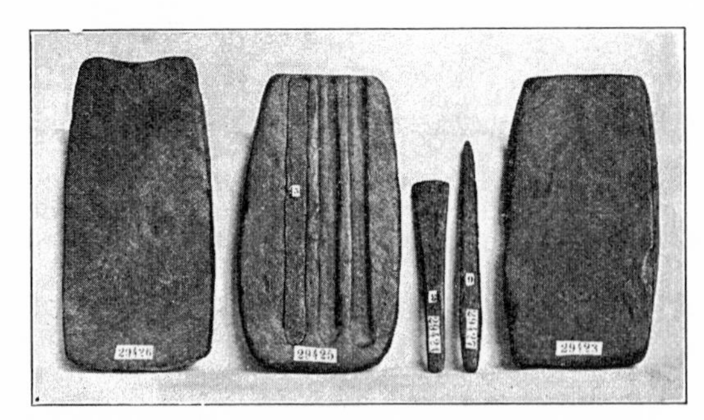

FIG. 73.—Prehistoric Stone Moulds for making solid casts of simple objects (Chisels)

Deutsches Museum, Munich

there were faults. The cast is an extremely thin shell, so that there must have been a nucleus or core which nearly filled out the mould and which left only very little space between it and the inner side of the mould. This narrow space was then filled with metal. As an example of how thin the ancients could make their casts we may quote the ' Praying Boy ' in the Berlin Museum ; this cast can be comfortably carried by one man. A stature of Hera [1] found in 1834 in Vulci and now in the Munich Glyptothek, weighs barely 100 lbs. (see Fig. 77) although it is nearly 6 ft. high ; a modern bronze statue of the same size would weigh nearly ten times as much. Some parts of it are so thin that they give the impression of having been embossed; closer investigation,

FIG. 74.—Egyptian Bronzes, solid and hollow casts
German Museum, Munich

however, shows that this is not the case. Statues of this kind were mostly cast in several parts which were afterwards joined together so skilfully that the joins defy detection.

The cast was produced in the following manner. First, a nucleus of clay, brick-dust and similar powdery substances was prepared, which was smaller than the cast to be made by an amount equal to the thickness desired for the shell of the cast. This nucleus was enveloped in a layer of wax which the artist used as a model. He very carefully shaped and kneaded the wax with his wooden modelling implements (which resemble those still in use) and so prepared the original of the casts to

[1] This supposed ' Hera ' is, in the light of recent archæological research, now called ' The Spinner '.

be made. He next took thin metal tacks and pressed or hammered them through the wax layer into the nuclear form. Their purpose was to keep the casting form, the 'mantle', at a correct distance from the nucleus after the wax had been melted out. The inner surface of this form therefore necessarily coincided with the outer surface of the wax. Further, at various points in the wax layer wax rods were erected as vertically as possible, which reached above the highest point of the wax model, most of them uniting at the top in a central drum above the figure proper.

FIGS. 75 and 76.—Greek Casting Workshop

Above on the left is the furnace, the upper opening of which is covered with a stone (?) which perhaps served to regulate the heat. In front is the opening for admitting fuel. Behind is an assistant, apparently working the bellows. Above on the right is an open mould from which the cast is being removed. Below is the centre in a finished cast (of a warrior) in a wooden frame; the cast is being chiselled and finished off. On the walls there are drawings, hammers, saws, parts of casts (feet), chiselling tools, and so forth. There are also assistants and onlookers. Taken from an Attic red-figured vase. First third of the fifth century B.C. Berlin, Altes Museum, Antiquarium

The whole was then carefully covered with very fine clay or a mixture of clay and brick-dust; this was in turn covered with thick loam which was in some cases surrounded by masonry or held together by iron bands (like the masonry itself). When the loam had dried the wax was removed by being melted, so that the hollow form was created into which the metal was to be run. The wax-rods previously erected were also melted away; in their place channels arose through which molten bronze was run into the hollow mould. The wax drum served as a funnel for the incoming bronze. A few channels that did not join at the top but were left free allowed the air that was displaced by metal to escape into the open (air-holes).

Fig. 77.—Statue of 'Hera' or 'The Spinner'

After the metal had become cold the covering (mantle) was cracked off and the cast was detached from the nuclear form, or the latter was shattered to pieces if the shape of the cast made this necessary. The projections due to the presence of the canals were then chiselled off and filed, and all other unevennesses on the surface were smoothed off. The cast was then complete.

The Romans made casts in the same way, employing for preference the method of hollow casts with 'break moulds'[1] just described, but they also practised solid casting in the case of smaller articles. As particularly beautiful examples of ancient Greek and Roman solid casting, and, indeed, of metal work of any kind, we must mention their mirrors, which are flat disks of bronze, one side of which is highly polished, the other being attractively engraved and ornamented; the mirror itself is mounted on an artistic handle. Later mirrors were also covered with a thin surface of silver; or the bronze plate was cemented on to a base, and in some instances, to prevent scratching, was enclosed in a sort of case provided with a lid which moved on a hinge.

Fig. 78.—The Wolf, with Romulus and Remus
Etruscan Bronze (hollow cast). Capitoline Museum, Rome

One branch of casting that became particularly developed in Imperial Roman times was that of casting coins. This was, indeed, also practised in the mints, but chiefly by forgers of base coin, who were very numerous at that period. A genuine coin was simply stamped out in clay, two clay discs being used, which were held in a round box. The clay was then dried and glowed out slightly in a fire. The two discs, each of which now bore the impress of a face of the coin, had previously been made to fit exactly and were provided above with a triangular incision which served for

[1] I.e. used for one cast only.

pouring in the metal. After the firing, they were placed together; usually, to save labour, a whole set of such coin moulds was made and was enveloped in loam to prevent them from shifting their position during the casting. The metal was next poured in. On cooling, the moulds were taken apart and the base coin was finished off by removing the peak caused by the aperture of the mould; this was done by polishing the rim and other parts (Figs. 83–86).

Even before the development of Greek and Roman art in bronze this same art had flourished in the north among the 'barbarians', reaching its zenith in the so-called La-Tène period, which began about 400 B.C. It was, however, at the same time supplanted by iron, which was now coming into use. Although

FIGS. 79–81.—Specimens of Hollow Casting
Berlin Museum, Antiquarium

bronze-work among the northern races refers to prehistoric discoveries, the consideration of which is not within the scope of this book, we must mention that the vessels made at that time, of which some are very beautiful, were first modelled in loam which was plastered on the nuclear form. The mantle was fitted over the loam and was cut when it was to be removed. The cut mantle was joined together later

FIG. 82.—Greek Folding Mirror with a soldered hinge, which also serves as a handle, and with a movable ring at the bottom fastened by hooks through holes. The design represents Skylla. Fourth to third century B.C.

Berlin Museum, Antiquarium

FIGS. 83 and 84.—The two halves of a Roman coiner's Casting Moulds, made of slightly burnt clay. At the top is the aperture for admitting the molten metal

Natural size. Collection of Dr. Cahn, Frankfort-on-the-Main

FIGS. 85 and 86.—Two halves of a Roman coiner's Mould with the triangular aperture at the top for admitting molten metal. Burnt clay. Very sharp impress

Natural size. Collection of Dr. Cahn, Frankfort-on-the-Main

and supported in loam during the process of casting. The loam model surrounding the nuclear form could now be detached from the latter, which could not, of course, be simply melted out like wax. The casting was done, just as described above, by allowing the metal to run into the space between the nuclear form and the mantle.

CHEMICAL TREATMENT AND COLOURING OF METALS

To the above arts of treating metals mechanically with or without the help of fire must be added the chemical treatment of metals which aimed in the first place at conferring a certain lustre on metallic objects. This was accomplished either naturally, that is, by mixing the metals in a perfectly definite way, especially in the case of alloys, in order to arrive at a desired tint, or else artificially, by colouring the metal.

Examples of the first method are 'electrum', 'Corinthian brass', bronze, and so forth, whose colours could be varied by suitably adjusting the relative amounts of the constituents of these alloys. Thus, three sorts of 'Corinthian brass', a species of bronze, were known; it was also produced in a whitish and golden-yellow colour, this being effected, it is alleged, by adding more gold or silver to the copper or bronze. Such bronzes, containing silver and gold, were indeed considered to be of a particularly fine colour. Liver-coloured bronzes (χαλκὸς ἡπατίζων) also occur. Metals were coloured artificially by various processes. Silver surfaces were given a golden colour by smearing them with orpiment (arsenic trisulphide, As_2S_3); copper surfaces were silvered by rubbing them with quicksilver (mercury). Gold coins containing high percentages of base metal were given a gold surface by being heated to a dull red glow with a mixture of common salt, dehydrated iron sulphate and brick-dust. The silver chloride produced melts and fuses with the brick-dust so that the surface of the coin acquires the appearance of pure gold. Among these processes we must also include the true processes

FIG. 87.—Roman Niello

Silver goblet with branches of ivy in niello; from silver finds made in Hildesheim. Berlin, Altes Museum, Antiquarium

of gilding and silvering, namely by means of gold- and silver-leaf [1]; further, hot gilding with the help of gold amalgam, which was early known, as it is described by various Roman writers (Vitruvius, VII, 8, 4; Isidore, Origg. XVI, 19, 2; Pliny, XXXIII, 64). Their descriptions show that it was practised exactly as is still done nowadays; and lastly, tin-plating, already known in prehistoric times, which was effected by dipping objects in molten tin and which was so skilfully done by the Gauls, for instance, that tin-plated objects could not be distinguished from silver ones. The Egyptians dipped the bronzes that came out of the casting moulds, while still hot, in molten resin which tinted the surface to the desired shade. The Egyptians were likewise acquainted with the method of colouring silver black, that is, with producing 'niello'. According to Pliny (XXXIII, 131) they accomplished this by melting together equal parts of silver, copper and sulphur (slightly in excess). Several of these Egyptian objects decorated with niello are known; for example, a vase found in Hungary, a very finely nielloed silver plate of Egyptian origin,

[1] See pp. 29, *et seq.*

now in Corinth, a clasp in the Imperial cabinet of coins and antiquities in Vienna; this clasp exhibits decorations exquisitely engraved in gold and filled in with a niello-like mass; there are also other specimens.

Egyptian niello, the age of which is estimated at 3,000 years, consists of compact layers which contain some enclosed stiffening substance, whereas Roman niello consists usually only of thin strata. It appears

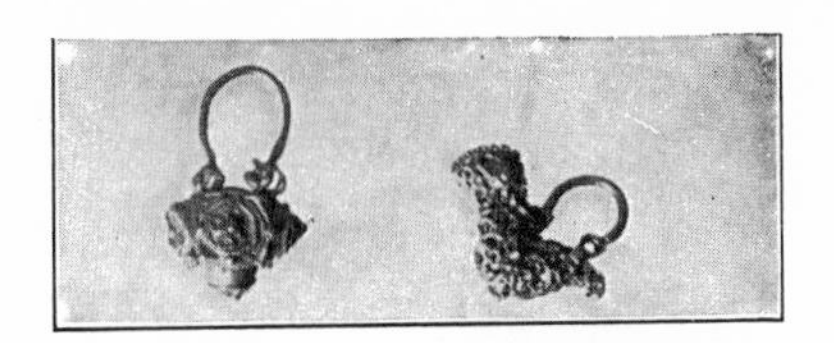

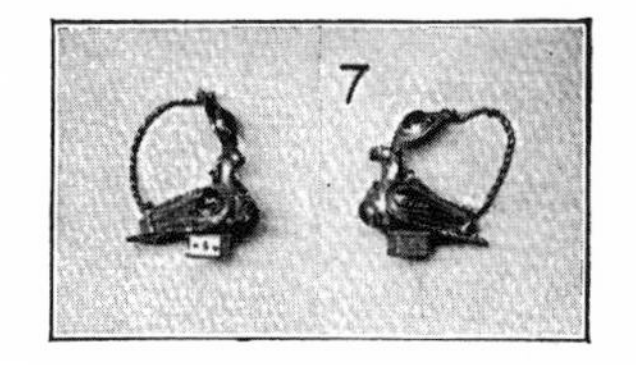

FIGS. 88–91.—Roman Filigree

Ear-rings, ornamental buttons, fibulæ (brooches), and so forth, partly chased and ornamented with gold wire that has been soldered on. Berlin, Altes Museum, Antiquarium

that the oldest Egyptian niello was worked on gold alone and that it was only later produced on silver.

The Romans made niello by melting together silver, copper, and lead with sulphur. After the mass, now become black owing to the production of silver sulphide, had been reduced to a fine powder, the latter was mixed with borax and melted over glowing coals on to the previously engraved silver and gold. After cleaning and polishing, the metallic foundation appears, the depressions in the surface being coloured black by the niello.

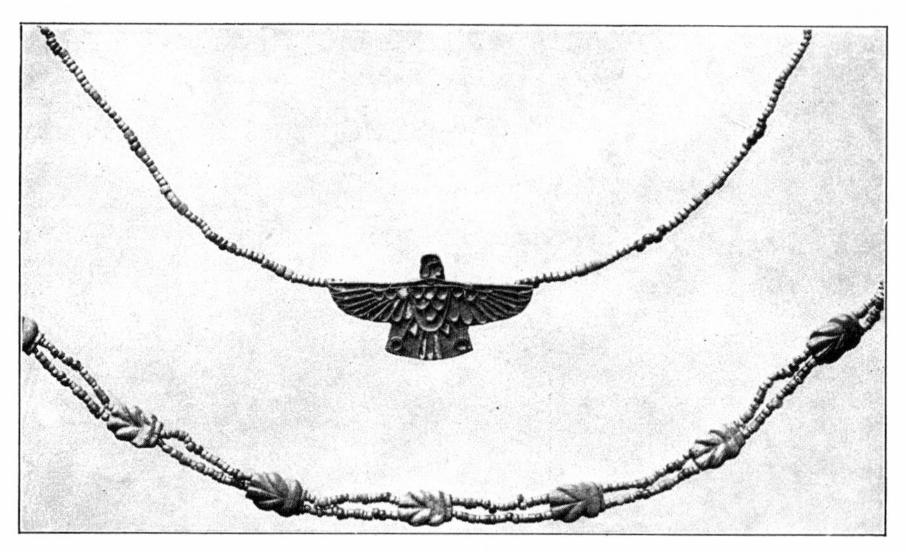

FIG. 92.—Egyptian Enamelling (above)

From the chain is suspended a soul-bird of gold with a human head. The inlaid enamel of the feathers and the head (light blue and black, partly fallen out) are made in cells (enamel cells). The width of wing is 1¾ inches. Below is a chain consisting of two strings of small beads of gold, lapis lazuli and cornelian, which are held together by 27 knots made of gold, lapis lazuli, cornelian, feldspar and glazed clay. Berlin Museum, Egyptian Section

A prescription by Pliny for making niello runs: 3 parts of silver, 1 part of copper, and 3 parts of sulphur (see Fig. 87).

SPECIAL METHODS OF WORKING METALS

Following on the above-described processes for treating metals we give several others which cannot be fitted into the scheme we have adopted but which likewise played an important part in antiquity. We are referring to the technical arts which chiefly fall within the range of the goldsmith, who was, indeed, a man of great experience and dexterity in various technical branches; he practised almost all the methods already mentioned of working metals. He knew how to chase metals, how to make alloys, how to colour metals; he cast smaller objects in precious metals in special furnaces, and so forth. To these must be added certain other technical accomplishments, such as chryselephantine work (that is, overlaying with gold and ivory). This technique was also practised by sculptors. It consists in covering individual parts of statues, in particular the flesh parts, with ivory, the rest being covered with richly enamelled gold. In the first place, it is now a lost art to join ivory plates without leaving traces or the joins and without the differences of external temperature giving rise to cracks owing to the resultant change

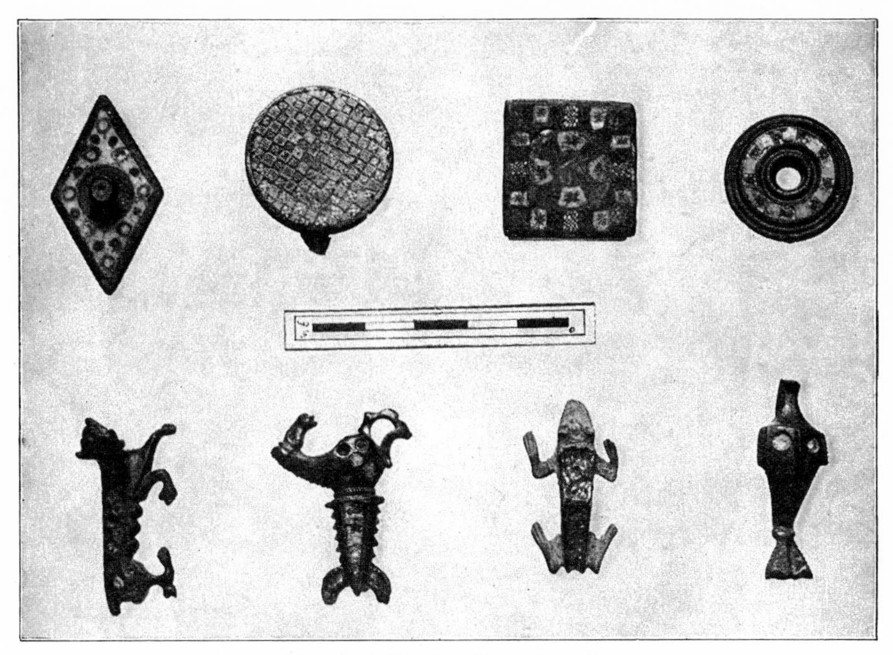

FIG. 93.—Roman Enamel-work

Bronzes with variously coloured enamel. Second and fourth ornamental button from the left in the top row are blue and white, the other objects are in widely different colours; the third button from the left in the top row contains almost all colours. Provincial Museum at Trèves

of dimensions. Next, they softened and shaped the plates; it is not known how this was done. Lastly, gold and enamel were applied in profusion.

A further accomplishment peculiar to the goldsmith was filigree work (Figs. 88–91, p. 63) which was probably common in Egypt and became transplanted into Greece; later the Romans carried it over into Germania, where, however, it never flourished particularly. Filigree work consists in soldering gold threads on to ornaments made of precious metal; in this way very delicate creations are often produced.

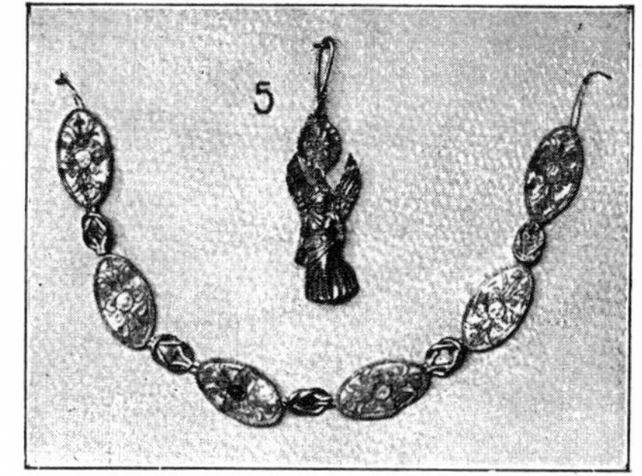

FIG. 94.—Roman Cellular Enamel

The chain, depicted below, is made of gold plate and is divided into cells by the gold wire that has been soldered on (Filigree); these cells are partly filled with stones and partly with enamel. (Some cells have now lost their fillings.) Berlin, Altes Museum, Antiquarium

Enamelling was also used for ornamenting jewellery (Figs. 92–94). Nowadays we regard Egypt as the origin of the art of enamelling, although some have claimed that it is Persia, which was certainly acquainted with the art at a very early date. The enamel for precious metals was produced in the same way as that for clay objects, and there is no chemical difference (see also the sections on 'Glass' and 'Pottery' below). The preparation of enamel is a branch of the ancient technical arts which suffered from various imperfections; these could be eliminated only later as the knowledge of physics and chemistry grew. If, for example, the enamel that is melted on metal

Fig. 95.—Egyptian Inlaid Work

Bronze Figure of the Goddess Neith. On her head is the crown of Lower Egypt; collar, eyes and crown are inlaid with gold. Height 6 in. Berlin Museum, Egyptian Section

or into its cells is to keep its position, the contractions and expansions due to variations of temperature must be the same for the enamel as for the metal. In physical terms, they must have the same coefficient of expansion. As soon as the one contracts or expands more than the other the enamel will either become loose and finally fall out, or it will

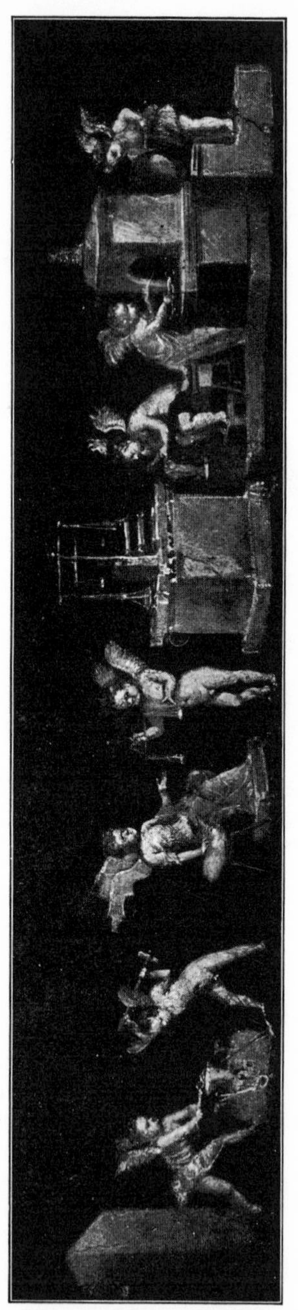

Fig. 96.—Cupids as Goldsmiths

The various activities in the workshop of a Roman goldsmith. From left to right: beating gold (probably preparing bars from lumps of gold) with a heavy hammer,[1] weighing, beating into thin sheets (with a lighter hammer), melting in a crucible or melting on ornaments or soldering with the use of a blow-pipe to increase and regulate the heat of the furnace, and lastly finishing off an object with the chisel-hammer (?) (The form of the hammer, whose head is indicated and can be recognized, is no longer sufficiently clear on the original at Pompeii to allow us to draw conclusions about the nature of the hammer. The head appears to be round at the bottom and pointed at the top.) Coloured wall painting in the house of the Vettii, Pompeii

[1] The assumption made by Mau (*Pompeii in Leben and Kunst* 1900) that 'the one workman is holding himself as far away as possible so as not to be struck by flying sparks', can hardly be correct, as gold in antiquity, as nowadays, was certainly always beaten while cold and not, like iron, while hot.

become so compressed by the contracting metal that it will fracture or split. If glasses of various colours are employed, their melting-points must either be the same or else lie close together. Otherwise the one glass will be melted before the others have even begun to get viscous. And if the temperature is raised to the melting-point of the coloured glass that melts least readily, it is very often so high that those glasses which melt more easily become changed, losing their colour or decomposing, or becoming dull, and so forth. Whereas nowadays we can successfully deal with all these factors and, in particular cases, interpose a special layer of enamel, the so-called ' counter-enamel', which counterbalances any difference of expansion that might be present, the ancients were helpless in the face of these difficult problems. Consequently there are relatively few well-preserved specimens of enamel work of those times, and in most cases the layer of enamel has been forced out or has fallen out of the cells.

Lastly we must consider inlay work. Inlaid objects occur at the earliest period of history. Assyrian bronze plates with inlaid silver ornaments are known, also an inlaid disc from Epirus, bronze appliances from Pompeii, and so forth. In Frankish and Alemannic tombs inlaid objects are found particularly often. Inlaying was performed in one of two ways. Either the metal to be ornamented was roughened with a roughening hammer (scraper) and the roughened surface was covered with a thin layer of gold and silver which easily adhered ; or the metal (in this case usually iron) was split to a certain depth and the other metal was inserted into the opening so made and the whole was then again subjected to the forging hammer, probably in the cold state.

WOOD-WORKING

PROCURING WOOD. FELLING TREES

WOOD was one of the earliest of the raw materials that served the purposes of the arts and crafts of antiquity. It need only be recollected that the habitations and their individual parts, such as the pillars, consisted mostly of wood before the time when they were replaced by stone. The wood was at first collected wherever it was found, particularly in the neighbourhood of where it was to be used. When it did not offer itself in the form of floating trunks, broken branches and so forth, it had to be obtained by felling trees. For this purpose fire was perhaps used in the remotest times, which was lit round about the trunk until it was so far charred that it fell of its own accord; later on, however, special appliances were used. As late as Homer's time, about 850–800 B.C., the Greeks still used stone axes [1] to fell trees and chop off branches, which, as Schliemann rightly points out, must have been a very laborious undertaking. The little saws of silex and chalcedony from the excavations of Troy were often only a few inches long and were probably used to saw up bones, perhaps also to smooth the surface of wood, which was necessary as it was not possible to cleave directly through a tree by means of stone axes. Consequently the resulting boards were rather uneven. The Egyptians, on the other hand, early made use of bronze implements for felling trees. They used both axes and pointed saws, the latter probably being used for subordinate purposes. On the other hand, for dividing up the felled trunk into boards the saw played an important part. These boards were made in the following way in ancient Egypt. A stake was stuck vertically into the ground. The trunk to be sawn was tied on to this stake and was also fixed in a vertical position. Sawing was then commenced vertically downwards and was continued until ropes could be used to prevent the sawn parts pressing together and jamming the saw (Fig. 104, p. 71). The most commonly used saw had straight teeth and did not have

FIG. 97.—Assyrian Woodcutters

Their equipment, consisting of a cross-cut saw, hatchet and props (which Layard interprets as spades), leads us to conclude that they are on the way to felling trees. The form of the 'spades' seems uncommon; we can imagine these being used only perhaps to dig out roots. They are more likely props which were placed alternately under the tree, as the latter began to lean over, so as to let it down gently without injuring neighbouring trees. Bas-relief in Kujundschik

[1] A blunder: iron or bronze axes were used, see *Iliad* IV, 485; XXIII, 118.—*Trans.*

its teeth set cross-wise like those of our day, that is, the teeth were not bent outwards first to one side and then to the other alternately, the purpose of which is to prevent the blade from getting stuck. Hence with the straight teeth, ropes which enabled the parts of the trunk to be held asunder were a useful adjunct in some circumstances. If the individual parts got loose, which made sawing difficult,

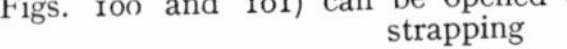

FIG. 98.—Roman Double-axe

With a bronze covering consisting of three parts. The lateral parts (see also Figs. 100 and 101) can be opened outwards. Hooks serve to attach the strapping

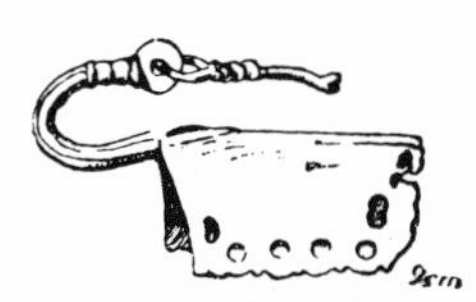

FIG. 99.—Covering of a Roman Axe

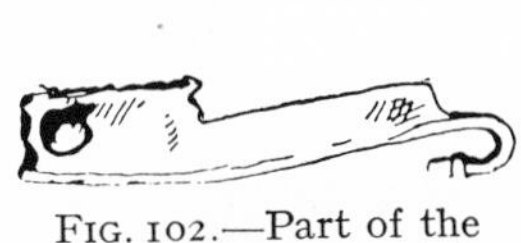

FIG. 102.—Part of the Cover of a Roman Axe

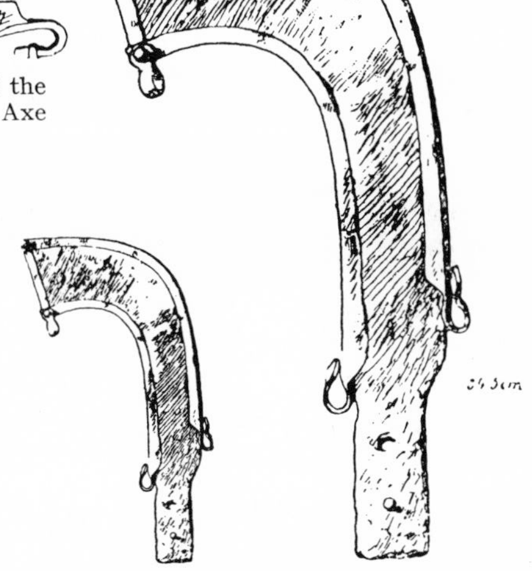

FIGS. 100 and 101.—Roman Hatchet-knife

With a strong back and two edges (a long one opposite the back and a short one at the front end) so that it could serve both as a chopper and as a light hatchet. The hatchet has a bronze cover in three parts, which fits closely. The two long parts are connected with the third, which protects the short edge, by pins and can be opened out. The handles, which are not shown, were riveted on, as is evident from the rivet-holes and pins. The objects represented in Figs. 98–102 were found in the Rhine at the Bleiaue near Mainz. Museum at Mainz

they were also bound with ropes until the trunk was sawn right through. The plane was not known to the ancient Egyptians; in its place they used a kind of adze, with which they smoothed the surface of the wood. It must be remarked that the axes used by the Egyptians to fell trees had no hole into which to fasten the handle; they were bound to the latter by cords. The Romans felled trees in much the same way as we do, namely, by chopping notches out of the trunk with axes, until the tree could be pulled down with ropes. The woodcutter of the present time usually guards himself against accidents by surrounding the edge of his tool with wooden guards which also serve to protect the edge. Similar devices were known to the Romans.

An iron double-axe found in the Rhine has around its wide edge a covering or sheath of bronze, consisting of three parts ; the two on the side can be opened out. They are provided with hooks at their ends in which no doubt straps were fastened ; these could be tied round the sheath to keep it in position. The marks of these straps are still easily recognizable on the blade. Individual parts of such axe-sheaths have also been found. The axes have a hole through which handles could be fixed ; their form seems to indicate that they were used for felling trees. Another tool, the hatchet-knife, which had also a sheath or covering, was probably used for sharpening stakes that were to be thrust into the ground, or for making fascines, and so forth. Strong rivets are still preserved on the short thick tang to which the solid handle was fixed (Figs. 100 and 101). These axes and hatchets were very serviceable. In the Taunus (Germany), for example, where no soft fir-wood was available at the time of the Romans, sturdy oaks had to be felled which were then cut into beams no less than 45 ft. long by means of a chip-axe ; such beams were used to fortify the banks of the Main at Stockstadt. Even in the early times of Theophrastus (390 to 300 B.C.) the Greeks had discovered the fact that it is by no means a matter of indifference what season of the year is chosen to fell trees. For Theophrastus (*Hist. Plant.* V, 1, *et seq.*) states that in the case of trees which are not to be lopped but only to be peeled it is best to fell them when they are full of sap, as the rind can then be more easily detached. On the other hand, the trees that are to be lopped are best felled when the fruits are ripe. Theophrastus formulates the following rule giving the best times for felling trees of various sorts : the silver-fir, fir and pine in the spring ; the holm-oak, the elm, the maple, the manna-ash, the beech and the linden-tree in the early autumn ; the oak, however, at the beginning of the winter.

THE TYPES OF WOOD

The trees just enumerated at the same time give us a survey of the various kinds of wood most in use among the Greeks. We must add that the Egyptians used, first and foremost, the Nile acacia (locust tree), which was difficult to treat on account of its twisted fibre ; they also used the sycamore, the date-palm, the dum-palm, several Syrian conifers, and the ebony tree. The Romans and Greeks used besides these the oak, the box-tree, the alder, the silver-fir, the cedar, the willow and a number of other less common woods. This gives us a general idea of the kinds of wood used in antiquity. Among them several, for example, ebony, were chiefly applied to making articles of luxury, whereas others, like the willow and the alder, were used for wicker-work. The cedar was valued as a building material. For the rest, the principle of procuring the wood from the nearest source was generally followed. For example, the cedar which occurs so often in the south as a building material is met with but seldom in the Roman provinces that lay north of the Alps, where its use was regarded as a luxury.

CARPENTER'S TOOLS AND CARPENTRY

At the time of the ancient Egyptians, even as far back as 3500 B.C., carpenters and joiners used bronze axes for wood-working, the heads being

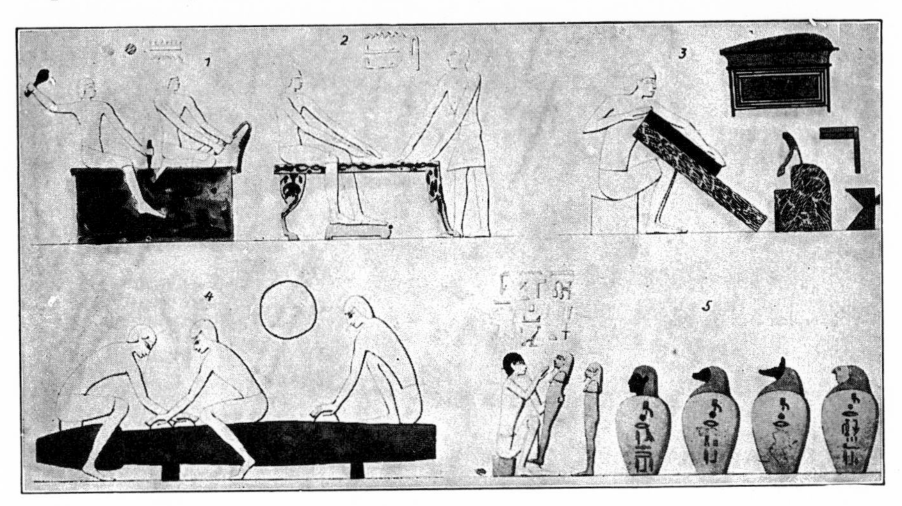

FIG. 103.—Wood-working in Egypt

(Upper row, left to right): 1. Working with a chisel and a hatchet, whose head is tied to a bent wooden handle (adze 2. Bench with inlay-work. 3. Planing. The man uses a piece of metal to test whether the wooden surface has been planed smooth. Adjacent is an adze, which serves as a plane, stuck into a block of wood; the curved surface is fastened to a handle by means of a piece of leather. We also see a set-square and a stand in which the rectangular gap, as in the case of the block into which the adze is stuck, serves as a rest for the pieces of wood that are to be worked (?) Above, a chest (?). (Bottom row): 4. Smoothing a wooden pillar; and 5. wooden coffins for mummies. Wall-paintings. Thebes.

tied to the bronze handles by leather straps. They also used chisels, having the blade part fixed into a wooden handle, which was struck with a wooden hammer. The form of the chisels resembled our own. As a plane they used a sort of adze the flat surface of which was fastened to a handle that was bent upwards. Wooden surfaces could also be planed by means of a peculiar little hatchet, whose blade was shaped like a half-moon or was bent (Fig. 103, top row, on the right: the axe is wedged into a wooden block). The curved side served as the edge; the flat side was tied to the handle. By turning this blade at right angles to the handle we get the adze, which was much used by the Egyptians.

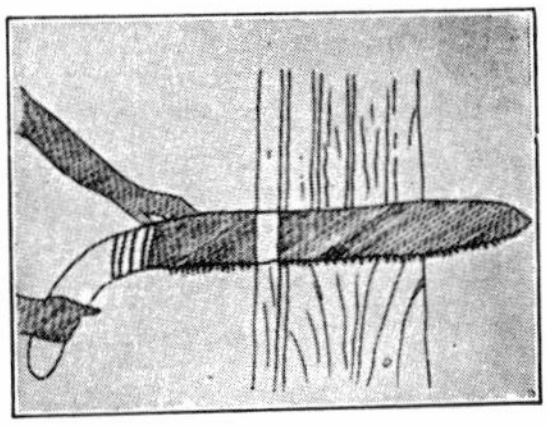

FIG. 104.—Egyptian Saw. A wood-cutter sawing through a vertical tree-trunk

The most detailed investigations about the tools used in ancient carpentry have without doubt been made by Blümner, whom in the main we shall follow in our present account.

The fact that only the pointed saw was used has already been mentioned; but, as our pictures show, it is often of considerable length and

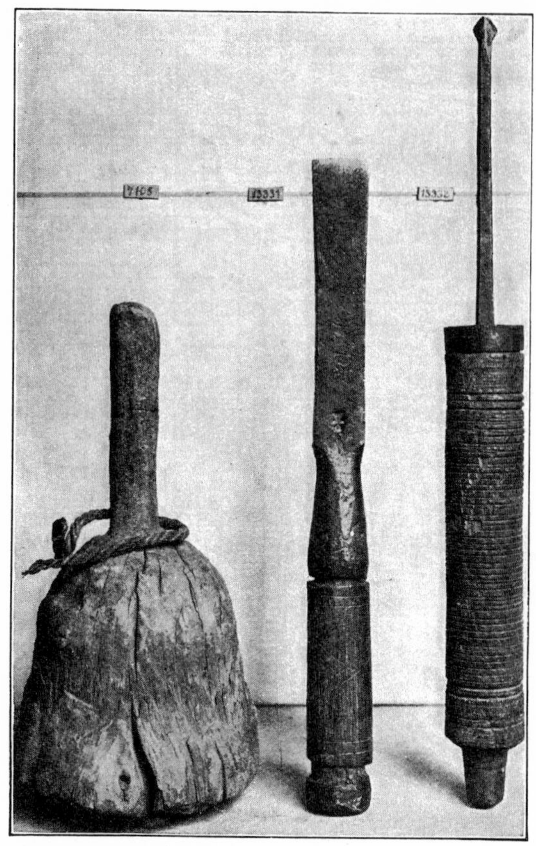

FIGS. 105–107.—Mallet, two-bevelled Chisel and Drill (Egyptian or Coptic)

To the drill there is to be added a hollowed-out piece of wood in which the thinned end of the holder turns. Berlin Museum, Egyptian Section

provided with a handle at the end, which also seems to have carried a pad or a guard near the blade. For boring the so-called bow-drill was used. It was fixed in a wooden holder which ended in a block held in the left hand, so that the drill could be pressed into the piece of material to be bored. The end block and the holder were probably not in one piece. Rather, the wooden holder rested loosely in the block (see Fig. 107). The string of a bow was passed round the holder, so that by moving the bow back and forth the drill was made to turn (Fig. 119). Borers were also used which were pressed against the chest. They were of similar form to the above and were manipulated by turning the holder by hand. The form of the drill-point itself is unknown. The older drills were probably in the shape of a nail with an edge. The drilling produced no chips, but only drill-dust, which was expelled by reversing the direction of drilling. Later, the screw-auger became known; the earliest picture of it occurs in an old manuscript copy of the poems of Hesiod, which dates back to the eighth or ninth century B.C.[1] This drill has the form of a nail with rectangular cross-section which has had its vertex turned through four right angles on its own axis

FIG. 108.—Egyptian Woodwork

Wooden Toys (animal and pitchers with and without a lid). Berlin Museum, Egyptian Section

[1] A curious confusion between that date of Hesiod himself and that of the MS. Save for a few fragments, no MS. of Hesiod is older than the twelfth century A.D.—*Trans.*

while the other end has been held fixed, so that four helical edges, rather blunt, remain. This drill, too, leaves only dust, no chips. Stones with a smooth face were used to polish the surface of the wood.

FIG. 109.—Working with a Chisel at a wooden statue of Hermes. Picture on an Athenian dish

Cabinet of Antiques, Copenhagen

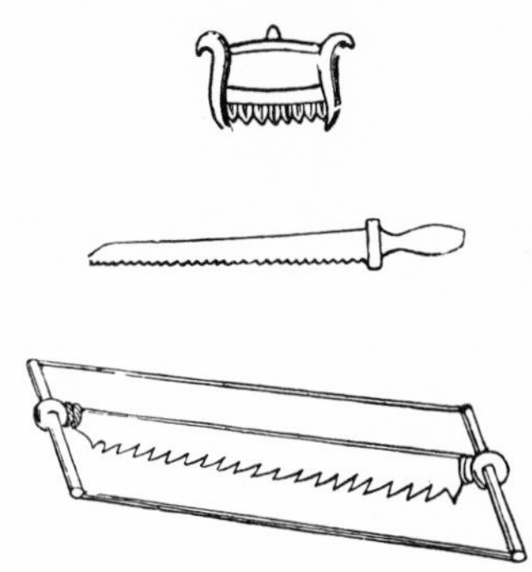

FIGS. 110–112.—Roman Saws

Frame-saw, pit-saw and fret-saw

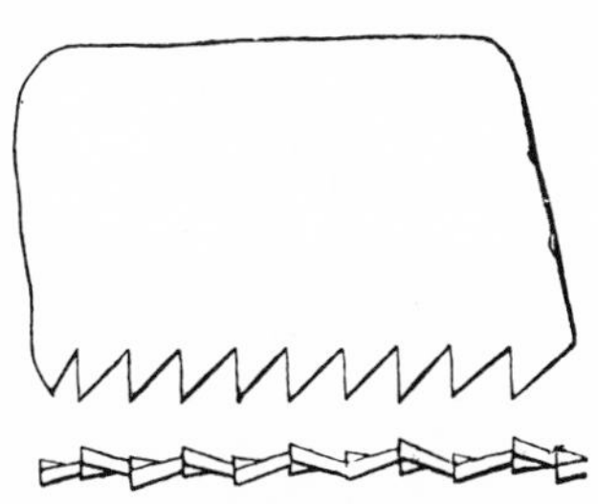

FIG. 113.—Roman Saw with crossed teeth

Below we see how the teeth are crossed. Museum, Zürich

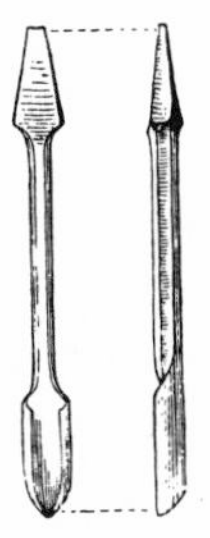
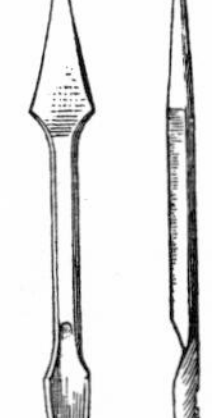
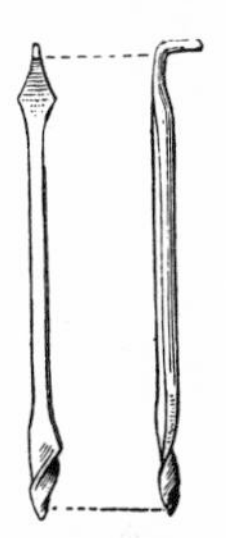
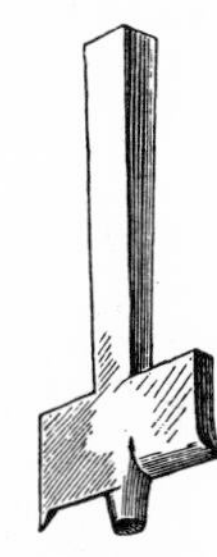

FIG. 114.—Various types of Roman Drills

Left to Right: Two double-edged drills, front and side view; ordinary drill, front and side view; centre-bit. Museum, Zürich

FIG. 115.—Roman Plane

With a grip at an angle inclined to the direction in which it is pushed, and with holes for the shavings to fall through. On a marble tombstone at Rastatt

FIG. 116.—Cupids as Carpenters

On the left, wooden folding doors, sawing-bench consisting of a board resting on two trestles; resting on it is a board on the left in the process of being sawn through (Rich here regards the blade of the saw as being in the middle, that is, a pit-saw; Oberbeck, Helbig, Blümner and others consider the blade as being at the bottom of the saw. The original is rather obliterated. On the right is a board fastened by a sort of screw-clamp. Below is a box. To the right, above, is a drill (?) resting in a hole in a shelf (Blümner assumes this to be a vessel or a lamp). Wall-painting in Herculaneum

In later times all of these carpenter's tools were further improved. Their form approached the modern types more and more nearly. Among the Greeks and Romans axes of very varied construction appear, in which the handle is stuck through a hole, mostly so as to project beyond the other side. The chisel persisted in its original form. The saw was made considerably handier. It is stretched in a curved frame, to which it is attached like the string to a bow. Then, it is held taut in a rectangular frame in such a way that it connects the mid-points of the two short side arms and runs parallel to the two long arms. The blade of the saw and its edge are either perpendicular or parallel to the plane of the frame. Finally our present form of saw also appeared, in which the blade of the saw is stretched by a cord. There are saws of this kind having sizes ranging from those of small hand-saws to those of large pit-saws. An ancient Roman saw in the Antiquarium at Zürich shows the crossing

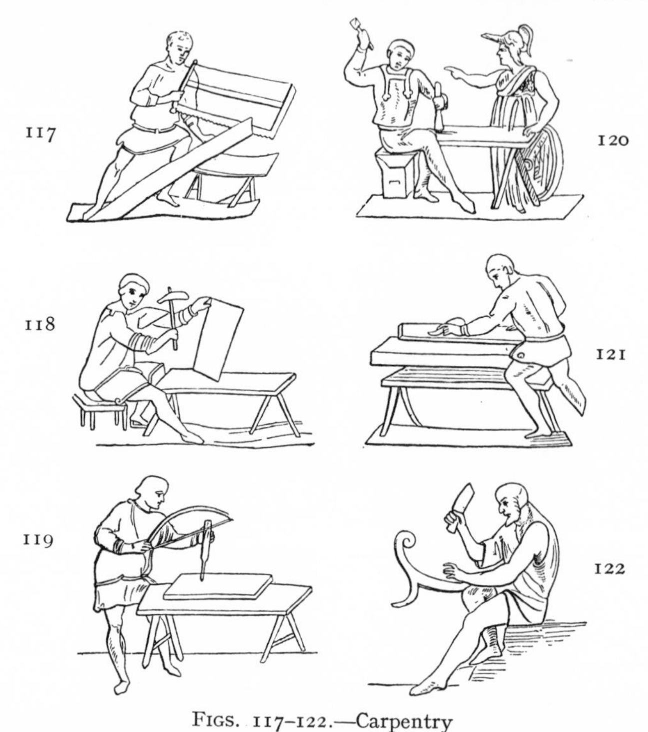

FIGS. 117–122.—Carpentry

FIG. 117.—Sawing through a board which is, as usual, propped up against a bench. In sawing through long boards a second workman, who guided the saw, stood on the board. The board was supported not only by the bench, but also by a tree-trunk against which it rested. FIG. 118.—Smoothing a board with the smoothing hatchet (or splitting a board, which Blümner also considers possible) . FIG. 119.—Boring a hole with a bow-drill. FIG. 120.—Hollowing out a board by means of a hammer and chisel. (Blümner assumes that the board is being split, but that could hardly be accomplished in this way.) FIG. 121.—Planing by means of a jack-plane. FIG. 122.—Trimming a piece of wood, which is to be carved or used for some finer purpose, by means of a hatchet. (Blümner assumes that finishing touches are being put to an object by means of a parer ; against this, however, there is the shape of the knife and the position of the arm, which seems rather to indicate rough chopping, that is, trimming.) Painted base of a glass vessel out of the Catacombs (Vatican Library)

of the teeth (Fig. 113). Among the Greeks and the Romans, too, the borer was at first a bow-drill, a type that is early mentioned by Homer (*Odyssey*, IX, 384) : . . . ' while I from my place aloft turned it about, as when a man bores a ship's beam with a drill while his fellows below spin it with a strap, which they hold at either end, and the auger runs round continually.' [1]

[1] Butcher and Lang, English Prose Translation, Macmillan & Co., London.

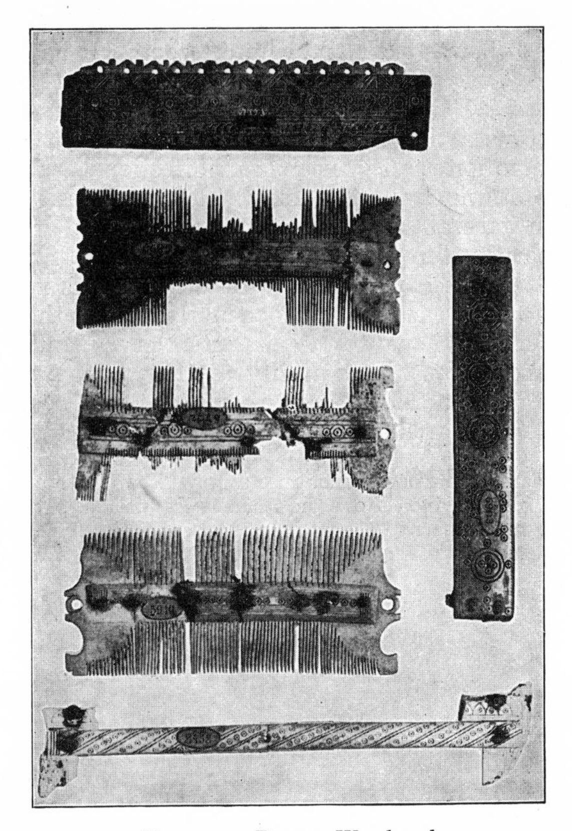

FIG. 123.—Roman Woodwork

Combs of wood and bone. The combs demonstrate to what pitch of refinement the Romans attained in woodworking. Provincial Museum at Trèves

FIG. 124.—Ancient Greek Woodwork from Mycenæ

A borer that became particularly important was that which, in the form of a Gallic drill, was used as a wimble-scoop. It had two edges, so that it could cut when turned in either direction. Since the borer was at that time worked by twisting the handle or by drawing a bow to and fro (Fig. 119), it was in both cases far more convenient to alternate the direction of the motion than to keep it unidirectional. In Zürich there is also a centre-bit which dates back to Roman times.

The plane in general preserved its original form; it had a spade-shaped blade sharpened in front, and was provided with a handle; later this blade was perforated with holes whose purpose is not clear. Still later the blade was fastened into a wooden block as at the present time.

The lathe was also known to the ancients. It is mentioned by Pliny (VII, 198), and numerous relics testify to the works performed on it. What its appearance was is not known. It can only be surmised that, like the grindstone, it was driven by means of a treadle.[1]

[1] The present-day Arab wood-turners use a bow-lathe (cf. the bow-drill in Fig. 119) which is probably derived from the ancient Egyptians. It still survives in Europe in the 'turn bench' of the watch and clock makers. See *Useful Arts and Handicrafts*, by Leland and Ward, Vol. 2, p. 17, Dawbarn & Ward, Ltd., 1900.—H. L. B.

PREPARATION AND TREATMENT OF LEATHER

TANNING

LEATHER played an important part in antiquity. Untanned hides, which were probably the oldest form of dress among all peoples, tended to decay and often lasted only a short time. So it may be presumed that steps were early taken to make them more durable by subjecting them to special treatment. It is not known what were the earliest methods of tanning. It is conjectured that the skins were first softened in water so that the hairs could be more readily removed. They were then treated with juices extracted from plants,—in some parts of Asia Minor possibly with the juice from *periploca secamone*, which is still used for tanning by the Arabians nowadays, and so probably served the same purpose in antiquity. Whether the Egyptians used it seems doubtful. It was at any rate a sort of tanning; for it must be presumed that the action was due to the tannic acid contained in the plant.

FIG. 125.—Preparation of Leather in Egypt
On the right, above, we apparently see the production of the tanning solution (the tanning substances are being pounded in a vessel). Below, on the right, the hides are being soaked; below, on the left, depilation is being performed on a scraping block. Further, we see hides, pieces of leather (above, the rectangular piece on the left), vessels, skins with borders (three superposed in the middle towards the right)

Many of the means nowadays used for tanning were also used in antiquity. Above all, every variety of tree-rinds, such as those of the alder (Theophrastus); further, parts of fruits, such as of pomegranates, acorns and so forth, were used. Besides this, numerous other plants and parts of plants were used, of which tannic acid is a constituent. Tawing was also known (Pliny, XXXV, 190) and salt was used; indeed, according to Wilkinson, the Egyptians are supposed to have used lime; but this seems little likely, as burnt lime can be used without harming the hide only if extreme caution is exercised, and unburnt lime is not a tanning agent at all. Nor has it been possible to prove whether oil was used (chamois-dressing). The methods of treating leather that were most prevalent in antiquity were thus probably ordinary tanning and tawing. Hides of very varied sorts were tanned by these processes, those of domestic animals as well as those of deer and other game and of beasts of prey. There was thus no lack of variety in the leather.

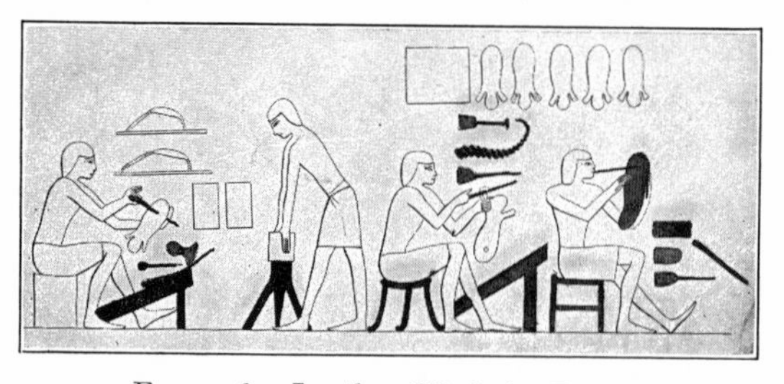

FIG. 126.—Leather Work in Egypt

On the left: Pieces of leather are being perforated by an awl; below is a scraping block with an iron scraper and punches; on the block is the hide that is to be worked (in the original painting it is spotted, so that probably it is a leopard skin); above it are rectangular pieces of leather. The next figure shows leather being stretched over a rack; the third and fourth men are engaged similarly to the first. Above are pieces of leather, hides and tools (for beating, scraping, and combing, etc.)

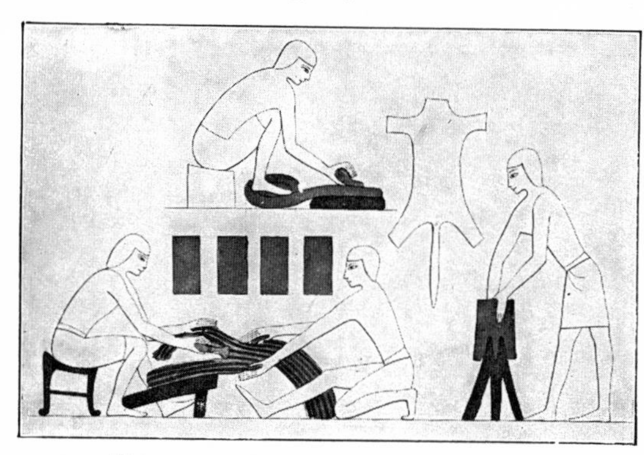

FIG. 127.—Leather Work in Egypt

Smoothing leather on a supporting base, with the help of a polishing stone (?), and (below) splitting leather with a knife. On the right: Stretching and softening leather by pulling it over a rack

FIG. 128.—Leather Work in Egypt

From left to right: Scraping a suspended hide by means of a scraper; pummelling, stretching and softening leather by drawing it over a rack. The activities of the two men on the right are not clear

The tools used for tanning are known to us only from a single discovery in Pompeii. They consist of a bronze scraper which is fastened by rivets to a wooden handle. Then there is a long concave scraping knife (two specimens have been found); and, thirdly, a small curved knife, whose probable use is indicated by the fact that nowadays furriers and other workers in leather still use a curved knife whose crescent-shaped edge is sharpened along its whole length. It is remarkable that in the ancient Egyptian wall paintings at Thebes similar knives occur where people are depicted dressing leather. Further, there were found in the same place stones for polishing leather, tablets which served as a rest when it was being cut, forms over which it was bent, and so forth. The pictures allow us to observe how the ancients used punches, knives, scrapers, borers and needles, and also racks for drawing and stretching leather.

THE USES OF LEATHER

It is seen from the preceding section that the Egyptians had at their disposal a fairly extensive set of tools for working leather. The equipment of the Greeks and Romans was probably

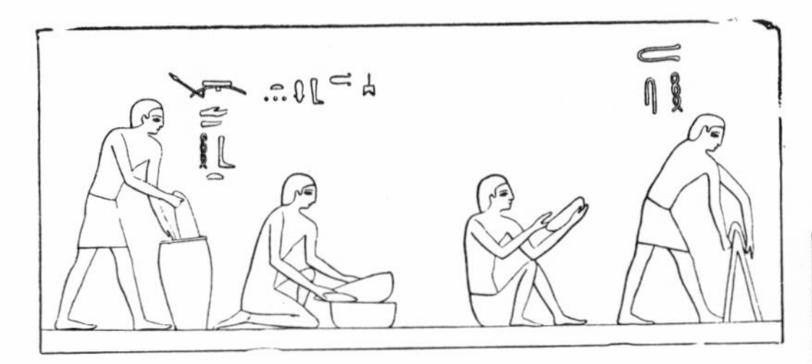

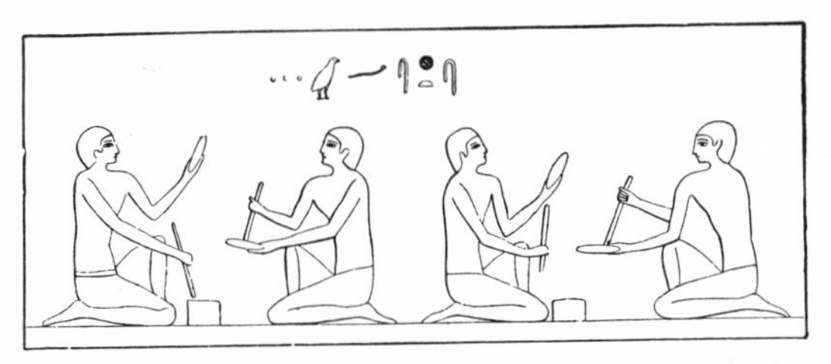

FIGS. 129 and 130.—Cutting Soles in an ancient Egyptian shoemaker's workshop

The picture is probably to be interpreted as follows: Above, from left to right, soaking the leather and softening it by pummelling or hammering between two stones; drawing and stretching it over a rack. The picture below: Cutting out soles on a support

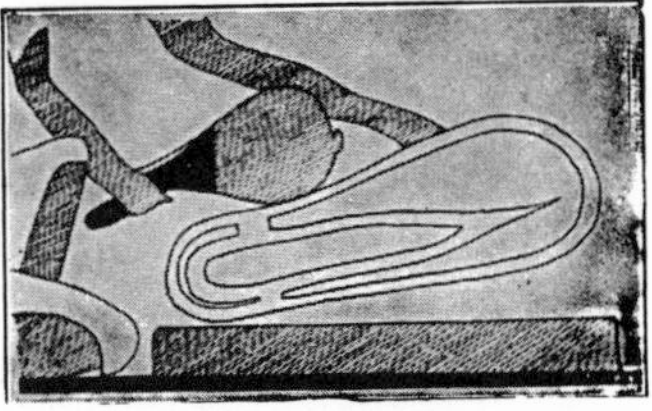

FIG. 131.—Pummelling a Leather Sole

There seems no other possible interpretation of this picture: it shows that even in those early times soles were treated just as at the present time

still more elaborate, as is known from numerous excavations and several descriptions. Knives have been found that resemble our own, and other finds show that shoemaker's awls mounted on wooden handles were used. An important point was established by the discovery of a tombstone in Rome which proved that shoemaker's lasts were in use, which were also provided with handles. These handles enabled them to be thrust into the shoes. The latter were first cut out and then sewn together. For sewing, the holes were first bored with the awl. The pieces of leather were then joined together by means of tendons from animals or by leather thongs. The joins were sometimes effected by riveting; indeed, pieces of leather

FIG. 132.—A Greek Shoemaker's Workshop

The customer is standing on the table on the piece of leather out of which the master (on the left) is about to cut the sole by means of the crescent-shaped knife. The assistant on the right (according to Blümner) is holding the piece of leather intended for the upper part of the shoe. On the shelf to the left, pincers and awls; on the wall, two pieces of leather suspended by a loop, two lasts and a basket. Below the table is a vessel which (in the opinion of the author) contains water for softening the leather, just as we find it under every shoemaker's table nowadays. The same sort of vessel is to be seen under the table in other Greek pictures. From a picture on a vase out of the Bourguignon collection in Naples, and now in Boston

were set with nails or rivets, partly for decorative purposes and partly to protect them. The soles consisted either of leather or of wood, and were sometimes nailed. There is every kind of shoe from the

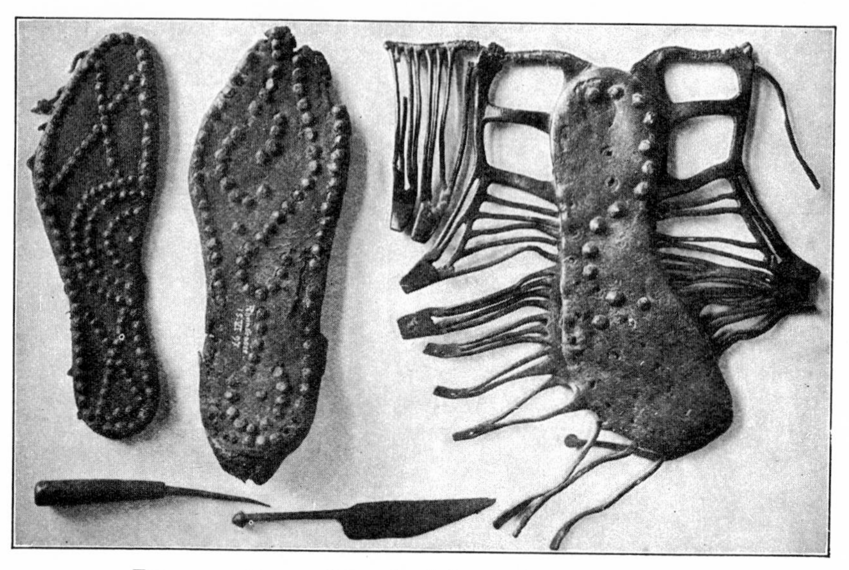

FIG. 133.—Roman Soles, Sandals and Shoemakers' Tools

From left to right: Two nailed soles for the right foot; a sandal spread out flat (it has a nailed sole, over which a second rests, and above the latter is the so-called inner-sole). Below is an awl and a shoemaker's knife. Found at Mainz. Museum of Antiquities, Mainz

daintiest women's shoes to the coarsest soldiers' shoes, sandals as well as boots. There were right and left shoes, made on the corresponding lasts. Dagger sheaths of leather and similar coverings were made over wooden forms that had previously been cut into the appropriate shape.

The chemical treatment of leather serves the purpose of colouring and preserving it. Madder and vermilion were chiefly used to colour it, and copper vitriol (sulphate) was used to stain it black; the black colour is due to the copper salt reacting chemically with the tanning substance in the leather. In general, however, the leather was worn in its natural colour. To preserve it, oil was rubbed in (Pliny, XV, 34).

FIG. 134.—Roman Sandals, Shoes, Nailed Soles
Found at Mainz. Museum of Antiquities, Mainz

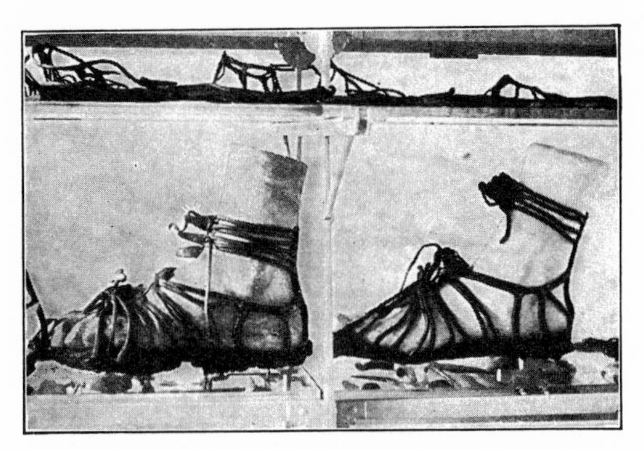

FIG. 135.—Roman Sandals fastened to the feet
Found at Mainz. Museum of Antiquities, Mainz

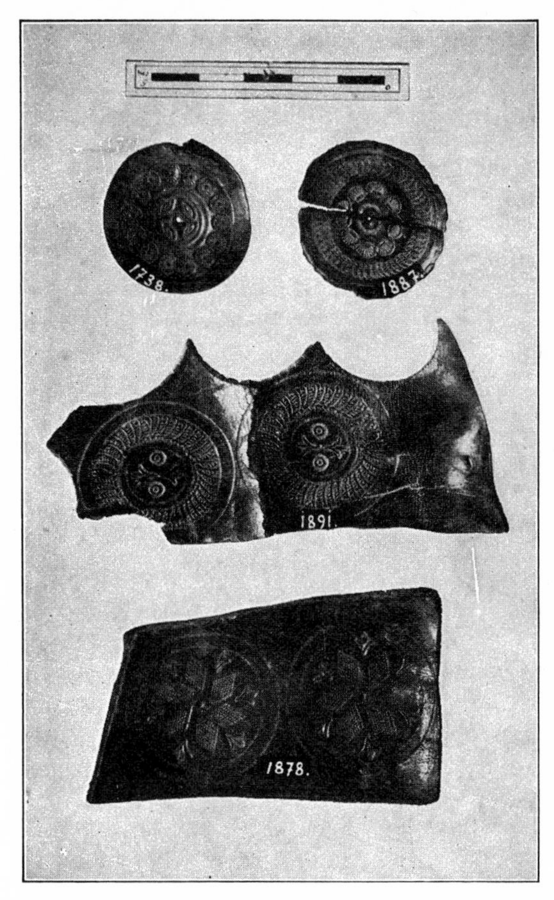

FIG. 136.—Ancient Roman Decorative Leather. Leather discs and pieces with impressed ornamentation
Provincial Museum, Trèves

AGRICULTURE

AGRICULTURAL IMPLEMENTS

THE oldest implement of agriculture is probably the digging stick, which has appropriately been likened to a lengthened and hardened finger. In antiquity this stick developed into the plough through stages of whose existence there are no records, but which are rendered probable by observations taken from primitive peoples. It may be supposed that the staff was early weighted by a stone having a central hole. In this way a digging stick was obtained such as is still used by the Bushmen of South Africa. By thrusting this stick into the ground and placing the foot on the stone, one obtained a

FIG. 137.—Bushman Digging Stick

FIG. 138.—In the foreground is the Mattock or Hoe, behind is the Hoe-plough of the Red Indians of Colombia

lever (Fig. 137); this enabled the ground to be loosened and turned over more readily than was possible with a simply pointed stick. To increase the rate of working the lower part of this primitive implement was broadened, and so the spade was evolved. A particularly convenient form of this spade offered itself now and then in nature: a strong bough with a branch inclined at an acute angle allowed greater power to be applied and one could thus dig more deeply. It was in this form that the hoe was first used (Fig. 138), and from it there developed the plough: for by reversing the hoe so that its blade is no longer directed forwards but backwards, and by harnessing draught-cattle to its long handle, we arrive at the plough (Fig. 138). It is in this form that the plough occurs in antiquity. It has preserved this shape throughout thousands of years (Fig. 140), although improved forms were also devised. Even in late Roman times such ploughs were probably not infrequently used.

FIG. 139.—The Iron Blade of a Coptic Hoe (form of the Egyptian hoe) used for loosening the soil
Berlin. Altes Museum, Egyptian Section

Alongside of this, however, a development occurs which shows rapidly increasing mechanical advantage in its various stages. The bough with the bent hoe-like limb for an end is not always easy to find in Nature in the exactly appropriate form, as the end is usually too narrow. This limb was therefore generally prepared separately and then either bound or fastened on to the branch by pegs. Ploughshare and shaft were likewise individually prepared. Joined together they formed a plough (Fig. 141). Wooden ploughs of this type were used by the Babylonians; they are preserved to us from Egyptian times. The Romans preferred special sorts of wood for making them, above all the common oak, the kermes oak, the laurel and the elm. The ploughshare was often made of metal, as it then wears off less soon and cannot be so easily damaged by stones as in the case of a wooden share; moreover, on account of its heavier weight and sharper edge the bronze or iron share cuts through the soil more readily.

FIG. 140.—Greek Hoe-plough. Vase painting
Berlin. Altes Museum, Antiquarium

But this plough had yet one fault: it could be guided only with difficulty. For this purpose a special handle, the plough-tail, was added, which served to direct it. In the course of time two tails were added, as this enabled both hands to be used in guiding the plough. Also, the plough-beam, the shaft, became lengthened, and finally, to facilitate manipulation, a special connection, the sole, was inserted between the beam and the handle. This improved hoe-plough is the form in which we encounter the plough among many peoples of antiquity, particularly among those of the Near East and certain of the Mediterranean peoples (Egyptians and Etruscans). It was also used by the Greeks and the Romans wherever the soil was soft owing to frequent rains. It was found to be particularly useful at places like the Delta of the Nile or the inundated parts of the Euphrates, where the rivers deposit a soft and therefore easily worked mud which is free from stones.

But wherever the cultivation of the soil made higher demands on the plough, the latter was improved still further. This was the case particularly with the Greeks and the Romans, who used improved ploughs simultaneously with the hoe-plough just described. The various parts, that is the beam (*temo*), the tail (*stiva*), the handle (*manicula*), and the tail (*buris* or *bura*), were retained (particularly by the Romans), but the share was placed obliquely to allow a special share-beam (*dentale*) to be added, by which the plough could be more effectively directed. The form of the plough was at first that of a wedge, and so it was called '*vomer*'. To

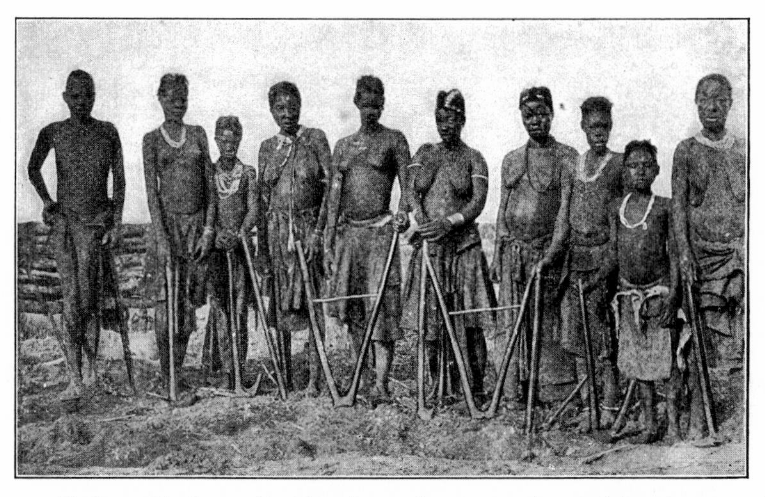

FIG. 141.—Kaffirs with Composite Ploughs, such as were also used by many peoples of antiquity, and Mattocks

turn the ploughed-up sod of earth over the share was turned to one side, being made in the form of a right-angled triangle, and was furnished with a board. Finally the ploughshare and the mould-board were curved into the shape of a helical surface (screw-like) and so an extended arched blade (*vectis rostratus*) was obtained which entailed a far less expenditure of energy in pulling the plough and turning the sod. But since the grassy surface of the soil can be cut only with difficulty by this share, so that it still requires considerable power to direct the plough, a special coulter is fastened in front of the blade to cut the surface before the share reaches it. This coulter (*culter*), as well as the frame which carries wheels (which was also added later), is to be found even in ancient Greek ploughs. In this way there developed among the Greeks, and more particularly among the Romans, a type of plough which in the later period resembled the simple farm plough of modern times. Numerous specimens, especially of the ploughshares and coulters, have been found.

THE METHOD OF PLOUGHING

Herodotus (II, 14) reports of the Egyptians that lived below Memphis: 'They do not need to break up furrows with the plough, nor to hoe, nor to perform any of the work which troubles other people in tilling, for the river comes of its own accord on to their fields and irrigates them, and when it has done so, it leaves them. Each husbandman then sows his field and drives pigs on to it; and when the pigs have trampled the seeds into the soil, he waits for the harvest-time, when he threshes out the corn again by means of pigs and brings it into his granary.' This passage might lead us to the erroneous conclusion that ploughs were not used in one of the most important parts of Egypt. But this certainly does not apply as Herodotus' remarks would lead us to believe. Concerning ploughing among the ancient Egyptians, Diodorus (136) in the first century B.C. and Columella (*De re rustica*, III, 25) in the first century A.D., narrate that the Egyptians made shallow furrows in the surface of the land by means of light ploughs, a mode of ploughing that the Romans called *scarificatio*. Pictures and manifold remains of ancient Egyptian ploughing have been handed down to us, which give us detailed information about the form and manipulation of the plough. According to these representations, the Egyptians seem to have had a preference for using the rake in addition to the plough. This rake was of wood and resembled the capital letter A (Fig. 142). The cross-piece of the A is made of a piece of twisted rope. Further, the seed was often scattered *in front of* the plough so that it was ploughed straight into the ground. In the case of dry sods of soil the Egyptian plough often seems not to have achieved its purpose. This may be inferred from the fact that on a drawing on the tomb of Kha-em-hat workers are seen walking in front of the plough who are breaking up the sods with a sort of hammer.

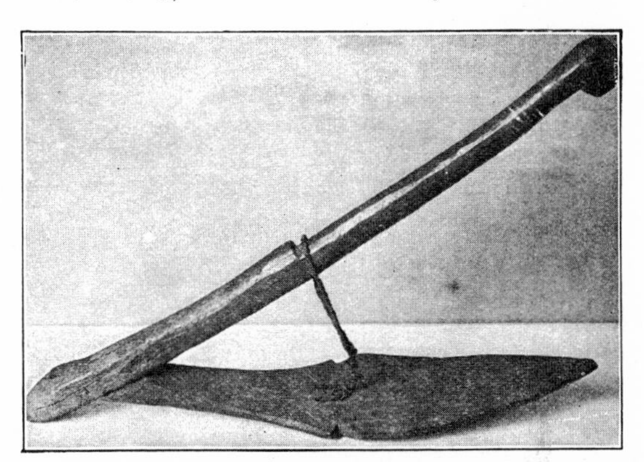

FIG. 142.—Egyptian Hoe. Length 28 in.
Berlin Museum, Egyptian Section

Deeper furrows than those of the Egyptians were made by the Romans, who were, indeed, excellent farmers. They were acquainted (as were also the Egyptians) with manures and the rotation of crops (Pliny, XVII, 6; XVIII, 53, and so forth), as well as intermittent farming (fallow one year, cultivated soil the next). The fallow fields were used as pasture land. The Roman husbandman did not simply plough to and fro, but mostly cross-ways; indeed, he sometimes ploughed the same field seven times before he proceeded to sow. Various accounts give us information about the advanced development of the methods of tilling the soil. M. Terentius Varro (116–27 B.C.) writes in his *De re rustica*, i, 29, 2: 'When ploughing is being done for the third time after sowing, little boards are attached to the share, thus covering up the sown seed in the rows and making furrows in which the rain-water may run off.' But Pliny, who was already acquainted with four types of ploughs (XVIII, 171), describes the use of the harrow (*rastrum*) (XVIII, 180) by which the clods of earth were broken up, the grass surface was destroyed and the weeds were removed: 'After the field has been ploughed for the second time it is harrowed either by means of a frame of interlaced twigs (carrying thorns) or with a proper harrow, according to whichever is necessary, and when the sowing has been done, the harrowing is repeated.' For the rest, the harrow was also known to the Egyptians and Jews; the Greeks, on the other hand, seem not to have used it.

Concerning the ways and means used by the Germanic tribes in agriculture, unfortunately only very little has been handed down to posterity, at least as regards the treatment of the soil. Tacitus merely states: 'The land to be cultivated is changed every year and a part is always left fallow. For they do not strive with industry to increase the productiveness of the soil and the area of cultivation by planting fruit trees, marking off pasture land or watering gardens. The German demands only corn from the soil. Therefore he does not divide the year into four seasons; he has the words and ideas of winter, spring and summer, but autumn, as also her gifts, are unknown to him.' Numerous finds of prehistoric times, and in particular of the La Tène period stretching from 400 B.C. to the birth of Christ, lead us to conclude that at the dawn of history agricultural implements, in particular ploughs, which resembled those of the Romans, were also used in Germania. It has been established that they used the movable mould-board (or breast) which could be set to the right or to the left, as well as the fixed mould board. Hoes were also used in cultivating the soil.

THE TREATMENT OF CORN

The sickle and the scythe likewise occur among almost all peoples of antiquity at the first dawn of history. At the beginning of Egyptian history blades were still made of flint, but later they were made of bronze and iron. The blade is often toothed. For the rest, these implements resembled our own fairly closely in form, manipulation and action.

The corn that had been harvested was threshed; originally this was probably performed by an extremely primitive method, namely by driving animals, chiefly oxen, over the scattered stalks. How old this method is can be gathered from the fact that it is mentioned by Homer (*Iliad*, XX, 495):

'For even as when one yoketh wide-horned bulls to tread white barley in a stablished threshing-floor, and quickly is it trodden out beneath the feet of the loud-lowing bulls. . . .'[1]

The oxen, which were urged on by drivers, were often replaced by other animals, such as mules, and probably asses and horses. Flails were also used; they were not, however, provided with a movable swingle but consisted only of rods with which the corn was beaten (see Fig. 167, above on the right, p. 101). The Romans had threshing-machines, of which a particular form, *plostellum Poenicum,* is supposed to have been invented by the Carthaginians. We do not know what its appearance

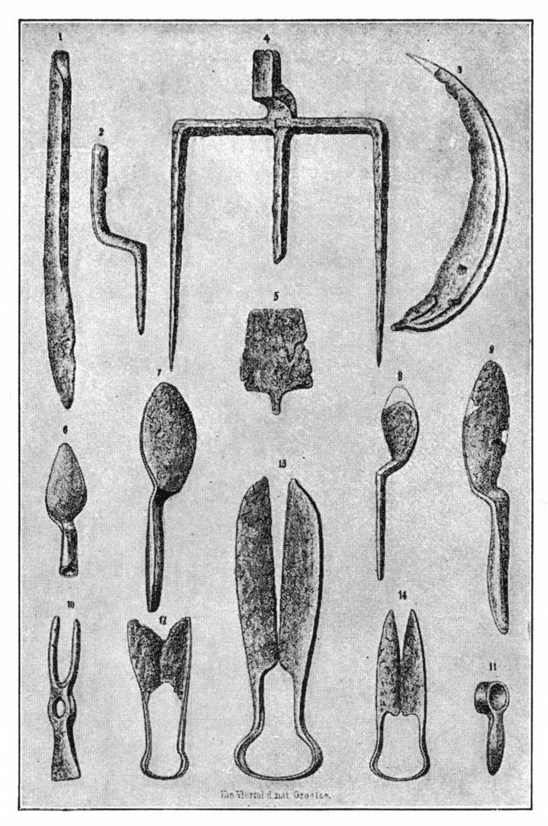

FIG. 143.—Roman Agricultural Implements

was, but probably it was shaped like a roller. Another type of threshing machine, *tribulum,* described by Varro (*De re rustica,* 152), was a wooden plate roughened underneath by stones or iron and weighted by means of stones as well as by the weight of the driver; this was drawn over the corn by oxen. The grains appear to have been pressed or squeezed out by the roughened surface. Varro's description does not give a clear picture of the implement, but it probably resembled that which is still used

[1] Prose Translation by Lang, Leaf and Myers, Macmillan & Co., London.

nowadays by the Syrians and some Arabian tribes. The latter consists of a wooden sledge in the shape of a chair, under the runners of which sharp stones are fastened; they are drawn by oxen. Varro's Latin text also allows this interpretation.

Threshing was followed by winnowing, that is, separating out the chaff. The corn was placed into shallow woven baskets shaped like a bowl or into flat wooden barrels of moderate size which could be conveniently packed together on their narrow sides. (It is proved by excavations that this was done by the Egyptians.) So soon as a strong wind blew, the contents were whirled into the air. If no wind was available, it was generated artificially, as old Egyptian pictures show, by fanning with a fan or a brush. The Greeks and Romans used a sieve. The heavy grains fell back into the baskets while the lighter chaff was scattered by the wind. The spade was also used for a similar purpose (see Fig. 167, above in the middle, p. 101). Wooden forks were in some cases applied to effecting this separation of chaff from the grain. By this process the corn was sufficiently prepared to allow it to be utilized for its proper purpose, namely, to making food, in particular bread, and to preparing beverages. It was kept as grain in granaries from which it was taken when required.

FERMENTATION

THE BAKERY

IN the case of probably all the peoples of antiquity, baking bread was a purely domestic matter which occupied the housewife and her servants. The profession of the baker came into being comparatively late, namely during the war against King Perseus of Macedonia in the year 582 from the founding of the city of Rome (Pliny, XVIII, 107). This was about 171 B.C. Until that date all the individual steps necessary for preparing bread, that is grinding the grain, mixing the dough, allowing it to rise, baking and so forth, were carried out in the home. Nor did the advent of the professional baker succeed in entirely stopping the making of bread in the home; just as nowadays in many households, particularly in smaller towns and in the country, 'home-made' bread is still met with. The baker was also the miller, as is proved by discoveries in Pompeii among others, where the mills and the bakeries lie together in one property. These two trades, milling and baking, became separated at a still later period.

This course of development was not without its influence on the process itself. The utensils used were at first so designed that they could also be manipulated by the weaker sex. Later, they were made larger, more efficient and adapted to trade requirements. Finally, however, milling proceeded along its own lines, producing at a far greater rate than was necessary merely for bakeries. The miller enlisted the help of machinery, and above all, water power, in order to provide as great a number of bakeries and households as possible with flour.

MILLING CORN

It may be generally assumed that the corn used for milling was in the state in which it was left after it had been cleared of chaff by being winnowed or passed through a sieve. In some cases, however, the milling was preceded by a special treatment aimed at facilitating the removal of the husk from the grain. This treatment consisted in roasting the corn. The roasting was performed either with or without moistening the corn; this was first applied to barley, but later also to other forms of corn, such as spelt (German wheat). The purpose of moistening the corn beforehand was to effect by an osmotic process a preliminary separation of the husk from the cells containing starch-flour in the grain. The husk and its content swell up by different amounts when soaked. The moisture first swells up the husk, soaks through it in virtue of osmosis and thus arrives at the grain, which likewise swells up. When distended to the maximum extent, they are pressed hard against each other. If the corn is then dried the husk and the grain shrink to different amounts and this causes a general loosening of the configuration. The roasting makes the husk brittle, so that when subjected to mechanical treatment, which consists of pounding, it easily breaks off. The corn was roasted either on or between hot stones or in an oven, after having been placed in a special vessel. The grains were separated from the husks, after the roasting and stamping were finished, by means of sieves.

> Grind, mill, grind!
> For Pittakos also grinds,
> The ruler of great Mytilene.

So runs an ancient song quoted by Plutarch (about A.D. 50–120), and since also in the Old Testament of the Bible and in the Edda such 'millers' songs' are mentioned, we may assume that in ancient times, too, milling was a cheerful occupation often accompanied by song; and this also shows that although the technical appliances used were very primitive the work involved was far less of a strain than might appear at first sight. The oldest form of milling consisted of rubbing and pounding the corn.

FIGS. 144 and 145.—Millstones of Trachyte
Diameter = 9 in. and 11 in. respectively. Found at Hissarlik (Troy)

Ancient Egyptian pictures and, in particular, beautiful carvings, as well as more or less roughly finished grave-gifts, disclose how this grinding was accomplished. A stone which in many cases had its upper surface hollowed out like a flat bowl was sloped off or set up so that its front end lay deeper than its rear end. The woman kneeled down on the latter and ground the corn in the hollow which sloped down in front of her by means of a second smaller stone. The motion was not merely one of pure sliding but consisted also of a knocking action. The Romans were therefore right later, when other kinds of milling came into use, in speaking of this kind of mill as a *mola trusatilis*, which may be rendered by the term 'knocking mill'. Since *trusare* indicates energetic knocking, this expression also betrays the important fact that in using these mills rubbing and crushing played a secondary part compared with striking. For rubbing and crushing we find stones employed that were not hollowed out; with them were used flat grinding-stones with a large area of base, such as we see in the ancient Egyptian carvings above-mentioned. Later improvements in milling did not succeed in supplanting these old grinding, crushing and knocking mills. On the site of encampments of Roman soldiers stationed on the borders of Germania, rubbing-bowls were found, which were made of clay, into which quartz fragments had been pressed. In them the soldiers rubbed up the grains of wheat, after having previously added water. By this means they obtained a pap ready for baking without requiring the immediate step of making flour. In view of the comparatively small amount of energy expended in milling by any of the above-named processes, the output was not strikingly large. At the suggestion of Héron de Villefosse Ringelmann made experiments in the *Institut National Agronomique* in Paris which showed that the grinding led to no proper flour but only to a sort of groats. In the course of an hour only about 10 ounces of ground corn was obtained. Villefranche infers from this that before mills were improved only comparatively little bread and bread-cakes were eaten and that they were probably a luxury. We are probably correct in surmising that the corn was soaked and then boiled, as is still done nowadays in the case of beans, peas and lentils.

FIG. 146.—Egyptian Grinding-stone for grinding down corn

Length = 5·4 in. Found at Thebes. Berlin Museum, Egyptian Department

FIG. 147.—A Servant grinding Corn. Egyptian Carving in Limestone

The body is painted reddish-brown, apron white, grinding-stone red. Length is 16 in. Found at Saqqarah. Berlin Museum, Egyptian Department

This is corroborated by two passages in Homer, *Iliad*, XVIII, 558–560, and *Odyssey*, XIV, 76, 77. The former mentions a 'mash' made of white barley, and the second relates that white barley-meal was used for sprinkling over the roast, 'crumbing' it, as we should now say. Pliny (XVIII, 19) also writes of pap or dumplings (*offa*) made of the crushed grain.

FIG. 148.—Rubbing Dish of Clay with quartz fragments embedded in it

Found on the site of an encampment on the Roman-German border. Museum at Mainz

The low grade of efficiency of these earliest mills which had been so long in use finally led to their being greatly improved among the various peoples. Without such progress, indeed, it would be impossible to imagine achievements such as, for example, those of the Papyrus Rollin in Paris which reports that 114,064 loaves of bread were on one occasion delivered by the master of the king's bakery. A first improvement was effected in Egypt by making the millstone higher so that the work was done in a standing instead of in a sitting posture. Such mill-stones sprang into being in the New Kingdom. The women who did the work were next replaced by men. For example, it is reported of Samson in the Bible (Judges xvi. 21) 'and he did grind in the prison house'; it is also corroborated by various drawings. In Greece and Rome, however, and probably also in other countries, free-men could not be forced to grind against their will. This was work for slaves and criminals, who were often prevented by means of a broad wooden collar placed round the neck from partaking of the corn or the flour.

FIGS. 149 and 150.—Mortar of Basalt and Pestle of Hard Limestone

Diameter of the Mortar = 13 in. and 10 in. Length of the pestle = 5½ in. Diameter of its rubbing and pounding surface = 1½ in. Troy

Besides the mill-stone the mortar was also much used for pounding the corn. Such appliances were found by Schliemann in the excavations at Troy; they consisted of a mortar made of basalt and a pestle of hard limestone which did not, apparently, belong together. Probably the two parts were always made of the same material. Furthermore, pictures on vases and, above all, a delightful Tanagra figure in the Berlin Museum, which dates back to the fifth century B.C., clearly shows how the pounding was performed. The mortar proper rested on a stand whose height was such that its upper rim reached about to the knee of the worker, or else it and the stand were made of one piece. The pestle was of wood, about 30 to 39 in. long, and narrowed down at the middle so that it could be conveniently grasped (Fig. 151).

The low efficiency of all these contrivances early created a desire for further improvements, and so, simultaneously with the mill-stone, there developed the mill, of whose existence there is some evidence among almost all peoples of antiquity. Thus, when the Jews were prisoners of the Babylonians, they had to transport mill-stones (Lamentations v. 13); and Deuteronomy (xxiv. 6) contains the commandment: 'No man shall take the nether or the upper mill-stone.' Homer writes in the *Odyssey* (VII, 104, and elsewhere) of 'mills', meaning probably querns or hand-mills. And in Egypt, too, the use of mills is confirmed, although no wall-drawings are preserved which depict them. All these mills were at first hand-mills and probably looked very much alike in all countries. The hand-mill consisted of two stones, of which the lower was fixed while the other was rotated on it. Originally the upper stone was probably always lifted off when fresh grain had to be added. Later, however, the upper stone had a hole in the centre while the lower had a projection which

FIG. 151.—Greek Women pounding Grain in a Mortar

Picture on a Greek vase

passed through this hole. Between this pivot and the hole enough space remained for adding grain when necessary. A grip was added to the upper stone to enable it to be turned more easily, and the lower one was provided with a rim which was to prevent the grain from falling out. When ground the grain was run off through leads into a receiver underneath (Fig. 152). In order to spread the grains entering at the central hole over the whole space between the two mill-stones, the latter had small grooves running out radially, between which further grooves were inserted inclined at acute angles to them. These grooves also increase the friction and in this way aid the crushing of the grain. There followed as a logical development of the hand-mill those typical Roman mills which have been handed down to us through excavations at Pompeii, and are represented in pictures and so forth. The earliest confirmation of the use in Rome of these mills, which Varro and Pliny report were invented in the town Volsinii (Bolsena), is given in the second century B.C. The improvement, made in order to grind more rapidly, was probably attained by attaching two grips to the upper mill-stone so that two people could grind simultaneously; they presumably did this by passing the grips from one to the other in rotation. But in the earlier stages they still used only their hands. The whole weight of their bodies could be applied only when larger mills were used, which consisted of a conical base of stone on which the milling-stone was rotated; the upper stone was, of course, hollowed out so as to fit over the cone. As the entrance funnel was fixed immediately above, the mill-stone assumed the form of two bells placed with their necks end to end and so the mill-stone presented the aspect of an hour-glass. In order to be able to rotate it two pivots were inserted at the outside of the junction of the necks radially, that is horizontally, so that rotating levers could be applied in the hollows of the pivots. In the case of large mills worked by animals these levers were riveted, or else strengthened by a scaffolding which passed over the whole entrance funnel as a sort of protective covering. The heavy

FIG. 152.—Roman Hand-mill
Saalburg Museum

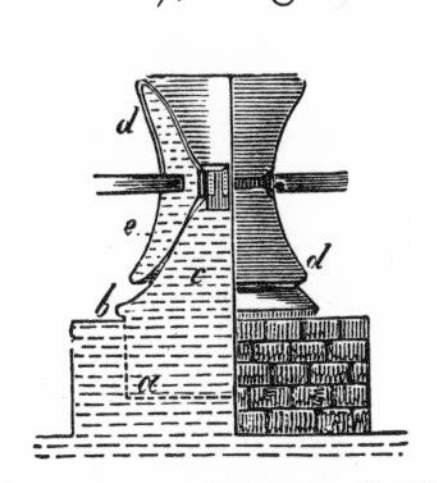

FIG. 153.—Roman Mill.
On the left is a sectional view; on the right is an exterior view. *a* is a brick foundation, *b* is a surface or a groove into which the flour collected, and from which it was run off; *c* is a fixed conically-shaped grinding-stone of the outline shown. This shape leads to a very narrow passage at *e*, at which the grain is most strongly compressed; *d* is a rotating counter-grinder in the form of an hour-glass, and it has a funnel-shaped opening at the top

grinding stone was not allowed to rest directly on the base stone as it could not then be rotated, nor could the grain have glided between the two. For this reason the base stone had an iron pivot on which the grinding-stone rested in such a way that a small space remained between them, which was particularly narrow at one point owing to the slight convexity of the grinding-stone. Connection between the mill-stone and the pivot of the base stone was made by a disc placed inside the mill-stone at the narrowest point and having five holes (Fig. 154). The pivot passed through the large central hole (socket), while the other four holes allowed the grain to pass through into the mill. By lengthening the central pivot or, in the case of larger mills, by extending the beam which supported the framework of the entrance funnel, coarser flour could be obtained. As already mentioned, the mills were turned either by animals, usually asses or mules, or by slaves and criminals (not by free men) (Figs. 153–156).

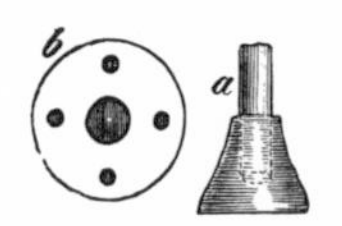

FIG. 154.—The iron Pivot (*a*) and the Disc (*b*) in the interior of Roman mills

FIG. 155.—Roman Mill worked by an Ass
Relief in a baker's shop in Pompeii

Later, the water-mill appeared, which Vitruvius describes (X, 5, 2)

FIG. 156.—Baker's Mills at Pompeii

The parts with the rubbing surfaces are in the shape of an hour-glass and are about 6½ ft. high. The holes for inserting the levers are clearly discernible in the two rear mills. On the left is the baking oven. In front of it at the side we see the trough for receiving the water

somewhat as follows : 'The water-mills are driven in the same way (that is, by means of the under-shot wheel). These mills are similar in all other respects except that they have a toothed wheel (*a*) at the end of the shaft. Working in this toothed wheel is another (*b*) at right angles to it and having at its upper end a double swallow-tail (*e*) which is plugged into the mill stone. Thus the mill stones (*d*) are rotated owing to the horizontal wheel being made to turn by the motion transmitted by the teeth of the vertical wheel attached to the shaft (the paddle-wheel). The mill-hopper (*f*) placed above the mill-stones feeds the grain into the latter, where it becomes ground up.' It is remarkable that this ancient Roman mill with the low-lying under-shot wheel as described by Vitruvius is still in use at the present time in some localities. It also serves as an example of how long some technical constructions last before they are superseded. Such regions also contain other relics which indicate that they once belonged to the Roman Empire. For instance, the author found an example of this mill in the furthermost parts of Val di Gardena, where a dialect derived from Latin is still spoken. A peculiar feature of these mills is that the undershot wheel described by Vitruvius was always used even when the conditions were such that much greater efficiency would have been obtained by the use of an over-shot or middle-shot wheel (cf. Fig. 297, p. 228).

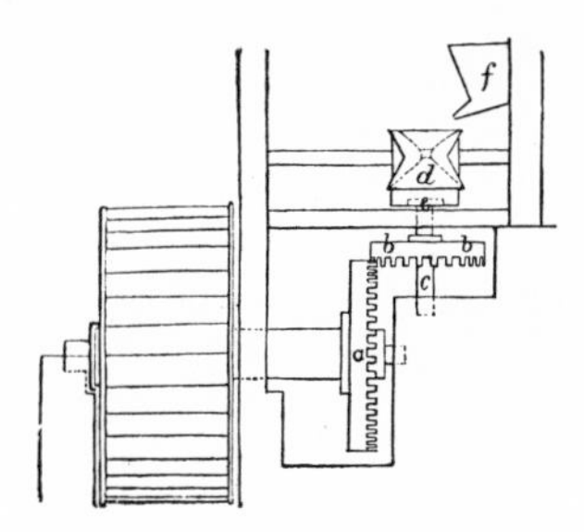

FIG. 157.—Roman Water-mill, according to Vitruvius

In place of the water-wheel a pulley was often used (see p. 209). In the sixth century B.C. the floating-mill came into use ; its invention was due to the circumstance that Vitiges, King of the Goths, had the water-channels blocked up when he besieged Rome in the year A.D. 536. The animals which had turned the mills had to be slaughtered on account of the shortage of water, and the slaves were required for purposes of defence ; so Belisarius had the mills mounted on ships that were afloat on the Tiber. Technically the floating mill had the advantage of working independently of the level of the water. The undershot wheel thus always obtained its supply of water. Hence its chief disadvantage, which often required special dams or weirs to be constructed, was eliminated.

BAKING BREAD

In antiquity many different sorts of flour were made, from which innumerable dishes were prepared. For baking bread, however, wheaten flour was chiefly used, although numerous other cereals (barley, rye, millet, oats, etc.) were used, and various ingredients (oil, milk, wine, poppy, sesame, and so forth) were also added. Herodotus reports that the Egyptians used spelt (II, 77, 78) in making bread, and also the seeds of the lotus-flower (II, 92). Ancient Nordic bread from Scandinavia, which was analysed by Rosendahl in the Stockholm Pharmaceutical Institute, was made of pine-bark and pea-meal. At first a mash of flour and water was probably eaten universally, that is, a sort of polenta[1] (see p. 791). In order to be able to preserve this mash, which easily turned bad, generally becoming sour, baking was probably resorted to; it was presumably carried out in hot ashes or perhaps on hot stones. At any rate the charred crust of some very old samples that have been found indicate that they were baked in some such way. This bread was unleavened and was mostly baked in the form of discs. The remark by Vergil, *Aen.* vii, 109, that the bread was used as a plate and afterwards eaten is explained by the flat shape of the unleavened bread. Leaven seems to be an invention of the Egyptians, by means of which the unleavened and unfermented flat cake became what is nowadays called 'bread'. The knowledge of leaven was then passed on from the Egyptians to the Greeks and still later to the Romans. Among the Greeks, who honoured Dionysus as the inventor of bread-baking, bread became the staple food of the meal. Besides being prepared from wheat, bread was also made from barley flour. The crust served as a spoon for the other dishes; it was not eaten, being thrown under the table after use. Both leavened and unleavened bread were eaten, and some bakers of Athens, such as Thearion, acquired great fame.

FIG. 158.—Egyptian Granary with a Bakery in front

In the yard a figure is seen grinding corn by rubbing it on the grinding-stone; next to it on the left we see two persons busy at the oven which is heated from the bottom and on the flat top of which bread is being baked. Behind is the storehouse in which bread and sacks of corn have been placed. A scribe is seen sitting on the roof, superintending operations and keeping a list. (Grave-gift.) Berlin Museum, Egyptian Department

To prepare the bread, flour of varying degrees of refinement was used, which had previously been put through a sieve. The Egyptians made their flour-sieves with meshes of different sizes from thin strips of leaves torn from papyrus-plants or from reeds. Roman flour-sieves were made of canvas or horse-hair procured from Gaul. In form they resembled our modern sieves. The dough was prepared by kneading. Although Herodotus (II, 78) remarks of the Egyptians that they 'knead dough with their feet and clay with their hands', this does not seem to be generally true, for old Egyptian reliefs show that in Egypt a trough of fine basket-work was used for kneading and that the hands were used, just as nowadays. The superfluous water passed out through the meshes of the basket into a stone jar placed below. Besides these, stone troughs were also used in Egypt for kneading. The Romans had in addition to similar stone troughs also wooden ones for use in the household; but in the bakeries, as for example in Pompeii, probably large flat stone troughs were exclusively used. An ancient Egyptian picture in the museum of Bulak shows us that great force was applied to knead the

[1] Italian porridge made of barley, chestnut meal, etc.—H. L. B.

dough thoroughly. In the endeavour to economize this labour mechanical kneaders were developed, about the construction of which we have

FIG. 159.—A Bakery in Egypt

The author regards the following interpretation as correct: (1) kneading the dough by means of the feet; (2) water-carriers bringing water for mixing the dough; (3) moulds of various forms; above, baked loaves, small and large; (4) the oven, which is heated from below, and on the flat top of which the loaves are baked; its construction agrees with that represented in the figure immediately preceding; (5) ?; (6) building up an oven for baking a different kind of dough; (7) moulds for this different dough—the man on the left seems to be cutting out the dough into shapes by means of these moulds; (8) the oven, filled with these cakes; flames are seen shooting out of the top.

information from discoveries at Pompeii. They consist of a kneading-trough of circular cross-section, carrying a wooden shaft pointing vertically upwards. It is provided with wings that reach almost as far as the inner walls of the kneading-trough. In order to scrape off the dough that collects between the wings, horizontal rigid rods pass through the sides of the trough into the interior. They were fixed in such a position that when the shaft rotated they came to lie between the wings, so that the dough remained hanging on the rods and then fell down of its own weight. As is shown in old reliefs the kneading-machine was turned either by human beings or by

FIG. 160.—A Kneading-machine

animals. To enable the machine to be turned the vertical shaft was furnished with a horizontal beam (Fig. 160).

The dough was salted and leavened before being kneaded. For leavening, the Romans used a mixture of sun-dried bran and fermenting must, which could be kept for a whole year. In Pliny's time, just as nowadays, leaven was kept over from one day to the next (Pliny, XVIII, 104). Pliny (XVIII, 68) is also acquainted with yeast, which he calls 'condensed foam', which forms when beer ferments (see below). He does not mention whether it was used by the Romans for making bread, but merely states that the Gauls and the Spaniards used it in place of leaven for baking bread. Not only was fermentation effected by means of leaven containing yeast, but other means of making bread rise were also known. Whether these actually included soda, as might be inferred from a passage in the Geoponica, II, 33, seems more than doubtful, as soda melts only at 850° C.; that is, at a temperature which could never be reached in the interior of dough that has been placed in a baking-oven. But even in the fused state soda does not give off carbon dioxide. Several reasons preclude the possibility of the dough having risen through escaping water of crystallization, so that we are urged to look for a different meaning of the word νίτρον. The juice of grapes that had been soaked and then pressed out was also

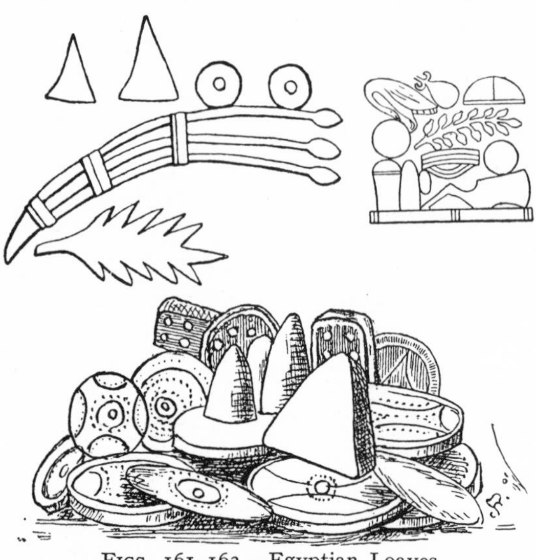

FIGS. 161–163.—Egyptian Loaves

The forms of the loaves are in part identical with those of Fig. 159. They disclose that some were obtained by kneading and forming, others by being stamped out of the flat dough. It must be recollected that the loaves of pyramidal shape (πυραμίδες) were prepared for purposes of worship; this is the origin of the name later given to the Pyramids (Diels).

FIG. 164.—Baker in Tanagra (5th century B.C.)
Berlin, Altes Museum, Antiquarium

used in place of leaven and was effective owing to its contained yeast.

As already mentioned, baking was carried out at first in glowing ashes or on hot stones, perhaps also on racks, the use of which appears

FIG. 165.—Oven in Pompeii

At the Casa di Sallustio. Below is the opening for fuel; next to it on the right is the remains of a water-container, and above is the depository for the bread with the space in front for placing aside the boards that have been used to thrust in the bread. In the courtyard there are remains of mills. Above is a chimney (a rarity)

to be indicated in a Tanagra figure of a man who is interpreted as a baker and which dates back to the fifth century B.C.; later, baking was done in ovens. Originally the oven had no particular space for baking. The loaves were laid on then in the same way as they had formerly been placed on ashes or between hot bricks (see Figs. 158 and 159). A picture of the court bakery of Ramses III (about 1200 B.C.) in his tomb at Thebes shows us an oven about a yard high which is heated from within; the bread was stuck on to the hot sides and was here baked. Later, the oven was arched and heated from below. Usually the apertures of the oven proper and of the heating space were situated at right angles to each other. The fire was lit in the heating space, which was open on both sides and which lay immediately below the bottom of the oven. Whether it was maintained during baking or was removed beforehand is not known. For thrusting the bread into the oven in the ordinary household probably the same board was used as that on which the dough had been shaped (this is suggested by Tanagra figures, etc.), whereas in the bakeries special long boards were used. In the larger bakeries, as for example in one excavated at Pompeii, ovens of considerable dimensions were used. Like many of the smaller ones they had small water-containers half built into the façade which perhaps contained the water with which the surface of the bread was moistened in order to obtain a good crust (see Fig. 156, p. 94). In the larger ovens (according to Overbeck) the inner arched oven proper *a* is surrounded by a rectangular space *b*, probably enclosed on all sides, which leads into it (Fig. 166) and which keeps in the hot air. The smoke due to the charcoal fire and the steam arising from the baking of the bread passed out through *d*; *e* is the ash-pit. The oven is connected by means of a moderately large opening *c* with the two adjoining chambers. Next to the oven are two clay vessels, half built in, which are situated to the right and left of an orifice leading from a fountain. These vessels probably served to contain the water used for wetting the half-baked bread in order to make its crust shine brightly. Other ovens, again, are provided with special chimneys. During baking the mouth of the oven was closed by an iron door furnished with handles.

FIG. 166.—Section of an Oven at Pompeii

BREWING BEER

According to Diodorus (first century B.C., in I, 20, 4 and 34, 10) the Egyptian god Osiris is supposed to have introduced into Egypt in the year 2017 B.C. a beer made of malted rye, which he first brewed in the town of Pelusium. Herodotus (II, 77) reports the same, and also Pliny (XIV, 149). Strabo (*Geographica*, XVII, 1, 14), Athenaeus (*Dipnosoph.* I, 61) and Aeschylus were acquainted with this Egyptian beverage (*ζῦθος*; Lat. *zythum*), which, so Diodorus states, could almost vie with wine in pleasantness of taste and power. In Strabo's time (60 B.C. till A.D. 20) large quantities of Egyptian beer were drunk in Alexandria; its mode of preparation is first stated in detail in the Papyrus Anastasi IV.

In view of all this it might seem that the origin of beer is to be sought in Egypt. But according to more recent researches by Hrozny, beer was already being brewed from rye in the year 2800 B.C. in ancient Babylon and was a favourite drink among many tribes of this empire. And there can be no doubt that the art of preparing it dates back much further still. The Babylonians made their beer not only out of barley but also out of spelt (*Triticum dicoccum*), which was probably first planted and cultivated by the Babylonians themselves.

The production of ancient Babylonian beer proceeded parallel with the baking of bread. The Babylonians knew how to malt and to make

FIG. 167.—Pictorial representation of Beer-brewing among the Egyptians

Wall picture in the sacrificial chamber of Achet-hetep-her (Old Kingdom). The most correct interpretation probably runs as follows: Threshing the corn, winnowing, grinding (by rubbing). In the middle row from right to left: Roasting the loaves by a flame held below (?); dividing up the bread and perhaps mixing with spelt or malt; making the malting apparatus and the fermenting oats. Bottom row, from left to right: Preparing the wort by mixing bread and malt or spelt in water (malting); filling the beer into vessels; sealing the vessels

malt-bread out of rye and spelt. From the malt-bread they also made a special kind of toasted bread, corresponding somewhat in its method of preparation with our toast. This bread was soaked and then allowed to ferment. This produced a sort of kvass. Kobert asserts that the Egyptians when they settled in their country discovered this kvass already in existence among the primitive Hamitic population living there. They made continual endeavours to increase the alcoholic content of kvass, which deprived it of its harmless quality, converting it into beer. A beverage of a similar nature was also drunk in many other countries at an early date. "Archilochus reports that about the year 700 B.C. the Phrygians and the Thracians knew how to prepare a popular drink of this kind. It is also mentioned by Aeschylus, Sophocles and Theophrastus, and was made partly of rye and partly of fruit, being

FIG. 168.—Egyptian Brewery
Spreading out and preparing the corn (model by Karl Runk). Deutsches Museum, Munich

called *βρῦτος* or *βρῦτον*. This also gradually developed into an intoxicating drink. The same applies to the fermented liquors made from corn by the Germanic tribes, the Gauls, the Iberians, the Lusitanians, the Ligurians, the Illyrians, and the Pannonians; also by other peoples,

FIG. 169.—Egyptian Brewery
(Model by Karl Runk.) Deutsches Museum, Munich

particularly in the North, whose names have not been quoted by ancient writers. Among some of these peoples, as for example the Germanic races, mead, that is, fermented honey, was also in use from early times" (Kobert). It was first mentioned by the navigator Pytheas of Massilia about 300 B.C. (Stübe).

The original form of beer was thus that made from bread and still found nowadays in many parts of Russia as kvass. It was soon noticed that it was not necessary first to make bread out of flour-pap in order to prepare beer. Quass (or kvass) also resulted when the flour-pap was allowed to ferment directly. It did not, indeed, then have the dark colour of the liquor prepared from the baked substance, nor did it have the pleasant taste and fragrant quality produced by baking on a hot stone. A further retrogressive step occurred in not preparing flour-pap at all but making the alcoholic liquor directly from roasted corn.

All these methods of preparing beer were practised early by the Babylonians, who thus had numerous varieties at their disposal. We are here using the term beer to mean a drink which, in contrast with kvass (which contains only a small percentage of alcohol), can produce violent intoxication. Whether it is prepared from hops or not makes no difference in this use of the term; save that among the Teutonic peoples the term 'beer' was used comparatively seldom of a drink containing no hops. The Babylonians were familiar with the following species of beer in the above sense. Firstly, they had a very 'cheap' beer, a sort of black beer prepared from barley to which, in some cases, spelt was added in amounts up to one-fifth of the substance to be brewed. Apart from these cases, the wort consisted only of barley materials, that is, of barley itself, or of baked barley bread or of malted barley. 'Good black beer' was produced from one-fifth of husked spelt and four-fifths of baked spelt-bread. 'Red beer' consisted of less than a quarter of spelt to which bread and ground malted-spelt was added. It appears to have been a thick beer. Beer of the best sort was made by using one-third spelt and two-thirds bread and malt for preparing the wort. The price of beer was higher in proportion to the amount of spelt used in preparing it. Strong and dear beers were probably also diluted with water in Babylon.

The fermenration of the wort was induced spontaneously in the case of all these over-fermented beers, just as is still done with kvass nowadays, no artificial yeast being added. Either fermenting agents floated in from the air, or they were contained in the bread that was added (this bread was probably made without leaven), in which they were likely to be present owing to its accessibility to air. Since yeast loses its vitality above 45° C. (113° Fahr.), and as this temperature was, on account of the method of baking used, not attained everywhere on the upper surface or even probably in the interior of the doughy mass, which was thumb-thick, the bread used for making beer probably still contained some living micro-organisms of yeast. Moreover, other species of fermentation fungi, particularly the one which produces the sourness of milk, probably played some part in the process. The fact that this was true beer—that is, an intoxicating beverage—is evident from the thirteenth maxim of the writer Ani, which was probably written at the time of the 20th Dynasty (thirteenth and twelfth century B.C.). The maxim runs:

'Do not get heated in the house in which intoxicating liquor is being drunk. . . . Your legs will become paralysed, and you will fall; no one will lend you a hand, your boon companions will drink and will leave, saying—" Go home, for you have drunk your fill." You are wanted for discussing your own private affairs; and you will be found lying helplessly on the ground like a small child.'

Like the beer itself, so also the habit of correcting its taste and giving it a certain bitterness by adding lupines comes from the East, probably from the regions of the Caucasus. In Western Europe, the use of hops cannot be traced until after the death of King Pépin (A.D. 768).

As for the beer made by the Germanic races, which they drank besides mead (this was prepared by allowing honey, diluted with water, to ferment), nothing was known for a long time except the very meagre information left to us by Tacitus (*Germania*, 23): 'Their drink is a liquid made from barley or wheat—a brew fermented into a certain resemblance to wine.'

According to the researches of Delbrück, we may assume that ancient Germanic beer was wine-like in character, that is to say, sour—not in the sense of beer that has gone bad—but rather on account of the taste of the ingredients from which it was made and the substances added to preserve it; hops were not known at that time.

Further passages in Tacitus, which however relate only to the manner of life of the Germanic races and to their pleasure in taking warm baths, lead Delbrück to infer that at that time vessels with a content of 500 litres could be constructed, which served for mixing the ingredients.

In order to heat the contents, hot stones were probably thrown into the vessel. Surface-coolers were apparently also known. The beer appears to have been stored in vessels with a wide aperture at the top, which were hermetically sealed—perhaps by means of resin used as a cement. Ancient Germanic vessels in clay have been found, to which a lid with a flange fits. In order to fasten the lid more securely by means of such flanges, holes were bored in them, and pegs of burnt clay contrived, to fit the holes. The temperature at which these vessels were kept when stored was, since they were buried in the ground, that of the earth—about 50° Fahr. We know that this is the correct temperature for beer brewed by surface fermentation.

The question whether the Teutons of ancient Germany and other northern countries used germinated corn is difficult to answer. But since it has been proved that very many peoples of primeval times, in particular Oriental peoples, prepared malt, this does not seem impossible in the case of the Germans also. But it is irrelevant whether malt was prepared from germinated corn or not, for the production of sugar is not necessarily bound up with the germination of corn. Natural corn may also be mashed. Delbrück assumes that the ancient Germanic beer, for the preparation of which the yeast was spontaneously supplied by the air, probably corresponded to the well-known Berlin 'Weissbier' of our own time.

THE PREPARATION OF WINE (VITICULTURE)

There seem to have been no enemies of alcohol among the peoples of antiquity; on the contrary, intoxicating drinks were highly appreciated, and the gods of wine were held in reverence. Wine was prepared from all substances that allowed themselves to ferment. Harnack has made up a list in which he shows that the Jews prepared intoxicating beverages from dates, figs, raisins, pomegranates, honey, and of course also from the grape-vine. Herodotus (II, 93) narrates that the Babylonians also drank palm wine. The god of wine was celebrated in Greece and Rome by special festivals, in which feelings ran so high that there have probably never in later times been occasions which could compare with them in immorality, riotous behaviour, and extreme debauchery.[1] This predilection for alcohol, which existed throughout the whole of antiquity, is not affected by the fact that wine drinking was forbidden among some peoples, as, for example, the desert tribes of the Rechabites, and that in some religious decrees we find abstinence prescribed for priests, women, and others. This preference for wine of course led to the cultivation of the grape-vine; the preparation of the drink itself was developed with very particular care. This in its turn led to the perfection of the technical apparatus connected with the manufacture of wine. The number of vineyards was particularly great in Ancient Egypt, where even at the time of the Old Kingdom (3900–3000 B.C.) no fewer than six kinds of wine were known. The vines were trained up on lattice works, or on palisades which carried trellises at the top, such as is still the custom in Southern countries nowadays. The vines were guarded by watchers, who chased away the birds. At harvest-time the grapes were collected in baskets, and the leaves were left for the goats, who ate them directly from the stalks. The next process consisted in pressing the grapes; this was usually done by means of the feet. The grapes were turned out into a large container made of wood from the acacia, provided at the side with holes through which the juice could escape. Ropes were fixed above this container to the ceiling of the room, from which men who carried out the pressing suspended themselves with their hands. In some of these wine presses, these ropes were replaced by wooden beams attached to pillars. The treading on the grapes was continued so long as juice flowed out, and the last residue of juice was extracted by placing the grape-skins in a long sack which was made of woven reeds or canvas, provided with loops at each end. One loop was fastened to one of the two vertical beams of a large wooden framework, whereas a stick was thrust through the other, which could be turned round, so as to squeeze up the bag, and cause the last remains of the grape-juice to flow out. Great power was applied in turning the stick, as is shown by the strength of the wooden framework, and also by the fact that on the pictures which have been preserved, we see three men twisting the stick simultaneously (Fig. 170). The wine was then filled into large stone jugs, in which it was allowed to

[1] A gross exaggeration.—*Trans.*

ferment. But large dishes also appear to have been used for fermentation purposes, which were provided with a lip, so that the lees remained behind when the liquor was poured off. It was then kept in stone or clay vessels which resembled amphorae in form, but which were often sharpened below, so that they could be bored into the ground of the wine cellar, and could thus stand firmly. Besides this, stone and wooden rings were used; vessels were placed in such to prevent them falling over. The vessels were closed by means of stone or clay stoppers of very varied form. But they all exhibit a wide rim, which fitted over the rim of the vessel. By smearing the surface of contact of the stoppers and the rim of the vessel with clay, resin or gypsum, the ancients attempted to

FIG. 170.—Preparation of Wine in Egypt (mural painting in Thebes)

Above: Plucking and collecting the grapes in baskets. Below and on the right: Pressing the grapes by treading with the feet. Above on the right: Making the wine clear by filtering (To the author it seems more probable, judging by the size of the vessels, and also from the person on the left who is stirring something in the vessel, that this picture deals with the preparation and filtering of additional ingredients for the wine. But perhaps it is the boiling up of the must, which was so much favoured in antiquity, that is here represented.) Below on the left: Pressing out the remains of grapes. On the right: Juice is being filled into pitchers

obtain an air-tight seal. The stamp of the owner was impressed on the substance used for sealing the vessel. In all of the wine-jars still preserved from the ancient Egyptians, we find at the bottom a resinous or asphalt-like substance, which was perhaps used for preserving the wine, but perhaps also—as later among the Romans—to obtain a definite flavour.

Among the Greeks and Romans too the maxim of Pindar, *ἄριστον μὲν ὕδωρ*, was colourless theory, which is easily recognized from the fact that the ode which begins with these words was performed for the first time in order to celebrate King Hiero of Syracuse at a feast in which wine flowed in abundance.

The greatest care was devoted to the cultivation of the vine, and to ennobling its qualities. In general, the technical part of preparing wine corresponded with that practised by the Egyptians. The grapes were likewise pressed out by means of the foot, but—particularly later—special presses were used, the construction of which is described in detail in the Section on the Extraction of Oils (see pages 110–115).

The juice was then passed through a sieve into a large vat or clay vessel (*dolium*) in which it fermented. The juice which was obtained before pressing out the grape-skins distinguished itself by having a higher percentage of sugar than the other acids; it was called *protopum*, and was allowed to ferment by itself. The juice from the grape-skins yielded a wine of poorer quality. In order to purify the wine, eggs were added. It was then filled into clay vessels or into leather skins, which were often of considerable size. For example, at a feast of Ptolemy Philadelphus, a skin made of panther-hides and filled with fine old wine was brought to the table, which had a length of 17 metres (18 yds.) and a width of 7 metres (7½ yds.). The fermenting vessels also were often of considerable capacity, amounting at times to over 500 litres. When fermentation was completed, they often served for storing the wine which was to be used soon afterwards. Wines of better quality, which were to be stored for a longer time, were later filled into wooden vessels. Before the latter came into existence, the wine was filled into smaller amphorae, provided with two handles, the inside of which had been covered with pitch or wax to make them watertight. They were sealed with a clay cover, which was fastened on by means of gypsum or pitch. Like the Egyptians, so also the Greeks and Romans mixed all sorts of ingredients into the wine. In Greece it was particularly the resin of the Greek pine which was added; this was supposed to make the wine keep better. The importance that was attached to this ingredient becomes evident when we recall that the Bacchic thyrsus always carries a pine-cone. Very early in Crete gypsum was scattered over the grapes to preserve them. Aristotle reports that wines were dried in skins, and then taken out in lumps, which were dissolved in water for drinking purposes. Other ingredients which were used were the needle-shaped leaves of cypresses, finely-divided myrtle berries, bitter almonds, honey, shells, gall-nuts, ashes from the vine, as well as all kinds of resin, of which some were more and some were less valued. (Pliny, XIV, 122–128.) For example, the resin of the sea-pine, which grows in Spain, was regarded with but little favour by the Romans, as it gave the wine a very bitter taste and unpleasant smell. In the east Roman provinces, the resin from the terebinth or turpentine tree was preferred. Pliny (XIV, 123) recommends Cyprian resin for lining the interiors of the vessels.

Such ingredients appear to have been added chiefly because the need was felt to do something to make the wine keep better. The wines often became poisonous owing to the action of bacilli, which produced rapid decomposition; and as the reason for this had not yet been discovered, the ancients did not know how to guard against it. Their method of working was, indeed, rather unclean. As Columella reports, even the must had to be boiled up so that it would keep at least until it was sold! As the boiling was effected in leaden vessels, the must (*defrutum*) naturally also contained lead. But this must was added to the wines of inferior quality, which had already fermented, in order to make them more appetizing. Hoffmann, who treated wine in the manner prescribed by Columella, found from his researches that 390 milligrams of lead were taken up in two urns of mountain wine; into the same quantity of valley wine, 582 milligrams of lead, and into bad must, 781 milligrams of lead, were dissolved. Considering, however, that poisonous lead salts such as minium (red lead) were also added and that the cement used to close the wine vessels was prepared—according to Cato—by boiling up syrup from the must (*sapa*) with iris powder in lead or bronze vessels, we are not surprised that the wines of the ancients often contained great quantities of poisonous acetate of lead. In cool weather, negus (*caldum*) was prepared from the wine, being again boiled in leaden vessels. Accordingly when we read of the many symptoms of poisoning that occurred after the feasts in antiquity, and when we learn of various Emperors being poisoned, we, in the light of modern medical science, are probably correct in regarding these alleged political assassinations and wholesale poisonings as nothing more than ptomaine or lead poisoning. The detailed researches of Kobert confirm this. Not only did people drink wine containing lead, but they also ate meat which they did not know sufficiently how to preserve from decay.

FIG. 171.—Trojan Wine Depository
Large earthenware jars (πίθοι) with their pointed ends placed in the ground, below the Temple of Athene at Troy

FIG. 172.—Transporting Wine in Casks: from a relief showing a wine-ship
Provincial Museum in Trèves

For the rest, wine was usually mixed with water, but very often, and on particular occasions, it was drunk undiluted. Data about the proportions of dilution with water are found for example in Homer, according to which Maron, the priest of Apollo, placed before Odysseus a wine which was mixed with 20 parts of water (*Odyssey*, IX, 209), and from which so delicious an aroma escaped that it was impossible to refrain from drinking.[1] These data, as Rhousopoulos has shown, are to be accepted with caution. The alcoholic content of the original natural wine did not probably exceed 14 per cent. by volume (equals 13 per cent. by weight). After the mixing, there would have been at most 0·6 per cent. by weight of alcohol; that is, the beverage could have neither tasted nor smelled like wine! We may assume that in antiquity also hardly more than an equal quantity of water was added to the wine; in most cases it probably was less.[2]

Vinegar was obtained by using sour wine, or allowing wine to turn sour for the purpose. There is nothing in the technical method by which the ancients prepared vinegar that calls for particular remark.

[1] 'There arose from the mixing-bowl an odour sweet past all telling; then none had a mind to refrain'.

[2] Wine was often mixed with three or more times its bulk of water, see Athenaeus, X, 27 (p. 426b) *et seqq.*—*Trans.*

THE PRODUCTION AND USES OF OILS, FATS, SOAPS AND PERFUMES

THE branch of the mechanical arts we are about to discuss is a province of applied organic chemistry which is intimately connected with numerous other branches, such as agriculture, the chemistry of nutrition, methods of preservation and the technical art of illumination, so that several of its departments might just as well have been discussed in the chapters devoted to these subjects. But as it is essentially built up on the use and manufacture of certain special derivatives of the organic acids of oils and fats, we shall consider it here as a separate subject ; this method of grouping is still in general use in chemical technology.

THE EXTRACTION OF OILS AND FATS

During the whole of antiquity, the cultivation of the olive-tree prospered exceedingly, for it yielded the oil which was so necessary for preparing foods, for filling lamps, for oiling or anointing the body, for cleaning purposes, for producing perfumes and cosmetics of every kind. This oil was the sort which we, who have such an abundant choice of oils, nowadays call olive oil. Even in very early Egyptian manuscripts we find the mention of the olive tree and the oil obtained from it, both of which are called ' Tat ' in the records of the 8th Dynasty (that is, about 2300 B.C.). The monuments of the 18th Dynasty (about 1550 B.C.) give representations of the leaves and fruits of the olive-tree. In the tombs of Egyptian kings of the 20th Dynasty (1100 B.C.) branches of the olive-tree and olive kernels have been found. Theophrastus (*Hist. plant.* iv, 2, 8) and Strabo (XVII, 1, 35) mention that it occurs in Egypt. The Bible also tells of Noah's dove which returned with an olive branch in its beak ; and even nowadays there are trees on the Mount of Olives near Jerusalem, which probably stood there at the time of Christ. In Greece, the olive-tree, as is established beyond doubt, was known in the time of Homer. The number of writers who mention it in later times is so great that it is impossible to enumerate them.

The extraction of oil from the olive-tree was probably carried out in the same way among all peoples of antiquity. From discoveries on the Island of Thera it appears to be established that the oil press which originated in Egypt or in the Orient later became introduced into Greece. Besides olive oil other oils were probably also obtained by the same process, in particular the pleasant-smelling unguents which were imported at later times from the Orient both into Greece and into Rome.

In order to extract the oil, the fruits were picked when they had attained the right degree of ripeness, or rather of unripeness. At the present day, particularly in Greece, oil is sometimes extracted from the olives that have already fallen, and have already partly begun to ferment. Consequently it is not seldom of bad quality. But better qualities of oil are also pressed out of fruits that are not fully ripe. In antiquity the unripe fruits were also used in order to obtain an oil of particularly good quality and pleasant taste and smell, both for nutritious and medicinal purposes.

FIG. 173.—Beating down the Olives from the Trees by means of Canes

Picture on a Greek vase. Berlin Museum, Antiquarium

According to the reports of Dioscorides (*De mat. med.* I, 29) this oil was called ὀμφάκιον, because it was produced from unripe fruits (ὄμφαξ = unripe fruits). When the fruits could not be plucked, they were beaten down by means of canes (Fig. 173). They were then put into the oil mills, in which they were first crushed, in order to release them from the kernels. (Our description is based on the researches and results of Blümner.) For this purpose, a mill was used, which appears to have been built similarly to that used for grinding corn. Supported on a lower fixed stone was a second stone which had a hole bored through the centre, to allow it to rotate on a vertical pivot. Other mills were also in use, which consisted of a stone tub in which there were vertically-placed stones which could rotate; and these represent the arrangement which modern technical science calls edge-rollers or vertical mills. When they first appeared is doubtful. They were used by the Romans and were known by the name *trapetum*.[1] The Greeks used a similar arrangement for pressing out wine; whether they also used it to press out oil, is not known. The *trapetum*, of which several specimens and descriptions are still extant, consists of a trough (Fig. 174), from the middle of which a round plinth or pillar projects, the whole being made of one piece of stone. The centre of this pillar has a

FIG. 174.—Vertical Mill or Edge-rollers (*Trapetum*) for pressing out oil

Found in Boscoreale

[1] Also *trapetus*. The term varies; likewise in the plural.

vertical iron pivot on which a horizontal axle turns. This axle rests on the pivot, with a special case made of wood and covered with metal plates. In order that the case may not shift upwards and jerk off the pivot, which is very easily possible if the mortar becomes stuck through foreign matter, the pivot is sometimes pierced by a hole. An iron pin is stuck through this hole. On the horizontal axle there now rest two crushing-stones which are shaped plano-convex, in such a way that their plane side is turned towards the pillar, whereas the convex side fits into the correspondingly hollowed out inner wall of the mortar. The crushing-stones were also held fast by means of a case provided with holes which had been bored through, and which allowed them to be fixed to corresponding holes in the shaft by means of a bolt.

Many of these vertical mills also had special devices in the form of interior parts which could be attached to the pivot in order to raise or lower the stones. The fastening of the horizontal axle and the shape of the pivot were subject to small alterations, so that we find differences in these parts of the *trapeta* that have been found and described. The whole machine had to be so arranged that the crushing-stones exerted only a gentle pressure. The skin and the pulp alone were to be crushed, while the kernels were to remain whole; oil was not yet to flow out. That is why exact dimensions still exist for each individual part, large as well as small. The dimensions of such vertical mills are carefully recorded by Cato (*de agric.*, 20–22: 136, 6–7); and he describes the adjustment of the crushing-stones down to the smallest detail. Besides the *trapetum*, there were also a number of other devices for crushing the olives, of which, however, we have no information.

The substance which came out of the mill, and consisted of crushed olives, was sorted out, in order to remove the kernels. This was followed by the pressing out of the kernel-less fruits. Very different devices were employed for this purpose. Originally they were probably placed in a kind of basket, and pressed out by placing stones on the basket. The oil ran out between the wickerwork of the basket, and was collected in a vessel placed below. Later, the method was made more perfect. The substance—or the wickerwork containing it—was placed between wooden boards, and several such layers were placed on a framework.

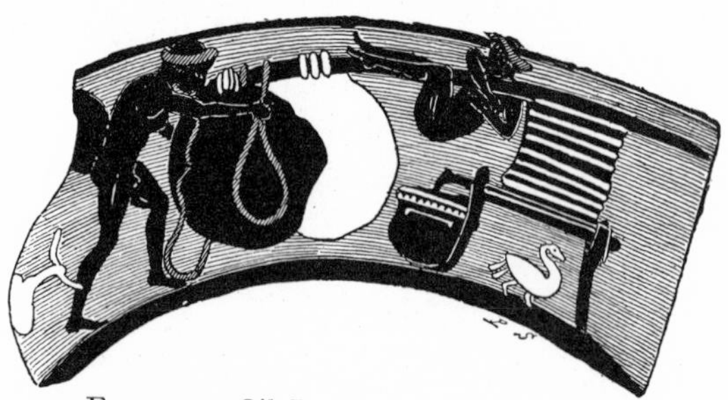

FIG. 175.—Oil Press with its Press-beam

On the right is a stool on which the oil fruits are arranged in layers with intervening layers of wooden boards or wooden discs (?), which are perforated, or perhaps provided with channels. Above them is the press-beam, which is weighted at its free end by means of two stones, and on which a man is jerking his weight, while a second man is striving to increase the power of the lever by means of the weight of his body. The oil runs out over the outer sides of the layers into the stool, which is furnished with a rim or a concavity, and thence by means of a tap into a collecting vessel. Picture on a Greek vase

A long lever beam was then fixed above, which was weighted in front with large stones, fastened by means of cords. By climbing up on the lever beams and jerking with the weight of the body, the effect was intensified. The oil ran out into the lower frame, and from here probably along grooves, into a larger gutter, the opening of which lay above a collecting vessel (Fig. 175). The most used kind of oil press is also described [1] for us by Cato (*loc. cit.*). His statements have been corroborated by various discoveries. Two stakes that have been rammed into the ground stand in close proximity to each other. At a suitable height between them, there is placed a long horizontal press-beam, which is movable. At the front end of the press-beam, situated again between the two stakes, a reel is fixed, by which this front end can be

FIG. 176.—A See-saw Press

pulled down with great force by means of ropes and levers. Reels also serve to raise the heavy press-beam, likewise a pulley or a block and pulley attached to the ceiling of the pressing chamber. The olives, from which the kernels have been removed, lie in a basket or woven bag, and this is placed on a frame and covered with a board—the purpose of which is to distribute the pressure of the lever-beam uniformly. The press-beam is then pulled down by means of the reels, and in this way a very powerful pressure is exerted on the mass of olives. This press probably developed from the still simpler see-saw press in which (Fig. 176) the press-beam simply had its one end stuck fast in a concavity made in a strong vertical post. Below, was a long horizontal canal-shaped trough (perhaps this is why the name *canalis* was applied to such presses) in which the fruits to be crushed were placed. The press-beam was weighted with stones, and was

FIG. 177.—Cupids extracting Oil

Wall picture in the house of the Vettii in Pompeii. From left to right: Selling objects; counter with toilet objects. Behind: a cabinet. Next to it: an oil kettle; mixing perfumes with the oil. On the right: a wedge press

[1] A description which tallies with this is also given by Vitruvius (VI, 9).

pulled down by jerking with the weight of the body. Later still, the screw was introduced. There arose a new type of oil press, in which the board resting on the olives was pressed against its base by means of a screw. This press probably corresponded in general to those represented in Fig. 240 except that it appears also to have been used with one screw alone. At any rate, Heron of Alexandria describes an olive press of this kind in his *Mechanics* (III, 20), and this tallies with one described by Pliny (XVIII,

FIG. 178.—Wedge-press (for pressing out Oil)
Mural painting in Herculaneum

317). From Pliny's writings it appears that cases weighted with stones were also used for pressing out oil. In Herculaneum, as well as in the house of the Vettii at Pompeii, wall pictures exhibit Cupids striking blows against wedges, between which the substance to be pressed out lies. A strong framework of beams serves as a buttress and holds together the alternating layers of wedges and oil-mass (Figs. 177, 178). In many oil-

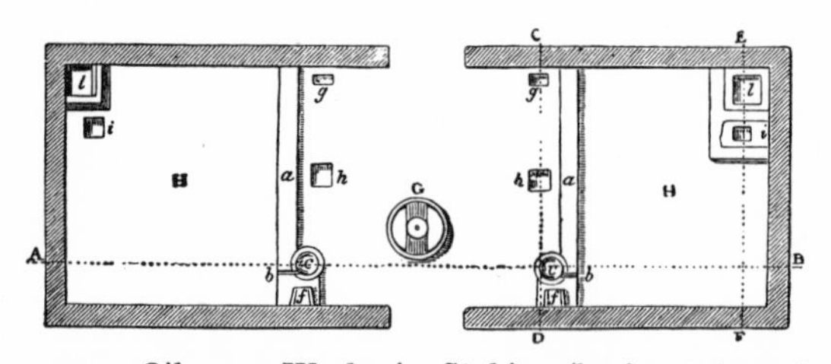

FIG. 179.—Oil-press Works in Stabiae (horizontal section)
G, vertical mill (*trapetum*). *ghi*, depressions for receiving the posts for the press apparatus. H, large receptacles shut off from the middle of the chamber by means of walls (*a*). The pressed-out oil was collected in these receptacles. The lowest point of the inclined floor is at B, where the oil flows out, and is conducted by leaden conduits into the receptacles *c*, from which it can be drawn. *f.f.* are ledges on which probably the pitchers were placed into which the oil was filled from *c*; and their inclined upper surface allowed the oil that flowed over to return to E

press works, the floor was sloped so that the oil flowing on to it collected in receptacles from which it could be drawn as required (Fig. 179). In a similar way, oil was extracted from nuts—from almonds—from sesame, various kinds of palm, mastic oil, and so forth.[1]

In order to preserve the oils, they were then mixed partly with salt,

[1] See also Herodotus (I, 94), in which a process for extracting oil by roasting and boiling out the fruit is mentioned.

and partly with gum and resin, which caused them to retain their smell. The extraction of purely ethereal oils was impossible, as the modern process of distillation was not then known. All sorts of other substances were also mixed with the oils, such as vinegar, fennel, must and honey.

The Romans obtained *sucus*, probably a rarely saponifiable ethereal oil from blossoms, as well as the *corpus*, which is obtained from fruits, and is always saponifiable. It was used for making ointments by adding *sucus*, and it was made to smell pleasantly by adding oil extracted from buds.

For preparing ointments, there were used, besides oil from fruits, also animal fats—in particular fat from wool (called *οἴσυπος* or *οἴσυπον*, also *οἰσύπη*, by the Greeks, and *oesypus* or *oesypum* by the Romans). This fat obtained from wool, after it had played an important part in antiquity, both as a medicine and as a cosmetic, sank into complete oblivion for several centuries until recently when it was introduced into medicine again by Liebreich, and is generally known under the name 'Lanoline'. Its preparation is known to us from reports by Dioscorides and Pliny: the best method of preparing it—according to Pliny—was as follows: The freshly shorn wool was placed into a bronze vessel filled with water, and the mass was heated up by means of a gentle fire. It was then cooled, and the fat swimming on top was collected in an earthenware vessel. This was repeated once or twice. The fat that had been scooped off was then thoroughly washed with water, strained through a piece of cloth, and exposed to the sun until it was white and transparent. This substance, which was most valued when it was obtained from the wool of Attic sheep, was held to be a remedy for various ills. Besides fat from wool, other animal-fats—in particular goose-fat, butter, and so forth—were used for all sorts of purposes, particularly as cosmetics. The reason for this was probably because fat obtained from wool, which, according to Ovid (*Ars amandi*, III, 213, and *Remedia amoris*, 354), was used to keep the skin tender and lustrous, very quickly became evil-smelling, by reason of its being insufficiently purified of albuminous material, which easily decomposes. According to Ovid, it smelt like 'the table of Phineus soiled by the harpies'.

THE USES OF OILS

The oils and the fats were at first used in the raw state in which they were obtained by the processes of mechanical extraction just described. Chemical separation by means of saponification was not known. In cases where chemical action perhaps really occurred, for example, in washing materials of raw wool by means of stale urine, by which the wool fat must have become decomposed owing to the action of ammonia, the ancients were not aware of it. When the resultant product, soap, became known, it was at first used for purposes other than cleansing. The method of cleaning woven and spun materials is reported in the sections which deal with these subjects. Personal cleanliness was achieved by various means: the Jews used potash and soda (Pinner); the Greeks used bran, sand, ashes, and pumice stone; the other peoples used similar materials, and also all sorts of ointments, especially oils, which they rubbed into the whole body, scraping off the excess (Fig. 180). Particular importance attaches to the baths as a means of cleansing; their preparation is described very early,—indeed, by Homer (Bath of Odysseus in the home of the enchantress Circe—*Odyssey*, X, 358 *seq.*):

'And a fourth (handmaiden) bare water and kindled a great fire beneath the mighty cauldron. So the water waxed warm; but when it boiled in the bright brazen vessel, she set me in a bath and bathed me with water from out a great cauldron, pouring it over head and shoulders, when she had mixed it to a pleasant warmth, till from my limbs she took away the consuming weariness. Now after she had bathed me and anointed me well with olive oil, and cast about me a fair mantle and a doublet. . . .'[1]

According to Pliny (XXVIII, 191), soap itself is an invention of the

FIG. 180.—'The Apoxyomenos.' The 'scraper', an athlete who is cleansing himself by rubbing oil into his skin and afterwards scraping it off with a strigil
Marble copy taken from a bronze statue of Lysippus. Vatican Museum, Rome

Gauls, who likewise, however, used it, not for purposes of cleaning, but as a means of embellishing the hair. It was produced from fats, particularly from that of goats, and from ashes (potash), chiefly from the ashes of the beech; and here a saponification of the fat actually occurs. Pliny mentions two kinds of soap—a hard and a soft variety. Reddening the hair, as mentioned by Pliny, could hardly have been effected by the use of soap alone (see page 121).

As elsewhere, so in Rome, soap was probably at first used as a means of cultivating the hair, and for medical purposes. Galen (A.D. 131–201) is the first to mention (XII, 170, 180) that soap served for washing.[2] He expresses preference for German soap, and puts Gallic soap second. It exerts a softening effect, so he reports, and is used to remove dirt from the human body and clothes. The distinction between hard and soft soap which Galen makes, and which Pliny (*loc. cit.*) already mentions, is due to the fact that German soap, being a potash soap produced from the

[1] From the prose translation by Butcher and Lang. Macmillan & Co., London.
[2] Wrong; it is mentioned by Theokritos, *Idyll.* XV, 30, some 450 years earlier.—*Trans.*

ash of the beech, proved softer than Gallic soap, which, being made from the ash of sea-plants containing sodium salts, was a sodium soap, and consequently hard. The doctor Serenus Sammonicus, who lived in the third century A.D., and was Physician-in-Ordinary to the Emperor Septimius Severus, mentions soap as a means of cleansing, but only in a poem which speaks of the treatment of various illnesses; so that doubts which have been raised in various quarters seem to be justified.

The varieties of products, besides soap, which were made from oils and fats, are innumerable. Even the ancient Egyptians prepared ointments having very different properties by mixing oils and fats with perfumes of every kind, which probably consisted of plant oils: these oils and fats had melting-points above ordinary temperatures, that is, they were solids. Perfumes obtained from the following vegetable substances were universally popular: tree oil, rose oil, almond oil, sweet calamus, cinnamon, cassia, ladanum, incense, spikenard, sesame, laurel, marjoram, lily, isis, pomegranate, cypress, amaravain, malabathrum, honey, oenanthe, resin from coniferous trees, and so forth. (Galen is our chief authority.)

Besides being used in the form of ointments, perfumes were also used in the form of oils and powders. A much-favoured perfume in Rome was *sussineum*, which consisted of lilies, oil from beans, honey, cinnamon, and saffron (Pliny). In ancient Aquileia, a perfume was discovered during the work of excavation, the analysis of which by Majonica showed that it was a resin obtained from the Cretan cistus (*Cistus cretinus*).

The use of cosmetics was very popular. Making up the face was practised by all ancient peoples, and the following words, in which the satirical Martial mocks at the Roman woman, probably applied to most of the women of antiquity.

> 'Though you are at home, Galla, and deck yourself in the midst of the Subura [a not over-respectable district of Rome], while your hair is abroad; though you take out your teeth at night as you take off your silk frock, and sleep tucked away in a hundred vanity-boxes; though you have not your own face for a bed-fellow; still you wink at men under an eyelid which you took out of a drawer that same morning.' (*Epigr.* ix, 37.)

It has been proved that cosmetics were actually manufactured by the Egyptians 4,400 years ago. At that time also, sticks of paint were made, which were probably of a fatty composition, although the existence of this fat can no longer be proved, as it has decomposed in the course of these thousands of years. This greasy cosmetic was poured into the hollow stem of graminaceous plants, one finger thick, which were cut off just below a notch, so that this notch served to close up one end. The fat that was used was probably obtained from wool, but perhaps it also consisted of olive oil. We may infer this from the fact that the sticks of paint were carefully wrapped up in the fibres of plants and grasses. Besides this, the paint was kept in pots of fired clay, in vessels of alabaster and ivory. Cosmetics of a pasty consistency were packed up in leaves; at any rate, some finds exhibit the impress of leaves from dicotyledons.

Ancient Egyptian cosmetics have been frequently analysed. For example, A. von Baeyer has investigated several black cosmetics derived from the mummy tombs at Achim, which had served to colour the eyelids and the eyebrows; and he has found that they consist of a mixture of lead sulphide and charcoal, and had without doubt been produced by combusting lead sulphate with charcoal. He believes that the Egyptians, in order to prepare the necessary lead sulphate, transformed lead (which was already known to them) by heating it in air to obtain galena (lead oxide), dissolving the latter in vinegar, and precipitating lead sulphate by the addition of alum. By combusting the lead sulphate with charcoal, one obtains—as Baeyer has proved by his own experiments—a product which exhibits the same properties as the cosmetics that were under investigation. A green cosmetic which was also studied by Baeyer, and which belongs to the British Museum, consisted of verdigris and some resin. Salkowsky, in his analysis of such cosmetics, also found lead sulphide present in most cases; and in one particular sample, he found mineral manganese. Ryssel believes that the mineral black-lead, which is likewise often found present in the black cosmetics but does not occur in Egypt itself, comes from Ispahan. In none of the samples investigated was antimony ever found, although Berthelot's researches make it certain that the Egyptians were acquainted with it.

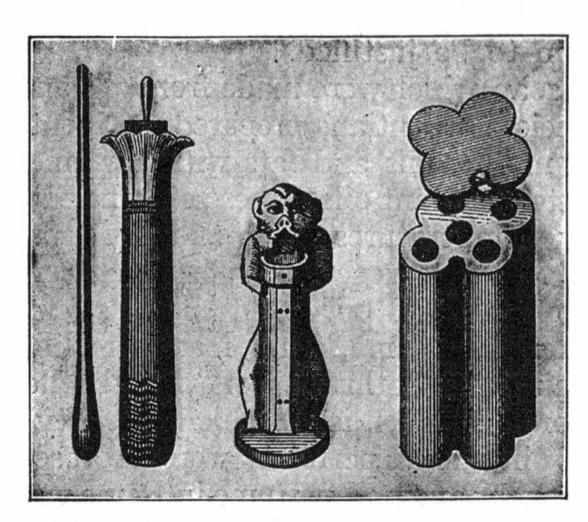

Fig. 181.—Egyptian Containers of Cosmetics
On the left is a spatula for taking out the cosmetic.

Later, the well-known Egyptologist, Ebers, as well as A. Wiedemann, presented to the University Laboratory of Erlangen a series of cosmetics which had been excavated by Flinders Petrie from the tombs near Illahûn, Kahûn and Gurob.

Fig. 182.—A Spoon for Cosmetics or Ointments, made of green glazed stone. On the handle is depicted a woman swimming between lotus flowers. The length is 3 in.
Berlin Museum, Egyptian Department

The cosmetics themselves were either fine powders of diverse colours, which under the microscope are shown to be either black crystals of the regular system, particles of quartz, remains of plants, fragments of green and red crystal, or they were in the form of cylindrical sticks as thick as a finger, which in consequence of having dried out for thousands of years, exhibit longitudinal cracks reaching almost to the middle. The cements used to make these cylindrical sticks could not be determined, as of course the fats had become decomposed in the course of time, and the presence of resin could not be detected. The analysis of the mineral constituents showed that black lead was mostly used for the black cosmetics, and in rarer cases, antimonite. As in addition lead sulphate was nearly always present, often in considerable quantity, there is reason for assuming that the black lead was either subjected to slight heating, or became oxidized under the action of some moist substance used as a cement. As neither of the ores mentioned occurred naturally in Egypt, they were probably derived from the great ore deposits in India, by way of Arabia. Pyrolusite (mineral manganese) was also used, but seldom alone; in the same way,

FIG. 183.—Containers (Egyptian) for Perfumers, Cosmetics, Pencils, etc.

copper oxide prepared from the carbonate by heating, and also protoxide of iron, occurred relatively seldom.

Clays containing a high percentage of iron were used for preparing brown cosmetics. The green cosmetics were either glass pastes, or else naturally occurring silicates, which were finely powdered and mixed with basic copper carbonate. These green cosmetics, besides serving as preventives against eye diseases, perhaps also, as suggested by Hille, served to colour the white of the eye ; but probably they were only used to paint the lid of the eye. The orange-red cosmetic used to colour the finger-nail was prepared from the plant henna (*Lythracee Lawsonia Inermis L.*). The coarse powder which is obtained from its leaves, stalks and buds, has been found in numerous ancient Egyptian tombs. Since the juice assumes an orange-red colour only when alkali has been added, it is probable that soda or burnt lime was used to produce this colour.

In contrast with the versatility of the Egyptians, the Jews were acquainted with only one cosmetic, namely, grey mineral antimony, which served to increase the brilliance and fire of the eyes. This cosmetic was called 'Puch', and reference is made to it in Jeremiah iv. 30—'. . . And though thou markest thine eyes with painting,'[1] It is to be assumed that this grey mineral antimony (antimony sulphide, Sb_2S_3) was brought from Arabia in caravans (Pinner).

The Greeks sought to beautify their bodies more by gymnastics than by means of cosmetics. In pre-classical times, however, they painted their whole bodies.[2] Later, the red extracts from plants mentioned on page 189 (organic dyes) served as a red cosmetic; still later, cinnabar (native red sulphide of mercury, HgS) was used. The white cosmetic

FIG. 184.—Egyptian Toilet Case made of Reeds (about 2000 B.C.)
Height, 13 in.; width, 8 in.; length, 11 in. Berlin Museum, Egyptian Department

was made of white lead. In trade it occurred in the form of round tablets, as is shown by discoveries from Athenian tombs dating back to the third century B.C. To remove hairs, orpiment (As_2S_3) was used (Rhousopoulos).

The art of using cosmetics, as well as the manufacture of cosmetics, reached its zenith among the Romans. A white cosmetic was provided by the finely divided excrement of crocodiles, earth of Chios, chalk, and, above all, white lead. The red colours were made of ruddle (red chalk),

[1] Painting = Puch in the German version of the Bible.

[2] I do not know on what evidence this extraordinary statement is based.—*Trans.*

cinnabar, minium (red lead) and archil (or orchil). We read in Martial: ' Lycoris, who is blacker than the colour of the mulberry when it falls from the tree, thinks herself beautiful when she covers her face with white lead.' (*Epigr.* i, 72, 5.)

Dioscorides and Pliny mention that all lead preparations (and hence also cosmetics) are poisonous; the recognition of this fact, however, seems to have been no obstacle to their use. The black cosmetic used for accentuating the eyebrows was made either of soot, lead, or powdered antimony sulphide (Sb_2S_3). This precious cosmetic, which was also used by the ancient Egyptians, was even at that distant period often adulterated with lead sulphide (Kobert). Particularly designing ladies used more expensive cosmetics, which were prepared from the ash of date kernels, spikenard or burnt rose-leaves. The men of Rome also used paint, but only on special occasions. The face of the victor who marched into the capital was smeared with red lead (minium). For the rest, the adornment of the men was limited mostly to wearing beauty patches (*splenia*). The hair was coloured black or blonde; black by the means just mentioned, or else by leeches which had undergone decomposition for a fair length of time in an earthenware pot containing wine and vinegar. A blonde or red effect was obtained by means of the soap imported from Germany, which was sold in the form of round cakes. Martial calls these cakes ' Mattiac balls ' after the Germanic settlement Mattium, where they were manufactured. (*Epigr.* xiv, 27.) This is nowadays believed to be the site of the present-day village Metze or Maden, near Gudensberg.

Ovid complains that this colouring matter was injurious to the hair. Probably an excess of alkali in it acted destructively. The fact that the Romans also knew how to make more harmless colouring pomades is proved by the analysis of a sample excavated near Ticino, which was found unimpaired in the vessel in which it was stored. According to Reutter, it consisted of a mixture of beeswax, fat, resin from the storax tree, and oil of turpentine. The presence of the potassium salt of tartaric acid leads us to conclude that it was moistened with wine. The yellow colour was produced by adding henna, this pomade being obviously used for colouring the hair blonde. In the times of greatest luxury, the hair was coloured with gold-dust.

REFRIGERATING AND PRESERVING

THE most important methods nowadays used for preserving were also practised by the ancients; that is, cold storage, salting, drying, and excluding the air. Just as now, cold served not only for preserving, but also for producing an artificial lowering of temperature. In this way, apart from preserving, processes of producing cold also developed, which were based partly on methods of conduction, partly on bringing about vaporization, as well as by lowering the temperature by dissolving substances.

The art of refrigeration is very old indeed. In the *Shih king*, the ancient Chinese collection of lyrics, we find an older section, earlier than the first millennium B.C., which prescribes religious ceremonies for filling and emptying ice-cellars. Unfortunately, nothing is known about the construction of these ice-cellars, nor in particular whether non-conducting layers were used as a protection against heat. The Jews, moreover, used snow for cooling their beverages. In the book of Proverbs, xxv. 13, we read—'As the cold of snow in the time of harvest, so is a faithful messenger to them who sent him; for he refresheth the soul of his masters.' The Greeks and the Romans, particularly the latter, constructed their snow-cellars in accordance with important technical rules. They were large pits which were covered with grass, chaff, or (according to Seneca) with earth, manure, or branches of trees; so the protection against heat was effected by the correct choice of non-conducting substances. Moreover, the snow was tightly pressed together before being introduced into the pits. As snow becomes ice under pressure, it is not improbable that artificial ice was at that time made by this process. The snow had often to be fetched from far away; perhaps pressure was used to economize space and so to facilitate transport. No further details are known to us.

Plutarch enters into a detailed discussion about the protection furnished by chaff against the melting of the snow; and from his reflections it is easily inferred that the snow was also wrapped in thick cloths in order to keep it longer. Moreover, the method of preserving just described was used, according to Athenaeus, by Alexander the Great. Snow was added directly to beverages. The water resulting from it when it melted was used for the same purpose, after it had been run through cloths or sieves in order to purify it. As mentioned by Pliny (XXXI, 21), the drinking of strongly cooled beverages produced illnesses of very different kinds. When this circumstance became known, the beverages were cooled from without, by placing the vessels in snow—an invention which is attributed to the Emperor Nero (Pliny, XXXI, 23);

so that we have to regard Nero as the discoverer of the champagne-cooler! Galen reports that Nero had also made the observation that water which had been previously heated cooled more rapidly than ordinary water. This observation, which, by the way, had already been mentioned by Aristotle (*Meteorologica*, I, 12), is correct. Ordinary water contains air and carbon dioxide, which retard cooling. Boiling the water drives off both of these gases.

For the rest, according to Galen, more extensive methods were used in Egypt to produce an artificial cooling of water. Water which had been previously warmed was placed into shallow earthenware dishes, which were allowed to stand on roofs protected from the wind during the night. The next morning they were placed into moist hollows dug out of the ground, and covered with moist leaves. So that in this case ample use is made of the cold produced by vaporization, which, as in the gullah (see the section ' Ceramic Art '), was used from the earliest times very appropriately for producing cool drink. According to the reports of Athenaeus, these earthenware dishes were moistened on the outside the whole night long by slaves, in order to increase the amount of vaporization. As to the amount of cooling effected, opinions differ widely; also as to whether the sun, in consequence of more rapid vaporization, or the shade, in consequence of vaporization in conjunction with the lower temperature, was more effective. Dollinger calculates that a vessel of 5 litres content, of which one-tenth is vaporized at a temperature of 33° C., incurs a loss of 58·5 calories of heat, which would correspond to a cooling of 12° C. (22° Fahr.); this would however never be actually reached, as some of the heat is furnished not by the water, but by the surrounding air, and since heat enters through the opening of the vessel. Von Luschan, on the other hand, was able to cool water or tea at 40° C. by 25° C. Experiments designed to determine the maximum possible amount of cooling, and to check theoretical calculations, were to have been carried out by the author himself in Egypt. These were intended for the winter of 1914–15, but had to be cancelled owing to the War. No record has been passed down to indicate that ice was produced in this way; nevertheless the ancient Indians were familiar in very far-distant times with a process for making ice artificially. It depended on the simultaneous action of vaporization and radiation. Shallow vessels filled with water and made of porous clay were placed on rice-straw in small holes in the ground, and left overnight. The water then freezes on account of the great amount of radiation and simultaneous vaporization; the next morning the vessels are covered with ice. This method of producing ice was probably prevalent among many peoples. An accident has revealed to us that it was also known to the Esthonians about A.D. 800. The cooling of air by means of fountains, jets d'eau, and by pouring water on marble tiles, which was very popular in antiquity, likewise represents a method of making use of the loss of heat due to vaporization. To what extent loss of heat by solution was used is not known. It seems fairly certain that it was applied. On the one hand, this emerges from the Indian work

'Panchatantra', which dates from the fourth century A.D. and states: 'Water is cool when it contains salt.' Moreover, when certain salts (in particular saltpetre), which were well known to the ancients and much used by them, are dissolved in water, considerable cooling occurs; and it is to be assumed that this did not remain unnoticed. The conduction of heat was also used for producing artificial cooling—although in a very peculiar manner. Persons placed cold-blooded animals about themselves, and used cold stones, in order to keep themselves cool. An account of the Egyptian women of the fifth century B.C. tells us that they used these means and also the method involving vaporization in order to make their existence more pleasant; 'they had the couch in their litters covered with a thick layer of green leaves and flowers, on which they stretched themselves out, covered with only a thin linen tunic. The curtains were drawn, and then wet with cold water. In addition, they rolled about their necks and arms two or three live adders, and in each hand they took a quartz sphere, a mineral whose temperature remains constantly below that of the surrounding air.'

METHODS OF PRESERVING

The fact that cold was used in antiquity for purposes of preserving is clear from various data—above all, from ancient Roman cookery books, in which it is advised to cover certain dishes, especially brawns, with snow. As these are particularly prone to decay, and as the snow can hardly have been regarded as a delicacy, we can interpret this only as a method of preserving. Other methods of preserving food-stuffs consisted in drying them in the air, in smoking them, in salting them, and in excluding the air. The latter was performed chiefly by placing the food-stuffs in oil (Columella, *De re rustica*, V, 8). Besides this, however, the food was also placed in vinegar, in salt, and in salt water (*loc. cit.*). Salting seems to have been used universally. Herodotus (IV, 53) reports of the river Borysthenes which flows in the land of the Scythians:

'At its mouth there is an enormous natural salt-pan, and it yields great sea-beasts without bones for salting purposes, which they call *antakaioi*,[1] and many other wonderful things.'

Preserved fish from ancient Egyptian times have remained unimpaired up to the present day. The method of preserving was certainly a little complicated. In the case of the ancient Egyptians, the particular fish used was one that resembled a perch and was regarded as sacred, the *Lates Niloticus*. Great quantities of this fish were found in a sandy desert stretching east of the town Esna; they have also been found in excavated tombs. The fish were wrapped round with linen strips, and were then placed into water of the Egyptian lakes, which contain much soda, and were left in contact with the water for some time. (The researches of French savants prove that sodium was present in some form; whether this sodium arises from the use of soda or of ordinary salt seems doubtful in the light of the more recent investigations into the preparation of mummies—which we shall presently discuss.) The fish

[1] A sort of sturgeon.—*Trans.*

were then packed into a mixture of sand and clay, and once again placed in brine. In some cases they still look nowadays as if they had just come out of the water. The skin is shiny and has colour, and in the eyes one can still clearly discern the iris. This method of preserving is a process in which pickling, excluding the air (clay), as well as drying, aided by the exceptional dryness of the Egyptian climate, probably acted in concert to produce this result.

MUMMIES

The greatest perfection in the art of preserving is probably exemplified in ancient Egyptian mummies. They have formed the object of many investigations, and yet, up to the present, it has not been possible to clear up every detail of their preparation. Nevertheless, more recent researches and analyses have at least proved that the account given by Herodotus (II, 86), as well as that given by Diodorus, is in general true. As the oldest of all known mummies probably date back to about 3,000 B.C., it might seem at first sight as if the process practised by the ancient Egyptians was appropriate for allowing complete corpses to be preserved for thousands of years. As W. A. Schmidt rightly points out from his researches, this view is erroneous. We shall revert to the results of these investigations below, and shall remark here only that in the mummies, blood or hæmoglobin and its derivatives have never been proved to be present. What has been preserved is only the skeleton and the skin, as well as the nails, hairs, sinews and bones. Muscular tissue has shrunken up to a small mass, and represents only a fibrous material resembling tobacco. Only in the more recent mummies, the so-called 'Coptic' mummies of the fifth century A.D., has the muscular tissue, according to Schmidt, been sufficiently preserved to justify one's speaking of preserving the flesh.

Mummies were made (so Herodotus and Diodorus state) by the following three methods, any one of which was used, according to the wealth of the person to be embalmed. The first process cost one talent (about £225); the second, 20 minae (about £75); the third was very cheap. In the first method, the brain was partly removed through the nostrils by means of a bent piece of iron, and partly by pouring in substances of which we are ignorant. A sharp Ethiopian stone was then used to make an incision in the side, through which the entrails were removed. They were then cleaned with palm-wine and sprinkled with pulverized aromatics. The abdomen was filled with finely-divided myrrh, with cassia, and with any other perfumery, except incense, and then sewn up again. The corpse was next placed for 70 days in *natrum* (see page 127). At the end of this time the body was washed, wrapped round with fine linen from Byssus, and painted with gum. The corpse was then placed in a wooden box, which followed the shape of the mummy. This box was placed upright against a wall.

The second method of making mummies was as follows: Syringes were filled with oil from cedarwood.[1] The body was not opened, and the

[1] Cedar-tree pitch (κεδρία).

stomach was not removed, but the oil was inserted through the anus, which was then closed. The body was again placed in the 'natrum' solution, and was taken out at the end of 70 days. The cedar-oil was then allowed to flow out, carrying with it the stomach and entrails in solution. According to Herodotus, the flesh was dissolved by the 'natrum', so that nothing remained of the corpse except the skin and bones.

The third method of embalming—the cheapest—consisted in washing and rinsing out the abdomen with a cleansing liquid, after which the corpse was placed in solution for 7 days.

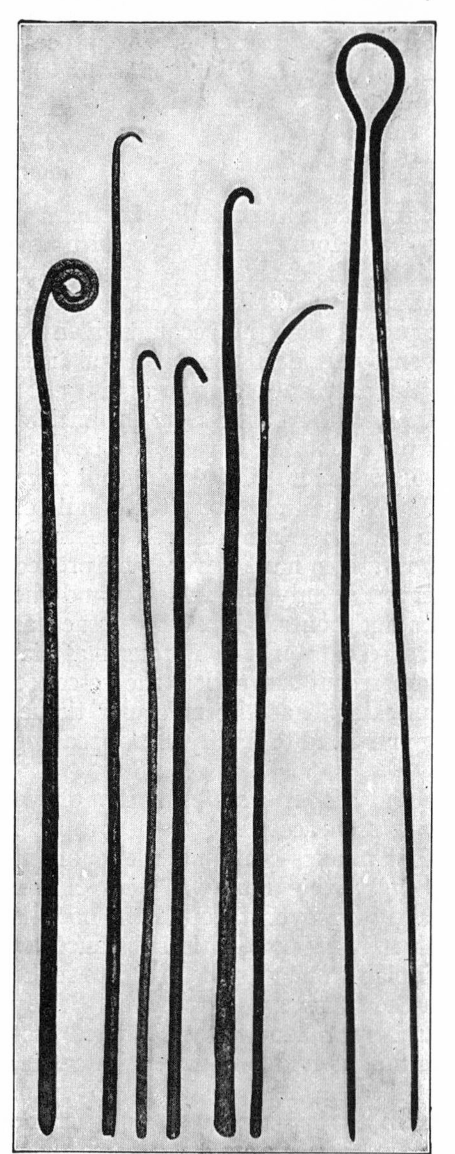

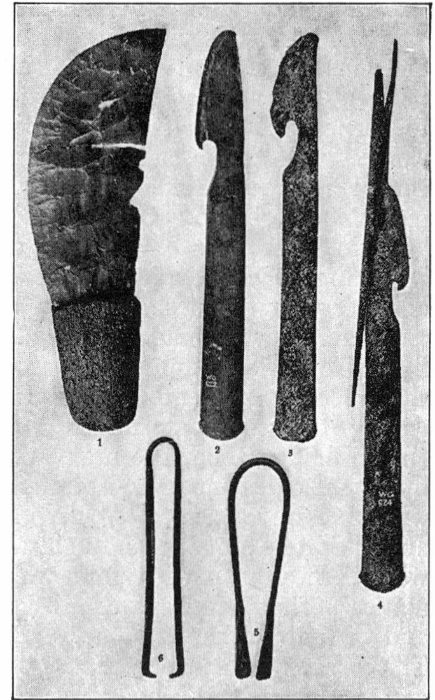

FIGS. 185 and 186.—Egyptian Instruments for making Mummies

The same general principles were applied to embalming sacred animals. These processes were, however, often modified slightly. Thus, many types of resin, asphalt, pitch, aromatic waters, expensive oils, flowers, and so forth, were often used. According to researches carried out by Elliott Smith on the mummies of forty-four priests and priestesses of the 21st Dynasty (eleventh century B.C.), a process was used, by which the natural form of the body was retained. In particular, the shrinking of the trunk and the twisting of the body was avoided. For this purpose, stuffing was adopted. The flesh was replaced by bringing under the skin more permanent substances, such as loam, sand or sawdust—aromatic substances often being mixed with them. Later, this process of stuffing was again given up, and an attempt was made to retain the external form by wrapping bandages round the limbs and the body. Still later, twisting was prevented by using pitch and bandages. The incision in the roof of the nasal cavity, which is mentioned by Herodotus, and through which the brain was removed, has been discovered by Smith in all mummies of the 17th and later Dynasties. The entrails, which were kept in the four 'Canopic vases' while the body was in solution, were placed in four packets in the interior of the body, after removal from solution.

FIG. 187.—Canopic vase, for entrails

This served to receive the entrails of the corpses of mummies. The lid has the shape of a human head. The lower part is covered with canvas and painted black. Height 13 in. Thebes. Berlin Museum, Egyptian Department

Of the numerous data derived from the analysis of mummies and their constituent parts, we mention only the following details, as being the most important, since they give us noteworthy information about the process of making mummies and the substances used in doing so. The ashes of three mummies, analysed by A. Lucas, contain 10 to 13·58 per cent. of substances insoluble in water, particularly calcium carbonate, also iron oxide, aluminium acetate, and sand. It has not been possible to determine whether the calcium carbonate is a transformed product of the embalming substances, or an accidental impurity introduced from the earth; nor has it been established whether the aluminium was used as a silicate or as a soluble salt. These substances seem to be the remains of the materials used for stuffing. Haas observed the high percentage of sodium in the ash of a mummy; this is due to the corpse having been laid in the 'natrum' mentioned by Herodotus. This 'natrum' or 'nitrum' has hitherto been regarded as a solution of saltpetre or soda, in particular of that form of soda (sodium carbonate) which occurs in the salt lakes of Egypt, and is now called 'trona'; it corresponds chemically with the formula $Na_2CO_3.3H_2O$. W. A. Schmidt failed to discover in the texture of mummies the slightest trace of saltpetre or sodium carbonate; on the other hand, there have always been found, in particular in 'Coptic' mummies, considerable quantities of common salt. According to Schmidt, the 'nitrum' bath therefore consisted certainly of common salt. The making of the mummies was thus effected by an actual pickling of the corpses. Trona was also much used in the solid form as a material to stuff the corpses. In no mummy was it possible to discover other chemical preserving substances, such as compounds of mercury, arsenic, lead, zinc, or antimony. The washing out of the bodies by means of palm wine had no preserving action, as it contains only a very small percentage of alcohol. Excluding the air by means of resin, asphalt and so forth plays a minor part, according to Schmidt, in comparison with the pickling and drying. The wrapping round with bandages, which were painted with gum and resins, is, however, of importance. The fact that drying without pickling can act as a preservative in the dry air of Egypt is proved by prehistoric mummies, perhaps 6,000 years old, which have lain buried in the sand; and no salting treatment could be traced in them. They were well dried before being buried. Probably the robbing of the corpses buried with ornaments and jewels, which often occurred, and also the improvement of tools which made it possible to construct wooden coffins, led to the old method of drying by means of air being discarded, and to the introduction of pickling and drying for making mummies.

FIG. 188.—An Urn for Entrails (Canopic jar)

The lid is in the form of the head of a sparrow-hawk. It is covered with asphalt, and then painted with a yellow pigment. It is made of wood. The height is 13 in. Berlin Museum, Egyptian Department

The 'trona' which was used to stuff the mummies was mixed with fats, probably with butter, but Schmidt, who has carefully investigated the question of the fatty acids present in mummies, has left the question open, as to whether other fats were also used, or whether the fat which was mixed with the trona was gradually derived from the body. It seems probable, however, that the trona was mixed with butter.

Concerning the preparation of the resins used for mummies, there are many researches by Reutter, Tschirsch, and others, which were carried out on mummies of various ages. It is shown that pure resins such as styrax, mastix, Aleppo resin, copal, asphalt, probably also turpentine from Chios, cedar resin and mixtures of these substances occurred. The presence of incense could nowhere be proved in these mummies, so that the remark made by Herodotus is confirmed. Its use was forbidden by religious decrees in Egypt. In Carthaginian mummies, on the other hand, where these decrees were not in force, we do find incense. The most varied essences were used for perfuming in Carthage; thyme and mint were favoured. According to Dörpfeld,

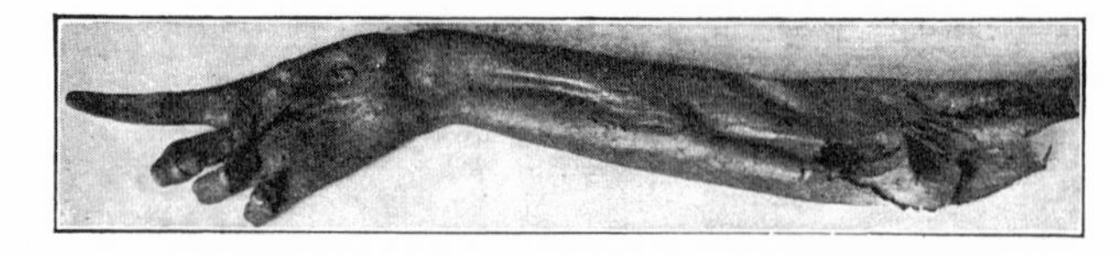

FIG. 189.—Fore-arm of a Female Mummy (without Bandages)

From a tomb in Thebes. Berlin Museum, Egyptian Department

the Greeks also preserved their corpses, namely, by smoking them. Burning was only resorted to when the ash was to be transported.[1] The

FIG. 190.—A Mummy with Bandages removed
Berlin Museum, Egyptian Department

fact that preserving was also effected by excluding the air, by placing bodies in honey, or pouring wax over them, is clear from the report of Plutarch (*Agesil,* 40) about the death of Agesilaus in the Harbour of Menelaus in Libya: 'As no honey was to be had, the Spartans poured wax over the dead man, and carried him thus to Lacedaemon.' Herodotus (IV, 71) makes a similar remark about the Scythians. In order to be able to transport the corpses of their kings, they covered the body with a wax, after having cut open the abdomen, cleaned it, and filled it with powdered saffron, with perfumes, aniseed, and other substances, and then sewed it up again. As this stuffing has no preserving virtues, the preservation must have been due to the exclusion of air by the wax.

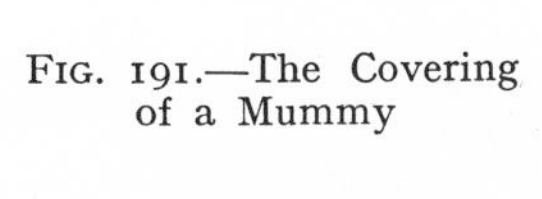

FIG. 191.—The Covering of a Mummy

Coloured painting on a white background. The face is dark red. Thebes. Berlin Museum, Egyptian Department

[1] This theory refers to prehistoric times.—*Trans.*

CERAMIC ARTS

THE DEVELOPMENT OF CERAMIC ART

ALTHOUGH ceramic art relates first and foremost to working in clay, that is, to moulding clay into all manner of objects of art and articles of daily use, we shall nevertheless in this section also touch on the production of various building materials, especially bricks. For in antiquity there were various relationships between pottery proper, and the extraction of building materials, due to the construction of the furnaces, the treatment of the material used, and other factors. Pottery is without doubt one of the oldest of all applied arts. It can be traced back to prehistoric times; indeed, we may well say, to the beginnings of the human race.[1] Rohland makes some noteworthy remarks about how vessels came to be made of clay. He mentions that the French navigator Gonneville discovered on the Brazilian coast wooden cooking vessels of the natives, which were surrounded by a layer of loam; if by chance the wooden shell became loosened from the earthenware envelope, an earthenware vessel was left. The German explorer Rau discovered in an old pottery of the Indians, on the Mississippi, reeds and rushes which were lined with clay. When they were heated, the wooden parts burned away, and the clay vessel remained behind. So it seems that wooden vessels and woven vessels were made water-tight by means of clay; perhaps originally only by rubbing clay in at the joints. When the clay became dry, it released itself from the vessel, and so the first unfired article of pottery was obtained. If now by chance a vessel of this kind fell into a fire, so that the wood was burned, it would at once be recognized that the clay not only withstood the heat of the fire, but indeed became harder and more rigid. So that, in primeval times, chance probably taught the firing of ceramic vessels. Other circumstances also conspired to make ceramic art one of the most ancient technical achievements: clay can be shaped; it is plastic. If a human being walked through a layer of clay, this property would immediately strike the eye. This property was then used in order to give the clay any desired shape by pressing and kneading it. Later, it was given its shape by means of tools, among which the most important was the potter's wheel. The date of the beginnings of the wheel cannot now be ascertained, but it occurs among all people of antiquity, and was probably first used in Asia Minor or Egypt. Very old ceramic articles which have come from these places prove that the wheel was used in making them; in very ancient Egyptian pictures we

[1] An exaggeration; but it is as old as the Neolithic period.—*Trans.*

see the potter sitting at work using it (Fig. 192). The fact that the potter's wheel was not discovered afresh by all the peoples who used it, but that it was spread abroad by inter-racial traffic and commercial relationships over wide areas of the prehistoric and ancient world, is supported by a remarkable circumstance, which perhaps proves that the art of firing clay became transmitted in the same way. In all fired clay of the first period, no matter whence it is derived, we find one and the same sign, namely the *crux ansata* (Swastika), 卐. We find this sign in Greenland, as well as at the southernmost point of America; we find it in Scandinavia, as well as in Africa. It suggests that the cradle of the clay industry, as regards the firing of clay and the use of the potter's wheel, was in Asia Minor or in Egypt.

In the most distant times, the clays used were from those uppermost

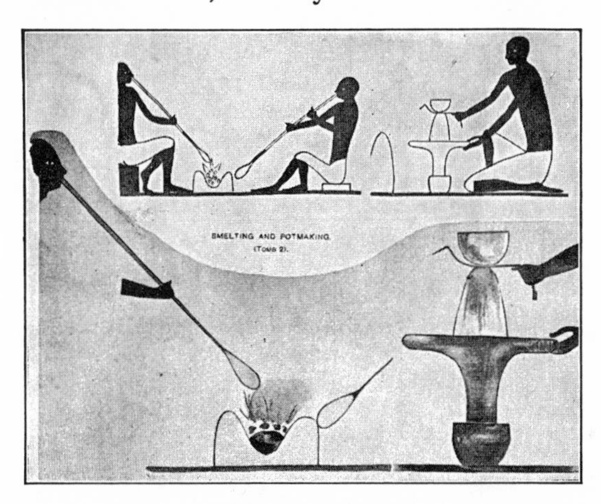

FIG. 192.—Use of the Potter's Wheel (on the right)

Among the Egyptians at the time of the Manetho's 12th Dynasty (2380 to 2167 B.C.). The meaning of the picture on the left is not clear. The suggestion that glass is being blown is probably wrong, according to the arguments used in the section on 'Glass', page 152. The disc is turned with the left hand, whilst the right hand uses the forming iron. Wall painting from Beni Hasan

layers of the earth which just happened to be available. Later, clay was specially selected; it was recognized that, after being fired, one clay assumed a different colour from another. The accidental admixture of compounds of iron, manganese and other metals brought about this effect. Perhaps experiments were made to discover the reason of this colouring, and thus the foundations of a new technical science were laid, which gave rise to coloured pottery, an art which in the course of time, particularly in Greece and Rome, became developed to a high degree of artistic excellence. We shall later treat coloured Greek and Roman ceramic art in greater detail, and shall describe the manner in which it was carried out. Glass fluxes also began to be used, and the method of using them was also probably due to an accident. For it does not seem impossible that sometimes, while earthenware vessels were being fired, coloured or uncoloured alkaline or calcium silicates, that is glazes, formed on the surface. These glazes are also found on very old specimens of pottery. Later still, the art of varnishing glaze also became perfected to an extraordinary degree. Moreover, in the course

Fig. 193.—A Tomb consisting of fourteen Bricks
Provincial Museum of Trèves

of time, the clay was cleaned and improved by artificial methods, especially by washing. The improvement of furnaces proceeded parallel with

Fig. 194.—Roman Tiles, with Stamps
Provincial Museum, Trèves

this development. At first, the clay vessels were probably fired by placing them on a charcoal fire and covering them with charcoal. It must then often have happened that the vessel, particularly when it was glazed, baked fast and stuck to its base. Methods were therefore devised for keeping the clay substances free so that they were brought into contact only with the flames, and not with the burning fuel. Furnaces were therefore invented, in which the fire chamber was separated from the oven in which the material to be fired was placed. The simplest furnace of this construction—in its fundamental essentials—is still much used, and is known in ceramic art under the name 'Cassel furnace.'

The extensive use of clay objects in art, in the household and in trade, made wholesale production necessary: all ancient peoples built factories, in which numerous workmen were occupied with producing the forms and with firing. Towns of considerable size required great quantities of clay ware; for these were used not only in the household and for building, but also for many other purposes, such as for making tombs (Fig. 193). In Rome there is still a mound 166 ft. high and 2,500 ft. in circumference, which consists entirely of broken fragments of pottery; it is known as Monte Testaccio. The fragments represent pieces thrown away during the unloading of goods despatched on the Tiber. Wholesale production led to the making of improved apparatus which could give a more rapid supply of earthenware. Forms were invented in which greater quantities could speedily be made than would have been possible by hand (Fig. 194). As nowadays, so in antiquity, the individual factories and workmen used stamps which were pressed into the clay. These stamps tell us the name of the maker of the object (Fig. 194). An extensive collection of ancient earthenware and brick stamps has been made by Ludovici.

FIG. 195.—Modelling Form, so-called Modelling Dish, with a cast relief in clay for the wholesale production of ceramic decoration
Berlin Museum, Antiquarium

CERAMIC ART AMONG THE INDIVIDUAL PEOPLES OF ANTIQUITY

The development of ceramic art sketched out above, took place everywhere along fairly similar lines, and therefore we have been able to treat it as a whole. We next discuss the special peculiarities of this art among the individual peoples.

THE BABYLONIANS AND ASSYRIANS

As already mentioned, the cradle of ceramic art was probably Asia Minor or Egypt. From here, this art spread over the Orient, and it first became a flourishing industry in Babylon and Assyria. The Babylonians and Assyrians not only made earthenware vessels, but also knew how to put an artistic finish to their bricks. In Assyria, we find bricks, as well as ordinary clay stones, which have been dried in the sun, also fired and glazed stones. Rathgen, with the help of a voluminometer, an apparatus which tells how much of the clay has disappeared during the firing, has determined the temperature that must have been reached in the ancient Babylonian furnaces at the time of Nebuchadnezzar (604 to 561 B.C.). He found that the bricks must have been fired at a temperature of 550° to 600° C. This is a very low temperature, and it explains why these bricks can be cut with a knife. The temperature of firing clay nowadays is about 1,000° C. For a long time, the construction of the ancient Babylonian furnaces was shrouded in mystery, until Hilbrecht, in excavations in Nippur, for the first time discovered one of these furnaces, dating from the year 200 B.C. Here, the fire-chamber and the flame-space have been separated from each other in a very curious way. For whereas among many of the ancient furnaces, and also in the case of the 'Cassel furnace' already mentioned, the flame-space lies at the side of the fire-chamber, it is here situated above it. The top of the fire-chamber is provided with a number of slits, through which the flames pass, and also the hot gases that are produced. The earthenware objects to be fired stood over these fairly long slits. Bricks were probably also fired on them; as Herodotus reports, the clay that was used for these bricks had been collected during the digging of the trench around Babylon. Herodotus had been in Babylon, as Friedrich Delitzsch has shown, and he can therefore be relied upon. He writes: 'As they (the Babylonians) made the trench, they fashioned bricks out of the earth which was thrown out of the trench; and when they had prepared a sufficient number of bricks, they burned them in brick furnaces, and then used hot bitumen as a cement.'

The last remark proves that even at that time the porosity of these bricks was put to good use in the case of ancient Babylonian structures, as a non-porous brick cannot be so tightly attached to other bricks with bitumen (asphalt). The great town-gate of Nippur, which was probably built about the year 3000 B.C., was also made rigid by means of bricks in the manner mentioned, which were joined together with asphalt. Great interest was aroused when, in the year 1851, pieces of brick were found in the ruins of Babylon, whose form and glaze led to the conclusion that they belonged to the figures of great lions. The prophet Ezekiel, and also the Greek writer Diodorus, tell of the splendid clay figures which adorned the walls of Babylon and depicted lion and tiger hunts. More recently, these wonderful terra-cotta figures have been rediscovered; they are coloured dark-blue, light blue, white, yellow, and green, and they show a black outline. It has also been possible to get an idea of how these works of art were made. The process was certainly a little circuitous, for since the bricks shrank during the firing, there was the danger that if they were first formed, coloured and glazed, they would afterwards no longer fit together. The following procedure was therefore adopted. The bricks were made wedge-shape, and then fired. By this means it was possible to make the outer joints fit closely. The bricks were then built up into a wall. On this the picture was painted in outline, by means of a substance which became red after the firing. Even if the building-up was not perfectly done, the drawing still remained regular. The stones were then marked, and the whole structure was again taken to pieces. The glaze was then put on the bricks within the outlines marked on them; and the bricks were then fired again—in which process they no longer shrank, and yet allowed the glaze to be burned in. The whole was then built up again, and the marks on the bricks indicated where every stone belonged. The great lions in the processional street of Nebuchadnezzar, which are 3 ft. high and 6½ ft. long, were at any rate first modelled or chiselled by a sculptor in a mould in which they represented a 'negative', so that the parts to be raised were depressed, and the depressed parts raised. The clay which served to make the bricks was then pressed into this form, so that a clay plate resulted which contained the 'positive'. This large clay plate was next cut up into several parts. Bricks were thus made which were marked in the manner already described, and then fired. A sort of wholesale manufacture of such gigantic specimens of plastic ceramic art is represented by the twelve warriors, which were discovered in the ancient Persian capital Susa; the close resemblance between several of them indicates clearly that they were produced from the same mould. The wall on which they are situated was first built up, and the warrior form was modelled on it. The model was then cut up in the manner demanded by the position of the stones of the wall situated beneath. Each brick so produced was then shaped, after it had been copied (and a negative had been obtained) as often as required. The outlines were then marked on the form-brick by means of clay—so that they came out as hollows in the negative but as prominences again in the final bricks. In this way, there were formed, on these final bricks, shallow spaces into which the glaze could be filled, and over which it spread itself when fired. These raised friezes, which are over 11 yards long, were made in this way about the beginning of the fifth century B.C. Similar plastic works are to be found in Babylon; for example, the ornamental animals on the triumphal arch of Ishtar.

In the above-mentioned city of Susa, terra-cotta vessels have been found, which give us information about the production and composition of ancient Persian domestic utensils. They are made from marly clay, are of rather rough form, and not smoothed on the outside. On some there are black ornaments which have been simply painted on the unbaked clay with a brush. The black colour appeared only after firing, but no lustre resulted. The firing temperature is estimated by Granger to have been about 1,000° C. The chemical composition of the vessels is as follows (according to Granger):

	Per cent.
Clayey substance	28·57
Sand, etc.	27·10
Lime	37·58
Moisture	2·70
Water (in composition)	4·05

THE EGYPTIANS

The ceramic art of the Egyptians closely resembles, in its main essentials, that of the Babylonians, Assyrians and Persians, which we have just described. Herodotus (II, 136) narrates of the brick pyramid of King Asychis that it bears the inscription ; ' Do not consider me mean

FIG. 196.—Making Bricks among the Egyptians (about 2000 B.C.)

A : Two men are taking water out of a pool, in order to moisten the raw material (Nile mud). B : Working the material and carrying it away. C : Brick moulds in wooden boxes ; next to them is the overseer. D : Piling up the bricks to dry in the sun. E : Collecting together the finished bricks that have been dried in the sun, and building up a wall. Deutsches Museum, Munich

in comparison with the stone pyramids, for I am as far above them as Zeus above the other gods. For they thrust a pole deep into a marsh, and collected that which remained of the mud on the rod, and made bricks therefrom. In this way they have built me.' This description of how clay was extracted is certainly noteworthy, but it can hardly have been the only method used. Pictorial representations that have been preserved, such as those shown in Figs. 196 and 197, which date back to the year 2000 B.C., give us sufficient information about the manner of making bricks in Egypt. It hardly varies from that practised by other peoples. The bricks were probably mostly dried in the air, but firing-ovens were also known, although none of these have yet been found. In the fifth chapter of Exodus, mention is made of the manufacture of bricks in Egypt by the Jews, and it is stated that straw was used in this process. The way in which the straw was used remained obscure for a long time. It was regarded by many as a mechanical cement. From experiments which were carried out by the American Acheson on the elasticity and tensile strength of the loam

FIG. 197.—Model of an Egyptian Brick-works

Forming and moulding the bricks by hand. Alleged to have been found on the eastern bank of Beliane and Nag Hamadi respectively. Made of wood. 14 in. by 11 in. Berlin Museum, Egyptian Department

used to make smelting crucibles, it was found that the addition of organic substances, and particularly of straw, to loam, which was afterwards dried, caused the breaking strength of the bricks so obtained to rise from 84 lbs. to the square inch to 269 lbs. to the square inch: hence the strength of the brick was increased by 244 per cent.

Acheson did not doubt that the Egyptians knew of this action of straw on the clayey mass, and he found that the presence of a substance in the straw affected the loam in the same way as tannic acid affects leather. The fact that straw was actually used for producing bricks in Egypt, is proved by the unfired bricks of El Kab and the bricks of the pyramids of Dahshur, in which, besides straw, leaves of plants and parts of grasses (*Triticum vulgare L.*, *Hordeum vulgare L.* and *Hordeum hexastichon L.*) were found. A further peculiarity of the ancient ceramic art of ancient Egypt is to be noted in the remarkable earthenware vessels which were used at a very early date for keeping water and are still in use nowadays on the Nile, namely, the so-called 'gullahs'. They were fired at a very low temperature and were consequently very porous. If Nile water was now poured into them on hot days, it passed through the pores and evaporated on the outer surface of the jar. As it derived the warmth necessary for this evaporation from its immediate surroundings, the water cooled very rapidly, in proportion to the rate of evaporation. Consequently, on very hot days, the 'gullahs' provided particularly cool water, since on such days the air would be at a temperature far removed from its saturation point. From theoretical reflections, however, Dollinger has arrived at the conclusion that the greatest cooling is effected by vessels placed in the shade and left in the draught. His opinion is not shared in all points by von Luschan. Further details are given in the section on 'Refrigeration and Preserving', page 122. For the rest, the ordinary earthenware vessels of the ancient Egyptians, such as were used in the household, exhibit no special peculiarities. They were made (Fig. 198) in very much the same way as nowadays. They were prepared from clay, which became red, yellow or brown after firing, and they differ in no wise from the earthenware vessels in use among the other peoples of antiquity. In contrast with them, however, the glazed ceramic works of the ancient Egyptians arouses the greatest interest; it was formerly called 'Egyptian Porcelain' or 'Glazed Faience'—two terms which are equally incorrect. They are due to Brongniart, who used them for the first time in his *Traité des Arts Céramiques.* They passed over into the archaeological vocabulary, although they can be justified neither from the technical nor from the chemical point of view. These pseudo-ceramic objects contain no clay at all as an essential constituent. Rather, they consist of sand, to which a small quantity of clay has been added. The analyses made by William Burton prove that the material of these vessels contains in general 94 per cent. of sand and up to 2 per cent. of clay. The rest consists of accidental ingredients, chiefly lime and magnesia. As the small quantity of clay contained in these does not suffice to bind the sand sufficiently for a plastic and hence workable mass to result, Burton assumes that the ancient Egyptians used, for preparing their glazed coloured vessels, simply the natural sandstone, which happened to contain a very small quantity of clay. The potter's wheel was not used at all; rather, the sandstone was hollowed out.

To prove the correctness of the view that this very peculiar ancient Egyptian art actually existed formerly, Burton quotes facts discovered in his detailed investigations. In the first place, there are found in the oldest Egyptian tombs small spheres, pendants from necklaces, and so

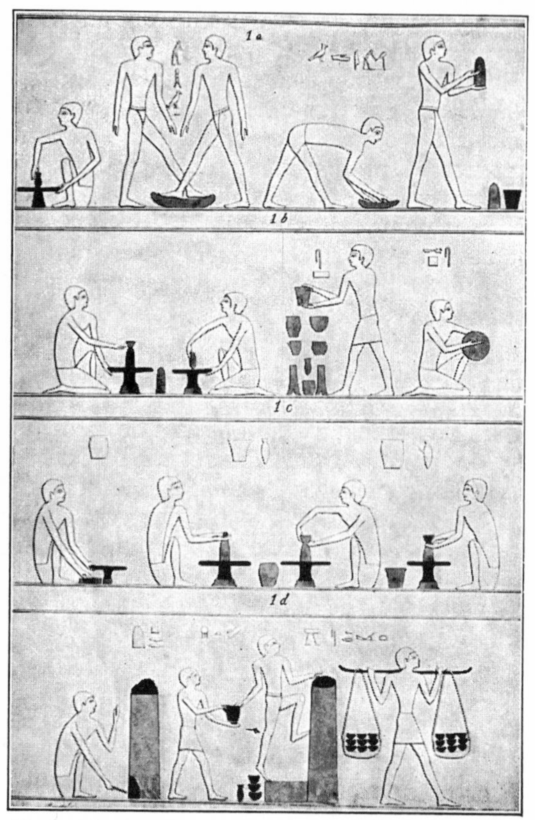

FIG. 198.—Making Earthenware Vessels in Egypt

Just as nowadays, the clay is soaked, stamped on, and then kneaded by hand, and left to 'rot' in lumps. It is then formed by means of the potter's wheel, which is turned with the left hand. The pieces are dried and fired in the furnace, which, as shown in the picture, is filled and emptied from above and heated from below

FIG. 199.—So-called 'Glazed Faience' or 'Egyptian Porcelain'

A thistle, probably from a chain. Above and below, a link. The stem and the cup are green, the rest is dark blue. Height, $\frac{4}{5}$ in. Found in Thebes. Berlin Museum, Egyptian Department

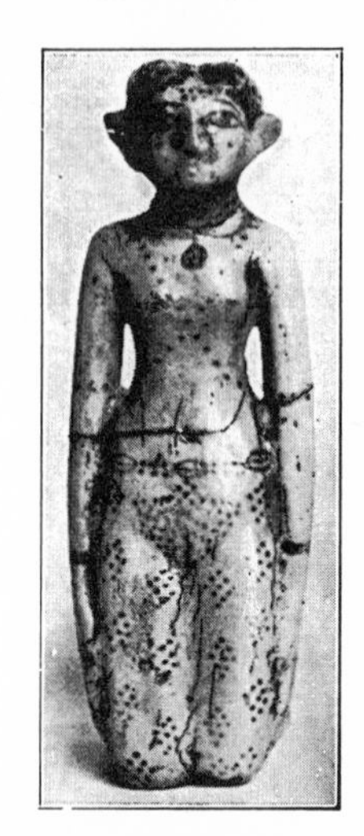

FIG. 200. — So-called 'Glazed Faience' or 'Egyptian Porcelain'

A child's doll. A blue glaze. Length, nearly 6 in. Berlin Museum, Egyptian Department

forth, which have been cut from stone that is harder than sandstone and has been glazed (Fig. 199). With the help of the polarization microscope, Burton further established that the basic substance of the earthenware vessels actually consists of sandstone or some quartz-like stone. This art was practised from the 18th Dynasty (1550 B.C.) onwards for 1,500 years in an unchanged form. Burton therefore suggests for these vessels the name 'Ancient Egyptian Silica Vessels' or 'Quartz Vessels'.

Since the sandstone itself has only a small coefficiency of rigidity, the strength of the quartz vessels depends solely on the glaze. The glazes are composed of alkaline silicates of lime ; they are for the most part of a beautiful blue colour and contain the colouring matter copper oxide. These glazes cannot be spread over ordinary earthenware at all, as they do not flow smoothly over them ; they form a beautiful smooth surface only on matter containing silica. It was only later, when the Romans had already penetrated into Egypt, that the method of applying such glazes to earthenware vessels was acquired. To do so, the device was used of applying between the earthenware and the glaze a slip

FIG. 201.—'Egyptian Faience'

Open-work or fret-work tablet, with 4 rows of figures of gods vertically above one another. The fifth row is broken. Light green glaze. Height, 3½ in.; width, 2 in. Berlin Museum, Egyptian Department

FIG. 202.—'Egyptian Faience'

A door in the lowest chamber of the stepped pyramid of Saqqarah. A line of hieroglyphic inscription runs around the three sides of the main portal. The inside, outside and the sides are ornamented with green glazed tablets of 'Egyptian Faience'. A replica in the Berlin Museum, Egyptian Department

containing a high percentage of silica. Polychrome glazes occur in Egyptian silica, but only in the later periods ; they reached the highest perfection and were made in great variety under the sovereignty of the Romans.

The investigations of Burton, which were at first much doubted, have been confirmed by the German investigators Pukall and Berge, who, entirely independently of him, came to the same conclusions from their experiments. Pukall and Berge succeeded in reproducing the turquoise-blue glaze from marble, soda, sand, and copper oxide. In this way, they obtained beautiful turquoise surface colourings. By using cobalt and manganese oxide, as well as chromium oxide, they obtained other splendidly coloured glazes. Le Chatelier in Paris also succeeded in copying the coloured enamels of glazed Egyptian stones, statuettes, and other objects. For the sandstone used, he finds exactly the same composition as Burton, and the glazes which he produced are composed essentially of silica, calcium carbonate, calcined soda, copper oxide, and similar substances. Besides vessels, the Egyptians also enamelled tiles.

Since the Persian ceramists who lived at the time of the Egyptian dynasties made tiles as well as vessels and vases, in which the sandy surfaces were covered with coloured enamels, we have reason for assuming that the art of enamelling had its origin among the ancient Egyptians, and that it then penetrated through the invasions of Cambyses (530–522 B.C.), who advanced as far as Nubia, to Persia, and thence to the rest of the ancient Orient. The Greeks and the Romans likewise learned the art of enamelling from the Egyptians. Later, in post-Roman times, this art was introduced from Egypt by Moors into Spain, whence it spread over the rest of Europe.

A question which has given rise to much discussion is whether the ancient Egyptians made porcelain. This question has in many cases been answered in the affirmative, probably on account of the terms mentioned above, and introduced by Brongniart. Now, porcelain is actually found in Egypt, but it has been proved that in all cases it is derived from China, and that it was introduced from China—probably rather late—into Egypt. Le Chatelier asserts that genuine Egyptian porcelain actually exists. He has examined a sample derived from the Morgan collection, and discovered exactly the same composition as that which white porcelain of Sèvres still has nowadays. The result of the analysis was:

	Per cent.
Silica	88·6
Aluminium oxide	1·4
Iron oxide	·4
Lime	2·1
Soda	5·8
Copper oxide	1·7
	100·0

Le Chatelier succeeded in producing the same substance artificially by using a temperature of 1,050° C. For the rest, it is known that porcelain was invented by the Chinese. It has not yet been possible to establish definitely when this invention was made, but the date is by no means so far back as was formerly believed. The existence of porcelain among the Chinese is established with certainty for about A.D. 600, although there are certain indications that the first porcelain objects were perhaps produced in China about 200 B.C. Little is known about the ancient Chinese method of making porcelain. Recent investigations by the Japanese savant Hirano have at least shown that the form of ancient Chinese furnaces for making porcelain still exists here and there. These furnaces, which consist of three or more chambers, are built up on a declivity in such a way that one chamber is always situated a little higher than the last. In this way, the draught necessary for burning

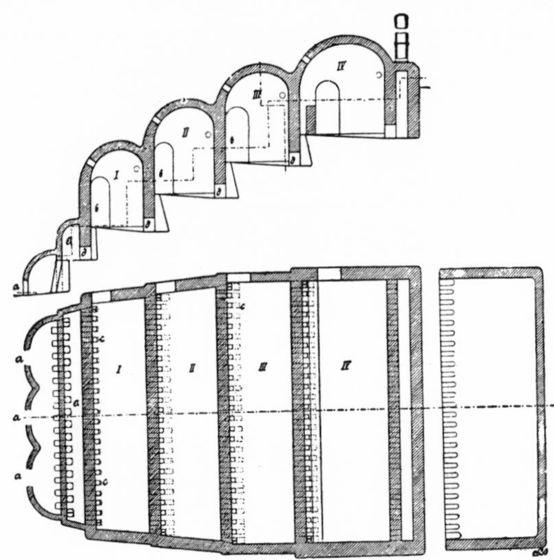

FIG. 203.—Ancient Chinese Furnace, consisting of various Chambers

is produced, and no chimney is necessary, which therefore is not present at all, or is very low and attached to the last chamber (Fig. 203). A special furnace was probably used for burning on the glaze.

THE GREEKS

The ceramic art of antiquity reached its zenith in Greece. The form and appearance of its products attained the highest degree of perfection, the clay and the object formed from it being a welcome field for artistic activity. All other arts were enlisted in the service of ceramic industry, indeed they were derived from it; for does not Greek fable [1] state that painting, as well as plastic art, was discovered in the workshop of the potter Butades? There is without doubt an element of truth in this myth—at least in so far as it refers to a definite branch of plastic art, namely bronze-casting. Before clay could be formed and fired, it was impossible to produce works of art cast from bronze. Thus, the casting of bronze must have been preceded by ceramic art, which served as a guide and a lead. There are intimate relations between Greek and Roman wall-paintings and the paintings on Greek vases. The painting of vessels among the Greeks became a model for the painting of friezes—indeed for the production of pictures.

In examining Greek vases, which represent the zenith of ancient Hellenic ceramic art, two aspects must be sharply differentiated; the artistic and the technical point of view. Although these vases are perfect in artistic respects, they are just the contrary from the technical point

[1] The reference is to a late and silly story told in Pliny, N.H. XXXV, 151.—*Trans.*

of view. In Greece, too, ceramic art attained a great age. The earliest excavations—above all, those of Schliemann in Troy, those at Mycenae and other places—brought to light numerous earthenware vessels. But even before Schliemann, in the twenties of the last century, numerous vases were discovered in Etruria, which, on account of their origin, were regarded as products of the Etruscans. Later excavations showed, however, that these were Greek products.[1] Since then, such vases have been excavated in enormous numbers in various places, so that we now have abundant material at our disposal. An endless number of publications have appeared about them, but they discuss the Greek vases almost in all cases only from the archaeological and artistic point of view. The technical aspect received less attention. Only recently, more attention has been paid to the ancient Greek ceramic art by the technical scientist. It was then discovered, as already indicated above, that the technical processes were by no means perfect. Above all, no very high temperature was reached, and consequently the clay remained too porous for

FIG. 204.—Greek Potter's Wheel. Corinthian Pinax. Paris, Museum of the Louvre

many purposes. It did not frit together sufficiently densely, and the glaze was not first applied in order to embellish it, but rather it served the necessary purpose of making the vessel water-tight, to make it impenetrable—which it would not perhaps be otherwise. Out of this necessity there then grew a virtue ; the glaze, and also the painting under it, were developed to a high degree of artistic excellence. In general, Greek vases are black, brown or red, and are more or less polished. At the end of the third century B.C. a glaze appeared on them. They are often so porous that we can understand that the glaze was necessary, for even if water—as in the Egyptian gullah—might have kept very fresh in many of these vessels, they were probably quite inappropriate for other purposes. The potter's wheel was used in the earliest times ; Homer mentions it ; he compares the whirling motion of dancers to the revolving of the potter's wheel (*Iliad*, XVIII, 600), while Diodorus names Talos (otherwise Kalos or Perdix) nephew of Daidalos, as its inventor. In all cases the potter's wheel is turned by hand. Moulds were not used, but forming rods. The construction of the Greek potter's

[1] Italy abounds both in important Greek pottery and in local ware, Etruscan and other, from Neolithic times on.—*Trans.*

wheel is made beautifully clear to us on a Corinthian votive tablet in the Louvre in Paris (Fig. 204). The disc is shown in cross-section, and has, as we see, bearings at the centre. This bearing consists of a conical hole placed over a pivot, which widens conically towards the bottom. To prevent the disc from raising itself up, the pivot, so it appears, is provided with a hole above the disc, through which a pin can be thrust. The part of the pivot which projects beyond the disc carries a cover, which is visible in the picture; and it is here that the clay that is to be worked is placed. The pivot is also hollowed out conically inside, and rests on a second massive conical pivot, about which it can turn. In order to keep his sphere of action clear the potter seizes the disc at the opposite side of the rim, or on the side remote from the body, and turns it. In the other hand he holds a bent forming-rod, which—judging by its appearance—we assume is used to shape the upper rim of the vessels. The potter must possess great manipulative ability. The rim of the vessels is always made thick, to give it greater strength.

FIG. 205.—A red-figured Greek Vase (best period).
Berlin Altes Museum, Antiquarium

The vessels were painted in manifold ways, and the colours were applied by means of a brush. In many cases the vases were painted completely black. The painting was carried out on the moist clay, which rapidly absorbed the colour. The figures were protected during the process so that they appeared yellow or red on the black background. Fine lines and other marks were scratched on the black background by means of sharp instruments. The black colour is always applied so thinly that it does not stand out in relief. Many colours, particularly yellow, which consists of yellow ochre, were always applied under the glaze; and others, above all white and red, occurred chiefly above it. Whereas in the older art only the colours mentioned were used, violet, green and blue appeared later. (For the chemical composition of Grecian colours, see the section on 'Colours.') The gilding of vessels is met with in the earliest times. For example, Mrs. Harriet Boyd Hawes excavated vases in Crete, whose age was probably about 3,500 years, and which were used for sacrificial purposes. They are so superbly gilt that they were at first thought to be gold vessels. Only a closer investigation revealed their real nature. At the same place, vases were found which were silvered in a similar way. In the Greek National Museum at Athens, there is an earthenware vase of this sort, which comes from the tombs of the Cyclades, going back to the year 2500 B.C. It is massive in form, in order to give the illusion of being a metal vase, and it has been silvered with great dexterity. The coating of gold and silver was applied by means of metal foil. The handle and other excrescences were made separately, and attached to the finished vase. Barbotine served as a cement. The beautiful black glaze of antique Grecian vases has been the subject of many researches. It was firstly found that the beautiful red of the clay resulted from its being burned in a natural way with abundant access of air. The analysis of the glaze, which was carried out in many cases, proved that only iron oxide was present, which could not explain the mystery of this splendid black coating, until Verneuil succeeded in making it by fusing together iron filings, soda and the marly clay, of which the vessel was formed, in an oxidizing fire. The result was an opaque black glaze with green fluorescence, which possessed the characteristic properties of Greek glaze. Verneuil considers it probable that the Greeks obtained finely divided iron through reduction of iron compounds by means of charcoal and soda, and that they then added this to the marly clay and soda. The beautiful black surface might also then have come about owing to the favourable circumstance that the soda used in Greece was not pure, but contained admixtures of carbon, sodium sulphide and sodium chloride. It does not seem out of the question, however, that finely filed iron (iron filings) may have been added in place of the iron obtained by reduction in the manner just described. Franchet confirms the use of iron, but he does not consider it probable that iron filings or reduced iron was used. Rather, he believes that the Greeks made use of the mineral magnetic oxide of iron, magnetite, which occurs freely in Nature, for producing their glaze; it always contains a small amount of manganese. By melting together 55 parts of quartz sand with 45 parts of soda, and by adding 100 parts of magnetite to the molten mass, he obtained a glaze which resembled exactly that of the Greek vessels, and which also exhibited their blue or green fluorescence. (For further particulars about the chemistry of black glaze see page 151.)

FIG. 206.—Tanagra Figure
Berlin, Old Museum, Antiquarium

If we leave out of account the ordinary articles of use, which do not differ from those of other peoples, we recognize a very particular product of Greek ceramic art in the so-called 'Tanagra' figures, which derived their name from the town Tanagra in Boeotia, where they were first discovered in 1874 in the necropolis on the Kokkali Hill. These pretty figures consist of a lump which has been burned red and painted with distemper. They were technically produced in this way; the sculptor first made a model, which was then pressed into a mould of plaster or clay, so that two negatives which fitted well together were made. The two hollow spaces in the middle were then filled with clay and pressed together. The result was a plastic figure surrounded by a kind of seam formed by the edges of the hollow mould. This seam was removed by means of a wooden spatula. The figure was then fired and painted with size colours.

Curiously enough, although so many and such different ceramic products were made in Greece, among them very large objects such as amphorae and decorations for the façades of houses, nothing was known until quite recently about the firing of these objects. On the vases there are indeed found pictures of ancient Grecian furnaces, on which workmen can be recognized who are looking through openings into the furnace, and to protect themselves from the glow, are holding their hands in front of their faces; but real potters' furnaces were not found till quite recently, when some specimens were discovered in Mycenae which in their essentials resembled the Roman furnaces, but differed from them by having the pillar which supports the arched roof round instead of rectangular (see page 149).

THE ROMANS

The ceramic art of the Romans was in many ways influenced by that of the Greeks. On the whole it does not differ much at first in its essentials; and indeed a common main stream runs through the ceramic art of the whole of antiquity, whose characteristics we have described in detail at the beginning of this section. Later on, in Roman ceramic art, just as in that of other peoples, particular methods developed, of which some did not even originate on the Italian peninsula. As an example of this, we may quote the barbotine process, which was practised in the Gallic and Rhenish provinces of the Roman Empire, and which was not known in Rome and in Italy. It has been discovered only recently that it was also known in Egypt and Asia Minor. It consists in washing the clay till it is very fine and then, by stirring it with water, forming a thin barbotine. This is then filled into a funnel provided with a fine orifice from which it escapes in a thin stream on to the earthenware vessels to be decorated. In this way, raised ornaments appear on the earthenware vessels. We see that this is the same process as that nowadays still used by confectioners in order to decorate their pastry with inscriptions and figures. Whereas, originally, simple ornaments such as circles and lines were applied, later, really magnificent show-pieces were made by the barbotine process, which exhibited entire hunting scenes and the like.

A further peculiarity of Roman ceramic art was the almost complete absence of glaze. The firing process is thus technically better than that of the Greeks. Where a glaze is present, it is mostly of a green colour, but there are also black glazes, and some with a touch of yellow. The black glazed vessels often carry inscriptions.

Besides the barbotine process, special effects were produced by throwing gritty particles on to the still wet vessels. In this way a rough surface is produced, such as we still use for covering the walls of houses. Roman ceramic art worked itself out most characteristically, however, in that species of earthenware which is called *terra sigillata* on account of its similarity with impresses of seals carrying relief, or else on account of its being decorated with raised figures (*sigilla*). (This term is of recent origin, and was not used by the ancient Romans.) The names 'Samian' or 'Arretine' pottery are used because the vessels were perhaps for the first time made on the island of Samos, and because the most important factories for producing them were in Arretium, in Etruria. The *terra sigillata* represented the finer types of earthenware that existed in ancient Roman times. We find vessels or fragments of *terra sigillata* wherever the Romans penetrated. They are sometimes of light, sometimes of dark red, simple in form, or of noble contour, smooth or ornamented. But all of them exhibit a beautiful velvety matt finish. It is this finish which constitutes their real beauty. The *terra sigillata* presented science with a problem that was difficult to solve. In spite of all endeavours, it was for a long time impossible to discover the secret of its production. Red earthenware vessels could be produced, but none of them had the beautiful and characteristic matt lustre of surface. Numerous chemists and ceramists spent decades seeking to solve the question. In the porcelain factory in Berlin no fewer than two thousand specimens were fired. Great sums of money, amounting to thousands of pounds, were expended on these experiments, in which experimenters went so far as to use the ancient clay deposits and instruments which had been discovered in the excavations. The most detailed scien-

FIG. 207.—'Barbotine' Vase (so-called 'Vase of the Gods from St. Matthias')

Black glazed goblet with a head and inscriptions painted. The rest is made in relief by means of a conical sprinkling bag Provincial Museum, Trèves

tific investigations were made in order to discover the secret. As an instance of the thoroughness of these efforts, we may quote an example. Many of the clays used by the ancient Romans contained microscopic particles of magnetic iron ore. During the firing, these particles assume a definite position, by setting themselves like the magnetic needle of a compass, so as to point along the magnetic lines of the earth. From the position of these particles of ore, scientists endeavoured to calculate the place at which the vessels were made, and also the temperatures which were used for firing. In short, no means were neglected which might serve as a clue. (Concerning this magnetic iron ore, see also page 151.)

The same happened as in many other cases. In a lecture given at the Association of the Friends of Saalburg, in Berlin, in 1907, Diergart spoke the prophetic words: 'With the solution of this problem of the *terra sigillata*, the same will happen as with the " egg of Columbus "; it is very simple when once it has been found.' Events proved that Diergart (who had spent nearly ten years of his life on this particular problem) was right. The solution has now been found. A simple potter in the little village Sulzbach in the Bavarian Oberpfalz, called Karl Fischer, succeeded, in collaboration with his son George Fischer, in lifting the veil from this secret of ancient Roman art; and how simple is the solution !—truly an 'egg of Columbus'. The new vessels of the *terra sigillata* type, which differ in no respect from the ancient Roman vessels, are made in three stages. At first, the rough objects which are either unfired, or only slightly fired, are covered with a coloured layer of clay mud. This clay mud must be in a very finely divided state, as it is this factor which produces the velvety lustre. It must have the further property of turning red when fired. There are a considerable number of such clays, so that it is not at all difficult to procure them. When this first stage is complete, namely covering the vessel with clay mud—the 'slip' as potters call it—the next step follows. This consists in polishing the surface by means of a brush until a very shiny surface is obtained. In the third stage, the earthenware is completely fired, and care has to be taken that the top layer of clay mud, the 'slip', becomes hard. The highest authorities in this branch of applied art, such as Diergart and Blümlein of Homburg, have asserted that the objects produced by the Fischer method differ in no way from their antique predecessors. The inventor has produced by his process a number of vessels from antique moulds that have been excavated, and even experts have not been able to distinguish them from the antique examples. The Curator of the National Museum at Munich, Dr. M. Halm, expressed the opinion that the new *terra sigillata* vessels resemble the originals so extraordinarily closely in their whole character, above all in their warm tone and their metallic ring, that only a specialist in archaeological studies would be able to distinguish between the original and the modern copy. He advised the inventor to affix the seal of his firm to all the copies, in order that they may be recognized, and may not be used for fraudulent purposes. Although it cannot be stated with certainty that Fischer's method is exactly the same as that of the ancient Romans, and certain doubts have been expressed in this connexion—it has been alleged, for

FIG. 208.—Roman Potters' Furnaces

On the left is the furnace of Castor in Northamptonshire. On the right is the furnace of Heiligenberg, near Strasbourg. Both were first described by Brongniart. Copies in the Deutsches Museum, Munich

example, that there are certain differences (such as those caused by drops that have fallen into the old vessels and have been fired with the clays, whereupon they assumed a brilliant lustre)—the similarity of the products to the ancient *terra*

FIGS. 209 and 210.—Roman Potter's Furnace in Heddernheim

As seen from the front space in which the workmen sat to supervise the firing. Fig. 209, a view of the fire-space and of the perforated bottom of the flame-space. Fig. 210, a view of the preserved part of the flame-space

sigillata wares makes it appear very probable that the processes were the same.

Concerning the method by which the Romans fired their clay objects we have received detailed information from numerous finds of furnaces, as well as potteries furnished with them. Although individual furnaces differ in small constructional details, they are fairly similar in their essentials. Above all, the fire-chamber and the flame-space are always separated. The fire-chamber is often so far away from the flame-space that the flames no longer enter the latter, but only the hot gases that are emitted. As a rule, the flame-space is of circular form; the bottom is perforated so that the flames or the hot gases, or both, can enter into it. The top is mostly arched, and supported in the middle by a square column. The diameter of the flame-space is nearly always small, amounting at most to 6½ to 10 feet, and often less. These small dimensions made it possible to remove the whole cupola from small firing apparatuses so

FIG. 211.—Model of a Roman Pottery in the Städtisches Historisches Museum, Frankfort-on-the-Main.
On the right is the muffle-furnace with an arched roof. (Constructed by Gondlach.)

that fuel could be inserted and extracted when burned out. Larger ones were provided for this purpose with a special aperture. Furnaces were either round or oblong. For instance, at Aquincum, nowadays called Ofen, a suburb of Budapest, seven specimens of the oblong type were discovered, in the vicinity of which there were five of the round ones (according to Doufrain), a proof that this was once the seat of a great industry. Of the oblong furnaces, some served for firing earthenware vessels, others for making roof tiles. The best preserved kinds are surrounded by walls about 3½ to 5 ft. thick. A fire channel 4 ft. high and 3½ ft. wide passes right down the centre of the whole apparatus. The distance from the upper surface of the arched roof to the floor is 2½ ft.; and from the bottom of the fire-channel to the floor it is about 6½ ft. The lower part of the masonry of the channel consists of trachyte blocks, and above them is some brickwork 2½ ft. thick. The channel projects 3½ ft. from the furnace proper, and thus forms the fire-space, the *praefurnium*. From the main channel, there branch off at each side eight side channels, about 10 in. wide. The mouths of these lateral channels are situated 2½ ft. above the base of the main channel. The lateral channels slope up from the main channel at an angle of 45 degrees, and end at the wall surrounding the furnace. The individual intervening walls, arches and buttresses, are 12 in. thick, and built up from unfired bricks of dimensions 12 × 12 × 4 in. Everything is covered with a clay layer nearly 1 in. thick, and here and there we find lumps of enamel hanging in the channels. To distribute the flames, there are holes 2 in. in diameter arranged in 12 to 15 rows. The furnaces probably had no arched roof, and it appears that before any firing was undertaken, they were covered up with earth. Of the circular furnaces, two are connected by a channel, which leads us to conclude that the smaller one was heated by the overflow of heat from the other, and that it served to fire objects (forms for moulds, stamps and so forth) which were not to be raised to too high a temperature. In some places, as for example near Waiblingen in Würtemberg, there are furnaces for firing clay, which date back to A.D. 150; they are not made of loam or tiles, but have been cut directly out of the clay soil. In the lower part there is the fire-chamber divided into two parts, and above this is the floor of the drying space, in which holes have been cut in order to allow the hot air to enter; above this, as can still be districtly recognized from the remains, rose a vaulted roof provided with a chimney. The inner walls of the furnace have become quite glazed, owing to the continual heat. On the floor in front of every furnace there is a depression, in which the workmen who served the furnace used to sit. According to the charred remains that have been found, beechwood was used as a fuel. The Roman potters' furnaces occurred in a particularly excellent form called 'muffle' furnaces, which are found here and there; in them, the fuel was enclosed in a muffle, which entirely prevented any gases from entering. The muffles did not look like those of nowadays. They were not closed on all sides, but rather the whole fire chamber served as a muffle. A number of pipes passed through it, starting from the opening of the base of the furnace, and becoming narrower as they led up to the arched top. The flames and the hot gases passed along these pipes and communicated their heat through their walls to the firing-space. There are certain indications which appear to signify that in some furnaces there was actually a sort of gas fuel used; at any rate, the fire-chamber leads us to conclude that here a combustible gas was produced, which was ignited in the furnace itself. Thus, the construction of the furnaces varied in very many ways, but in all of them we see that the Romans had an eye to what best answered the particular purpose.

THE TEUTONS

It must yet be mentioned that the high excellence of Roman ceramic art also exerted a fruitful influence on the technical science of other peoples, in particular of the Teutons in ancient Germany. Under Roman rule, numerous Germans became expert potters, as is easily recognized from the stamps on the bricks and other earthenware objects. These Germans at first made their vessels of unwashed clay and dried them in the sun, or else they fired them in an open flame, so that they remained fairly soft and porous. The invasion of the Romans changed all this. The clay was washed; the clay furnaces allowed higher temperatures to be obtained and therefore harder earthenware, while the potter's wheel gave rise to better forms. According to reports of Heuser about Ludovici's researches, the red glaze of the earthenware *terra sigillata* was subjected to a process of smoking, the air being excluded. The colouring of the carbon gave rise to a brilliant black glaze. Ludovici has established that another process for producing these *terra nigra* vessels had its origin in the fact that insufficient access of air caused the red iron oxide of the glaze and of the clay to be transformed by reduction into black ferro-oxide. The author is of the opinion that it was probably not the black ferrous oxide (FeO), as this is not at all known in the pure state, on account of its great affinity for oxygen, but that rather Ludovici's remark relates to the well-known lustrous black powder which consists of metallic iron and ferrous oxide—which is obtained by the action of carbon monoxide and carbon dioxide on red-hot ferric oxide (Fe_2O_3). Owing to the insufficient supply of air, both these gases were probably present during the heating process. This magnetite (Fe_3O_4), which was already mentioned on page 147 as being present in the *terra sigillata*, however, also makes the conclusion possible that some compound was also formed in the case of the *terra nigra*, which had been formed in considerable quantities from the red iron oxide (Fe_2O_3). That may easily be determined by means of micro-chemical analysis. According to Forster, the black glaze on Greek vases consists of a ferrous oxide compound (that is, not of the pure ferrous oxide), probably combined with silicon dioxide. (Concerning the supposed addition of metallic iron to black glaze, see also page 144.) The black smoked ware was then sent out, particularly at the time of the Emperor Augustus, as *terra nigra* from the land of the Treveri, and from other places of manufacture, to all parts of the world.

FIG. 212.—Roman-Germanic Earthenware, of a particularly good form

From a cremation grave. Provincial Museum, Trèves

GLASS

THE ORIGIN OF GLASS

FOR a long time it was believed that the Phoenicians were the inventors of glass ; this belief is traced back to Pliny. But we must consign this story to the realm of fables, for, long before the Phoenicians, the Egyptians manufactured glass and made the most varied objects from it, above all, ornaments. The oldest of all known pieces of glass is to be found in the Egyptian section of the Berlin Museum.[1]

It is a greenish glass bead, which was found with other objects in a prehistoric Egyptian grave containing a body in the contracted position. This antique bead, which is about 5,400 years old, was for a long time regarded as a stone, and indeed as being made of quartz, until a little crack was found in it, which made it possible to fracture off a minute particle, which could be subjected to a chemical microscopic test. This test, which was carried out by Rathgen, showed that when the stone was treated with iodized eosin solution, a strong red colour was produced, which proved that the object was made of glass—since quartz does not change colour under the same treatment. By the addition of powders and treating with ammonium fluoride and sulphuric acid, it could be established that besides silicon dioxide the bead also contained calcium and sodium, which means that it must be regarded as a calcium-sodium glass. We shall leave it an open question whether it was made intentionally, or whether it was derived as a by-product from brick glazes. But the analysis of the bead proves that the Egyptians had knowledge of a number of noteworthy technical methods even 3500 years before the beginning of our calendar. They were not only able to heat quartz (silicon dioxide) to its melting temperature, but they also knew that the silicon dioxide contained in rocks could form a glaze-like compound, when salt or soda[2] was added to it.

Moreover, they knew how to give the molten mass a definite form. They were also aware very early of how to produce colourings ; proof of this is furnished by a glass rod which is also among the Egyptian objects in the Berlin Museum. This glass rod consists of a number of blue and whitish strips of glass, which have been fused together in such a way that

[1] Flinders Petrie makes mention in his book *The Royal Tombs of the Earliest Dynasties*, in relation to Plate XXXVIII, Figs. 53 and 57 (age of Seti), of a piece of green glass, which is perhaps older than that in the Berlin Museum, but details of this piece of glass are wanting.

[2] Which of the two sodium salts was used is not known ; the author is inclined to believe that it was the natural soda, that occurs in Egypt.

they make up the name Amenemhat III, who lived about the year 1830 B.C. (Fig. 213). A somewhat more recent piece which is in the British Museum, dates back to the year 1500 B.C. It is the oldest known glass

FIG. 213.—Glass Stick with the name Amenemhat III (about 1830 B.C.)
Millefiori Art. Length, 1·56 in.; width, ·4 in.; thickness, ·2 in. Berlin Museum, Egyptian Department

vessel and is made of light-blue glass with brown stripes. Since it bears the name Tutmosis (Thothmes III), it was easy to determine accurately the date when it was made.

EGYPTIAN GLASS MANUFACTURE

We next inquire how the Egyptians manufactured their glass, and how they succeeded in converting it into the very different objects which are discovered in excavations. In a tomb at Beni Hasan there is a relief, which is probably of about the year 1900 B.C.; on it we see men apparently working at a glass vessel by means of long pipes. For a long time it was believed that these were glass-blowers, and that the pipes were the usual pipes of the glass-blower. But Kisa and others have proved that this relief represents not glass-blowers but metal-workers, who are blowing up a furnace. An excavation made about 25 years ago by Flinders Petrie in Tel-el-Amarna, part of which passed over into the Berlin Museum (Figs. 214 and 215), gives us information as to how the ancient Egyptians prepared and treated their glass. This excavation represents an ancient Egyptian glass works of the year 1370 B.C. According to the researches of Flinders Petrie, the glass was obtained by fusing together quartz and alkaline salt in clay crucibles. A colourless product resulted, to which coloured frit was added, whose preparation we shall return to presently. During the fusing process, tongs were used to take samples of the fused mass, which served for testing the colour. When the glassy flux had the right colour, it was cooled, and the crucible was broken, in order to release the glass. In this way, a shapeless mass was formed, which had to be given a suitable form, to enable it to be worked. For this purpose, the pieces of glass were separately softened in the furnace, and then rolled on a hard base by means of a metal stick. In this way, a cylindrical glass stick was formed, which represented the raw material and served for making objects of the most varied kinds.

The coloured frit which was used to tint the glass proper, is simply, according to its chemical composition, finely divided glass flux, whose origin was probably due to an accident. The raw materials used for

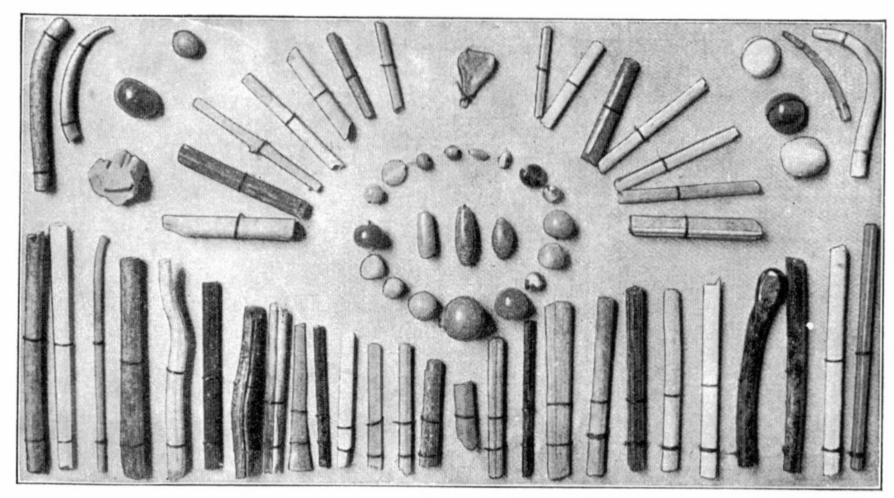

FIG. 214.—Pieces of Glass out of the glass factory of Tel-el-Amarna (about 1370 B.C.). Variously coloured Sticks, Fragments of Beads

Berlin Museum, Egyptian Department

FIG. 215.—Fragments of coloured glass Sticks and Vessels from Tel-el-Amarna (about 1370 B.C.)

Berlin Museum, Egyptian Department

manufacturing glass probably in many cases contained iron. Now, if the glass flux contains iron, it acquires a different colour, according to whether it is treated in an oxidizing or a reducing fire, namely reddish-brown or green respectively (as in the case of red and green wine-bottles). As it is probable that before the use of crucibles, the glass flux was melted together in pits dug in the ground, and as the fire could not be accurately regulated, even when crucibles were used, red and green masses were obtained indiscriminately, which were used for colouring the glass. Later, further colours were added, which arose from various impurities which were contained in the materials used. There are violet glasses, which contain manganese, blue and red glasses which owe their colour to the presence of copper compounds, and so forth. Experience and accident served as a teacher, and gave rise to an ever-lengthening scale of colours. In the course of time, it was also learned how to remove the colour from a glass tinted through the presence of iron, by adding substances containing manganese; and before this, it had been recognized that when very pure Nile sand was used to make glass, a colourless product resulted. The colourless glasses of Ancient Egypt are indeed opaque nowadays, as they have become dull owing to the action of time. But it has been established that from the first century B.C. onwards, the old coloured glasses had to make way for the colourless glass; that is, coloured glass went out of fashion. Although this signifies an advance technically, it also denotes the decay of the glazier's art, which was at its zenith in the 18th and 19th Dynasty (1550 to 1200 B.C.). At this zenith, there was an abundance of colours and of forms, such as had never existed before, and never occurred since.

FIG. 216.—Egyptian Hand Mirror, with a glass inset

From a tomb at Meidum. Height, 10 in.; width, 4½ in. Berlin Museum, Egyptian Department

The cylindrical sticks which came out of the glass crucibles were, as already mentioned, the supply which was used for further working the glass into all types of vessels, vases, amulets, ornaments, and even imitation jewels, and so forth. The relief from Beni Hasan, quoted above, has led some archaeologists to surmise that the art of the glass-blower was indigenous in Egypt in very early times. But it has been shown that the vases and other hollow vessels were not blown, but were formed in another way. A clay core was first made, which had the shape of the vase to be formed. It was fastened on to a stick, so that it could be conveniently manipulated. A glass stick from the supply made as above was then taken, softened and placed in this state about the clay core. A second glass stick was next treated in the same way, and a third, and so on, until the whole core was covered with the glass mass. The whole was then held in the furnace, where it was further heated, whilst being constantly rotated, so that the sticks fused together well. When the vase was ready, the clay core, which had become shrunken during the firing, was broken, and its pieces were taken out separately. In the first century B.C. another method of producing hollow vessels arose. Clay models were again used, but in this case they were not solid, but hollow moulds, which could easily be prepared by means of the potter's wheel. After they had been fired, the liquid glass mass was poured in, and was swung round inside, until it covered the inner walls. When the clay model was removed, a glass vessel remained behind. Even large objects were produced in this way from glass. Thus Sesostris had a statue cast in glass as early as 1643 B.C.

Fig. 217.—Glass Rosettes from the case of a mummy. The glass particles have been fixed into a layer of stucco

Discovered at Abusir el Meleq. Berlin Museum, Egyptian Department

Fig. 218.—Statue of a Man. Made of Limestone; the eyes are of glass

Of the Old Kingdom in Egypt. Found at Saqqarah. Height, 2 ft.; width, 11 in.; length, 14 in. Berlin Museum, Egyptian Department

Glass-blowing was unknown in Egypt as late as the time of the Ptolemys (311–30 B.C.). It is without doubt an invention of the Phoenicians, which was made some time between 20 B.C. and A.D. 20 in Sidon. How the idea of blowing glass came up can probably no longer be established. The assumption of Kisa that it arose through observing soap bubbles is probably hardly in agreement with the facts, as the use of a soap which would be appropriate for producing bubbles is more than doubtful among the Phoenicians. The Phoenicians learned the art of making glass and working it from the Egyptians, and they spread it over wide parts of the Orient. The discovery of glass-blowing gave their glass industry a new impetus. The first products of glass-blowing were small vases, as well as vessels for balsams and essences. They were ornamented in relief, and on them—mostly on the handles—the artists, who were not a little proud of their art, perpetuated their names. The best known of them was called Ennio.

We must here mention another ancient Egyptian form of the art of making glass, which was communicated to the Phoenicians by the ancient Egyptians, and thence to other peoples. We mentioned above the peculiar prismatic piece of glass, dating back to the time of 1830 B.C., which was prepared from blue and white strips of glass, and which exhibits at its two ends the name of the King Amenemhat III; the letters are in blue written characters on a white background (Fig. 213). There are other examples of similar pieces of glass with coloured stripes of this kind. They were prepared by laying the glass sticks which had been produced in the furnace side by side and heating them up until they fused together. While they were still hot and soft, they were pulled out lengthwise. This is a method of working glass which is still used in many cases nowadays, and is called millefiori-work. (See also Figs. 215 and 217.)

Another branch of ancient Egyptian glass-work was the production of artificial eyes, which were placed in mummies, as well as in statues (see Fig. 218, p. 156). These artificial eyes are made of all sorts of substances, and are in some cases compound. The iris and pupil consist of glass; the sclerotis (white skin of the eye) of a metal alloy, ivory, pearl, felspar (South Kensington Museum, 5th or 6th Dynasty), marble (Musée du Parc du Cinquantenaire, Brussels) or else entirely of glass (National Museum, Stockholm, 700 B.C.). Whether the ancient Egyptians also made artificial eyes for living beings is not known. Ebers considers it not improbable.

PHOENICIANS

In antiquity, as we have already mentioned, besides the Egyptians the Phoenicians were also excellent workers in glass. They seem to have monopolized the trade with glass, for in Syria and Judaea there was no glass industry at all until the time of the Roman Empire. According to Pinner, the name for glass is to be found only once in the Bible (Job xxviii. 17), that is, in one of the latest books of the Old Testament, where it is mentioned as a precious substance, of equal value with gold. This leads us to infer that in the ancient Jewish Kingdom the glass derived from the Phoenicians was very dear. The high price may be explained, if we consider the technique necessary to work it, as well as the fact of its being fragile, and the consequent difficulties of transport. In Mesopotamia, too, glass seems to have been imported, but not to have been made on the spot. It appears doubtful whether the famous vase of King Sargon, in the British Museum, which dates back to the eighth century,—it is bag-shaped, and made of semi-transparent green glass,—is actually an Assyrian product.

THE GREEKS

Nor did the Greeks practise the art of making and working glass to any considerable extent; indeed it appears doubtful whether glass was known at all in wider circles in Greece at the time of Aristophanes (450 to 385 B.C.). An indication that it was very little in use is given by the fact that it was considered quite astonishing when the Persians, as was reported, drank out of glasses. Besides this, the price of glass was as high as that of jewels. Nevertheless, Kurt Müller brought to light, among his excavations in Pylos—which produced objects of the Mycenaean period (1600 to 1200 B.C.)—a beautiful transparent blue piece of a vase, which, when examined by Rhousopoulos, was found to be a potassium glass, which it was difficult to fuse and was coloured blue by a compound of copper oxide. From this Rhousopoulos concludes that glass was made in Greece even at that time, and endeavours to support this view by quoting other objects from the Museum at Athens.

THE GLASS-WORK OF THE ROMANS

Glass-work attained an extraordinarily high degree of excellence among the Romans, but their knowledge is probably also of Egyptian origin, and is presumably traced back to the glass-blowing works at Alexandria. Among the Romans, glass became an object of common use. Even in the first century B.C., it displaced the gold and silver goblets from the banquets, and even at that early time windows made of glass were to be found in the towns of the Roman Empire,—later they were made of a considerable size. Panes of the dimensions 1 ft. by 2 ft. have been preserved up to the present day. It may well be assumed that still larger panes—probably made by casting—were also prepared, for in Pompeii there are bronze frameworks for panes, in which there are fragments of glass from sheets that must have been about 21 in. by 28 in. in size. The *apodyterium* (dressing-room) of the small hot baths of Pompeii had a very large pane, whose dimensions were 40 in. by 28 in., and half-inch thick. The pane is matt on the one side, and it is assumed that it was made matt by grinding it. The pane was fixed in a frame of bronze, which turned on two pivots attached half-way up. Otherwise, the frames of glass windows were mostly of wood. The Egyptians also used cast glass plates for covering their paintings. Since the art of making glass is to be traced back to the Egyptians, it was carried out by the Romans in exactly the same way. Above all, the process of decolorizing glass was used, and in the main colourless glass was prepared, which was afterwards ornamented with coloured glasses in a particular way. From the researches of Roters, who examined fragments of colourless glass found in Saalburg, we know that manganese was used throughout as the decolorizing substance; so we see that the Romans used exactly the same means as we do nowadays. The colouring substances likewise very much resemble our own. In general they are the same as those used for the glazes of earthenware objects. According to Roters, ferrous oxide was used for green, cobalt for blue, ferric oxide for reddish brown, brown-stone containing iron for black, manganese for violet; further, according to the analyses of K. A. Hofmann, copper was used for red, blue and green, chromium for green, antimony and uranium for yellow and orange. Gold was fused into the glass mostly in the form of gold-leaf. The Roman gold glasses are vessels which contain figures and so forth made of gold-leaf between two layers of glass. Lines and whole pieces were scratched out of the gold-leaf, so that the back ground lay bare. Heated glass, particularly glass thread, was dipped into gold-dust before being further used. When being blown, a drop of glass so treated or covered with gold-leaf grew to a great size, the gold becoming very finely distributed, and giving a very beautiful effect. A very beautiful antique red glass flux, which was first found in Pompeii in 1844, is the so-called 'Haematinum', which was investigated by Pettenkofer, and was found to be a silicate of sodium and calcium, containing also lead, of which the brilliant lustre was due to the lead, whereas the striking blood-red colour was due to cuprous oxide. Pettenkofer arrived at the following values:

	Per cent.
Silicon dioxide	49·90
Sodium	11·54
Lime	7·20
Magnesia	·87
Lead oxide	15·51
Cuprous oxide	11·03
Ferrous oxide (with traces of manganese oxide)	2·10
Aluminium	1·20

The method of producing this excellent glass, which was called obsidian or obsian by the Romans, is described by Pliny (XXXVI, 197): 'There is also a kind of obsian artificially coloured, for table utensils; likewise a glass which is quite red—the so-called *haematinum* (blood-colour)—and is not transparent.' *Ibid.*, 193, he writes: 'But the glass is fused with light dry wood, copper and nitrum (probably soda) being added. It is fused in furnaces uninterruptedly like ore, and gives blackish masses of very rich colouring. In the workshop these masses are again fused up, and are coloured.'

Pettenkofer has succeeded in reproducing this ancient obsidian glass of the Romans by the method prescribed by Pliny, and he discovered that the black mass first obtained acquires a blood-red colour when melted again. Hence the expression of Pliny, *tinguitur*, is not to be read as meaning 'it is dyed', but rather that 'it colours'.

To the art of colouring glass in manifold ways, there later became added further devices by which various effects were produced. Above all, it was understood how to give glass objects metallic reflections. We do not mean those peculiar reflecting surfaces, which we nowadays see on almost all the excavated ancient Roman or antique glasses. The iridescence of these glasses is sometimes due to an insufficient decolorization, but is mostly due to the fact that in the course of centuries the glass has become decomposed through the humic acids (that is, acids in the vegetable soil) and other substances on its surface, which covered it with an iridescent layer. The iridescence here referred to first appeared in late Roman times, and was brought about by applying compounds of metals with resins to the glass, and burning them in at a dull red heat. Red tints were obtained with copper, gold tints with silver, and blue tints with bismuth. Franchet has succeeded in recent times in obtaining exactly the same results by copying the Roman process. The fact that similar iridescence can be produced by marking very fine lines on the surface seems to have been already known in Greece, where no glass was used, but transparent quartz plates were placed on a silver base, and riffled by tracing straight lines on them; the purpose of these was probably to produce an iridescent effect (Rhousopoulos, No. 2708 of the Collection of the Greek National Museum).

FIG. 219.—Roman Glass-blowing

A pot from a cremation-grave, and also various other glass objects obtained by blowing. Provincial Museum, Trèves

The celebrated myrrhine vessels (*murrina vasa,* also *pocula murrina* or *myrrhina*) of the Romans, which were first brought to Rome (64 B.C.) by Pompey from the treasures of Mithridates, were made of a milky mass of glass with red and white spots; the milky appearance was due to an addition of calcium phosphate, which had probably been added in the form of bone flour. It showed vivid opalescence, and cost a great sum. According to Pliny, the Emperor Nero paid 300 talents (about £731,000) for a myrrhine goblet.[1]

Thus the Romans had at their disposal excellent raw material coloured in manifold ways, from which they knew how to make objects by ingeniously working them; these objects still excite the greatest admiration, on account of their technical perfection and artistic beauty. The means they used were the blow-pipe and tongs of the glass-blower, so that the tools were the same as those now in use; and since the feet, handles, and so forth, were specially added, the ancient Roman method of working glass hardly differed from ours in the essential points. The glass was blown in moulds which—like ours—could be opened out so as to allow the glass object to be freed. Numerous pieces of ancient Roman glassware exhibit

[1] Pliny, N. H. XXXVII, 20; the figures are doubtful, but a very large sum is meant.—*Trans.*

the seam of the mould; this is the case not only with vessels, but also with the figures of animals and so on. To this general method of working glass, there are also special branches, of which we must mention, above all,

FIG. 220.—Roman Flasks in Glass. Blown and ornamented
Provincial Museum, Trèves

FIG. 221.—Roman *diatreta* Vessels (collection of Rath)
Berlin, Altes Museum, Antiquarium

the serpentine windings, in which all manner of ornaments and twisted lines and other designs were applied to the vessels, in such a way that the glass thread—often coloured—was fused on to the corresponding windings of the object. The late Roman vessels called *diatreta* were made by melting on the glass threads; they were covered with a raised network of such threads. These threads do not, however, touch the vessel all along their length, but only at particular points. How they were made is not known; some believe that the network was ground out of the thick glass. However, coloured and sometimes also uncoloured drops of glass of the most varied size were dropped on to the glass vessel. In this way trinkets arose, which have again become the fashion with us.

Engraving on glass was developed to a particular degree in the Roman glass-works. At first, simple ornamental lines were engraved into the glass, and later, whole scenes were drawn on it. These engravings were effected by means of grinding wheels. Afterwards, flashed glass was produced by covering one kind of glass with glass of a different colour. When engravings were then also cut out of the upper glass, so that the lower layer came to view, beautiful effects arose, as for example in the famous Portland Vase, which till recently was in the British Museum; in it a blue background is covered with a white opaque glass one-fifth inch thick, on which artistic designs have been engraved.

FIG. 222.—Roman Pane of Glass with an engraved representation of a chariot race in a circus
Provincial Museum, Trèves

We must here just touch on some special points which are closely connected with glass-making. Firstly, we must make reference to the often repeated story of unbreakable glass, which plays a part among various ancient writers. According to the narration of Pliny (XXXVI, 195), a man is supposed to have come to the Emperor Tiberius, and to have shown him a flexible glass. The Emperor had his workshop destroyed in order that this glass should not lower the value of metals. Petronius likewise reports in his *Dinner of Trimalchio* of an Emperor to whom a man is supposed to have presented a glass vessel which did not break when it was thrown on the ground. The Emperor had this man executed, in order that gold and silver should not lose their value through the invention! This story is often repeated in this form, indeed so often that we feel constrained to believe that there is some element of truth in it. In spite of all efforts to explain it, as for example those of Lippmann, Rathgen, and so forth, it has not been possible for us to trace back the tale of the malleable or unbreakable glass to any ancient art that has in the meantime become known to us.[1]

A further question which is connected with glass, is whether the Romans knew of glass mirrors and spectacles. The first question is without doubt to be answered in the affirmative, and we do not need even to support the remark by reference to Pliny, who states that glass, and particularly black mirrors, were invented at Sidon. Fragments of glass mirrors have been found in the Roman camp at Saalburg, as well as in other places, for example at Ratisbon (Regensburg) and so forth. They were made by pasting thin leaves of gold, silver, copper or tin as a backing to the glass. As the glass was not polished, it was not very smooth, and so the mirrors probably gave distorted images. But in the Roman and Gallic tombs at Reims, mirrors have also been found which date back to the third or fourth century A.D., which were presumably made by a quite different method. These mirrors resembled watch-glasses, that is, they were curved and round pieces of glass, two inches or one inch and a fifth in diameter, which had lead pasted on the back. The curved glass surface, which was perhaps cut out of a glass balloon, was at any rate first warmed in order to avoid cracking, and the lead was then poured in. The mirror of course likewise gave a diminished and distorted image.

FIG. 223.—Millefiori Dish (Roman)

Green and white flowers, with red cups. Berlin, Altes Museum, Antiquarium

Spectacles were not known in antiquity; indeed, the effects of concave and convex glass lenses had not apparently been observed, or they were not made use of. The only report derived from antiquity concerning the use of an arrangement resembling spectacles, comes from Pliny, who relates that the Emperor Nero used a polished emerald to observe the contests of the gladiators. From this it has been concluded that the Emperor Nero was short-sighted, and that he used a sort of lorgnon or monocle. 'Lenses' which have been found (in the ruins of Tyre, a

[1] A method of making elastic glass has recently been discovered in Vienna.—H. L. B.

grave at Nola, Pompeii, Troy, and so forth) served as ornaments for leather belts and similar objects, but not as magnifying glasses. On the other hand, the Greeks and the Romans were familiar with the magnifying power of glass ' spheres ' (or glass globes filled with water, used by shoemakers for concentrating the lamplight).

ARTIFICIAL STONES

A particular branch of the ancient glass industry was the production of artificial gems, which flourished at a very early date. In ancient Egypt we sometimes find in the jewellery buried with kings genuine stones mixed with artificial stones made of coloured glass fluxes. This need not lead us to think that a fraud was intended ; as at that time the physical and chemical processes, which later allowed natural and artificial stones to be differentiated, were not yet known, a glass flux which accidentally was particularly beautifully coloured, may have been mistaken for a precious stone. It is true that later the making of artificial stones developed into a particular art, for which there are numerous rules ; for example, the ' new Stockholm Papyrus ', which dates back to the third century, contains quite a number, which very often seem of little value. In Rome, too, Seneca reports that there were whole factories for making artificial stones. In Egypt these false stones were produced by soaking minerals that were of a leafy or porous constitution, above all pyrites and topaz, with coloured solutions, which were then absorbed ; whereas in Rome abundant use seems to have been made of the property of lead to impart to glass a high refrangibility. Stained glass fluxes were produced, whose colours were brought about by the ingredients already mentioned above, and lead or lead compounds were added in abundance. A glass flux was then obtained which exhibited two of the most important properties of the genuine stone, namely the beautiful colour and the high refractive power. The hardness of these artificial stones was, just like that of the Strass or imitation diamond nowadays, made in the same way, much less than the genuine stone, but this was difficult to prove, owing to lack of appropriate methods of investigation. How little was known about these methods of investigation is clear from the fact that Pliny could say no more about hardness tests than that ' the diamond scratches all stones, genuine ones and false ones.' For the rest, according to researches of Rhousopoulos in Greece, it appears that even in pre-Mycenaean times artificial pearls were made, namely by melting together lime, magnesia and silica ; these were likewise coloured. Thus the imitation of precious natural products seems to be a very ancient art.

SPINNING AND WEAVING (YARNS AND TEXTILES)

GENERAL REMARKS

CONCERNING the textile arts of antiquity, that is, the production of yarns and textiles, we are in a curious position. We read everywhere of the beautiful robes which were at that time made, but nowhere do we find clear descriptions as to the actual process, as to what devices were used, as to how the raw materials and the finished textiles were treated, and so forth. Taken all in all, the textile industry must have reached a high standard and flourished among all peoples of antiquity. Even the Old Testament describes the precious hangings of the Tabernacle of the Lord (Exodus xxvi.), which were skilfully made and artistically executed. Homer tells us of the masterly way in which the Grecian women spun and wove ; Helen of Troy knows no better way of giving expression to her interest in the battles between the Greeks and the Trojans, than by representing the mon her loom in richly coloured pictures. In Egypt, as well as among the peoples of the Orient, gorgeous robes were worn, and Greek vases and wall pictures at Pompeii bear witness to artistic weaving. In spite of all this, however, the secrets of the actual art are fairly well preserved from us. From all these descriptions and representations, we get acquainted only with the products. Nevertheless, laborious investigation has succeeded in finding out at least a few details of the textile arts of antiquity, so that we at least get a glimpse of them, even if we cannot get an unbroken view.

SILK

The material about whose extraction and working we are best informed is silk, which however was introduced into Europe fairly late. The origins of silk culture are to be sought in China, where it was a home-industry as early as 3000 B.C. The historical work *Shu-king* reports of that time that Shön-wung, the successor of the Emperor Fu-Hi, made efforts to spread the cultivation of mulberry trees and the breeding of silkworms, as widely as possible, in order to encourage the art of making fishing-lines, which were drawn from the intestinal contents of the worms. These threads also served as strings for musical instruments. The actual unwinding of the cocoon, such as is nowadays practised, is supposed to have been introduced by the "lady of Si-Ling," the wife of Huang-ti ; according to other reports it was her daughter Liu Siu in the year 2698 B.C.

While observing a silkworm, she conceived the idea of re-tracing the winding process carried out by the worm and then using it for weaving.

In grateful commemoration of this invention, which was so important for Chinese civilization, the Empress was elevated to the rank of a goddess. For twenty centuries, the silk industry then flourished exclusively in the province of Shantung, where the silk was not only produced but also dyed. In the ancient Chinese textile industry, silk was obtained and worked on the whole just as we are accustomed to do nowadays. Above all, the cocoons were wound off before the moths had escaped, which was quite in contrast with the processes among the other peoples of Eastern Asia, where later, when the silk industry had spread from China, the moths were first allowed to escape, and the silk thread was then unravelled from the cocoon. On this account, the separate parts of the twisted threads of course became shorter, and consequently less durable. After the silk thread had been unwound, it was scoured, that is, the gum was boiled off from it, for which purpose probably a mixture of plant-ash and oil was used. This was followed by dyeing. The silk was ornamented in various ways, partly by painting, partly by embroidering, but later also by weaving in all sorts of ornaments. As among almost all peoples of antiquity, so also among the Chinese, gold threads were woven into the material, indeed even birds' feathers. A quite particular art developed, which consisted in producing a sort of 'half silk', which was obtained by making the warp, around which the weaving was effected, out of linen, into which silken threads were then interwoven in such a way that these warp threads became covered. This woven material then had the appearance of pure silk.

In the fourth century A.D. the silk industry spread from China into Japan, after it had previously passed over into India. The Indians indeed had their own silk industry before, in which—as already mentioned—the cocoon was not killed—for religious reasons. The moth was allowed to escape, and the silk was then wound off. In this way, a sort of 'wild silk' was produced, an inferior product, which was so different from Chinese silk, that when Chinese silk was introduced into India, the Indians had no idea that this wonderfully lustrous textile could be obtained from the same animal as that from which the Indian silk goods were derived. The introduction of Chinese silk into India probably occurred about the third century B.C. Among all other peoples, silk appeared at a rather late date, and although there are certain passages in Herodotus, in the Bible, and so forth, treating of textiles, which suggest silk, there may be opposed to such assumptions that only the external appearance of this textile is described in these passages, and that there is not a single datum which allows us to draw inferences about its chemical or physical constitution. Nor has it been possible to ascertain when silk came to Europe. Although silk materials are mentioned among the booty of Alexander the Great in his Persian campaign (331 B.C.), we cannot assert definitely any better than before whether it is really silk that is meant. We have more trustworthy data from Pliny and Aristotle, who mention that the first Chinese textiles that appeared were unravelled, and that the threads so obtained were split, in order to increase their number. They were then woven into finer, almost transparent, tissue. This is a proof of the great value of silk at that time, which in Caligula's reign was as dear as gold. A pound of purple silk at that time cost about £100. At the time of the Persian wars, when there was a lack of raw materials, the price of a pound of silk rose to £350, and that of purple silk to almost four times this amount.

OTHER RAW MATERIALS AND THEIR EXTRACTION

If we disregard silk—as we know so little about when it was first worked by the different peoples of antiquity—we get approximately the following picture of the fabrics used in the textile industry. All yarns and textiles used in ancient Egypt and Babylon consisted solely of linen, cotton, wool, as well as 'byssos' or 'shell silk', which was obtained from a river shell (see below). Cotton first appears around A.D. 500 in Upper Egypt, and seems to have been introduced from Persia. The Assyrians and Babylonians also made use of cotton, besides wool. Moreover, the hairs of certain species of goat were used; among many Oriental peoples, yarns were made from this hair. In India there arose in this way the industry of Kashmir (Cashmere) shawls at a very early date. Jute was also cultivated in India.

The Greeks and Romans presumably were at first acquainted only with flax, to which there soon was added sheep's wool. Many investigators, however (including Blümner), consider wool to be the older material. In the fifth century B.C. they became acquainted with cotton. Further, *bombykia*, probably a sort of wild silk, was introduced from Kos before real silk appeared. It probably resembled wild Indian silk, and was derived from the wild silk moth *Bombyx Otus*. It served for making the famous Coan robes, mostly coloured with purple and worn by elegant Roman women. According to unconfirmed reports (see above), Chinese silk was then supposed to have come into being at the end of the first or at the beginning of the second century B.C. At any rate, Tacitus (*Annal.* II, 33) writes of the luxurious display that was made of the silk textiles that entered Rome with the war booty. The Germanic tribes chiefly cultivated flax. They further attired themselves in animal skins, and Tacitus (*Germania* 17) reports that the women often wore linen garments decorated with purple stripes. For the rest, we must again emphasize that all ancient writers are fairly untrustworthy in their remarks about the textile industry. The terms for the different materials are confused, and are not always correctly translated. For example, it has not been possible to determine whether silk was known to the Jews. The word 'schesch' which occurs in Exodus and is translated by Luther as silk, was, according to the researches of Forster (*De Bysso Antiquorum*, page 8) probably only fine linen. Further, the name 'byssos' [1] seems to have denoted sometimes shell silk, and sometimes cotton.

[1] Concerning the meaning of βύσσος, see the detailed data in Pauly-Wissowa, *Real-Enzyklopädie der klassischen Altertums-wissenschaft*, Stuttgart, 1899, Vol. III, Column 1108–1114.

What confusion there is among the different terms may be illustrated by the following example ; Herodotus (Book 3) asserts that 'bombykia'[1] is derived from the wool of a wild tree in India ; Theophrastus regards silk as the product of a plant ; Strabo (Book 15) states that it is derived from the red bark of a tree ; Servius confuses silk with wool ; Pliny (XI, 22) relates that on the island of Cos, the blossoms of the cypress that have been struck down by rain become transformed into silkworms ; Ammianus (xxiii, 6, 67) speaks even in the fourth century A.D. of a fine wool-like substance which comes from the leaves of a tree ; and so forth. Thus the textile industry of the ancients presents an almost insoluble mystery for the technical invsetigator, at least so far as the literature is concerned. To this there is to be added the fact that the method of working up these manifold raw materials is nowhere described, probably for the reason that it was in general practised at home, and because the ancient writers for that reason assumed that the details were known. They therefore preferred to write of other more interesting things.

So far as any assertions can be made at all or conjectures can be justified from the finds available, we may make the following remarks about the technical working-up of the raw material.

Wool was at first probably obtained, not by shearing the animals, but by pulling out the hairs, a method that persisted to some degree as late as in Pliny's time (Pliny, VII, 191). The shears were used later, probably first by the Romans, by whom this method was then spread among other peoples. They had the form of the shears nowadays used for shearing sheep, but were larger and clumsier. The wool was then washed (see below), dried, and beaten, in order to remove impurities that were still clinging to it, and then pulled apart—which must have been done by hand—and combed. In that way, the product which we nowadays call 'top or sliver' was produced. This was then spun and woven, after having been previously coloured when circumstances demanded it.

Flax, which was grown in great quantities in Egypt as early as the year 2500 B.C., and which was even earlier worked in the Orient, served for making linen, which was a universally used material in Egypt, whereas in Homer's time it was worn in Greece only by the *élite*. In Rome, too, it was at first used as the dress of the rich, until it later became universally worn. The statement of Tacitus (*Germania* 17) that among the ancient Germans the woman was more often dressed in linen garments than the man, allows us to conclude that here too linen was dearer than animal skins. Besides flax, hemp was also grown in later times, but it remained a rarer article.

Flax was prepared in a manner which resembles that still in use to-day —as we can recognize from the excavations among almost all peoples of antiquity, and as is supported by the report of Pliny (XIX, 16–18). The stalks were, however, not cut off, as nowadays, but were pulled out. In this way all sorts of weeds were pulled up with them, which were not particularly carefully sorted out, for Hübner found, by microscopically

[1] This is the present-day Indian cotton obtained from a shrub which dies down after the second year.—H. L. B.

examining two mummies of the 12th Dynasty (about 2500 B.C.), that the material consisted exclusively of linen. Between its threads, however, there were fibres of China-grass, nettles, and other plants which had grown in between the flax. The stems were then soaked for several weeks in water, by means of weights, so that the fibres became loosened from the stem. This was followed by drying in the sun, further drying on hot stones, and beating with clubs. For breaking up the flax wood seems to have been used, which was provided with diagonal strips also of wood. In this way flax fibres were obtained, which were then combed. After the fibres had been loosened by the wood they were laid parallel by means of combing (' hackling '), and the too short threads (oakum) were removed, and the spinning could begin. The woven linen was then beaten by means of sticks—a sort of milling.

Concerning the preparation of cotton, strictly speaking we know nothing at all. It seems to have been obtained from various plants; at any rate Strabo mentions materials which were produced from a nut that occurs in Egypt, the contents of which were suitable for spinning and weaving. This can therefore refer only to cotton. That this was actually used, is supported, not only by various excavations, but also by further data of occasional writers, whom we mentioned above, and whose statements appear to mean that what was alleged to be ' silk ' was obtained from the bark of trees. This probably also refers to the extraction of cotton. Herodotus distinguishes carefully between linen and cotton. Concerning the mail-shirt of King Amasis he relates (III, 37): ' This is made of linen, and many pictures are woven into it, and it is adorned with gold and cotton.'

SPINNING

The fibre which was obtained in the manner just mentioned, no matter whether it consisted of wool, flax, hemp or cotton, was next spun, in order to produce the thread adapted to weaving. Spinning was probably carried out among all ancient peoples according to the same method; at least excavations and pictorial representations lead to this conclusion.

The spinning whorl, a disc provided with a round hole and often ornamented, is everywhere used for spinning. It is made of all sorts of materials, sometimes of bone, sometimes of stone or glass, or of various metals. The whorl has been used since the earliest times; it is found among the ancient peoples of Asia as well as among the Egyptians and the Trojans, as the excavations of Schliemann have shown. Spinning and weaving, these important branches of the textile craft of antiquity, were exclusively domestic arts, and, with rare exceptions, the affair of women. In many cases, the whorl used by a woman in her lifetime was buried with her. Spinning was carried out in much the same way as nowadays in the South of Italy, in Greece, and in other countries along the Mediterranean. The combed fibres that are to be spun are placed on a distaff mostly made from cane, which the women set up next to themselves in their homes. When they went out, or chatted in front of their doors while they were spinning, they took with them a distaff which they could thrust through their belts. The whorl was then placed on the spindle. This spindle was a round rod of wood, metal, or bone, 10 to 14 in. long. Since wood rots, many whorls have been preserved but very few spindles, and these were then of metal or bone. But we know them from pictorial representations. Further, metal spindles are known. The wood spindle carries a notch at the top, whereas the metal spindle is mostly provided with a hook. The woman who is spinning draws down some of the raw material from the distaff, and jams it in the incision of the spindle, or fastens it to the metal spindle by the hook. She

FIG. 224.—Egyptian Distaff for Spinning

(Made of the straw of Durra or Turkey millet.) Length 10½ in. Berlin Museum, Egyptian Department

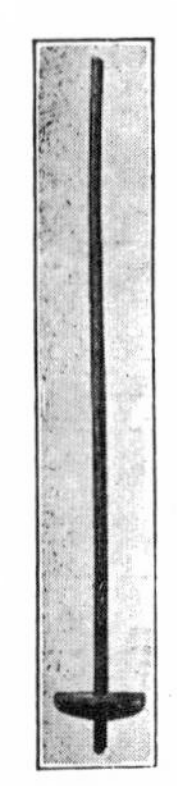

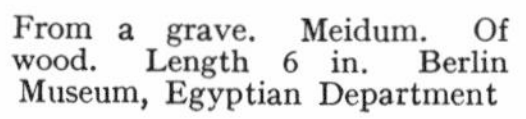

FIG. 225. — Egyptian Spindle, with an attached Whorl

From a grave. Meidum. Of wood. Length 6 in. Berlin Museum, Egyptian Department

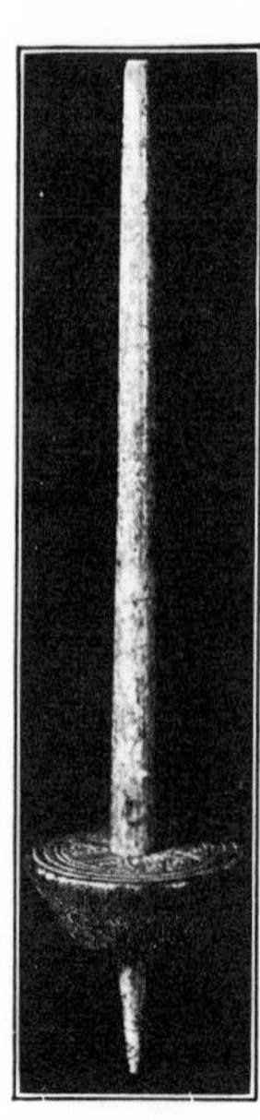

FIG. 226.—Roman Spindle with Whorl. Found at Mainz

Museum of Antiquities of the City of Mainz

then turns the spindle with a skilful movement of her hand, which gives the whorl its necessary momentum to keep up the motion a little longer than would be the case otherwise, and throws it into the air. Hanging by the thread, the spindle continues to turn, winding up the thread. As soon as the thread is long enough, the spindle dances on the stone floor of the house, where it continues merrily to turn during the whole process of spinning. The finished thread is wound up on the spindle (see also Catullus, LXIV, 311—where the process is described in verse). The whole process is still carried out unchanged in form nowadays in certain parts of Southern Italy, for example in the neighbourhood of Naples.

The spinning was not always carried out in this popular way. There were also derived methods. Thus a picture on a Grecian (Attic) vase of the fifth century B.C., which is in the Berlin Museum, allows us to see that the combing, or the other raw material, was sometimes simply taken up in the left hand, and laid across the thigh and forearm (Fig. 227). The naked right leg was then supported on, and firmly held against, a wooden framework. The right hand draws out the thread and compresses it, by rubbing and turning it on the leg. The finished thread falls into a work-basket. Perhaps this process served only to prepare a somewhat coarse 'rough thread', which was then placed on the distaff, in order to be spun into 'fine thread'. Instead of the thigh, a special vessel was often used in Greece for milling the thread; it was a clay pipe, which was supported over both thighs, the legs being crossed. This pipe, called ἐπίνητρον or ὄνος, which has the form of one half of a pipe 10 to 12 in. long, and closed in front by a plate, is often beautifully decorated with paintings (Fig. 228). After the spinning, the thread was further worked, and sometimes indeed it underwent various kinds of preliminary treatment. Thus it was strengthened by twisting together several single threads. Herodotus (III, 47) relates the following about the mail-shirt of Amasis, which we have already mentioned: 'What excites our wonder in it, however, is every single thread; for the threads are not coarse, and yet each one consists of 360 single threads, which can all be distinguished.' Further, gold

FIG. 227.—Spinning on the Thigh
Attic vase of the fifth century. Berlin Museum, Antiquarium

FIG. 228.—ὄνος (spindle)
Athens, National Museum

thread was spun into these threads, for the gold-workers of antiquity were able to draw out this metal into very fine wire. In this way garments threaded with gold were obtained (Herodotus, IX, 80). Asbestos threads also seem to have been added to the ordinary threads, in order to obtain fireproof garments, and sometimes asbestos was even used in the pure state in which it was derived from Germania and Britain.

WORKING-UP OF THE THREAD

The further treatment of the thread was performed by plaiting or knitting it, and further by knotting, embroidering and weaving it. The first-mentioned methods of working require no further explanation. On the other hand, weaving is of particular interest to us, for, as we know, through this branch of industry most splendid carpets were made—in addition to those that were knotted—and gorgeous figured garments as well as all the various kinds of textiles required in the household. Weaving too was a work for women and for the home, and was carried out by means of a loom which fully deserves to be called primitive. Although the looms made of wood are no longer preserved, we can recognize them from pictures on vases, for example on some that date back to the year 500 B.C. and were excavated in Thebes (in the British Museum in London) (Fig. 231).

The ancient loom—probably among all peoples—consisted of two vertical wooden stakes, which were at first simply thrust into the earth, but were later fastened on to a horizontal bar. They were likewise united at the top by means of a bar, to which the threads of the warp were attached. To keep them tightly stretched, each single thread of the warp was weighted by means of a little ball of clay or of metal, called ' weaver's weight ' (loom weight). In some cases perhaps several of these threads were tied to one such ball, or a stone, and united below. Looms in which the weaving was carried out from below upwards (see below) have a beam instead of the stones (Fig. 230). In the middle of the loom, there are two horizontal rods (the canons), which served to separate the threads of the warp into a front and a back row, so that the rows pass in turn in front of and behind the thread of the woof. Of course this process had to be alternated after every throw of the woof. The picture on the vase mentioned (Fig. 231) allows us to see clearly in the vertical stake on the left a gap or notch (or something similar) by which the alternation was perhaps made possible. How it actually took place is not clear. There is perhaps some truth in the conjecture that the rods were simply pushed in and drawn out from the side, and so produced the alternation. Before the alternating devices were applied for the threads of the warp, perhaps the method used was to hold the two rows apart by fastening them on two beams, and then a shuttle or a bobbin was sent around each thread in turn, once behind and once in front—certainly a laborious process. The shuttle probably consisted originally of a rod provided at the top and bottom with notches, on which the threads of the woof were wound. The fact that bobbins were also used in place of the rods, on which the thread was simply wound, is clear from the pictures on vases which have been preserved. The shuttles of later times (see Fig. 232)

FIG. 229.—Penelope's Loom (picture on a Greek vase from Chiusi). Each thread is weighted by means of a loom weight

The different heights of these weights show that half of the threads are hanging down behind the cross-bars. The position of the cross-bars with respect to the threads is not clearly recognizable. Bucher (III, 337) assumes that the warp-beam also served as the cloth-beam, and that the weaving was conducted from below upwards. Above is the finished woven fabric. On the topmost horizontal bar, the author suggests that there are shuttles, some empty and some carrying their full complement of thread. The figures in the finished fabric are embroidered, as Blümner is probably correct in assuming, for they could not have been produced by weaving on this loom

resemble those of the present day. They are made of wood or bone, pointed in front and provided with a handle at the back; they were

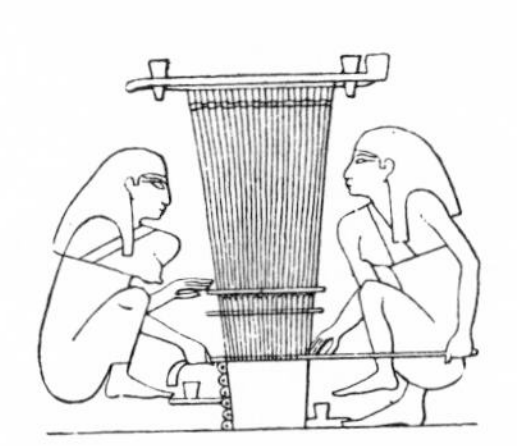

FIG. 230.—Egyptian Loom

The threads are not stretched by means of loom weights, but by a horizontal bar. On the right and left below, there is a forked end, which is worked by foot; by treading these down alternately, the sheds or intervals between the warp-threads are produced. In the hands of the women weaving, we see the weaver's reed or slay. Below is the finished woven fabric. Thus the weaving is effected from below, upwards (see also page 175). Mural painting in Beni Hasan

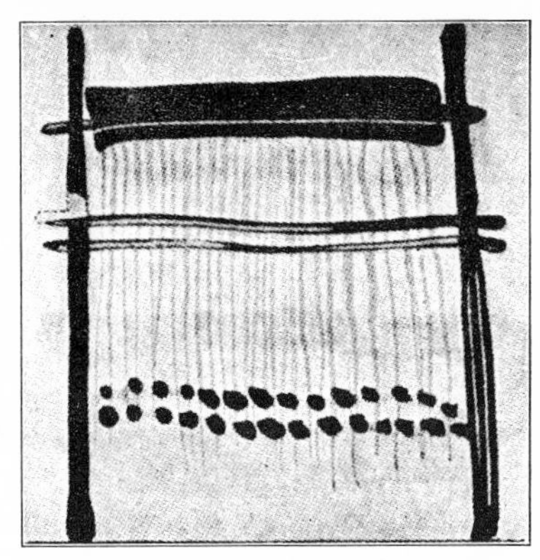

FIG. 231.—Ancient Grecian Loom. Picture on a vase from Thebes, fifth century B.C.

British Museum, London

hollowed out, and possessed two apertures or slits for fastening the thread. The shuttle was not two-sided, that is, provided with two points—which would have given it symmetry,—so that it could not simply be thrown to and fro; it had to be turned round each time, so that the point came in the direction of throw. The thread of the woof which was drawn through was then energetically projected by means of a flat piece of wood into the angle formed by the threads of the warp, in order to give the fabric the necessary firmness.

In order to drive together the threads, use was made at first probably in all cases of the simple bar called the batten (σπάθη, spatha) (see Fig. 233 centre), which was later provided with teeth, so that it became a slay which had the shape of a comb (κτέις, pecten). The slay is first met with among the Egyptians, either in the true form of a comb (Fig. 233, above and below), or in that of a grate (Fig. 234). The slays of the first sort were made of wood, the surface to which the teeth were attached being slanted off in order to moderate the blow against the chain of threads, and prevent their becoming destroyed. The grate-shaped slay (Fig. 234), which is probably of Byzantine origin, consists of a frame covered with leather, carrying teeth made of thin flat pieces of wood.

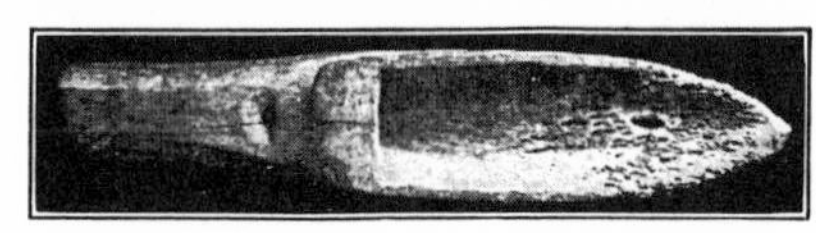

FIG. 232.—Weaver's Shuttle made of Bone. Found at Mainz
Altertumsmuseum der Stadt Mainz

In order to weave large fabrics there was probably used, instead of the topmost horizontal bar, a roller on the loom, on which the finished

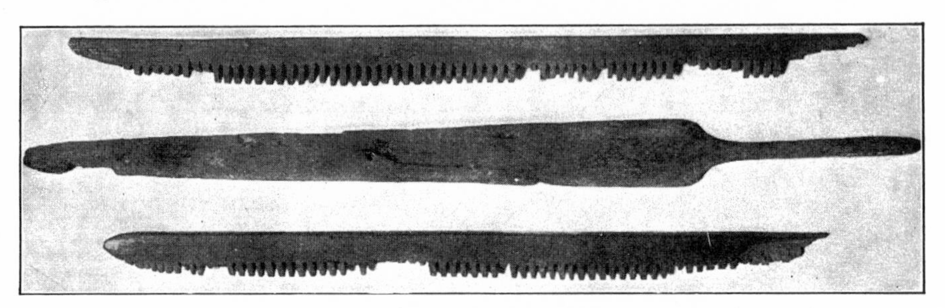

FIG. 233.—Egyptian Weaver's Batten (in the middle) and two Slays of Wood
Berlin Museum, Egyptian Department

piece was rolled up. According to a passage in Homer (*Iliad*, XXIII, 760 *et seq.*), it seems probable that cords were tied to the first, third, and fifth, etc., thread, in order to raise them for passing through the shuttle, that is in order to form a shed, to use the technical expression.[1] But this is known with as little certainty as so many other details of the making of textiles in antiquity, about which, as mentioned at the beginning, we are very largely restricted to making conjectures. Weaving was carried out, according to the construction of the loom, either in the standing or in

[1] This much discussed passage is to be translated as follows, according to Blümner: 'The cane rod remains near the chest of the weaver, when she draws it in order to pass through the bobbin.'

the sitting (or crouching) posture, and either from above downwards, or from below upwards.

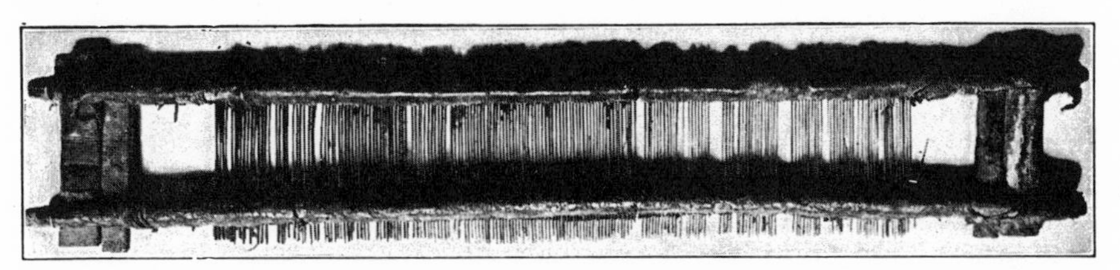

FIG. 234.—Grate-shaped Slay (used in Egypt, of Byzantine origin). Length 2 ft., width 4 in.

Berlin Museum, Egyptian Department

Herodotus writes (II, 35): 'The men sit at home and weave; other people weave by inserting the threads of the woof from above; but the Egyptians insert them from below' (see Fig. 230). The result of the weaving in the case of the simple looms of antiquity was the so-called canvas-weaving, which represents a chessboard pattern on account of the regular crossing of the threads. By this process there were produced in Egypt, as is proved by remnants that have been preserved, examples of weaving which are as fine as the finest veils of the present day. The embroidering mentioned under Fig. 229 probably hardly differed at all in its manner of execution from that of the present day. The fact that the embroidery frame was also used is evident from the various pictures that have been preserved (Fig. 235).

FIG. 235.—A Woman embroidering by means of Embroidering Frame

THE CLEANING OF TEXTILES

The process of weaving was followed by that of cleaning, which was necessary in particular whenever the woven materials were later to be dyed. At first, soap wort or fuller's herb was used for cleaning materials; Dioscorides makes particular mention of its being used for washing cloths and dresses. Both among the Oriental peoples, and among the Greeks and Romans, the fuller's herb that was in general use was probably *gypsophila struthium*, whose root still serves nowadays in the East for washing shawls, and is exported to our countries under the name of soap root. That it was used by the peoples of the Mediterranean, may be inferred from the circumstance that Pliny mentions it under the name *struthion*, and relates that it served for removing the fat from wool. In India, the roots and crushed fruits of various kinds of soap tree (*Sapindus emarginata, maduriensis, saponarius, senegalensis*) were used.

Moreover, urine, which these washers or millers, who were the *fullones* of the Romans, collected in pitchers which had been placed for use at the street corners, served as a cleansing material, after it had become decomposed; [1] in consequence of its content of ammonia, it removed fat and also acted as a cleansing agent. The cleansing action was further increased owing to the fat becoming partly saponified by the ammonia, that is, soap was formed. Of the inorganic bodies which served to cleanse materials, we must mention raw potash, which was obtained by lixiviating the ashes of various plants. Likewise, the residue from the evaporation of waters from several Egyptian lakes in which soda occurred naturally, which is called *neter* in the Bible, was also used.

The cleansing of the materials was advanced a further stage by combining a mechanical process with the chemical treatment effected by soap root, potashes and so forth. This mechanical process was at first very simple. From Egyptian pictures it is evident that the materials were placed on an inclined plane, of which the lower end sometimes dipped into the washing vessel, and they were then beaten with apparently rather heavy stones. The wall paintings of Cività, as well as the excavations of Pompeii, make it clear that among the Romans the workman stood in a wide vessel filled with the cleansing lye, and trod on the materials in the vessel with his feet, and partly milled them with his hands (Fig. 236). As the Indians still cleanse materials mechanically by beating them with stones and wooden hammers, it may be assumed that the process was no different in ancient times.

THE DYEING OF TEXTILES

Chemical and mechanical cleaning was followed by dyeing. This process was applied either to the thread, or—perhaps less often—to the finished material. Dyeing was effected either directly, by placing the materials in the dyeing solution, or by the method of so-called corrosive staining, which Pliny (XXXV, 150) describes in detail as practised among the Egyptians. It must be remarked parenthetically that he bases his description on Herodotus, who knew the process from personal observation, and can therefore be regarded as trustworthy in this matter. Pliny reports:

> 'In Egypt, garments are dyed according to a remarkable process. They are first cleaned, then soaked, not in dye, but in various substances that absorb dye; these substances do not at first show in the materials, but when the materials have been dipped into the dyeing tun, they can be removed after being stirred about, completely dyed; and the most wonderful thing about this is that although the tun contains only one kind of dye, the materials suddenly appear dyed in various colours, according to the nature of the dye-absorbing substances used; and these colours are not only resistant to washing, but the materials so dyed actually wear better.'

For the rest, the use of mordants in dyeing was also known in other connections. For instance, in purple dyeing, an alum mordant was used; further, tartar appears to have been used for fixing the dye to the fibre. Perhaps lacquer was also used in dyeing; in the baths of Titus, red

[1] Urine was largely used in England up to forty years ago for scouring cloth. It produced a full soft handle in the fabric.—H. L. B.

colours have been found, which, on examination by the English chemist Davy, proved themselves to be madder lacquer containing aluminium salts. (Concerning the colours used in dyeing, see the section on Dyes, where further details regarding the production of colours are given so far as is necessary.)

MILLING AND MAKING CLOTH

The production of yarns and textiles as above described, was probably that which predominated universally over a long period. Later (it is not known when) the textile industry advanced a further stage, when the milling of textiles was introduced, which was supposed to have been invented by a certain Nikias in Megara. The purpose of milling is to unite closely the comparatively loose fibres of the woven material, so that cloth is produced from them. The process brought about by milling is felting. This converts the texture into cloth. As already mentioned several times, the woven materials are sometimes beaten, as well as trodden on, and milled by hand.

FIG. 236.—The Milling of Cloth
Mural painting from the Fullonica in Pompeii

We must regard this process as differing from that of washing only in the length of time required, and in the energy expended. When washing alone was done, one worked for only a short time, and with less expenditure of work; in the case of milling, more power was used, and the process was continued until its aim—the production of felt—was achieved. The apparatus used for both purposes was probably fairly similar; it consisted of troughs or pits situated in the vicinity of flowing water. The material was trodden on in the manner already described in the washing process, while soda was added (*νίτρον*, Latin *nitrum*, which, on account of its resemblance to saltpetre, is often confused with it by the ancients),—or else decomposed urine, or clayey substances, which easily combined with fat. There was even a fuller's earth, known as 'Kimolian', because obtained from the island of Kimolos, one of the Cyclades in the Aegean Sea. Such earth was also brought to Greece and Rome from Samos and other places. The methods and the means were probably the same among most peoples of antiquity, namely, when the material had been sufficiently milled, it was subjected to washing and beating, which completed the process of felting (we here follow Blümner's view). As is still done nowadays, the felted material then had its surface dressed, for which purpose thistles were used, fixed in appropriate implements with handles (Figs. 237 and 238).

In the textile industry these thistles are now called fuller's thistles or teazles. They were mounted in a framework and brushed up and down over the stretched cloths (Fig. 238). The prickles of the hedgehog were used

FIG. 237.—Pieces of Cloth hung up to dry, and the mounting or cleaning of the thistles to be used for dressing the Cloth

Mural painting from the Fullonica in Pompeii

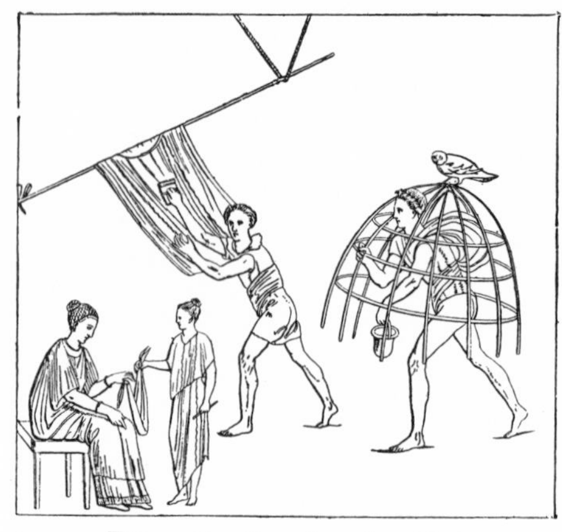

FIG. 238.—Dressing the Cloth

The man on the right is carrying a frame used for bleaching by means of sulphurous vapours (see page 179), and a vessel with a handle, in which perhaps the sulphur used was ignited. On top, we see what is probably a domestic pet in the shape of an owl, accidentally immortalized by the painter. Mural painting from the Fullonica in Pompeii

for the same purpose, perhaps also metal combs, provided with sharp teeth, or brushes. The wool fibres scratched off in this way were carefully collected and were a favourite means for stuffing cushions.

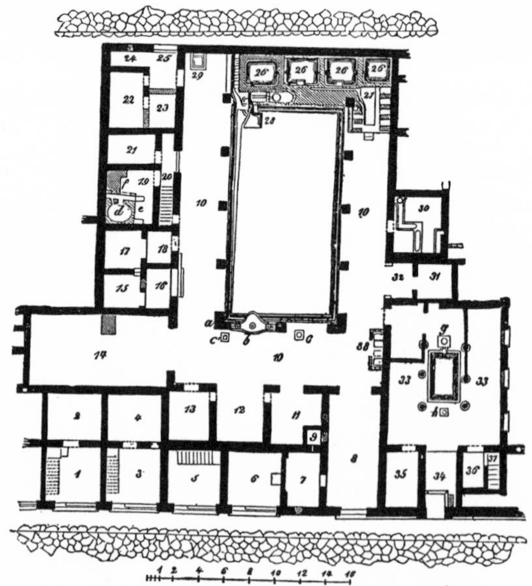

FIG. 239.—Plan of the Fullonica in Pompeii

The production of pieces of cloth by the succession of individual processes described above was a trade that was practised on a large scale by the Romans; its importance and special peculiarities made it necessary to adapt buildings to its purposes. In this way, factories for milling cloth arose, in part after the manner of our present day factories, as regards their technical equipment. The milling factory (Fullonica) in Pompeii, (Fig. 239) in the Street of Mercury consists of four shops (1, 3, 5, 6), which, as was mostly the case with Roman houses (see the Section on Buildings, p. 321) had no communication with the house. But the shops 1 and 3 have each a backroom, 2 and 4. The back rooms of 5 and 6 were on the first floor; 8 is the vestibule; 7 is a sort of porter's room; 10 is the atrium, in the middle of which a shed built on pillars, having a fountain (*b*) playing in front of it, was situated. On the pillar *a* there is the painting partly reproduced here. Room 14 was probably the drying room, whereas 22 and 23 represent the workshop. In 22 the washed materials were probably dressed; in 23 the press (see below) appears to have stood. The dyeing may have been carried out in the four troughs 26; the two outside troughs are higher than the two middle ones, which are of equal height and connected with each other, so that the solution flowed into them from the outer troughs. The troughs are of varying depths, the first being 46 in. deep, the last 20 in. deep. 28 is a water basin, which presumably served for rinsing the milled material. In room 27, which was divided into six cells, which are also clearly recognizable in Fig. 236, the pieces of cloth were milled by means of treading. Room 30, in which there were found a bath and stone table as well as great quantities of soap (?),[1] was the washing room, in which the cloth was beaten on the stone table by means of a wooden beater. The other rooms are private chambers. Among them we must mention in particular room 19, which contained a bakery.

BLEACHING AND PRESSING

In spite of the thorough treatment to which the finished cloth had been subjected, it had not yet the brilliant white colour that was desired, and that was prescribed among some peoples for certain garments, such as those of priests. In the case of white cloth, therefore, and perhaps also of others that were properly dyed, a bleaching process was next applied. Bleaching on grass was unknown in ancient times; bleaching was effected by using sulphurous fumes. For this purpose, a cane framework resembling a round bird-cage or a crinoline was used, which was placed on the ground (Fig. 238). The cloth was spread over this framework so as to cover it completely, and a pan or pot containing ignited sulphur was placed underneath. This primitive arrangement did not of course allow the bleaching process to take place uniformly, and darker patches must have remained in the cloth. To cover up these patches, and to give the cloth the brilliant white appearance which was

[1] The excavation of this Fullonica, which was discovered in 1825, was carried out in 1826. It can therefore no longer be determined whether the substance found was actually soap. After what has been said about soap (see pp. 110, 116), it is more likely that it was not.

so much desired in antiquity, it was then rubbed with certain white earths, as well as with gypsum. If bleaching was undertaken with materials that were genuinely dyed, probably correspondingly coloured earths such as ochre and such-like were used for rubbing in. An after-treatment then followed, which consisted in brushing, and perhaps also

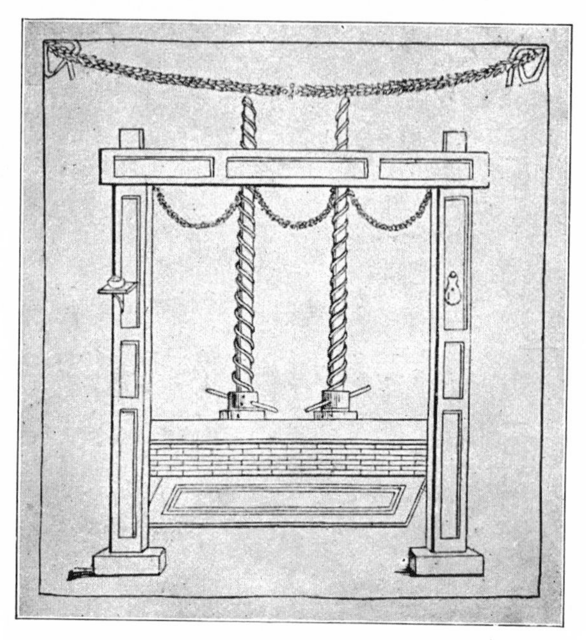

FIG. 240.—Cloth Press
Mural Painting from the Fullonica in Pompeii

in fleecing, in order to make the surface more uniform. Finally, the cloth was pressed, after having been previously moistened by sprinkling. A press was used, as is shown in a further mural painting of the great milling works of Pompeii; in it the threads of the two screws run, curiously enough, in opposite directions (Fig. 240).

TREATMENT OF THE CLOTHS

Concerning the further working of the materials into garments, there is not much to say. The pieces of cloth and textiles were made of the right size at the beginning, so that they could be worn without alteration later. Figs. 241 and 244 show us a number of Greek and Roman garments, from which we easily see that the pieces made were often of considerable size, so that it required experience and skilful manipulation to treat them by milling, bleaching, and dyeing, if reasonably good results, and in particular uniformity with regard to thickness, colour and so forth, were to be obtained. It has already been mentioned that this uniformity could not always be achieved. To make the garments, various processes of sewing were necessary, as for example for making the facings, for sewing on the purple and other strips on the tunics of the dignitaries, in particular of the senators and of the aristocracy, for

FIG. 241.—Greek Garments
Tanagra figures
Berlin Altes Museum, Antiquarium

FIG. 242.—Roman Garments
Relief: Return from a Hare Hunt
Provincial Museum, Trèves

attaching the much-favoured trimmings, and so forth. For these purposes, as well as for darning, needles were used which were made of very different materials, such as ivory, bone, bronze, iron, precious metals, and others. As now, so at that time, thimbles and scissors were also in use.

FIG. 243.—Roman Garments
Paying Tribute
Provincial Museum, Trèves

Nowadays, worn-out garments are unstitched, and are used to make artificial wool (shoddy and mungo); from these the artificial cloths are then obtained from which cheaper clothing materials are made. No such process was, however, known to the ancients. But they knew a process for making use of rags, which they sewed together in special workshops to make all sorts of articles of daily use, coverings which served for

FIG. 244.—Roman Garments
Sepulchral Cippus, with a Farewell Scene
Provincial Museum, Trèves

soldiers' equipment—further, extinguishers for placing over burning objects, curtains for inner rooms and shops, cheap dresses, and so forth.

FELTS, ROPE-MAKING, WICKER-WORK

The process of felting was used not only for making cloth, but also for its proper function of making felt. Felt was chiefly obtained from goats' hair, but probably the hair of hares, camels, sheep, and so forth, was also used. It served as a covering for the head, also for footwear, coverings for horses, and so forth. How it was actually made is not known; nor do we know by what apparatus the finished felt was pressed into the form of head-coverings and so forth. The assertion that felt prepared with vinegar can resist even iron, as Pliny (VIII, 192) writes, is probably exaggerated. Rope-making must be regarded as a special branch of

FIG. 245.—Egyptian Wicker-work of Palm Bast
Berlin Museum, Egyptian Department

textile work; it consisted in subjecting plant fibres to a process resembling that of spinning, and then twisting them round one another. Among almost all peoples of antiquity, there was used as the raw material, not only flax, but also hemp, and among the Romans esparto grass (*Stipa tenacissima L.*). The hemp and the espartos were prepared on the whole

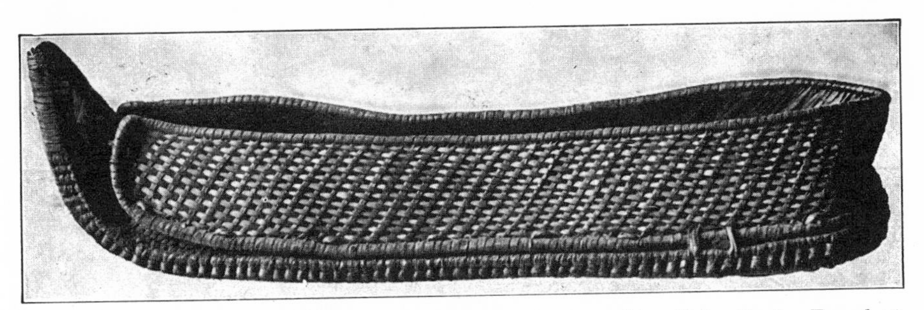

FIG. 246.—Egyptian Child's Shoe, fully woven (also the sole). Palm Bast. Found at Thebes
Berlin Museum, Egyptian Department

by the method already described in dealing with flaxes. By retting, drying, beating and so forth, the desired fibre was at last obtained. But these were not the only raw materials used. Rope was also made of straw. In Egypt, and later in Greece and Rome, reeds, rushes, willows, papyrus, bast (the inner bark) of the palm, were partly used for making ropes, nets, and so forth, but also, like cane, for weaving chairs, baskets, mats and hats. Moreover, ropes were sometimes made by simply twisting the material together, especially if it was of a coarser sort, such as straw, reeds and similar materials. For the rest, rope was probably made in precisely the same way as nowadays—this was so, indeed, even among the Egyptians—as is confirmed by mural paintings.

Either the finished skein of thread was taken, or it was pulled off from the belt during the process of rope-making, or from a sort of distaff,

FIG. 247.—Woven Cane Chair. (Relief)
Provincial Museum, Trèves

which, as we may surmise from the mural painting just mentioned, was held in one hand. In the other hand, the ropemaker, who, as nowadays, walked backwards, carried the piece of wood (laying-top) which effected the twisting together, and was at any rate provided with the appropriate notches. A frame with a hook for attaching the ends of the ropes does not seem to have been known. Rather these ends seem to have been held by some assistant (Fig. 248). Then as now ordinary rope consisted of three strands, or, in the case of stronger ropes, of a number of

FIG. 248.—Egyptian Ropemaker. Above are Coiled Ropes
The method of making ropes is difficult to interpret. The explanation given in the text seems the most probable one

single ropes wound together, and thus consisted of 9, 12, 15 or more threads. Strong ropes contained as many as 45 threads. Besides these, there are also ropes containing groups of four threads.

DYES

DYEING is without doubt one of the most ancient technical arts, for even in the oldest reports (for example, the Book of Genesis xxxvii. 23, and Exodus xxvi. 1 and xxxix. 1; and in later times Esther i. 6), we read of coloured garments, of which some are described in detail. It is true that the Old Testament mentions only three colouring substances—purple, kermes (a scarlet dye) and madder (a red dye)—(see Pinner). As dyeing had necessarily to be preceded by the preparation of the dyes, this branch of chemistry must also have had its beginnings in very early times. In the most ancient Egyptian graves dyed fabrics have been found. The Phoenicians were famed for their skill in dyeing, and, in particular, gorgeously coloured materials and carpets were made in the capital, Tyre, which were transported as highly desirable products of commerce to all parts of the ancient world. According to E. Curtius, the art of dyeing is supposed to have come into Greece from Phoenicia with the worship of Aphrodite.

PURPLE

The dyes used in antiquity were probably at the beginning exclusively organic by nature, that is, derived from animals or plants. Mineral colouring substances, at any rate, came to be used only later. The most renowned of all the colouring substances of antiquity was purple, which was supposed to have been invented by the Phoenicians in Tyre. A fable relates that a dog tore to pieces a murex (sea-mussel yielding purple dye), and the splendid and deep crimson colour which then adhered to his snout caused a shepherdess to use the juice from this mussel for colouring her garment. The Phoenicians succeeded in hiding the secret of purple-dyeing for hundreds of years. Trade with purple fabrics brought them a considerable amount of wealth. In antiquity, purple stood as the symbol of wealth and distinction. In Rome, only the senators had the right of wearing a broad purple stripe (*latus clavus*) around the opening of their tunics. The knights had a narrower stripe, and in the case of the higher state and city officials, the *toga praetexta* was edged with purple. Only the general who entered the city in triumph was allowed to wear a robe coloured entirely in purple and interwoven with gold. Later, particularly in the reign of Nero, and again in that of Theodosius (A.D. 379–395), laws were promulgated, by which only the holy person of the Emperor was allowed to carry entirely purple robes—a right which was afterwards transferred to the high dignitaries of the Church; and we still see a survival of this privilege in the robes of cardinals. Although we have accurate information about the importance of purple in the history of civilization and of manners, and also know what high prices were paid for purple substances, which amounted in Rome at the time of the Emperor Augustus to £30 for one pound of purple-coloured wool from Tyre, we did not until comparatively recently know what the purple dye actually looked like, nor how it had been produced in practice. New and very careful researches have disclosed that there were various ways of dyeing in purple, by means of which different shades of colour were obtained, according to the process adopted and the ingredients used. In general, the price of purple increased with the darkness of the colour. The deepest and darkest purple, which was made from the boiled-up juice of the mussels without any other ingredients, was obtained in the necessary shade of darkness by performing the dyeing twice (dibapha, *δίβαφον*). It was so dark, that in looking at the materials dyed with it, the impression of colour was almost lost in the general sense of darkness of the material. This also explains the terms used by Homer—'purple night', 'purple death', and so forth. The double dyeing was carried out 'by dyeing the material at first in *pelagium*, that is in the prepared juice of the *murex* (*πορφύρα*, *purpura*), the latter being in a half boiled-up state; and then in *buccinium*, that is in the juice of the trumpet murex (*κήρυξ*, *buccinium murex*).' Lighter hues were then obtained by diluting the dyeing bath with water or urine, as well as by adding other red colouring substances, such as orchil, kermes, and so forth. In this way, colours ranging from violet to red were obtained, for which special terms were used (such as hyacinth-purple, etc.).

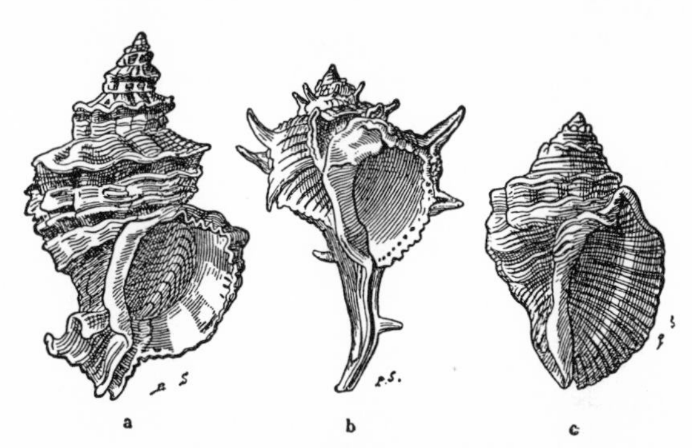

FIG. 249.—Purple Mussels

a, Murex trunculus. *b*, Murex brandaris. *c*, Purpura haemostoma

Descriptions in particular by Pliny (IX, 132; XXI, 45), as well as the evidence of broken shells found on the site of ancient purple dye-works, now accurately inform us about the nature of the purple mussels. For purposes of dyeing, various species of these mussels were used; they are classified by Pliny under the generic name 'purpura'. The precious substance was delivered not only by the real purple mussel (*Purpura lapillus*), but also by several species of the genus *Murex*. Each of these creatures yielded a special kind of purple. In Tyre, the juice of the mussel *Murex brandaris* was used for preference; in Sidon, dyeing was carried out by means of *Murex trunculus*; the second kind was also called amethyst purple. When the mussels were small, they were pounded up together with their shells, whereas the bigger ones were killed and cut up, and then the juice was extracted. After having been treated with salt, they were left for three days. The mass was then washed with water, and was cooked in a leaden vessel at a moderate temperature, produced by means of steam, for ten days. From 8,000 lbs. of juice, the ancients obtained in this way abont 500 lbs. of residue. The foam which formed, consisting of fibres of flesh, albumen and so forth, was scooped off. The clear liquid was used for making dyeing tests. If these were not successful, the boiling was continued, until the necessary concentration of the dye was obtained. Later, namely after the sixth century A.D., the dead mussels were allowed to lie for six months, probably so that they should dry out. This dried mass was then taken up in water, and treated as above described.

The real dyeing substance of the purple mussels is situated, according to the information of ancient writers, behind a small white membrane situated between the liver and the throat. Pliny calls this organ, which had already been described by Aristotle, 'vena' (vein), and asserts that the colouring matter is contained in it in an 'unripe form' as a whitish slimy juice to the amount of one small drop. After the treatment just described, the dye was supposed to come out when exposed to the air, and with particularly striking effect in the sun. This action of the sun was in early times regarded as a miracle proving the divine origin of the substance. The observations here stated are tolerably correct. More recent researches have confirmed that the slimy fluid is exuded by an organ in the coat of the mussel. A fermenting substance is assumed to be present, namely 'purpurase', in the purple gland of the mussel, in which it is secreted. The slimy juice is also in contact with other substances, the purpurines (madder purples), which are different in the various purple mussels, whereas the purpurase is the same in all. Through the action of the purpurase on the purpurine, the various colours desired are produced, of which, for example, *Murex trunculus* yields two, one that is reddish violet and the other dark blue. The juice is still colourless when exuded. It then changes to yellow, later becoming green, and ultimately purplish red. This transformation occurs—so we may nowadays assume—owing to three different kinds of influences: the first is chemical, due to the action of the purpurase on the purpurine; the second is due to heat; and the third is some kind of effect of light, that is, a photo-chemical action. The transformation occurs with the generation of a strong and extremely unpleasant odour, which is mentioned in the most ancient literature. An ancient Egyptian poem of about 1400 B.C. contains this passage about the purple dyer: 'His hands stink, they have the smell of putrid fish.' But Plutarch says in his *Pericles*: 'We often value a work and despise its creator, as for example in the case of salves and purple: we derive pleasure from them, but we regard the dyers and the makers of salves as vulgar and narrow-minded fellows.' Contempt of the purple-dyer is probably connected with this unpleasant odour which clung to them. The dye that was finally obtained is insoluble in water, and withstands change so effectively that this property is sufficient in itself to explain its great value to the ancients.

But their value is also to be attributed to another factor. Friedländer, who has made careful investigations of the purple dyes, obtained from 12,000 specimens of *Murex brandaris* only 1·5 grammes of dye. In view of this fact, it is not surprising that, according to the calculations of Friedländer, the price of a pound of purple dye in antiquity amounted to between £2,000 and £2,500; and that the ancient purple dye-works used up immense quantities of purple mussels. On the coast of Saida, where such a dye-works was situated, the remains of *Murex trunculus* covered the shore to a height of several yards over an area 80 ft. wide and several hundred yards long.

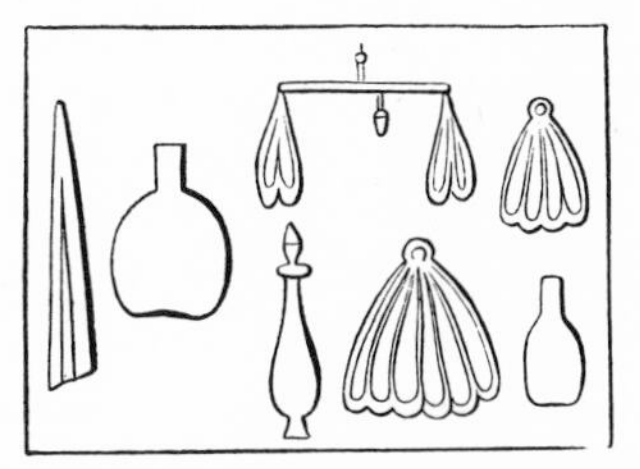

Fig. 250.—The Instruments of a Purple Dyer

Relief on a Roman grave. On the left, a stirrer for stirring the dye-brew; variously formed bottles; coloured strands of wool (?) (Blümner regards them as shells, but their shape seems to indicate strands which have been hung at the top over a bar, in the way that dyers are accustomed to do when washing them out). Next there is a pair of scales for weighing the dyed wool, from which strands likewise appear to be hanging

The detailed investigation of purple dye carried out recently by Friedländer, showed that it is a derivative of indigo containing bromine, being 6 : 6′ dibromo-indigo, with the chemical formula:

```
          CO          CO
             C  =  C
Br        NH          NH        Br
```

This body [1] has been known for some time, and was first obtained by R. Sachs synthetically, that is by building it up chemically from its component parts. Before the War, this dye could be produced synthetically for a price round about £1 to £1 5*s*. per lb. by chemical factories. But it would no longer occur to anyone to make this ancient purple in quantity. For this dye, which in the opinion of the ancients was so gorgeous, is of a dull shade, inclined to be reddish, and tending towards violet. It would give little pleasure to our eyes, and could be replaced in a much more splendid form, and equally genuinely, by far cheaper products of chemical industry, above all by various thio-indigo-derivatives.

These latest researches concerning indigo have thus deprived us of an illusion.

OTHER ORGANIC DYES

Other organic dyes of antiquity which were used in particular for colouring materials are chiefly represented by the following, which we know from data given by Pliny, from the Stockholm and Leyden Papyri, from other texts, also from analyses of ancient Egyptian and other textiles (the ancient Egyptian by Hübner, the others by Blümner, Hübner, Lippmann, and so forth). The chief source of red was the kermes tree or its berries (Pliny, IX, 141; XV, 8), a parasite resembling cochineal and living on the oak. The name kermes or alkermes first occurred in the Middle Ages; in antiquity it was called the scarlet berry,

[1] Known as Tyrian purple.—H. L. B.

'coccum' (among the Greeks, κόκκος). It was used for dyeing in scarlet. Another familiar red dye was madder (Pliny, XIX, 4; XXIV, 2), which was much used under the name 'rubia' (ἐρυθρόδανον) and, like kermes and orchil, was added as an ingredient to purple. A further red dye was anchusa, which was obtained from the root of the bugloss. It is now generally known under the name alkanet. It served not only for dyeing garments, but also as a red cosmetic (Pliny, XXII, 20). The term *hyacinthus* used by Pliny (XXI, 26), the 'purple flower', is probably to be interpreted as a species of mallow, which was also utilized as a spurious purple. The bilberry (*vaccinium*) was used, particularly in Gaul, for dyeing slave dresses (Pliny, XIII, 77), probably causing them to look a dirty-red (blackish). Yellow dyeing was effected in the main by means of saffron, and was practised from time immemorial. Bindings of Egyptian mummies of the 12th Dynasty, that is about 2500 B.C., were dyed by means of the Egyptian safflower (*Carthamus tinctorius*), according to Hübner. Among other kinds of safflowers, the *genista* was also used in Rome (Pliny, XVI, 18). It is the yellow broom plant, which gives a beautiful and genuine colour. Saffron itself was not seldom adulterated with litharge (Dioscorides, *Mat. Med.*, I, 25). Dyer's woad (*lutum*) was reddish-yellow and was used in Roman dye-works. Another yellow dye was obtained from the root of the lotus tree (Pliny, XVI, 124). The bark and the root of the elstree berry (*Lotos medicago arborea*) were the source of brown dyes (Pliny, XXVI, 30); further, the rind and the green shell of the walnut was used. There was an abundant choice of blue colours. First we have the woad 'glastrum' or 'vitrum' (ἴσατις). It appears that it was allowed to ferment, that is, it was placed in a sort of vat. For Pliny (XXXV, 46) writes of two kinds of 'indicum', of which the one 'forms a purple-coloured foam, which swims on top in the dyeing vats, is scooped off and dried by the craftsmen'. Whether this was actually indigo or some other dye cannot be stated with certainty. It seems, however, to be established that the ancients did not know how to dissolve indigo, for it appears only as a colour used for painting, and not for dyeing materials. A further blue colour was litmus, which in its fresh state also served for dyeing in red, and, according to Theophrastus (H.Pl. I, 6, 5) was still more beautiful than purple. Litmus (orchil), when washed with alkaline substances, did not however retain its reddish colour, as this can exist only in the presence of acids. The colour became changed to blue. Whether conscious use was made of this fact seems doubtful. The Stockholm Papyrus gives a whole series of rules for making the rose-colour of the orchil dye and also of the alkanet dyes more lasting. The means recommended include the use of sheep's hair, juice from the onion, a juice extracted by boiling henbane, and also from the leaves of lemon-trees, and so forth. Litmus (*fucus marinus*) was used in varying degrees of quality: some kinds were more highly valued, some less. Those from Crete were considered especially good (Pliny, XXXVI, 10; XXII, 6; XIII, 136).

The most important black colour was probably made from the bark of the oak (Pliny, XIII, 15).

Besides the dyes enumerated above, which were most used, there were a considerable number of others, less often mentioned, and therefore used probably only in special cases, the nature of which cannot always be ascertained.

INORGANIC DYES AND PAINTERS' COLOURS

Whereas the organic dyes, as we have already pointed out, were chiefly applied to colouring woven materials and cloths, the inorganic dyes were used for glazes and for painters' colours. So far as they served as a colour for glazes, as well as for colouring glass, all that need be said about them has already been stated in the section on Ceramic and Glass Industry. We therefore concentrate our attention here on painters' colours.

Historians of antiquity relate that the ancient painters for a long time knew and used only four colours, namely—white, yellow, red and black. This statement seems hardly credible, for, besides the various organic dyes, there were also inorganic dyes present in nature; they needed only to be powdered to be ready for use. We need only recall that the important colours blue and green, which are missing in the scale just mentioned, must have been known in ancient times, in the form of the copper-ores, malachite, and copper glaze. All peoples of antiquity seem to have derived much pleasure from colours and painting. The Egyptians in particular, as far back as can be recorded, painted the walls and columns of their buildings, temples and palaces, as well as the mummy-cases, using seven different colours, namely:

Black (for the hair and beard).
White (iron, water, mountains).
Blue (iron, water, mountains).
Yellow (sandstone and lime, rough wood, lions).
Green (crocodiles).
Cinnabar-red (the sun's disc).
Brownish-red (horses, hares, antelopes, tree trunks, iris, and the tear-glands in the eyes; granite, etc.).

The colour most often used was of a brownish-red hue, which corresponds to the so-called Pompeian red. In chemical composition it was a mixture of iron oxide, obtained from the red iron deposits of Egypt, with clay. The grain of this colour is so fine that we would almost be tempted to assume that it was made by precipitation from solutions. But it is probable that the iron oxide was brought into this convenient form by pounding it up for a long time under water, and washing it. To obtain yellow, there was used, besides gold-bronze and gold-leaf, iron oxide, to which various shades of colour were given by adding varying amounts of clayey soil, lime and so forth. By heating it, brown tints were obtained; and by mixing it with red, orange colours were produced. The blue colours consisted of glass fluxes in which copper salts had been dissolved. The fineness of the grain makes it appear probable that the glass fluxes, while still hot, were poured into cold water, and that the brittle mass so obtained, which was lined with innumerable cracks, was powdered and then washed. As this glass mass would probably have adhered only with difficulty to the background that was to be painted, possibly some gum or other binding material was used with it. To obtain a white colour, gypsum was used, and it was also applied to obtain a pale-red colour by adding an organic substance. From what material this organic substance was obtained can only be guessed, but it is to be assumed that it was madder, which the Egyptians knew how to extract from the madder root. It is interesting to find that the ancient Egyptian architects were well aware of the durable and immutable quality of their colours. Thus, on one of the works of Neh-Fermad (4000 B.C.), the builder of pyramids, there is an inscription which gives us information about the manner in which the colours used by him were produced, and it contains the words: 'Colour decorations for temples must be as eternal as the Gods themselves.'

More richly varied than the palette of the Egyptians was that of the Greek painters. As early as 2000 B.C. the Greeks had in general the same colours as the Egyptians, and in addition, colours containing manganese and mercury. In the sixth century B.C. cinnabar appeared. According to the researches of Rhousopoulos, there was even in 2000 B.C. a rich variety of blues alone. A vase of that time contains a blue colouring matter, which was composed of copper, iron, silicon dioxide, and carbonic acid, and thus perhaps represents a mixture of copper silicate and iron carbonate. Another blue colour of the same time contains carbonic acid, silicon dioxide, copper, iron and mercury. A third blue of the time 1600–1200 B.C. was composed of a basic silicate of copper oxide, in which there was mixed argillaceous earth to the amount of one part in four by weight. So that even at that time there were three different blues available, while further shades could be obtained by blending them with clay. About the ninth century B.C. there was added to these a further blue, namely a basic copper carbonate, which corresponds to our present-day mountain blue or blue verditer (powdered azurite). There was a similar rich variety of other colours. In the fifth century B.C. a black was produced from manganese and iron salts; a violet and a green were also obtained by mixture, the latter being produced from iron and copper salts and argillaceous earth; and there are many further examples.

Among the Romans, the manifold variety of colours reached its zenith. For every colour, almost, there are various representatives. There was a considerable number of whites; first of all, the chalk from Selinus in Sicily, which was particularly highly valued; it was washed and then stirred in milk. It also served as a cosmetic. Further, *melinum*, a white earth from the island of Melos, was used, although it was not suitable for wall painting. Another popular earth was obtained from Eretria on the south-west coast of Euboea. According to its chemical composition, it was a chalk which is supposed to have been used particularly over other colours. *Praetonium*, a chalky substance derived from Egypt, was rather dear, and was therefore very often adulterated. To these, there is to be added white lead, which was the only white colour of the Romans that did not occur naturally, being obtained artificially. It was known as early as the fourth century B.C., when Theophrastus, in his essay *περὶ λίθων*, described its preparation, which is also given by Dioscorides, Pliny and Vitruvius. From these descriptions, it is evident that the *ψιμύθιον*, *cerussa*, was made in the following way: lead was placed on a vessel filled with strong vinegar, and both were wrapped up as tightly as possible, so that the vapours from the vinegar should attack the lead. White lead was produced, which was scratched off, ground up and passed through a sieve. The poisonous character of white lead was known as early as the 2nd century B.C., when Nicander mentions it in his *Alexipharmaca* (verses 74–76). As a yellow colour, ochre was chiefly used; it was dug up, and applied in all shades, ranging from yellow through brown to red. The yellow ochre which was obtained in the vicinity of Athens was regarded as the best. Before ochre deposits were discovered in Italy, Athenian ochre was so dear that it was often adulterated, or cheap substitutes were used for it. According to the report of Vitruvius, these substitutes were made by ancient wall-painters, by boiling out dried yellow flowers in water. The yellow fluid obtained was then mixed with chalk. In this way a colour was produced which resembled in its shade Athenian ochre but resisted exposure to light considerably less, which is not very surprising, since organic colouring substances in general have less resistive power to light than mineral substances. Besides ochre, there was used as a yellow colour orpiment, that is arsenic trisulphide, having the chemical formula As_2S_3.

There was a great choice of reds in very many different shades. First of all, red ochre was available naturally. Among the various sorts, 'Sinopian' earth was particularly favoured; it was probably brought from the town of Sinope by traders, and was a red chalk obtained from the mines of Cappadocia. No less famous was the red chalk from the islands of Lemnos and Keos, from which the city of Athens had secured the contract rights of extracting the substance. Moreover, Athens had special ships built for its transport. It was also known that yellow ochre, when subjected to heat, passes over into the red form; this is a process of oxidation which is still used in factories making mineral dyes. It is supposed to have been invented by the painter Kydias, about the year 350 B.C. Further, powdered bricks were used as painters' colours, which also became converted into a brighter red when heated. Later, however, when better colours were obtainable, they were only used for lime-washing. Like ochre, the arsenic compounds with sulphur gave various tints between yellow and red, particularly when the red realgar (disulphide of arsenic, red orpiment) was mixed with the yellow orpiment; these two substances almost always occur together in nature. Of course the extraction as well as the use of these colours was associated with great dangers to health. No less harmful were the production and use of minium, which was made by heating white lead. This red colour (Pb_3O_4) was supposed to have been discovered owing to a vessel containing white lead having fallen into the flames when a decorator's workshop had caught fire, with the consequence that the white colour was changed into red. To these numerous red colours there then became added the cinnabar extracted from Spanish mines, which is early mentioned by Theophrastus about 300 B.C. (*περὶ λίθων*, 59). Besides being imported from Spain, it was also obtained from Cappadocia (Strabo, III, 144). The use of cinnabar (mercuric sulphide, HgS) was also very dangerous to health. The discovery by the Athenian Kallias (about 405 B.C.) of an 'artificial cinnabar' made from red sand, which came from Ephesus, while being a retrograde step as regards beauty of colour, certainly marks an advance in hygienic respects. Artificial cinnabar is supposed to have been made from the sand which occurs, as just mentioned, near Ephesus, by dividing it up finely, washing it in water, and then again letting it precipitate. The deposit was then dried and used as a colour.

As a blue colour, there was used above all 'Egyptian blue', which was made by heating a mixture of copper-ore, sand, lime and soda. A. P. Laurie has recently endeavoured to produce this colour from its component parts, and has succeeded in his efforts. According to the investigations made by him, Egyptian blue was a crystalline substance, which has the property of double refraction. Fouqué obtained it by glowing a mixture of 24·4 parts of copper oxide, 50 parts of quartz, 21 parts of chalk, and 4·6 parts of soda. According to his researches, the quartz had to be used in the finest state of division, as success depended on this point, and indeed the finely divided state of all components was a necessary factor in the process. The temperature to which he glowed these substances amounted to 900°–950°C.

Besides this artificial blue, there was also a natural blue colour available, which the Greeks called *kyanos* and the Romans *caeruleum*. It was found in Egypt and Cyprus, and was probably lapis-lazuli, from which a blue colour was obtained by powdering and washing—which probably corresponded to our washing-blue—that is, to ultramarine. The price of a pound was as much as £45. A fraudulent substitute was obtained by using white chalk, which was coloured by a decoction of woad. Besides these, indigo was used as a colour by painters, as has already been remarked under the section on Organic Dyes.

The most important green colour was malachite (chrysocolla), which was extracted from numerous deposits, above all in Macedonia, Armenia and Cyprus. There were further used the green earth obtained from Smyrna, and also verdigris. It was made by leaving copper in wine lees until a green layer had formed, which was then scratched off. Since in this way only comparatively little verdigris could be obtained, the colour was rather dear, so that it was often adulterated by adding marble dust or iron sulphate. A method of detecting the fraud was also known; it consisted in glowing out the suspected colour, whereupon the resultant change of colour of course showed clearly whether or not a pure copper compound was present. A green discovered in Crete consisted of Egyptian blue mixed with ochre. The Romans used green earth.

For making black, soot was the chief source. It was produced, as nowadays, in special works. Pitch, resin, chips from the pine, beeswax, dried remains of the grape and other substances, were burned in chambers whose walls were as smooth as possible and in many cases made of polished marble. The soot which deposited itself was scratched off. Further, bone black was also in use; it is supposed to have been discovered by the most celebrated painter in Greece, namely Apelles (about 325 B.C.), who produced it by charring ivory. Bone black was extraordinarily dear, and was only seldom employed. On the other hand, wood tar was sometimes used, as well as a black derived from India, which is probably identical with our Indian ink, and so likewise represented a product from soot.

Gold dye was also used in antiquity, namely in the form of finely-divided gold-leaf, that is as that kind of metal colour to which we nowadays apply the collective name 'bronze dyes'. The word bronze applies not to the chemical composition, but rather to the physical constitution of the material. Theobald surmises that at first the scraps from the workshop of the gold-beater, that is fine strips of gold, were used for producing this dye, by rubbing it up into a powder, and applying it as a paint. From excavations in Mycenae, Hostman concludes that gold bronze must have been in use very long ago. In Egypt, however, it appears to have been applied rather late. To make the bronze powder and the gold bronze adhere to a surface, cements were used; above all, probably gummy or resinous juices of plants, and also mercury. Only small traces of mercury can however have been used, as the addition of a larger quantity would have resulted in an amalgam, white in colour. The mercury gradually vaporized from the alloy, while the gold bronze clung by adhesion, or was perhaps attached by a residual trace of the amalgam, which did not decompose.

It has yet to be mentioned that among the ancient writers definite and characteristic expressions for the individual dyes are not always to be found. The ancients revelled in speaking in extravagant terms of the beauty of these dyes; thus we read of the 'green of the myrtle', 'the colour of the acorn', 'the blue of the heavens', and similar picturesque expressions.[1] So it is very often difficult to establish which colour is meant in a given passage.

[1] Such terms, which can easily be paralleled from other languages, especially those of savages, result from a restricted vocabulary of colour-names, not from rhetorical tendencies.—*Trans.*

THE TECHNIQUE OF PAINTING

PAINTING AMONG THE EGYPTIANS AND BABYLONIANS

THE technique of painting in antiquity probably reached its zenith at first among the Egyptians and then among the Babylonians. The resistance of these paintings, as well as the dyeing of garments, to decay, which has been much praised, is due less to the perfect method of painting than to other favourable circumstances, above all, to the dry air which—in contrast with that of our cities—contained no harmful gases, and in particular no sulphurous fumes. Further, the complete exclusion of air, as for example in the Royal tombs, was favourable for the preservation of antique paintings. Their durability is, as Heaton, Immerheisser, Lessing, and others have rightly pointed out, only relative. The production of Egyptian wall paintings was carried out by first smoothing the surface of the rough stone wall by means of a layer of slime or loam. On this base there was superimposed a second layer of straw and asphalt. Then the actual background for the painting was added, but only in a very small thickness—of about $\frac{1}{25}$ of an inch—which consisted of chalk, and sometimes bolus. Later, in the time of the Ptolemies (in the third century B.C.), gilding also appeared, particularly on the wrappings of mummies. The water or tempera colours applied to this background were then fixed by means of gum or glue. The real nature of the means used in painting has not yet been determined. It is only known that water-colours were involved. When these paintings are made wet, they can be washed out together with the background. The brushes were made of reeds, of which one end was split up into fine pieces by knocking it against a surface, also perhaps by chewing it. Later, however, brushes made of hair were also used. The palettes (Fig. 251) were of wood, and were provided with hollows for containing the colours. Besides this method of wall painting, there was also another practised by the Egyptians, which was even more common. The pictures and inscriptions were cut or engraved in the stone, and the incisions giving the outlines of the drawings were filled with a colour paste. The two methods of decorative painting just mentioned remained predominant until the time of the Ptolemies. They had continued in use for nearly three thousand years.

PAINTING AMONG THE GREEKS AND ROMANS

In the meantime, there developed in the Mediterranean countries, particularly in Greece, a new method of painting, the beginnings of which go back to the time of King Minos, as is borne out by the fresco paintings in the palace of Knossos. The fact that the art of fresco appears to have originated in Crete, whereas it was possibly unknown in Egypt, is probably due to the circumstance that in Crete simple distemper pictures of the Egyptian kind could hardly have outlasted the colder and moister climate. It was therefore necessary to find a new method of painting which would give enduring productions. The analyses of the materials used for Cretan fresco paintings showed that the lime was derived from a subterranean quarry situated some miles from the palace of Knossos. To obtain the

FIG. 252.—Greek Painter

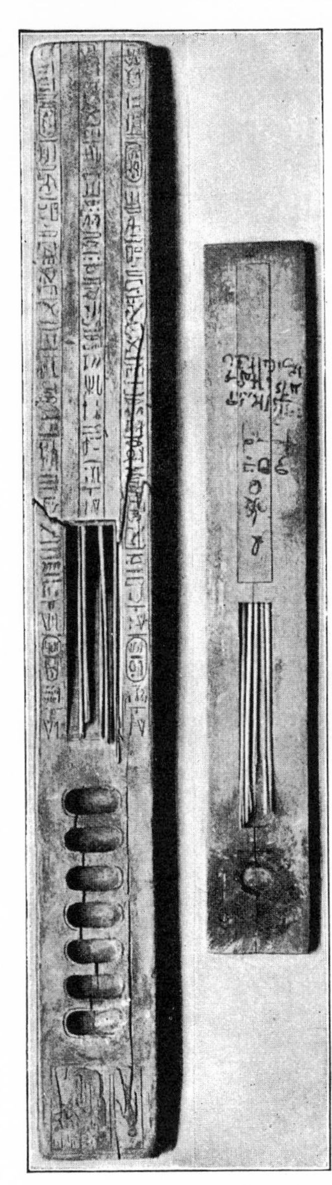

FIG. 251.—Egyptian Painter's Palette (with depressions for the colours and grooves for the brushes)
Of wood. Length, 21 in.; width, 2¼ in. (Below is a writer's palette, with five reed pens.) Berlin Museum, Egyptian Department

different colours, lime was used for white, ochre for yellow, and burnt yellow ochre or ground haematite for red. Black was made from slate containing coal. Blue was the Egyptian blue already mentioned above, therefore a silicate of copper and sodium. A uniformly constituted green was not used; this colour was always mixed from Egyptian blue and ochre. The lime of the earlier frescoes is not so white and is coarser than that of later periods. Moreover, it contains a considerable quantity of aluminium silicate in the form of zeolite. This mineral was probably added in order to help the hardening process, which strangely enough is not completed even at the present day. The hardening of frescoes, as we know, is due to the lime (calcium hydrate,

$Ca(OH)_2$), taking up carbon dioxide from the air, and becoming converted into ordinary lime (calcium carbonate, $CaCO_3$). Even nowadays, several thousand years after the production of these frescoes, we still find at the deepest points of the frescoes in Knossos traces of unchanged calcium hydrate.

The Roman fresco paintings were made in a way similar to that of the Greeks. The method was improved in various directions. In particular, Vitruvius (VII, 3) describes the preparation of stucco (*tectorium*), in a passage which, in spite of all attempts at explanation by Weigmann, Donner, Blümner, Raehlmann, Keim, Berger, and others, does not seem sufficiently elucidated in some respects. From the technical point of view, the explanation given by Berger, and supported by experiments, has much to recommend it; according to it, a shining smoothed stucco surface was at first produced, being either coloured or white, on which a painting could be made, according to the method adopted (tempera, stucco, and so forth). It must be especially mentioned that one of the green colours used by the Romans, malachite, lost some of its beautiful quality on the lime. Wherever it was to be applied, therefore, a thin coat of black was first painted on the white ground, over which the green could then be applied.

FIG. 253.—Painting on Canvas (late Egyptian)

Portrait of a girl on a mummy. A golden wreath in the hair, gold earrings and necklace. Hawara. Berlin Museum, Egyptian Department

PAINTING ON TABLETS

The ancients painted not only on walls but, later, also on tablets. They used tablets made of wood from the cypress, larch or pine. Canvas was hardly used at all as a painting material, although there are isolated examples of such portraits (those found by Flinders Petrie in Hawara in the Fayum). The dried wood was covered with a coat of white, and then painted. The ancients also painted on stone tablets, in particular on tablets of polished marble. Such paintings were used in Greece at a very distant date on monuments. It was not usual to varnish the paintings, although it is reported of Apelles that he covered his beautiful creations with a protective layer, whose composition he kept secret. As all the colours were water-colours, the paintings had to be preserved from decomposition, and this was effected by providing them with folding doors. But the Egyptians are also supposed to have used glass for this purpose. Oil-painting was unknown throughout the whole of ancient times.

BINDING SUBSTANCES

The number of binding substances, that is of those substances by means of which the colours were mixed and made to adhere to the ground, was comparatively large. But if we look carefully into their chemical composition, we find that they are nearly always substances of the class of carbohydrates or albumens, or of a mixture of both. At any rate, no substances from the class of oils and fats were used, so that it was a question simply of tempera painting in the original sense—that is, painting that was entirely free of 'fatty substances'. Fischer enumerates the following binding substances:

'1. Gum arabic and tragacanth.
2. Animal glue; that from Rhodes was particularly valued.
3. Blood of the hippopotamus.
4. Egg, and white of the egg.
5. Milk for smearing over the *tectorium* (wall surface) with earth from Selinus. The *tectorium* in the Temple of Athena at Elis was painted on with milk and saffron. Later, the milky juice of figs was also used. It was mixed with the yellow of the egg and added to the colours.'

THE ENCAUSTIC PROCESS

Besides water-colours and the tempera painting carried out with the use of egg, gum or glue, the ancients were also acquainted with a special form of painting, 'encaustic painting', about which Pliny writes (XXXV, 122): 'We do not know who first conceived the idea of painting with wax colours and burning them into the picture'; *ibid.*, 149: 'There were only two methods of making encaustic paintings in ancient times, with wax and on ivory. It was done with the cestrum (a stump), that is a tool resembling a spit (*vericulum*). When people began to apply paint to ships a third method arose, consisting in making the wax colours fluid by means of fire, and using brushes; what was painted on ships was thus not damaged either by the sun, salt water, or winds.'

Ever since the sixteenth century, this passage has been the subject of lively discussion as to the method of encaustic painting. The explanations which are chiefly based on philological reasoning began in the year 1585 through Louis de Montjosieu, and have continued right up to the present day. A comparison of texts undertaken by Mayhoff brought out the important fact that the three methods of encaustic painting mentioned by Pliny (*qui encausto cauterio vel cestro vel penicillo pinxerit*) are the following:

FIG. 254.—Tools used for Encaustic Painting, obtained from the grave of a woman painter.

Below, from left to right: glass jug, knife with a cedar handle, bronze box with colours in four sections, which are covered with a perforated silver plate; below is a basalt tablet, a bronze spoon, a mortar; in front is a shovel made of rock crystal

(1) Cauterium-encaustic, that is placing on the colours and working them in with a hot instrument.

(2) Cestrum-encaustic—working with only a pointed stump on ivory (miniatures).

(3) Brush-encaustic—adding the hot fluid colours by means of a brush.

A difficulty was at that time encountered, in that no encaustic paintings were discovered, so that it was even believed that encaustic painting had never actually existed. Not even eminent chemists like Chaptal (1809) and Davy (1815) succeeded in proving the presence of wax or mixtures of resins in ancient wall frescoes. At last, however, at the end of the nineteenth century, encaustic paintings were discovered on the ancient Egyptian tombs at Rubayat in the Fayum, of which, according to the opinion of Ebers, the oldest dated back to about the second century B.C., and the most recent ones to the fourth century of the Christian era. Chemical analysis showed that wax was present in them. As a Roman painter's grave had previously been discovered at St. Médard des Prés, in which a complete outfit was found, these two discoveries have made the ancient method of encaustic painting clear to us

FIG. 255.—Instruments used for Encaustic Painting, from the grave of a painter (woman).

From left to right: a grate made of crystal, bronze spoon, large mortar; behind is another grate, a case with two small bronze spoons two blobs of colour in front

In the grave of the painter there were found—in a small box with iron mountings (Figs. 254 and 255): (1) A bronze box with a sliding cover (in which were contained colours of an irregular shape); (2) a basalt tablet;

(3) a mortar made of bronze; (4) two delicately worked little spoons of bronze in a case of the same metal; (5) the handles of two brushes. There were also found in the grave amphorae, which were partly filled with beeswax, partly with a mixture of resin and wax; also, clasp-knives, colour grates, and an alabaster mortar with a spout, and other things.

The presence of wax, which was investigated by Chevreul, the eminent expert in the industrial chemistry of oils and fats, made it seem probable that this outfit was that of an encaustic painter; this possibility becomes a certainty, when we compare the above with the data of Pliny and with the manner in which the Egyptian encaustic paintings were carried out. The little box with the perforated silver cover served to contain glowing coals. The heat that escaped through the apertures softened the wax colours placed above. The two long-handled spoons with the thickened ends, which could be warmed alternately, were used to distribute and smooth out the wax smeared on the surface of the painting and to work it in. Experiments made by the artist Ernst Berger with models of these implements made for the Deutsches Museum, Munich, showed that it was possible to make an encaustic painting in the antique style. According to the researches of Berger, the spoon-shaped end of the instrument—which seems to be the *cauterium*—served for the first application of the wax, which was caught up in the fluid condition, being hot, and was spread immediately over the surface (the first method of Pliny); the final touches were carried out with the other warmed end of the cauterium. Or else, at the beginning, the third method of Pliny was practised by means of the brush and hot fluid colour, and the process was completed with the cauterium.

The ancient Egyptian encaustic paintings also allow us to distinguish two processes: in the one, an instrument differing from the brush was exclusively used, the traces of which are clearly visible; whereas in the other this instrument was used only for delineating the parts of the face; the background, however, as well as the garments, jewellery and so forth, were made with the brush, and that mostly quite superficially with softened wax colours. Encaustic painting later gave rise to oil-painting. Resin was mixed with the wax mass, and, later, oils, probably in order to retain it fluid for a longer time. In this way, there originated an oil-resin method of painting, and finally painting with pure oils, which the Greek doctor Aëtius mentions for the first time in the sixth century A.D. with the words, 'The oil of the walnut is useful to the encaustic painters, on account of its drying power.'

TECHNICAL MECHANICS AND MACHINES

MANY of the technical achievements of antiquity excite the greatest admiration in us on account of their massiveness, of the colossal conceptions embodied in them, and of the splendid manner in which they have been executed. This admiration is still further increased when we realize that all these achievements were accomplished with comparatively simple machines, with contrivances which throughout result from exploiting a few easily recognizable physical laws. 'Work' is the product of 'time' by 'power.' We can understand how these achievements were possible in spite of the simple machines used, if we bear in mind that there was an abundance of both time and power available at that period. Time was of practically no account; in order to produce a definite piece of work, any amount of time could be used. There was likewise no lack of power: the existence of slavery provided more than enough labour, and it could be used to the fullest extent. In view of this profusion of power and time, machines could well be of a simple kind.

THE SIMPLE MACHINES

Aristotle (384–322 B.C.) enumerates in his *Mechanical Problems* [1] the contrivances used by the ancients. Among these he includes the lever with its counter-weight in the case of the draw well, the ordinary balance with equal arms, the steel-yard, the tongs, the wedge, the axe, the winch, the roller, the wheel, the pulley, the compound pulley, the potter's lathe, the sling, the oar, as well as the cord-wheel of iron or bronze capable of rotating in different directions, which must probably be interpreted as toothed wheels (see page 215). If we consider this enumeration, as well as the definition which Vitruvius (1st century B.C.) gives us of the 'machine': 'A machine is a connected construction of wood, which gives very great advantages in raising heavy masses; it is set into action artificially, namely by rotation', then we recognize at once that the ancients were chiefly concerned with making use of the simple devices which in mechanics are usually classified under the generic term 'simple machines'. Their name is due to the fact that they cannot be analysed into still simpler machines; they are the lever, the inclined plane, the wedge, the pulley and the toothed wheel. By combining these, we get compound machines. Let us now see in what way the ancients derived advantage from the 'simple machines' and combinations of them.

[1] A work probably not by Aristotle.—*Trans.*

It has been assumed by many, among them Wichelhaus, that the Egyptians were acquainted only with the lever, the wedge, and the compound pulley. This view is supported by the circumstance that it seems doubtful whether the inclined plane was used in building the Pyramids, as has been assumed by some investigators. If, for the present, we therefore disregard the toothed wheel, to which we shall return later, and examine in detail the technical achievements of ancient peoples, as well as how they were attained, we find, as the elementary mechanical appliances of the ancients, the lever, the inclined plane, the wedge, and the pulley.

THE LEVER AND ITS APPLICATIONS

Of these appliances, the lever offered itself naturally; it was fairly certainly used by all peoples of pre-history. The assertion of Pliny (VII, 195) that it was invented by Kinyras of Cyprus can therefore be regarded only as a contribution to mythology, and of no value for the history of technical mechanics. The theory of the lever exercised the greatest minds of antiquity, above all Aristotle[1] and Archimedes (287–212 B.C.), of whom the former regards the action of the lever in the light of related circular arcs, whereas Archimedes discovered the law of levers by calculation. This law states that the product of the force by the arm must have the same value on both sides of the fulcrum, if equilibrium is to be maintained. Thus, in order to raise a weight that is a thousand times heavier than can be lifted with the strength of our arms, it suffices to make the lever-arm at the end of which the force is being applied a thousand times longer than the lever-arm supporting the weight. 'Give me a fixed point in space, and I will move the earth!' was the proud boast of Archimedes. Whether the knowledge discovered by him influenced the mechanical development of later times must remain an open question. At any rate, the method of using the lever, both alone and in combination with other devices, was known long before. We meet it among the ancient Egyptians in the form of numerous tools, and comparisons with the achievements of other peoples show us that the latter also knew how to make appropriate use of it. Thus we find manifold devices for raising water, which depend on the action of the lever, such as the 'shadoof' among the Egyptians, the Babylonians and Assyrians, and the 'picotah' among the Indians. As we may recognize, for example, from the reliefs at the Palace of Nineveh, which date from the seventh century B.C.,

FIG. 256.—Shadoof in Babylon. The two-armed lever used for drawing water

(The efficiency of the shadoof, with three people working it, is about six cubic metres of water per hour.) From a relief of the seventh century B.C. in the Palace of Nineveh

[1] Meaning the unknown author of the *Mechanical Problems*; see p. 202, n.—*Trans.*

and also from other pictures, the shadoof was used in antiquity as well as nowadays on the delta of the Nile: a two-armed lever, with a weight attached to its rear shorter arm, carries on its longer arm the scoop-

FIG. 257.—Shadoof for raising Water from the Nile into Irrigation Trenches

The contrivance used nowadays still exhibits the same form as that which was in use among the ancient Egyptians

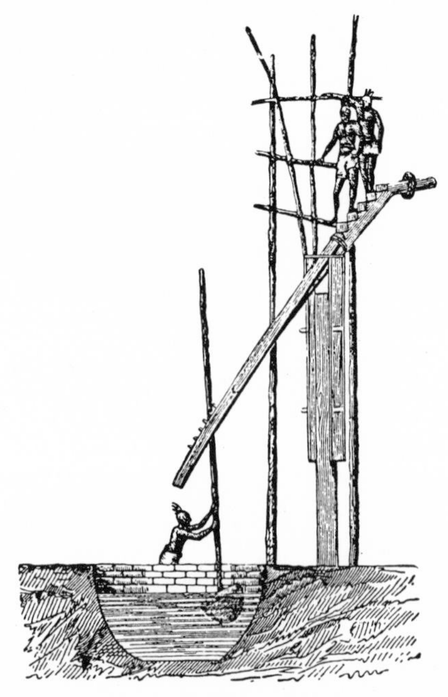

FIG. 258.—Picotah of the Indians

ing vessel (Fig. 256). The workmen apply their strength to the longer lever arm. In opposition to this, Philon of Byzantium (about 230 B.C.) describes a device resembling the shadoof for drawing water, in which there is attached to the rear shorter arm a treadle contrivance. The bucket is then raised by the workman walking up this treadle (a simple board—see Fig. 259).

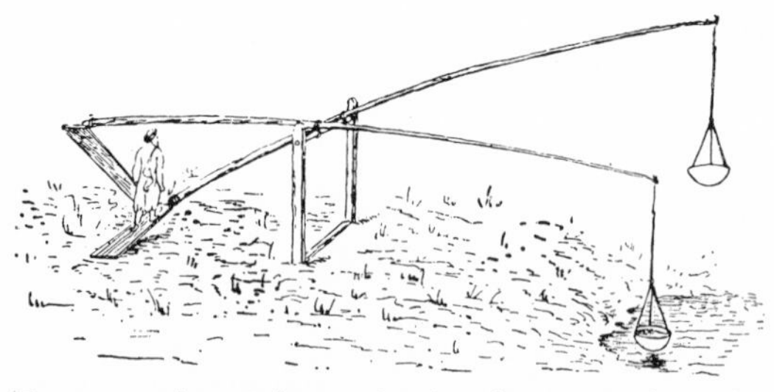

FIG. 259.—A contrivance for drawing water, in which two Levers are used in combination: the Treadle Lever works the Drawing Lever

According to Philon of Byzantium

The old 'picotah' or 'kuphar' of the Indians worked in the same way; In it, the shorter arm carries a few steps, on which the workers walk up or down, and so cause a bucket to be raised or lowered (Fig. 258).

In view of the active trade relations which the ancient Egyptians maintained with all sorts of countries, the scale-balance (Figs. 260–263)

could be dispensed with neither in these countries nor in Egypt itself. Numerous ancient pictures give us information about its structure, which

FIG. 260.—Roman Balance or Steelyard

A two-armed lever with unequal arms. To the shorter is attached the mass to be weighed ; on the longer arm there is a movable weight, the 'runner' (here shown in the form of a bronze figure consisting of a woman in a sitting posture). By moving along the runner, equilibrium with the mass to be weighed is effected, and the weight of the latter can then be read off from the division at which the runner happens to be on the long arm. A specimen derived from Greece. Berlin, Altes Museum, Antiquarium

resembles that of the ordinary balance of the present day. (See also Figs. 48 and 49.)

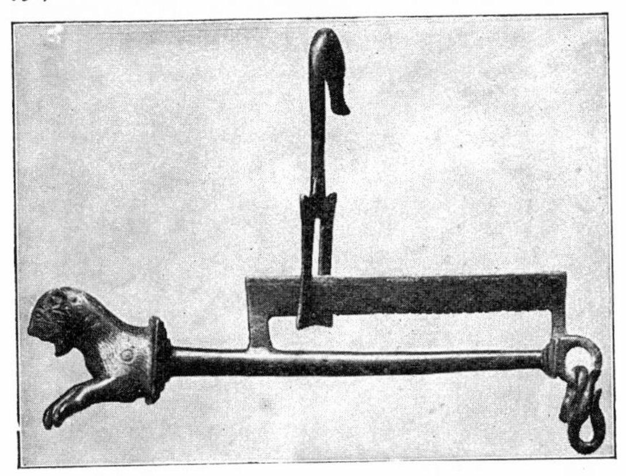

FIG. 261.—Steelyard. Another form

The weight (in the form of a lion's head) and the mass are both fixed. Equilibrium is obtained by shifting along the whole yard and so varying the position of the point of suspension. The weight is then read off at the point of suspension of the fine division on the beam. Berlin, Altes Museum, Antiquarium

An ingenious use of the lever, perhaps derived from the law of Archimedes, was made by Heron of Alexandria (first century A.D.). He constructed numerous automatic machines, which for the most part depended on the use of the lever. A typical example is given by his automaton for supplying holy water (Fig. 264), which he describes as follows (*Pneumatica* i, 21, p. 110, Schmidt) :

'Many vessels for offerings are arranged so that holy water for sprinkling flows out when a five-drachma piece is inserted.

FIG. 262.—Steel Jack; in use
From a Roman memorial at Neumagen. Provincial Museum, Trèves

'Take a libation-vessel (*σπονδεῖον*) or a money-box (*θησαυρός*), (*αβγδ*, Fig. 264), of which the aperture α is not closed.

'Let there be in the money-box (or the libation-vessel) a (small) vessel $\zeta\eta\theta\varkappa$ with water and a box from which an exit-tube μ leads outwards. Next to the vessel place a vertical rod $\nu\xi$, about which another $o\pi$ rotates like a scale-beam. Let $o\pi$ be widened at o into a thin plate which (in the state of rest) lies parallel to the bottom of the vessel. At π attach a small vertical rod, $\pi\sigma$, to which there is attached at σ a lid exactly fitting the cylinder, so that it can interrupt the escape of liquid through μ. Make the lid of the cylinder heavier than the little plate ϱ but lighter than the combined weight of the lid and the coin. When the coin has been inserted into the aperture α, it drops into the plate ϱ and so, depressing the cross-beam $o\pi$, brings it into an inclined position while drawing up the lid of the cylinder ; as a consequence of this the water is allowed to flow out. So soon as the coin has dropped (from ϱ) the lid again closes the box and arrests the flow of the water.'

FIG. 263.—A Balance consisting of a Lever with equal Arms
Greek pictures on the 'phiale of Arkesilas'

More important than these and many other automatic devices of Heron, who was ex-

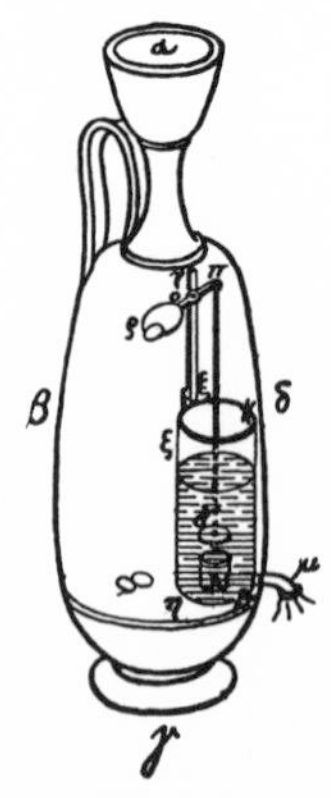

FIG. 264.—The Automatic Device for supplying Holy Water, invented by Heron of Alexandria

tremely clever in making such inventions, were the manifold technical applications which were made of the lever, particularly in Roman times. Among these we must mention the cord-wheel, which was used for turning the grindstone, and probably also the lathe. Further, numerous and often very complicated lever appliances were used in the theatre in order to raise or lower planks and so forth, of which isolated beams, as well as panels let into the walls of Roman theatres, also give evidence. Lastly, very important war machines, dependent on the use of the lever, are supposed, according to Diodorus (first century B.C.), to have been invented by Pericles (492–429 B.C.), who had them made by a mechanic, Artemon, for besieging Samos (439 B.C.). We shall discuss these machines in greater detail later.

THE INCLINED PLANE

The inclined plane was also recognized in antiquity as a convenient means of raising heavy loads. Whether it played a part, as is thought by many, in the construction of the Pyramids (about 2800 B.C.) is doubtful. According to Herodotus (II, 125), the Pyramids were built in the following way with the help of lifting machines, whose exact nature he does not describe.

> 'This Pyramid was made like a stairway with tiers, courses or steps. When this, its first form, was completed, the workmen used levers made of short wooden logs to raise the rest of the stones. They heaved up the blocks from the ground on to the first tier of steps; when the stone had been so raised it was set on another lever that stood on the first tier, and a lever again drew it up from this tier to the next. It may be that there was a new lever on each tier of the steps, or perhaps there was but one lever, and that easily lifted, which they carried up to each tier in turn. I leave this uncertain, both ways being told me. But this is certain, that the upper part of the pyramid was the first finished off, then the next below it, and last of all the base and the lowest part.' (Transl. by A. D. Godley.)

If we disregard the last sentence, which Lepsius interprets as meaning that 'the uppermost step of the Pyramid was completed first, before the one lying below was finished, the process of filling in each step was carried out from below upwards', then the remarks of Herodotus tell us only of the use of elevating machines of an unknown kind in the building of the Pyramids. But it does not seem improbable that ramps, in the form of inclined planes, were present, which served to bring the stones up to these elevating machines, if we consider the method by which the Egyptians and the Assyrians, and probably also other peoples of the East, transported their heavy burdens, which they always placed on runner-shaped supports (sledges). Such a support can easily be pulled up an inclined plane. It cannot however be imagined that this inclined plane, as Diodorus writes, reached to the top of the Pyramid; it probably served only for bringing building materials to the elevating machines that had been erected. An extensive literature has gathered round the use of the inclined plane in the building of the Pyramids, from which we wish to point out only that Hirt does not consider the use of the inclined

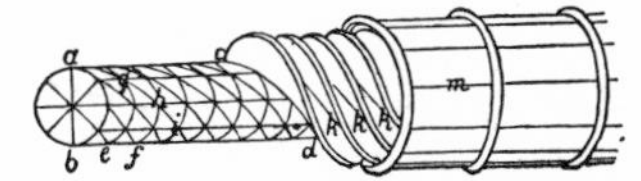

FIG. 265.—The Construction of Archimedes' Screw, according to the description of Vitruvius (X,6)

plane as probable, whereas Erman refuses to allow that a complicated mechanism was involved at all, and asserts that ‘these marvels were achieved by only *one* power—by innumerable human hands, which were ruthlessly exploited’.

The inclined plane acquired particular importance by being used in the form of the screw, which is supposed to have been invented by Archimedes while travelling in Egypt. But it is to be assumed that it had long been in use in that country, namely for pump-work in mines (‘Egyptian or Archi-

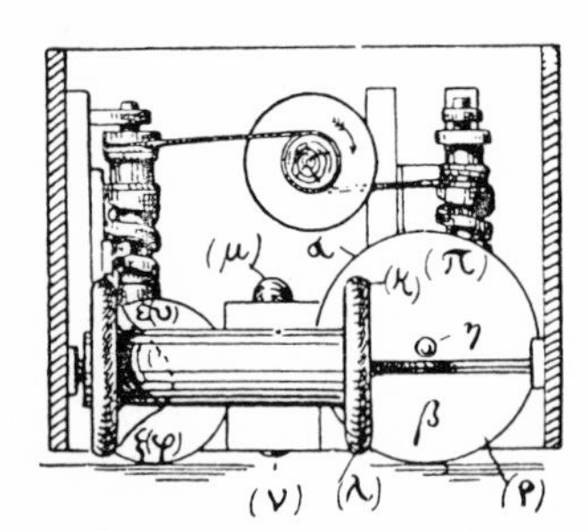

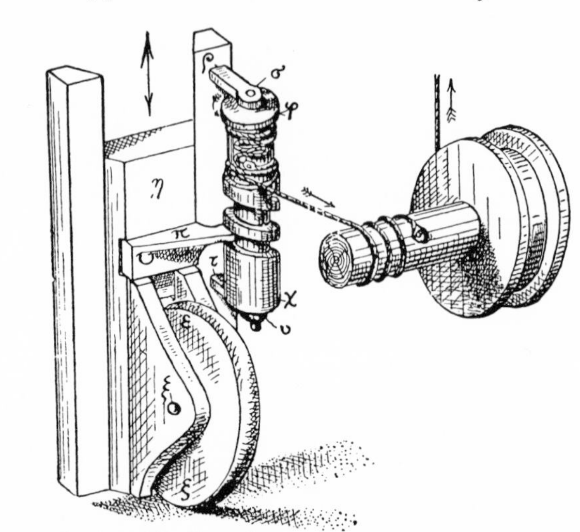

Figs. 266 and 267.—‘Endless Screws’

Worms of screws, compounded with pulleys and cords, used in the automatic machines of Heron of Alexandria. The device serves to raise and lower the wheel automatically

medes’ screw). The method of making it is described in detail by Vitruvius (X, 6). From this description, we see that the screw or worm was made of wood, and served at first exclusively for drawing water. It was in the shape of a long worm *k, k, k* (Fig. 265), whose grooves were enclosed in an envelope *m*, bound by hoops and covered with tar. The lower part of the worm, which ran obliquely and was fixed in scaffolding and driven by means of a treadle, dipped into water; by continual turning, the liquid was raised. Later, the screw was used for the single-screw olive-presses (Pliny, XVIII, 317), and in the double-screw cloth-presses (see the Section on Yarns and Textiles) and so forth. In other mechanical constructions, it was also used in the form of the ‘endless screw’ (Figs. 266, 267); in fibulae we find little screws of gold; iron screws do not seem to have been used by the ancients, as they have never been found.

THE PULLEY AND THE WEDGE

The pulley was even used by the Assyrians, and probably also by the Egyptians. Heron of Alexandria (? first century A.D.) used a combination of several pulleys of unequal size, for altering the rate of movement of dancing figures; that is, he used the device which we nowadays call ‘gearing’ (Fig. 269). From it there was then derived the much-used compound pulley (tackle of pulleys) which was particularly favoured by the Romans (Fig. 270). It may be surmised that it was also known to the Egyptians; at any rate Arnondeau assumes that it was used for raising obelisks; this is in agreement with Krusemann, who holds the opinion that these immense stones were raised with the help of a tackle of pulleys, which was fixed at the top of a pylon, and the rope from which was wound round the point of an obelisk that had been lowered on to a sand-heap from a slope. If Krusemann's view is correct, the raising of the obelisk on to this slope would again imply the use of an inclined plane by the Egyptians. In Roman times, the compound pulley was often used for oil presses, for theatrical machines, in the tackling of ships, and so forth; indeed it was even used in the Imperial Roman palaces for lifts and cranes. In the so-called 'hall of machines' excavated on the Palatine at a depth of 66 ft., niches were found in which the lifts worked, and also the tubes and grooves through which the

FIG. 268.

Use of Pulleys among the Assyrians for drawing water in a besieged town

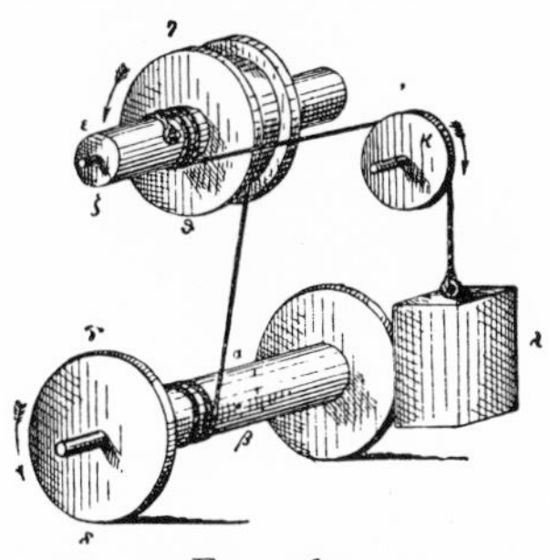

FIG. 269.

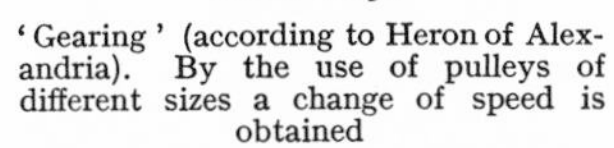

'Gearing' (according to Heron of Alexandria). By the use of pulleys of different sizes a change of speed is obtained

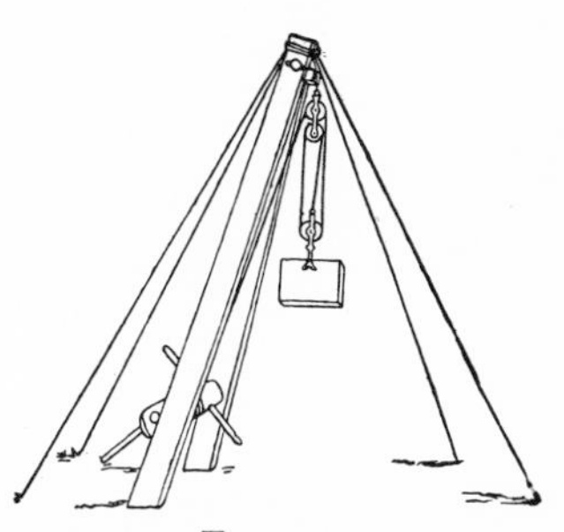

FIG. 270.

Roman compound pulley (according to the description by Vitruvius, X, 2)

pulleys passed. According to the number of pulleys used in the compound pulley, Vitruvius (X, 2) distinguishes between elevating machines, 'tackle of pulleys', which work with three pulleys, that is *trispastos*, and those with five pulleys, *pentaspastos*. For heavy loads, the *polyspastos* was used. The last offers the advantage of having to be fastened to only a single tree, as it works easily and quickly on account of its many pulleys. It was therefore used as a crane; 'the circumstance, however, that only one tree is present has the advantage that before the load is set down, the machine may be inclined at will, either to the right or to the left side' (Vitruvius, X, 2, 10).

In this process, the lifting machine is placed now upright and now horizontal on crane-discs (Vitruvius, *loc. cit.*). It also served for beaching ships.

A special variety of the pulley is the windlass, which is set into motion by lever action, and which was also a much-used machine; wire ropes were used with it, as perhaps also with the pulley, even in Roman times. In Pompeii such a rope made of bronze wire has been discovered.

All ancient peoples were expert in the use of the wedge. It served for a great number of purposes, at first in the form of numerous tools, such as the chisel, the hatchet, axe, and so forth, since primeval times. Later, large stones were split by means of it, and wedges were placed underneath loads in order to transport them more easily and to raise them.

OVERCOMING FRICTION (SLEDGE-RUNNERS, WHEELS AND VEHICLES)

It was early understood how to convert sliding friction into rolling friction. As already mentioned, the Egyptians used to transport huge masses on a kind of sledge-runner. Whether round logs were placed underneath to reduce the friction may be left an open question. It is likewise doubtful whether we must regard as round the logs which appear under such sledges in the pictures of the Assyrians (see Figs. 271 and 272). The direction in which they lie in some cases favours this interpretation, in others contradicts it. At any rate it is certain that the round log origi-

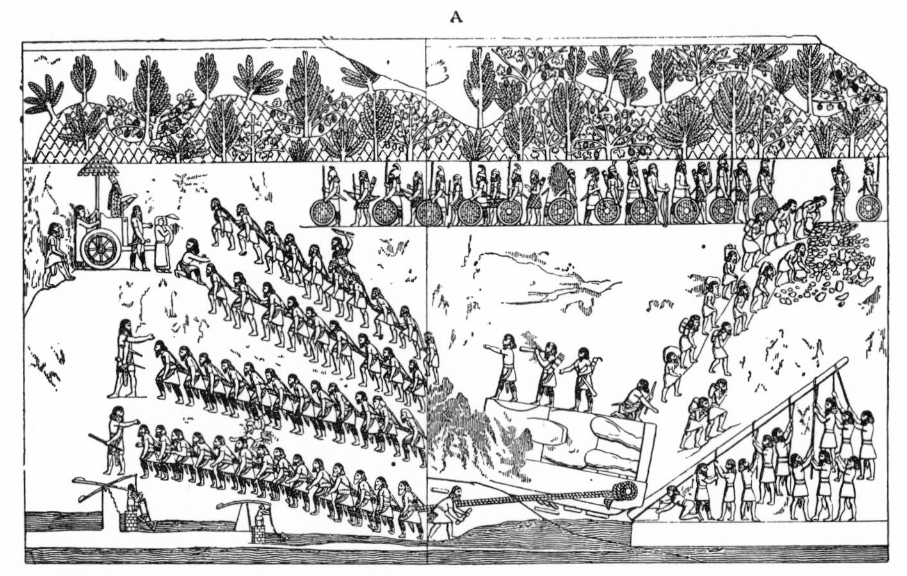

FIG. 271.—Assyrians using Sledge-runners for Transport. Bas-relief at Kujundschik

The load, placed on runners, is drawn from the front, and a lever used to assist the operation at the back is prevented from slipping off by having a block rammed against its lower end. There are pieces of wood, probably of circular section, under the runners, probably intended to convert sliding into rolling friction. The view that the wood is placed in the appropriate transverse position for this is supported by the way in which the man is holding the piece of wood that he is about to place underneath and by the foreshortening of the log behind his head due to its being drawn in perspective. Evidence against this view is, however, given by the position of the pieces of wood immediately in front of the lever. We may assume that they have been laterally displaced or discarded in the motion.[1] (Below on the left there is a shadoof: see also Fig. 257)

nally applied to use rolling friction, which facilitates transport, gave rise to the *wheel*. The wheeled vehicle necessarily appeared simultaneously with the wheel, but its beginnings are likewise lost in the obscurity of time. The vehicles of the Assyrians and the Egyptians used to have wheels with six, eight or more spokes, whereas the wheels of the Greeks were better constructed and had only four spokes. The earliest form of wheel was probably a simple wooden disc of moderate thickness. The spoked wheel was also of wood originally, and later was bound in metal; finally, it was made entirely of bronze. Bronze wheels of this type that have been preserved have round spokes and a felly with a deep groove. The

[1] They are certainly rollers, here and in Fig. 272, their apparent position resulting from the artists' lack of skill in foreshortening.—*Trans.*

segments of the circular wooden felly were fastened together with rivets. The tyre which bound together and served to fix the parts of the felly,

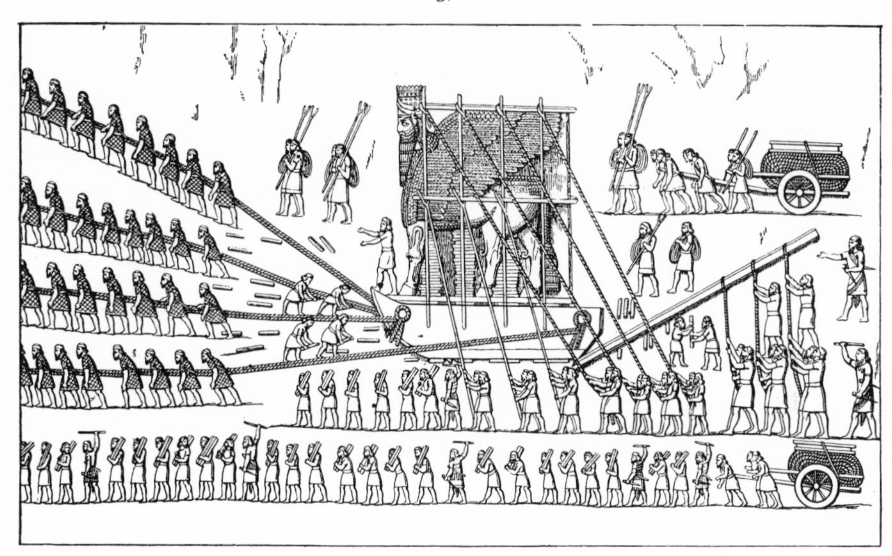

FIG. 272.—Assyrians transporting a gigantic Monument on Runners. Bas-relief at Kujundschik

A lever at the back, pieces of wood (logs) in front, behind and below the runners, lying partly lengthwise and partly transversely

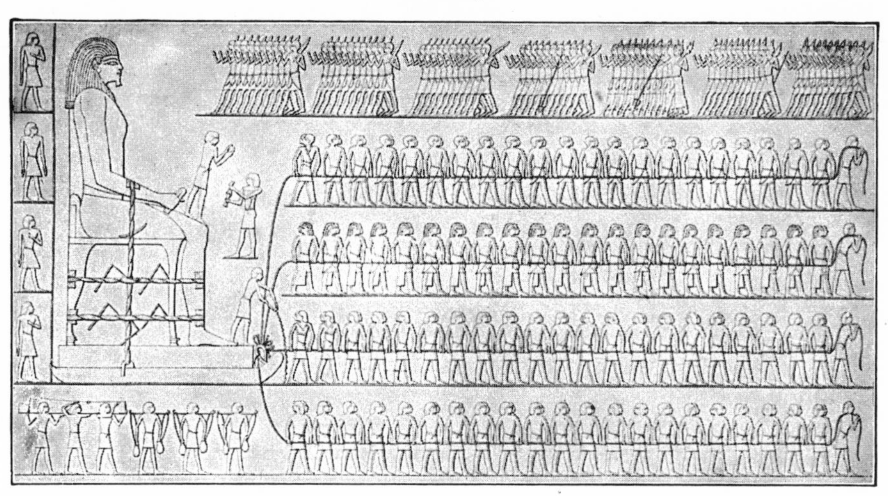

FIG. 273.—Egyptians transporting a Monument on Runners

The logs do not occur here; on the other hand, a man on the fore-part of the base is pouring water from a vessel just in front of the path (or the artificially-prepared slide (?)), in order to reduce the friction. Twelfth Dynasty (about 2000 B.C.). From a rock-tomb at Bersha

first rendered the wheel capable of surmounting the obstacles in its path. They were first made of nails, the heads of which were close together and covered the wooden fellies like scales. The tyre was only later made of one piece and fastened only by a few nails. It was first made of bronze, later of iron. The body of the ancient Egyptian chariot rested directly on the axle, which was connected with the movable shaft (Fig. 277). The round frame of the wheel consisted usually of six segments, which was

FIG. 274.—Egyptians transporting Monuments on Runners

In the two pictures on the left, the path, which has apparently been artificially constructed, is being watered. Funeral procession of Maia. Berlin Museum, Egyptian Department

certainly the easiest way of constructing it ; for it was already known at that time that the radius of a circle can be stepped off six times round the circumference. Each segment was usually attached to the hub by a spoke. But wheels also occur with more spokes, as already mentioned.

FIG. 275.—A large Vessel carried on Sledge-runners

From the tomb of Sheshonk. Abu Shehr. Berlin Museum, Egyptian Department

The revolving hub was pushed over the rounded ends of the axle. The gudgeon or bearing part of the axle was pierced with a hole and secured by a peg to prevent the wheel from slipping off. The axle itself was straight and had a square cross-section. The shaft was fixed to it and was inclined upwards. It was provided with two yokes to which the horses were harnessed. Besides these vehicles, there were also others for agricultural and similar purposes; they had solid wheels and were drawn by oxen. Four-wheeled waggons were also known, but were mostly used for religious purposes.

The vehicles of the Greeks resembled those of the Egyptians, but like

FIG. 276.—Assyrian Vehicle with Wheels of Eight Spokes

the Persians and the Romans they also used four-wheeled waggons for transporting heavy loads. The 'harmamaxa', in which the corpse of Alexander the Great (who died 323 B.C.) was conveyed from Babylon to Alexandria, was drawn by sixty-four mules, and also had four wheels. Regarding Persian vehicles special mention must be made of the scythed chariot [1] which was used in war. This form was not applied to this purpose

FIG. 277.—Egyptian Chariot (war-chariot). 8 ft. long
Museum, Cairo

by the Romans; nor was any other. In Roman times this was done only by the uncivilized peoples such as the Gauls, the Belgians, and the Britons.

There were very many different kinds of Roman vehicles. Some were drawn by two horses, others by three or four, which were always harnessed side by side (*bigae, trigae, quadrigae*). The drag-chain (*plaustrum*) was also known. It was wound through the back-wheel and chained to the body of the vehicle so as to prevent the rotation of the

[1] Wheels mounted with sharp sickle-shaped blades.—H. L. B.

FIG. 278.—Egyptians building Vehicles

Above : sawing the wood ; shaping the shaft; wheel (of four spokes, a rare form in the older Egyptian vehicles). Below : fastening the shaft to the body of the chariot ; bending and preparing wooden parts; stretching leather parts over a trestle

FIG. 279.—Greek Vase, showing a chariot with wheels of four spokes

Berlin, Altes Museum, Antiquarium

wheel. The usual method was to wind the chain round the felly between two spokes. The felly was not always cut out in a curved shape, but was bent artificially after the fibres of the wood had been softened in

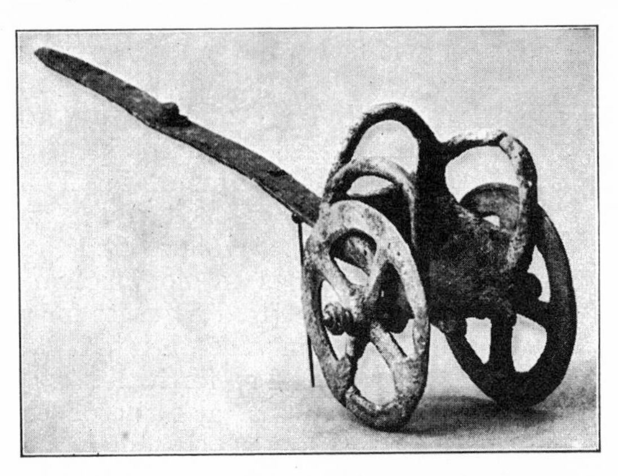

FIG. 280.—Greek Bronze Chariot with two wheels of four spokes (Model or Toy)
Berlin, Altes Museum, Antiquarium

hot water. The process seems to date from very early Grecian times; at least we may infer this from the following passage in Homer (*Iliad*, IV, 486): 'This (the poplar) hath a wainwright felled with gleaming steel, to bend him a felloe for a goodly chariot.'

TOOTHED WHEELS AND THEIR USES

The wheel also gave rise to one of the most important of the simple machines, namely the toothed wheel. If the teeth of two such wheels catch in each other, the wheels always rotate in opposite directions. It has not been possible to ascertain when this contrivance first came into use. Nor do we know whether Aristotle [1] (384–322 B.C.) is referring to toothed wheels (as Beck and Pregel hold) when he talks in his book on 'Mechanical Problems' of 'tools that set many circles in motion simultaneously by means of a single circle, like those votive offerings in the temples which consist of bronze or iron wheels, arranged as follows. When the wheel AB is turned forwards, while in contact with CD, the latter moves backwards, and, at the same time, for the same reason, EF revolves in the original direction, and so forth if there are still further wheels.' There are many reasons for believing that this refers to toothed wheels.

Vitruvius, on the other hand, often mentions the toothed wheel; and Heron of Alexandria applies it elegantly in an appliance like the modern taximeter which served the purpose of measuring the distance covered. In this hodometer (Fig. 281) a pin attached to the axle of the wheel (in the right-hand bottom corner of the diagram) catches in the radial pegs, and turns them when the axle rotates. This rotation is transmitted by means of endless screws and further toothed wheels to the indicator in line with Δ and carrying a small hand. The greater the

[1] See note on p. 203. The reference is to [Arist.] *Mechan.* 848a, 24.—*Trans.*

number of toothed wheels the greater the distance covered for one revolution of the indicator (that is, the more slowly the indicator moves). Each turn of the indicator denotes a definite distance traversed by the chariot. The small hands on the left of the figure serve to measure subdivisions of this distance. For the rest, Heron makes plentiful use of toothed wheels in his automatic machines and puppet shows, in which he sets the arms of the figures into motion by means of such wheels and lever devices (Fig. 282). We also find them mentioned in his writings in conjunction with winches: they were used together for a contrivance in temples in which a bird is rotated and made to sing and so forth (Fig. 283).

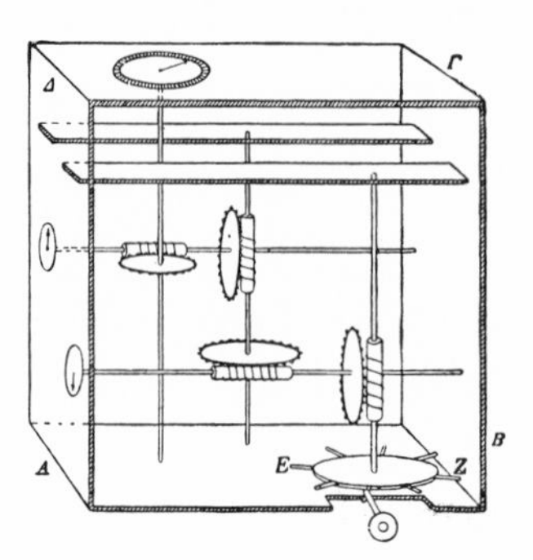

FIG. 281.—Apparatus for measuring distances (according to Heron of Alexandria). With toothed wheels and 'endless screws'

Vitruvius also describes a meter for carriages in which stones are used to record the distance covered in place of Heron's indicators.

'Let there be attached', he says, 'firmly to the nave on the inner side a (vertical) drum having one projecting tooth. Above it, on the carriage-body, let there be another (vertical) drum with 400 teeth, geared on to the lower one. Let it have a

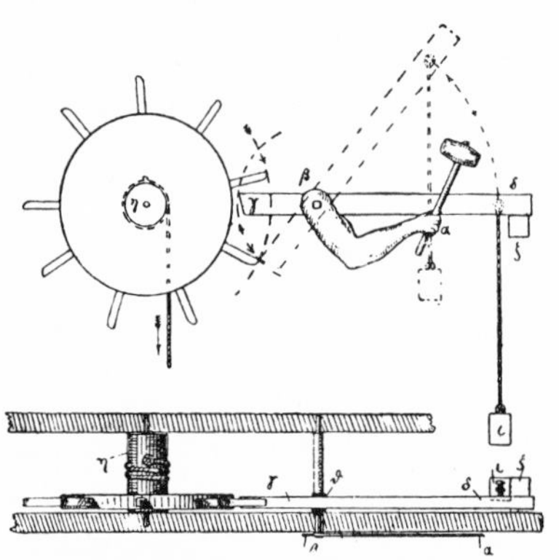

FIG. 282.—The Arm of a Puppet being moved by a toothed wheel (according to Heron of Alexandria)

The toothed wheel is here fixed to a spindle (so-called cam-wheel). When the spindle is turned by means of a weight it depresses the end γ of the lever. After the cam of the wheel has slipped over γ, γ is restored to its old position by the weight which acts on the other arm $\beta\epsilon$ of the lever, whereupon the next cam again depresses γ. This causes the arm $\beta\alpha$ to carry out a hammering motion. (Below is a sketch of the apparatus as seen from above)

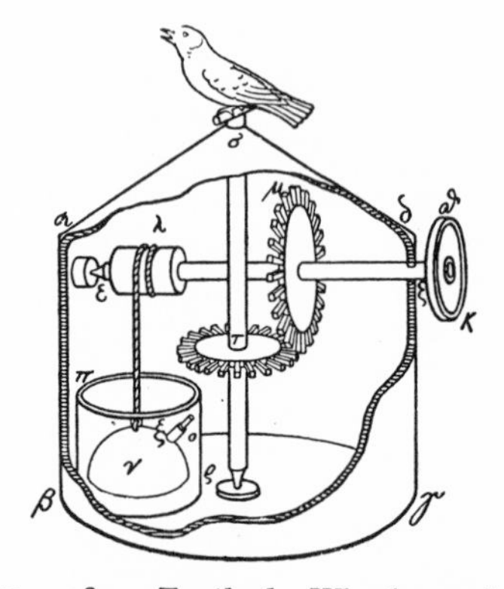

FIG. 283.—Toothed Wheels and Winches (according to Heron of Alexandria)

The apparatus consists of a bird which rotates and whistles when the wheel $\theta\kappa$ is turned. The whistling is produced by the air-chamber ν after it has been raised by turning $\theta\kappa$ and then, by releasing $\theta\kappa$, allowed to fall under its own weight into the vessel πo which is full of water. This forces the contained air through the pipe ξo.

stud which projects laterally. Geared on to this stud let there be a third drum, fixed horizontally, pierced with as many holes as the maximum number of miles the carriage can go on a day. In each hole place a pebble. In the case or covering of this last drum let there be a single tube, through which the pebbles, as they come over it, may drop into a bronze vessel placed underneath in the carriage-body. In this way, 400 revolutions of the wheel will move the second drum once around;

its stud will thus move a tooth of the horizontal drum ; a pebble will fall and its rattle will record the completion of a mile'. (Abbreviated from Vitruvius, *de archit.*, X, 9, 2–4.)

CAPSTAN AND TREAD-WHEEL

Very important forms of application of the wheel were the capstan

FIG. 284.—Gear propelled by a camel. Consisting of two wheels, with plugs mounted on the circumference. A construction for drawing water from the Nile—identically the same in form as that used by the ancient Egyptians

and the tread-wheel. The capstan is mentioned by Vitruvius, who is well aware of the difference between the capstan (or whim, *ergata*) and the windlass (*cula*). The first of these two kinds has its axle placed vertically ; in the second the axle lies horizontally. The capstan was chiefly used in Roman mills, where it was worked either by man-power or by animals, particularly

FIG. 285.—Capstan, consisting of a horizontal axle carrying one wheel with radial pegs on the circumference and another carrying a series of jars ; set up in the manner customary among the ancient Egyptians

FIG. 286.—Tread-wheel connected with a Bucket-system (Chain-pump)

asses. The oldest form of the toothed wheel occurred among the ancient Egyptians; it consisted of a wooden wheel the circumference of which was provided with plugs.

The tread-wheel served for pumping water, for moving loads, and also for erecting columns and similar objects. In the amphitheatre of Capua there is a relief still extant which represents a tread-wheel in which two naked youths are shown running. The motion of the wheel causes a rope to wind up on a pulley suspended from a framework of beams. A heavy column is fastened to one end of the rope. Alongside it a youth is seen chiselling a capital. Minerva is holding her hand in protection over the whole. For the rest, Philon of Byzantium (about 230 B.C.) mentions that the tread-wheel is used for drawing water.

ELASTICITY AND ITS APPLICATIONS: THE BOW, THE CROSSBOW AND BALLISTIC MACHINES

The elasticity of bodies was exploited by the ancients particularly for devices used in war. The simple bow is the oldest of all weapons for projecting missiles: this is true for almost any part of the world. In it the elasticity of wood is applied to shooting of the arrows. In the age of Homer it did not yet play a prominent part; and in the combats around Troy other arms were more important. In ancient times the wooden bow was made of the yew-tree or *taxus*. H. Menge assumes *τόξον* and *taxus* to be cognates. Besides the ordinary wooden kind a composite bow which was much more efficient was also used.[1] Odysseus mostly carried a bow of this sort. It had been given to him, to seal their friendship, by Iphitus (*Odyssey*, XXI, 13). It was made of horn carefully smoothed and of reflex curve (*παλίντονον*), and so large that it was not simply laid on the ground, but propped up against the door. When unused it was kept in a decorated case and hung up on a peg. When it was to be

FIG. 287.—Ordinary Wooden Bow from ancient Greece, the 'specifically' Greek Bow

In the separate drawing on the right the ends are shown too far bent

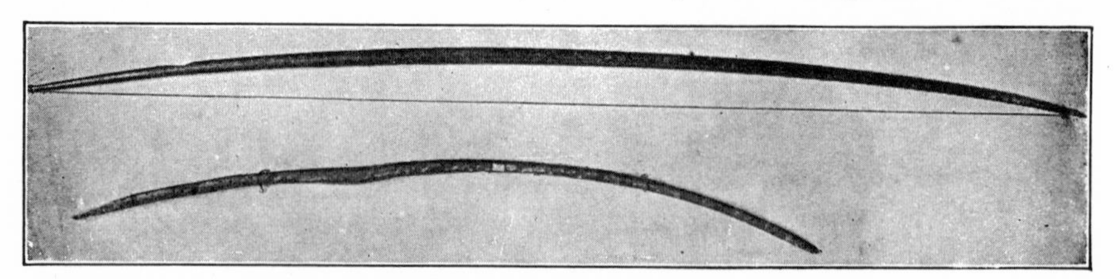

FIG. 288.—Egyptian Bows from tombs in Thebes

Above: Simple bow (length of string, 5 ft). Below: Artistically made composite bow (length of string, 3 ft. 6 in.) Berlin Museum, Egyptian Department

[1] See H. Balfour in *Journ. Roy. Anth. Inst.*, li (1921), p. 289.

restrung tallow was rubbed in, while it was warmed over a fire. From Homer's descriptions we may draw the further conclusion that the bow was normally kept in a relaxed condition, and that the string was fixed just before use. This was done in the following way: the loose end of the string was undone from the lower end of the bow and was hooked into the upper end (ἐνταvύειν). For this purpose the bow had to be bent (τιταίνειν). Then the arrow was placed on the bow, and the string further stretched to shoot it off. In *Iliad* IV, 105 *sqq.*, it is asserted that Pandaros' bow was made of the horns of a wild goat (pasang, *Capra hircus aegagrus*): a physical impossibility, for they will not bend. It must therefore have been composite, probably of horn, sinew, and wood. The composite bow was better and stronger than the simple wooden bow, but required more skill for its manipulation. Long before Homer the composite bow was used by the Egyptians (Fig. 288). One relic dates from the time of Rameses II, that is, from the thirteenth century B.C.; another originates from an Egyptian tomb of the seventh century B.C., that is, from the post-Homeric era. A very difficult matter in the manipulation of the bow was the fixing of the string. It is for this reason that the 'prudent' Penelope required this of her suitors. The composite bow which comes from Asia, where it still continues in use among some peoples (Fig. 289), is made of horn, wood and sinews, and recoils, that is, when unstrung it curves back in the opposite direction. If it is to be bent again, it has to be stretched first and then crooked in the

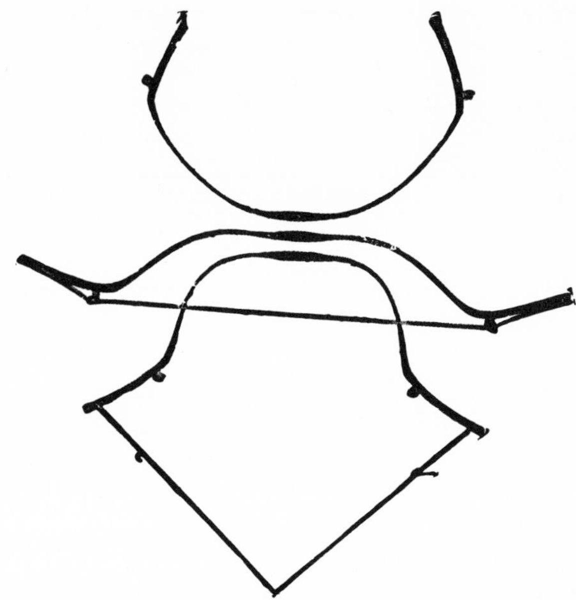

FIG. 289.—Greek Composite Bow of the Recoiling Type
Above: Unstrung. In the middle: Provided with a string. Below Bent for shooting

FIG. 290.—Greek Vase showing a Man in the act of bending a Bow of the recoiling type

reverse direction. To perform this a certain strength is needed, but above all a familiarity with the special trick involved. Penelope's suitors were ignorant of this knack, whereas Odysseus, being the owner of the bow, knew it well. The way in which a bow of this kind had to be strung is described by Buchner as follows. 'One loop of the string is fixed into the cut specially made at the top of the bow and is held fast there by the right hand. The back of the bow faces downwards. The right leg is then placed between the bow and the string, and the lower half of the bow is laid on the left knee, which thus takes over the pressure of reaction. In this position the lower loop of the string is fixed into the corresponding cut in the lower end of the bow by the left hand which has now become free.' Buchner states that this method of stringing a bow, 'which must obviously be the same as that practised by the Turks, was probably usual among the ancient Greeks, who had similar bows at a later period.' It can also be strung in a sitting posture, and it is in this way that Odysseus is likely to have done it.

These statements are in accordance with those of an anonymous writer in the *Tägliche Rundschau* (22nd June, 1914) describing the bending of a compound bow which came from the Dutch East Indies. The string is thick and solid; it is made of animal gut twisted together. 'The bow was made of black horn. It was from two to two and a half inches wide, about two-fifths of an inch thick and five feet long. In the middle it had a round piece of wood four to five inches long and two inches thick, which served as a handle. To it the two long pieces of horn were fixed by means of two iron rings. Threads were artistically twisted round the handle.'[1] The string had a loop at both ends. A first attempt at bending the bow was unsuccessful. It slipped through the hands, twisted around and assumed its original form. It was only when laid on the upper and lower thigh that the string readily allowed itself to be fastened to the notch in the bow. Less force was necessary for bending the bow than for shooting, but it could be done only by someone familiar with the trick. The full strength of a man was needed to produce the necessary tension for shooting. The arrow would then travel over thirty yards. As the driving power of the bow increased considerably for a small increase in tension, the composite bow, which gradually superseded the wooden bows in Greece, would carry to remarkable distances if used by strong and skilled archers. The arrow dispatched by a composite bow can fly as far as a thousand yards and is capable of shooting right through a bison, as is known from an investigation of the bow of the Sioux Indians, which is likewise a composite bow made of horn. This achievement cannot be equalled by the heavy Colt revolver used by the American army. A great number of Assyrian, Babylonian, Egyptian and Greek pictures, showing the simple or composite bow or the bending of the latter, are still extant.

A natural development of the bow was the arbalest or crossbow.

[1] The description shows this to have been a compound bow, *i.e.* one made of two pieces of the same material joined together. The Homeric bow was probably composite, *i.e.* made of a combination of different materials.—*Trans.*

The ancient Greeks knew of a species of crossbows which were bent by a winch or spanner. The front end of the stock was firmly planted against the ground, and the back end pressed down by the lower part of the body in order to hold the weapon tight while it was being stretched. In the Middle Ages, too, ample use was made of the crossbow. It is hardly necessary to describe it, as the details of its construction and manipulation are well known. Here again it is the elasticity of a bow stretched into a frame that shoots off the missile—in this case the arrow.

Although the achievements of the ancient bows are amazing even from the point of view of the modern science of ballistics, they were surpassed by the ancient ballistic machines, whose action likewise depended on the exploiting of the property of elasticity. In these the tension was generally brought about by twisting a cable composed of several strands. The same principle is still observed nowadays in the way in which the strings of saws are tightened, as was also done by the ancients in the case of saws. When such a saw is loosened the wooden peg held fast in the twisted string recoils with great force against the middle part of the saw-frame. A single extra turn of the peg considerably increases the tension. In the ancient ballistic machines, designated by the generic term *tormenta*,[1] the tension was extraordinarily increased by means of levers and winches. While the use of ballistic machines attained its zenith with the Romans, they were undoubtedly also used by the peoples of the East. In the Second Book of Chronicles (xxvi, 15) it is said of Uzziah, King of Judah (779–740 B.C.), 'And he made in Jerusalem engines, invented by cunning men, to be in the towers and upon the bulwarks, to shoot arrows and great stones withal'.

The essential constituent part of all these ancient ballistic machines is the twisted cable, consisting of intertwined cords resembling a sinew-pack. According to the number of these cables we may distinguish between weapons with one arm and one cable, and those with two arms and two cables. Hemp and flax, the usual materials for making ropes, attract moisture from the air and particularly in rainy weather absorb large quantities of it, which causes a change in length and also in the resistance to torsion. For this reason substances were chosen as a rule whose sensitiveness to moisture had a less troublesome effect. Among materials of this kind there were, above all, the sinews of animals, horse-hair and women's hair. One way of producing tension is by twisting. In order to save time and energy, however, the separate strands of the cable were tightened as much as possible beforehand. The method of doing this, which was also adopted in the reconstructions at Saalburg, was probably as follows: a cord was fastened at one end to a peg in a specially constructed frame; it was then wound to and fro through holes and over pegs until the other end was reached, which was then also fastened. During the whole process the cord was kept stretched to the utmost.

Ammianus Marcellinus (XXIII, 4, 4), who died about A.D. 400, gives us a description, complete in all details, of one particular kind of ancient

[1] Ballistae and catapults are terms often applied to such weapons, but they do not characterize them in the least.

one-armed ballistic machine, the *μονάγκων*, or onager (wild ass), a nickname given to it by the soldiers since by kicking out with its hind legs, a wild ass flings earth and stones ; it is also called *scorpio* because the slinging arm of the weapon, which is curved upwards, resembles the telson, the hooked tail, of the scorpion.

It appears from the exhaustive and standard investigations of Schneider, whom we here follow, that it consisted of a lower part made of two solid horizontal beams of oak, firmly joined by cross-beams 'like the runners of a threshing-sledge' (*hique in modum serratoriae machinae connectuntur*). The beams are higher in the middle, carrying bosses through which holes are bored to take the horizontal cable which is tightly stretched to and fro over the tension-pegs fixed outside in the manner already described. Fixed in the middle of this bundle of cords there is a wooden arm which usually projects obliquely upwards and is capable of motion backwards below or forwards above. To its upper end there is attached a sling made of cords into which the missile, a stone, is placed. The slinging arm could be moved backwards by means of a windlass and held in that position by a bolt. This movement still further tightened the already taut bundle of cords. When the bolt was now knocked off the arm was suddenly dragged forwards by the cords, striking a buffer which was protected from the violent recoil by a cushion. In obedience to the law of inertia the sling retained its forward motion even after the sudden stopping of the arm, so that the stone flew towards its goal in a high trajectory. The sudden check to the motion of the arm, however, caused a recoil which made it necessary to mount the machine on a base which yielded to pressure, such as turf or air-dried bricks. A platform of solid stone would have been split asunder under the strain of the recoil.

FIG. 291.—'Onager' (Ballista with one arm). Tightening the slinging arm
Reconstruction by Schramm

Reconstructions of the 'onager' as well as of other kinds of ballistic machines have been made by Schramm. The wrenching power of the stretched cords, which amounts to an initial pressure of about 14 tons in the two-armed machines to be discussed presently, was increased to 70 tons in the great onager at Saalburg: this is equal to the tractive power of a very powerful locomotive. Experiments in which this initial pressure was used showed that it was possible to hurl a stone sphere over 4 lbs. in weight a distance of nearly 400 yds.

By exploiting the elasticity of two bundles of sinews in place of that of one there developed from the one-armed ballista that with two arms, which can shoot forth either arrows (*ὄργανα ὀξυβελῆ*) or stones (*λιθοβόλα*).

There are thus two kinds of two-armed ballistae, a lighter one for shooting arrows, the *euthytona* (εὐθύτονα) and the heavier type for hurling stones, the *palintona* (παλίντονα). So we may talk of a light and a heavy artillery even of the ancients. The weapon projecting arrows could be of a lighter structure, as less power was necessary to produce the necessary tension. Those of the second kind were built more solidly. They were specially strengthened at the back and were bent, not by man-power, but by the aid of winches or compound pulleys.

FIG. 292.—Onager. In a state of tension, ready for shooting
Reconstruction by Schramm

The two-armed ballistae are not crossbows, although their appearance might easily lead one to mistake them for such. The difference consists in the fact that the crossbow is merely an improved bow, shooting the missile in virtue of its elasticity. The two-armed ballista, on the other hand, is an advance on the onager: the missile is projected by the tension of the bundle of cords. It is not a compound bow. Its two halves have no connection with each other; each acts independently of the other. Their sole purpose is to transfer the power from the two bundles of cords to the sinew (string). In stretching the crossbow the bow is bent, whereas in the case of the two-armed ballista the two halves of the bow act merely as levers, transferring the tension to the bundles of cords.

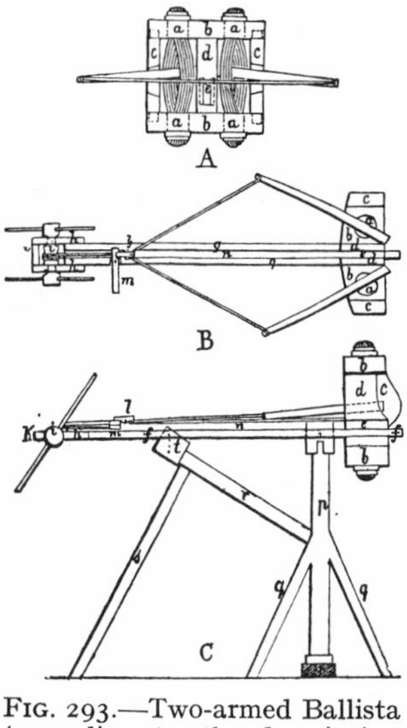

FIG. 293.—Two-armed Ballista (according to the description of Vitruvius, X 10)

f, groove between bars with strips *g* on each side; *hik*, windlass for stretching; *ml*, trigger (or handle); *n*, middle bar on which the arrow was placed; *bcd*, stretching frame; *aa*, the two bundles of sinews; *pq*, stand with three struts; *rst*, props (when movable, presumably a means of directing the aim of the arrow)

The ballista with two arms was furnished with devices for sighting, altering elevation and traversing; all these things were accomplished with great ease and accuracy, so that their aim was true to a high degree, see for instance the *de bello Africo*, xxiv, 4). In Schramm's model a lead ball weighing 1 lb. was carried some 330 yards. The light *euthytonon* reconstructed from a stretching frame found in 1912 at Ampurias in Spain was capable of shooting short arrows 340 yds. against the wind. Four arrows, each 4 *spithamai*, that is 3 ft. in length, like those of ancient Greece, when dispatched from a two-armed ballista built according to Vitruvius' descriptions, 'pierced an iron-plated shield 1¼ in. thick, half of the arrow (1½ ft.) passing through it: thus a man carrying it would have been put out of action when hit' (Schramm).

Notwithstanding these achievements, however, the ancient ballistae had various defects, the greatest of which was the slackening of the cords through being continually subjected to tension. Philon of Byzantium (about 230 B.C.) therefore suggested improvements in the construction, as described in the fourth book of his *mechanica syntaxis*. His first advance consisted in making a 'wedge-spanner' by which wedges

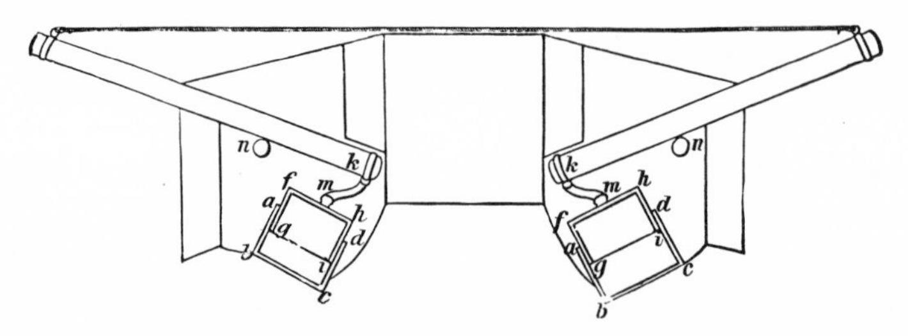

FIG. 294.—The Pneumatic Spanner of Ktesibios

The airtight pistons *fghi* move to and fro in the cylinders *abcd*. When pushed into the cylinders they compress the contained air. By means of the joints *km* the pistons are linked up with two arms, which turn on the axles *n* and are connected at their upper ends with the string, which discharges the missiles. When the string was stretched the pistons moved into the cylinders, and when it was released they were forced outwards by the compressed air and in turn forced the string against the missile with great violence so that it was propelled in a trajectory of considerable range

were forced into the bundle of cords in order to keep up the necessary tension. It is clear that any slackening can be counterbalanced in this way. A further improvement was the 'bronze spanner', *chalkotonon* (χαλκότονον), in which the defective cords were replaced by bronze, that is, metal. But it is doubtful whether all these good ideas were actually put into practice, for no mention is made in the literature of antiquity of the actual use of the spanner with wedges or the brass spanner. They have been reconstructed by Schramm, but the results they gave were in no wise better than those of the older machines. If they were constructed at all in antiquity their advantages must have been that they worked more consistently and were unaffected by the weather rather than any ballistic superiority.

Another invention of this type originates from Ktesibios, who probably lived in the second century B.C. It is the 'pneumatic spanner' (ὁ κληθεὶς ἀεροτόνος, see Fig. 294, above). By this device the string of the bow was stretched by cylinders in which pistons compressed the contained air. Although Philon praises this 'pneumatic spanner', it does not seem to have become popular either. Reconstructions by Schramm gave no noteworthy results (Fig. 294).

More important than these machines was the multiple charged

polybolos (πολυβόλος) invented by Dionysios of Alexandria. It is a kind of machine-gun in which the tension is generated by turning a crank. By this action an arrow is at the same time automatically placed ready for a fresh shot. The arrows come out of a funnel situated above the arrow-groove and first slide on to a reel which is turned by the crank and which has a groove for receiving the arrow. After a half-turn this groove is at the bottom and allows the arrow to drop into the arrow-groove ready for discharging. The machine was worked by one man. It is also praised by Philon, but to what extent it came to be used is not known. The reconstructed models are surprisingly accurate in their aim, the only defect being that all the arrows were directed at the same spot, so that there was no 'scattering'. Under certain circumstances this is an advantage, for example, when it is a matter of preventing the enemy from climbing up scaling-ladders or ramparts or from making their exit through a gate.

To understand fully the ancient art of constructing ballistic machines it is essential to know that in his descriptions Vitruvius expresses the dimensions of the machine in terms of the given length of the shaft of the arrow as the unit,[1] The diameter of the holes through which the sinews are stretched is one-ninth of this unit, and is the derived unit, that is $d = \frac{1}{9}(l)$ where l is the length of the shaft, in terms of which all the other measures are given.

HYDRAULICS

In hydraulics it is the siphon, above all, that was used in antiquity for manifold purposes: it occurred in the form of the ordinary siphon as well as in that of the plunging-siphon and the hydraulic press. The Egyptians were foremost in using the ordinary form as an every-day appliance. A great number of ancient representations inform us that they not only transferred liquid from one vessel to another by means of it but also used it in drinking. The forerunner of the siphon may have been a pipe used for sucking as depicted in Fig. 295: such a pipe cannot be regarded as a true siphon although it makes use of the atmospheric pressure on liquids to raise them out of a vessel to the level of the mouth. If, while sucking or drinking, the longer limb of the bent pipe were allowed to fall quickly enough and if by accident the lower surface of the liquid in this limb came to lie below the free surface of the liquid in the vessel, siphoning would occur automatically, and the liquid would flow out in spite of its having first to flow upwards in the shorter limb. Perhaps Fig. 295 actually depicts how a siphon is started by sucking. The three points which favour this view are the length of the one limb (which is apparently being supported to prevent the snapping of the bent pipe), the fact that there is a bend, and that the youth is holding in his left hand another vessel which is probably to be filled and offered to the woman waiting on the right.

[1] Vitruvius says (X, 10, 1): 'The proportions of these engines are all computed from the given length of the arrow which the engine is intended to throw, and the size of the holes in the capitals through which the twisted sinews that hold the arms are stretched is one-ninth of that length.'

An extraordinary number of applications of the siphon are given by Heron of Alexandria, who also occupied himself with the theory of the action, making liberal use of the teachings of his master[1] Ktesibios.

The plunging-siphon was also used for extracting and transferring drinks. Philon of Byzantium gave a theory of its action as well as of the ordinary siphon. It occurs very often in the form of an inverted poppy ('Aristotle's sieve'), such as was also used in the oldest form of water-clock, the clepsydra, as early as 522 B.C. The clepsydra consisted of a narrow tube open at the top and widening out in the shape of a poppy at the bottom, the base being perforated over a fairly small region. The clepsydra represents nothing more than a plunging-siphon: it was filled by being plunged into water and left until it had become full. The upper aperture was then held closed in order that the pressure of the air should prevent the escape of the water through the narrow orifices. So soon as the upper aperture was uncovered, the water escaped at the lower end. The interval which elapsed while the vessel emptied itself could serve as a measure of time. The rate of flow was of course not uniform, being quicker at the beginning and gradually decreasing. The chief use of the clepsydra up till 422 B.C. was for physical experiments (by Empedocles and others) and also to a smaller degree as a kitchen-clock for boiling eggs. After that date it became the universal instrument for measuring time, for example, in the law-courts, where the time allocated to orators for their speeches was measured by it. Doctors also used it for counting pulse-beats. The action of the famous water-clock of Ktesibios (Fig. 296) is based on that of the plunging-siphon. For Philon of Byzantium writes that Ktesibios had made a fine tube by boring a small hole in a piece of gold or a precious stone through which the water flowed out regularly into a large vessel beneath. The rising water in this vessel raised a float

FIG. 295.—A Sucker in use

A seated Syrian sucking up liquid out of a jar by means of a bent pipe. A painted tombstone in the form of a door. Made of limestone. Height, 1 ft.; width, 10 in. Berlin Museum, Egyptian section

[1] That Heron was actually a pupil of Ktesibios is by no means certain.—*Trans.*

carrying a rod provided with little teeth which caught in toothed wheels and brought about all the motions necessary for recording time. The Deutsches Museum in Munich possesses a reconstructed model of Ktesibios' water-clock made by Speckhart. The internal mechanism is as just described. The rack and pinion and other toothed gearing are connected with a column 4 ft. high, on the cylindrical surface of which the hours of the day from one to twelve twice over are marked from below upwards. On the right at the foot of the column there is a female figure from whose eyes tears are continually falling. These tears collect in a vertical tube and gradually raise a float which supports a second female figure on the left of the column, whose purpose is to indicate the hour by means of a rod while moving past the column. When the figure has traversed the twelve hours of day and the twelve hours of night, a valve opens in the large collecting chamber and allows the water in it to flow out on to a water-wheel which makes the toothed gearing turn by a certain amount and so causes the cylindrical column to register the advance of a day. Thus the

FIG. 296.—Ktesibios' Water-clock as reconstructed by Speckhart

Deutsches Museum, Munich

column moves once round its axis in 365 days. In this process the collecting chamber empties itself completely, and the figure with the supporting float rapidly sinks to its initial position, closing the valve, and then begins to indicate the succession of hours of the new day. Each new day is recorded by means of the tongue of a serpent in the act of rearing itself up. Similar water-clocks were in use in Egypt as early as 300 B.C.

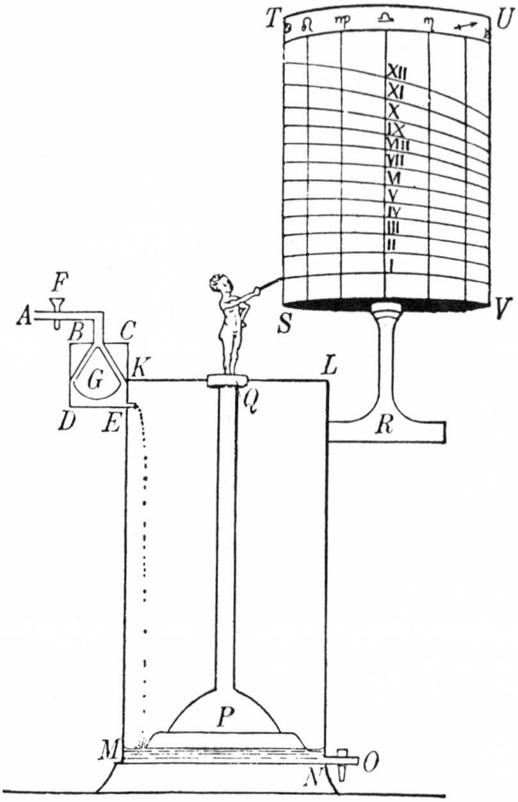

FIG. 297.—Ktesibios' Water-clock as reconstructed by Diels
See the additional note on p. 232.

The principle of its action is sufficiently clearly seen in this reconstructed model. There may be differences of opinion about the details, such as how the rate of flow into the collecting chamber was regulated, how the length of the hour was adapted to the prevalent season, for according to the convention of the ancients the hours were shorter in winter than in summer, since the time between sunrise and sunset was simply divided into twelve equal parts. As pointed out by Diels, the apparatus could be adapted to meet the varying length of the hour in two ways: either by altering the rate of supply of the water according to the season, or by making the indicating device variable. In the latter case the inflow of water must remain quite constant. Diels solves the problem of producing a regular supply in his reconstructed model (Fig. 297) by following the directions of Vitruvius[1] (IX, 8, 6). The second method of overcoming the difficulty raised by the varying length of the hour in the different seasons was very simple. It is visible in Speckhart's model as well as in that of Diels, and is as follows.

The signs of the Zodiac are written around the top of the rotating column. Below each sign twelve equal spaces are marked out, but the space under each sign differs in size from those under any other sign; that is, only meshes in the same vertical column are equal. As we pass along the signs of the Zodiac in the direction of the winter months, the

[1] See p. 232.

meshes in the corresponding columns become successively narrower, since the hours become shorter. On the other hand, in the direction of the summer months the meshes become broader, corresponding to longer hours. As mentioned above, the column performs a complete revolution once in 365 days. In this way the figure standing on the float indicates with its rod shorter hours in winter and longer hours in summer.

The hydraulic press served in antiquity to convey water over hills; in this way water was sometimes raised to considerable heights (over 1,000 ft. at Pergamon). Further details will be found in the Section on Water Supply.

THE PRESSURE OF WATER: THE WATER-WHEEL

To exploit the pressure of water the water-wheel was used, but it was known only in the under-shot form. In Roman times it was used both on land and on ships. The frequent assertion that over-shot water-wheels were also used for technical purposes is not corroborated by trustworthy evidence. One important form in which the under-shot wheel was universally used in antiquity was the Persian wheel or noria. Vitruvius (X, 5, 1) writes as follows about it:

'Wheels are used in rivers in the same fashion as has been described above. Around them boards are attached and these being struck by the rush of the stream move forward and force the wheel to turn, and in this fashion they draw up the water in buckets and carry it to the top without workmen to tread the wheel. Thus, being turned by the flow of the stream, the wheels furnish what is necessary for the purpose in hand.

'Water-mills are turned in the same fashion.'

FIG. 298.—Use of the under-shot Water-wheel in the manner of the ancient Romans. Near Wolkenstein in the Val di Gardena

For the rest, the under-shot water-wheel has survived up to the present day in many Alpine valleys, whose civilization dates back to Roman times even in places where the middle- or over-shot wheel would have been equally suitable on technical grounds.

EXPLOITING GAS-PRESSURE

Gas-pressure was made use of in antiquity only in isolated instances, but both atmospheric and steam pressure found some applications. We have already described how Ktesibios made use of air-pressure in the brass spanner for bending bows. A more important application is the force-pump, also invented by Ktesibios, of which several descriptions have been handed down to us. We will quote that of Vitruvius (X, 7), which seems to be the best:

'It is made of bronze, and has at the bottom a pair of cylinders (*aa*) set a little way apart, and there is a Y-shaped pipe (*c*) connected with both (*bb*), and joining them to a vessel (*d*) which is between the cylinders. In this vessel are valves (*e*) accurately fitting over the upper vents of the pipes, which stop up the vent-holes, and keep what has been forced by pressure into the vessel from going down again.

'Over the vessel a cowl (*f*) is adjusted, like an inverted funnel, and fastened to the vessel by means of a wedge thrust through a staple, to prevent it from being lifted off by the pressure of the water that is forced in. On top of this a pipe is jointed, called the trumpet, which stands up vertically. Valves are inserted in the cylinders, beneath the lower vents (*g*) of the pipes, and over the openings (*h*) which are in the bottoms of the cylinders.

'Pistons (*i*) smoothly turned, rubbed with oil, and inserted from above into the cylinders, work with their rods (*k*) and levers upon the air and water in the cylinders, and, as the valves stop up the openings, force and drive the water, by repeated pressure and expansion, through the vents of the pipes into the vessel, from which the cowl receives the inflated currents, and sends them up through the pipe at the top; and so the water can be supplied for a fountain from a reservoir at a lower level.'

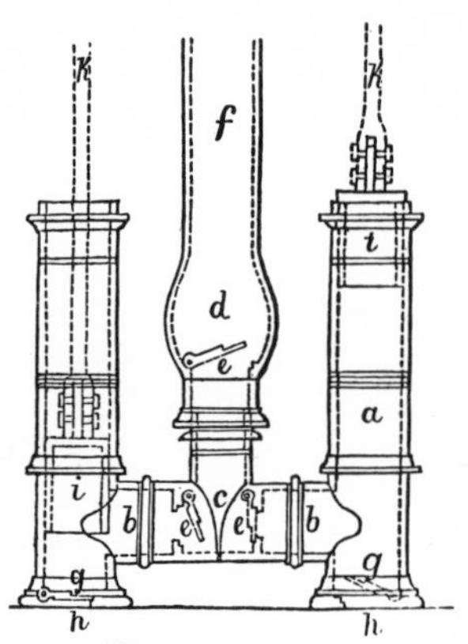

FIG. 299.—Fire-pump. Reconstructed according to the directions of Vitruvius

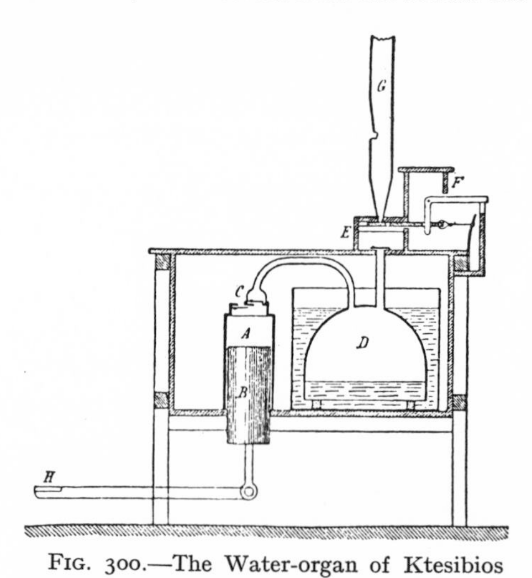

FIG. 300.—The Water-organ of Ktesibios

If the lever-arm H is pressed down by foot, the piston B is pressed upwards in the cylinder A. This forces the air in A to pass through the valve C into D. If the piston sinks under its own weight, air is again drawn into A and is again forced over into D. The air in the receiver D presses down the contained water and causes the level of the water outside to rise. The pressure of this water makes the air in D and E rush through the organ pipe G and causes it to sound whenever E and G are brought into communication by striking the key F

There were no hoses to the pump. The architect Apollodorus, who lived in the reign of Trajan, sought to overcome this defect by using the intestines of oxen for hoses. To one end of them was attached a reservoir made of skins sewn together and filled with water. The water was expelled by pressing together these *siphones*, as they were called. Firemen's work was carried out in Rome by the *siphonarii*.

In the ruins of Castrum Novum a pump was found which in the main agrees with the above description, except that the two pipes are not oblique but run horizontally into the air-chamber; this chamber is weakly constructed, being of one piece with the cowl, whereas Vitruvius prescribes two pieces.

The action of Ktesibios' water-organ (Fig. 300) likewise depends on the effect of air-pressure. Air is compressed by a piston and forced into a receiver. It displaces the water in this receiver. The displaced water causes the level of the water in a larger surrounding chamber to rise. This outer water transmits its pressure to that within the receiver and therefore also to the contained air. When a valve attached to the receiver is opened, the air rushes out and is directed into the organ pipes situated immediately above. While the air is being expelled the water gradually enters the receiver from the outer chamber owing to the pressure of the outer water, until the receiver is at last full of water again.

Furthermore, air-pressure is utilized in the apparatus known as Heron's fountain, invented by Heron and still called after him. We may assume

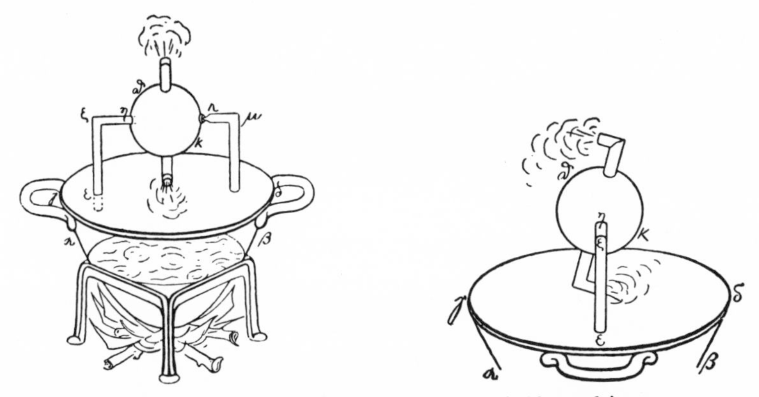

FIG. 301.—The Aeolipile of Heron of Alexandria

that the reader is familiar with its construction. It was probably of no particular technical value to the ancients. On the other hand, Archytas of Tarentum (about 400–365 B.C.) set into motion a flying-machine in the form of a wooden dove by means of compressed air (Gellius, N. A. X, 12, 9 *et seq.*).

The pressure of steam was exploited in the aeolipile (nowadays called Barker's mill) of Heron: it may be called the first turbine that was made. Heron himself gives a description of it somewhat as follows:

> 'The object is to make a ball move on a pivot over a heated vessel. Let $\alpha\beta$ (Fig. 301) be such a vessel, containing boiling water. Let it be closed at the top by a lid $\gamma\delta$, to which is fixed a bent tube $\varepsilon\zeta\eta$: this tube is connected by an air-tight joint with a hollow ball $\theta\varkappa$. Diametrically opposite η there is a pin $\lambda\mu$ resting on the lid. The ball is furnished with bent hollow arms also diametrically opposite one another; these arms and tubes are connected with the ball and are bent in opposite directions. The bends must be imagined right-angled and perpendicular to the line $\eta\lambda$. When the boiler is heated the steam enters the ball through $\varepsilon\zeta\eta$ and consequently issues forth through the bent arms, impinges upon the lid, and so causes the ball to rotate in a manner similar to that of the dancing figures.'

(In the latter the motion is produced not by steam but by means of hot air.)

For the rest, steam pressure was not only used in the above form, in which it exerts a dynamic effect, but also in the form in which it is nowadays exploited in Papin's digester, that is, for cooking meat. The Greek physician Philumenos reports of this about A.D. 250 as follows.

> 'The meat is placed in a pot containing rain-water. This pot is then closed and greased (*clausam ollam illiniri*) and placed at night in an oven filled with glowing coals. It is left all night. The steam causes the meat partly to dissolve and produces a thick gelatinous brew.'

In a later passage he remarks about the preparation of a kind of aspic : ' Many people also cook calves' feet (*ungulas vitulinas*) in the broth all night long, until they dissolve, and then the liquid becomes stiff and gelatinous ' (*spissus fit et glutinosus*).

Diels' Note on the action of Ktesibios' Water-clock depicted on p. 228 :

The water from the pipe A passes through the tap F by which the supply can be cut off ; it passes into the regulating chamber BCDE and through E by way of a fine tube out into the reservoir KLMN. If the pressure in the main-pipe A is great the water in the small chamber will not pass in the ordinary way through E, but will accumulate and so raise the float G whose upper surface is conical, so that the supply from the main-pipe is cut off. As the water flows out through E the level of the water gradually falls and with it the float, so that the water from A can flow in more readily until the normal level is again reached.

METHODS OF PRODUCING FIRE: LIGHTING AND HEATING

FIRE—APPLIANCES

THE technique of lighting and heating was bound to remain on an elementary plane so long as the kindling and keeping up of fires were more or less a matter of chance. The real development began with the time when man had acquired a certain skill in making up fires, and when he possessed those contrivances which may be summarized under the name of fire-appliances. The place and date of their origin is lost in the obscurity of prehistoric ages. Whereas many archaeologists maintain that the art of kindling a fire at will must have 'reasoned out', others are of the more justifiable opinion that this art owes its existence to observation and experience. It is very probable that in the making of primitive tools and weapons it was frequently observed that the piece of wood which was about to be pierced by being bored with another piece of wood ignited spontaneously, if both pieces were sufficiently dry and covered with boring dust.

At any rate such appliances, which produced ignition by the friction of wood against wood, are found among all the people of antiquity and even in prehistoric periods. In the 'Homeric' Hymn to Hermes we read :

> 'And he brought together much wood, and sought after the art of fire. A fair bough of laurel he took and smoothed it to a point (?) with iron *and therewith drilled*, for well it fitted his hand, till a hot breath arose. Yea, Hermes first of all produced firesticks and fire. And much dry wood he took ; in a trench in the earth, in bundles (?), did he lay it in great abundance ; and the flame gleamed, shooting forth afar a jet of fire that is mickle of might.' (108–114 ; see Sikes and Allen's notes.)

If this corrupt and difficult passage is rightly interpreted, and it seems certain that something equivalent to the words in italics must be supplied, we have a description of the fire-drill in a simple form. Wood of the laurel was employed by the Greeks and Romans for a very long time for the purpose of ignition. A large piece of soft wood was taken, preferably ivy or clematis, in which several holes were bored. In one of these holes a rod of hard wood was placed which was provided with a handle of hemispherical form similar to that of the bores used in the same way. One hand was placed upon the handle and this hard pointed end of the rod was pressed into the soft piece of wood. Then it was rotated quickly by a bow and bowstring till the easily inflammable material, the 'tinder', placed in the hollow space, took fire. For tinder such things as charred canvas, wood-dust, dry grass, dried mushrooms, leaves and so forth were used. Pliny (XVI, 208) describes this method of making fire as follows:

FIG. 302.—Bow and Sinew for lighting a fire (so-called fire-drill of the Eskimos)

'Wood is rubbed on wood and this friction causes fire which is attracted to the dry tinder. There is nothing more suitable for this purpose than ivy and laurel, the former to be rubbed and the latter to produce the rubbing. But clematis and other creepers have also answered the same purpose well.' Besides these fire-appliances, others were also known to the ancients. In Greece and Rome steel and tinder were used in combination with not only ordinary flint but also pyrites, and other kinds of suitable stone. The 'steel' was either a longish piece of steel, a nail, a key or another piece of the same stone (Pliny, XXXVI, 138). Furthermore, fire was made with the help of concave mirrors composed of bronze and covered with silver-foil, which were already known in 640 B.C., and lenses were made of rock-crystal or glass, as has been proved by Layard's discovery in the palace of Assur-nazir-pal at Nineveh. Aristophanes (450–385 B.C.) says in his comedy *The Clouds* (767) that a burning lens, such as Strepsiades uses in order to rid himself of a debt of five talents by melting a wax tablet, is also used for lighting fires. If the sacred flame went out in Rome it was ignited again, according to Plutarch, by means of bronze or silver concave mirrors or burning lenses. Pliny (XXXVII, 28) and Isidore (XVI, 13, 1) mention that the latter were sometimes made of rock crystal. The assertion that Archimedes had set the Roman fleet on fire by means of concave mirrors at the siege of Syracuse arose falsely at a later period, and there is no doubt whatsoever that such an act was technically impossible.

LIGHTING

THE OLDEST METHODS OF LIGHTING

The earliest method of lighting was by means of the hearth-fire. According to Homer, for instance, Hermes finds the nymph Kalypso weaving by the fireside. There followed the use of splinters of smouldering pine-wood. This method persisted throughout the whole of antiquity and has not been entirely discarded even to-day. In its place amber seems to have been used only by the inhabitants of the Baltic coast. At least, Pliny says that they used it 'pro ligno ad ignem', that is, in the place of pine-wood splinters for producing fire and heat. In proportion as civilization and the sense of beauty developed, however, these splinters could not entirely satisfy all needs. Better and finer methods of lighting were sought. First of all, the splinter was improved, that is, it was elaborated into the torch, which may have served originally as a fire-

FIG. 303.—Vase with Torch-bearer

Boeotian Vase with red figures from the middle or the second half of the fifth century B.C. Altes Museum, Antiquarium, Berlin

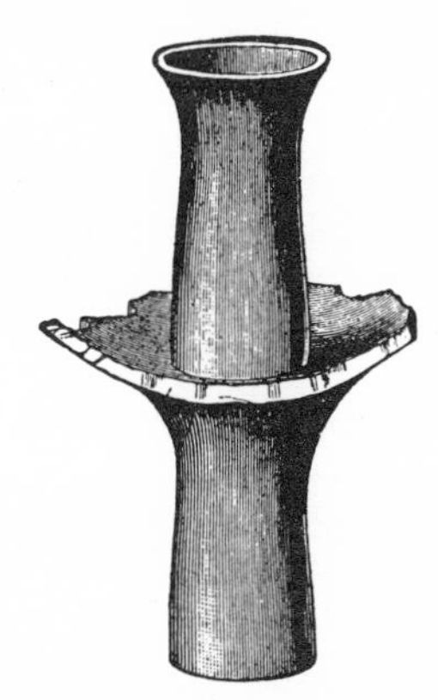

FIG. 304.—Torch-holder from Tiryns

brand, in time of war, to judge by ancient Assyrian representations of the ninth century B.C. Several splinters bound together were dressed with pitch, asphalt or resin. Later on, sprigs of vine were interlaced and saturated in a similar way. At a further stage of development the vine was succeeded by fibres which were able to absorb a great quantity of such-like fuel, especially when they were old and decayed. In order to handle the torch more easily people made use of manifold devices. At the time of Homer great pans of clay or copper (*Odyssey*, XVIII, 307), probably placed upon plinths, served as receptacles for very dry wood which had been mixed with resinous wood (δαΐς or δᾷς) and then burned. From the sense 'resinous wood' is derived the meaning 'torch' (Schliemann); it occurs in Thucydides, Plutarch, and so on. Later on, little cases (φανός, Lat. *funale*), were used as torch-holders; an example of this kind of carrying cup was unearthed by Schliemann in the city of Tiryns near Argos, which was destroyed in 468 B.C. This torch-holder was made of brownish-red clay (Fig. 304).

LAMPS AND CANDLES

But the torch could not satisfy the love of beauty of the ancients, who required a mode of illumination more in harmony with their standard of life. The lamp and the candle were the next stages in lighting, the lamp being the older. In Greece the candle does not seem to have been known till the time of the Roman emperors, but doubtless both the lamp and the candle have developed out of the torch. As a first step, the above-mentioned Homeric torch-pans were filled with oil instead of resinous wood, and so lamps arose. On the other hand, candles came into existence in the following way. The actual inflammable matter was increased in the torches and at the same time substances were chosen which made as little smoke as possible, and the proportion of fibrous to combustible material was continually diminished.

Lamps were unknown at the time of Homer and did not appear in Asia Minor until the sixth century B.C. Previously to this, torches and fire-pans and basins filled with burning resinous wood were used in those countries for the illumination of houses. There is no conclusive evidence that lamps were used even in ancient Egypt in pre-Roman times. Not a trace can be found in ancient Egyptian pictures which suggests the use of a lamp. On the other hand, paintings of funeral processions sometimes show a person carrying a sort of candle or torch, more likely the latter. It is true that Herodotus (II, 62) mentions an Egyptian lamp-festival and accurately describes the lamps in the words, 'these lamps are vessels filled with salt and oil on the top of which the wick floats'. But nobody has ever found an Egyptian clay-lamp of pre-Roman times. If we bear in mind the frequent use of glass by the Egyptians the conjecture cannot be dismissed that the lamps here referred to were of glass, if we assume that 'lamp' is the correct term at all. In Allahun and Hawara in Egypt clay bowls of some 3 in. in height, partly oval-shaped, were found similar to the small night-lights filled with tallow in use at the present time. They show no provision for the reception of a wick. Although the hieroglyphic probably represents a lamp of this kind, it is doubtful whether such a lamp is meant in this instance. The Egyptians used limestone stands for illuminations at festivals. They were about a yard in height and supported a flat granite bowl which had no device for the reception of a wick. It is probably no more justifiable to call them 'lamps' than the similar stands which date from the Minoan period of Crete (Fig. 305). It was not till the Romans used

FIG. 305.—Stone Lamps of the Minoan Period of Crete
From reproductions in the Deutsches Museum, Munich

the lamp for all kinds of purposes that it spread to all peoples of antiquity and became a much-used common article. The number of ancient lamps handed down to modern times is unusually large and among them are some of very high artistic merit. The lamp, originally nothing more than a crudely-shaped bowl, became in the course of time an object of the highest luxury. Although it developed to a high standard of artistic excellence, its progress from a technical point of view was slight, apart from a few irrelevant improvements.

FIG. 306.—Lamp-mould. On the edge four bosses to secure an exact fit with the companion mould

Found at Pergamon. Altes Museum, Antiquarium, Berlin

The bronze lamps developed from the cast and beaten vessels, the execution of which has been discussed in detail in the section 'Working in Metal'. On the other hand, the more ordinary forms of clay lamps were chiefly shaped on

FIG. 307.—Closed Clay Lamps (Roman) with two or more openings

(In the top left-hand corner a bowl. In the bottom right-hand corner fibulae.) The lamps are of different form (foot and so forth), and have a different number of openings. The three small holes beside the bigger hollow in the middle of the lamp in the top left-hand corner are intended to accelerate the filling of the vessel, the air escaping through them while oil is quickly poured into the centre. The lamp has a rim in order that if too much oil is poured in, it will not soil whatever the lamp stands on, but flow back into it. There is a similar rim on the lamps in the top right-hand and the bottom left-hand corner: the latter has an oil reservoir and two passages for wicks. The slit behind the apertures for the wicks serves partly to allow spilt oil to flow back, for it is unable to flow into the big opening on account of the rim, and partly for adjusting the wicks backwards or forwards. Found at Nidda. Städtisches Historisches Museum, Frankfort-on-the-Main

the potter's wheel. The better ones, however, were made in moulds as follows. A lamp-form was modelled by hand and covered all round with clay which was then cut through horizontally in such a way that two moulds were made, one for the lamp proper and one for the lid. Sometimes, however, the lid and the vessel seem to have been shaped separately. In order to secure a close fit for the two parts of the lamp the forms were marked with corresponding symbols, sometimes with letters of the alphabet. Still more frequently the form of the lamp proper exhibits bosses on the edge which fit into corresponding notches in the mould of the lid.

FIG. 308.—Bronze Lamp with Open Bowl and funnel-shaped Spout for the Wick

Altes Museum, Antiquarium, Berlin

FIG. 309.—Closed Roman Lamps (Safety Lamps)

In the completely closed lamps the opening for refilling is very small, always smaller, indeed, than the opening for the wick, so that the oil is prevented from igniting. In the lamp on the left above, there is a small hole visible between these two openings; it is on the inner side of the concave surface leading to the opening for the wick. The idea of this was to allow the wick to be easily adjusted while it was burning. The opinion that the wick might have been prevented from slipping by a pin fixed in this hole can hardly be supported because the swollen soaked wick does not easily slip and could hardly have been held in position by a smooth pin. Provincial Museum, Trèves

The two moulds were separately lined with lamp clay, firmly pressed in; before this clay had dried too much, they were placed on top of one another and were then probably tied together. The lid and the vessel thus came into a suitable position and adhered together to form a uniform whole. After the mould had been opened the lamp was taken out.

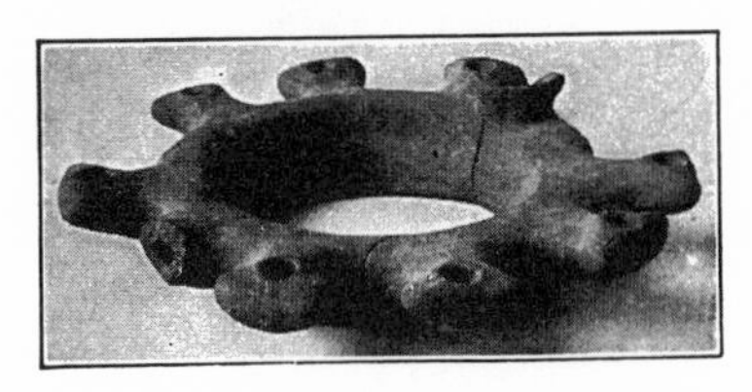

FIG. 310.—Annular Roman Lamp, of reddish micaceous clay. With eight openings for wicks and one opening for refilling, on the right above

Found at Rottweil, Würtemberg. Rottweil Museum

FIG. 311.—Annular Roman Lamp with crossed arms, used as a chandelier

Römisch Germanisches Zentralmuseum, Mainz

The clay, having dried and shrunk a fair amount, is further dried in the air and finally burned at a low temperature. Before the latter process was carried out, details such as handles, ears, adornments (dolphins and so on) were sometimes added, which were either formed by hand or made in

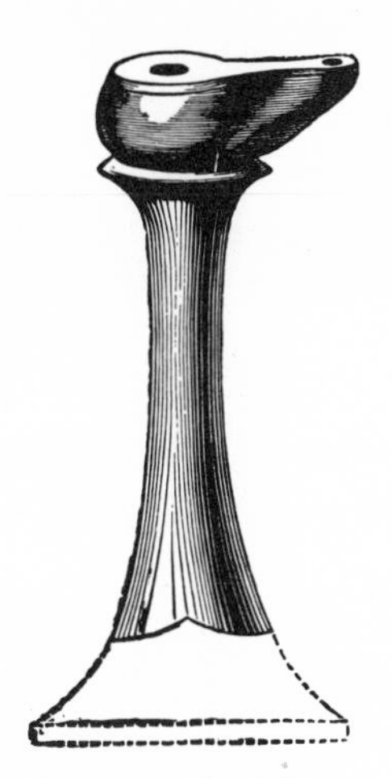

FIG. 312.—Greek Lamp on a Stand; one quarter of its natural size.

Found at Novum Ilium

FIG. 313.—Bronze Stool serving as a lamp-stand

Altes Museum, Antiquarium, Berlin

large quantities by pressing the clay into moulds. Technically lamps improved very little, as already mentioned. First of all open bowls filled with oil were used, on top of which the wick floated. Afterwards the lamp was provided with a lid which was intended to prevent the oil from being spilled when the lamp was being carried about and, more important still, to minimize the chance of the oil surface catching fire from the burning wick. An opening is kept free in front to enable the lamp to be refilled

FIG. 314.—Bronze Lamp-stands
Found at Pompeii

and also serves to take the wick. Later on there were two separate openings, one for filling and one for taking the wick. In course of time the opening for the wick was made conical in shape. Some lamps have separate funnels for the wicks, sometimes as many as twelve (δίμυξοι, τρίμυξοι, πολύμυξοι). The poet Kallimachos (310–238 B.C.) even mentions a lamp with twenty

FIG. 315.—Greek Lamp-stand for suspending four lamps
Found at Priene. Altes Museum, Antiquarium, Berlin

FIG. 316.—Greek Chandelier for suspending five lamps
Found at Priene

wicks. Lamps of this kind, often shaped like wreaths or flat round bowls, were frequently suspended in the manner of our chandeliers (Figs. 310, 311).

To enable the lamps to be set down special lamp-stands were used, which were often of high artistic perfection and were so devised that they could support several lamps at the same time (Figs. 313, 314). On other stands, the lamps are suspended by little chains (Figs. 315, 316). Finally the lamp was provided with a hollow cylinder leading through it vertically from top to bottom and projecting beyond it, by means of which the lamp could be moved along a vertical rod attached to the stand. By shifting the lamp either upwards or downwards the flame could be brought into a suitable position. This motion of the lamp as well as the adjustment of the wick was effected by means of small tongs suspended from tiny chains or sharp thorns, both merely signifying a primitive method of altering the intensity of the illumination. It is not the absolute but the relative illumination which is altered, that is, the luminosity remains the same, but by altering the distance between the lamp and the place of work, however, the amount of light received is now a greater now a smaller fraction of the total quantity of light emitted. Replenishing the lamp with oil is a troublesome task. Methods were therefore sought to enable the lamp to be fed for longer periods by means of receptacles holding reserve supplies.

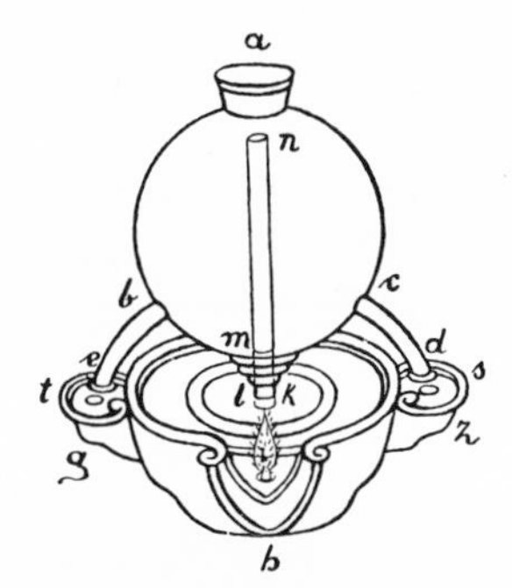

FIG. 317.—The Lamp of Philon of Byzantium

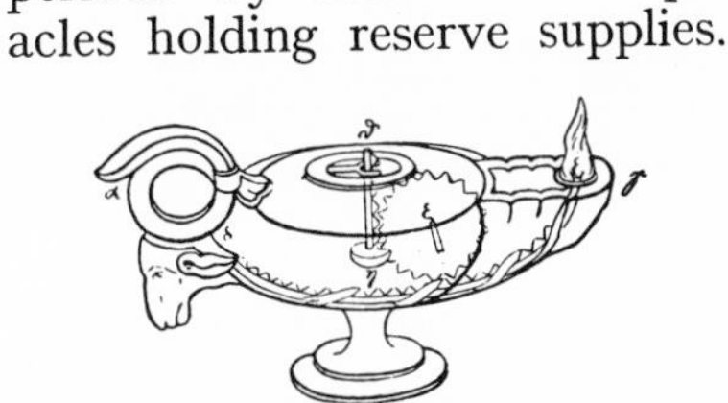

FIG. 318.—The Lamp of Heron of Alexandria, with an automatic adjustment of the wick

Philon of Byzantium (230 B.C.) improved this oil reservoir by making the oil flow automatically and thus maintain the same level (Fig. 317). In his oil-lamp a tube *klmn* with a lateral hole stands vertically in the centre of the body of the lamp, which is filled with oil. The oil reaches above the hole of the tube, the upper part of which is surrounded by the reservoir *a* containing the reserve supply. The reservoir has two lateral orifices *be* and *cd* near its bottom. According to a simple physical law the oil can flow out of these orifices only if the external atmospheric pressure acts on the surface of the liquid in the reservoir. So long as the lateral opening of the tube is covered with oil, the surface of the liquid is shut off from the air outside. If the flame has consumed sufficient oil to free the lateral opening of the tube from the oil in the body of the lamp, the external atmospheric pressure exerts itself through this opening and the tube, and so acts on the surface of the liquid in the reservoir: the oil flows out till the lateral aperture is again covered with it. Then the connection between the reservoir and the air outside is again interrupted: the reservoir supplies no more oil until the opening is once more free. This process is repeated so long as the oil supply lasts. Philon's lamp shows that the physical laws concerning atmospheric pressure had been well mastered, and it gives an excellent solution of the problem in question.

Like the refilling of the lamp, the process of pushing the wick forward continually is an unpleasant accompaniment in the handling of these lamps. Heron of Alexandria therefore constructed another kind of automatic lamp in which the motion of the wick is brought about by means of a floater and cogged wheels. Heron (I, 34) describes his lamp somewhat as follows (p. 162, Schmidt):

'Let us assume the lamp to be αβγ. Through the orifice or socket we push an iron pin δε which moves freely about the point ε. Round the pin we loosely twist the wick and place beside it a toothed spindle (cog-wheel) ζ which easily moves around a small axle. The teeth of this wheel grip into the rod in such a way that when the spindle is turned the wick advances through the action of the teeth. Let the lamp have another opening in the middle of its body. When oil has been filled in, let a vessel η float on its surface. With the latter connect a small toothed vertical rod θ which grips into the teeth of the small spindle. In proportion as the oil is used up the tin sinks, and by means of the teeth of the small rod the cog-wheel ζ is made to turn. The consequence is that the wick moves forward.'

The last-mentioned stage of development as well as the mechanical contrivances in the lamp cannot be called improvements from the point of view of the technique of illumination: they do not increase the luminosity. The manufacture of large lamps and the application of thick interlaced wicks are not an improvement either as regards the transmutation of the energy contained in the fuel into light. In spite of the comparatively large consumption of oil the ancient lamp gave forth only a weak light, though it was warm in its colouring. It smokes and smoulders excessively, owing to the insufficient supply of air and the comparatively low inflammability of the oil. Juvenal (A.D. 60–140) says (VII, 222) that the fumes of the lamp brought in by boys blackened the busts of Horace and Virgil in the schoolroom. The lamp needed constant attention. On account of the air-supply being insufficient the wicks deposited oil-soot which had to be removed by snuffing with the above-mentioned small tongs. The oil used in the lamps was olive, castor, rapeseed or linseed oil; the castor oil gave only a weak flame. Petroleum (naphtha) is said to have been used in Babylonia. Tallow is also used, being poured as a liquid into the lamp, where it solidifies. Herodotus (II, 62) talks of salt having been added to the oil. The idea of this admixture of salt probably was to remove the danger of the oil or tallow catching fire. This danger did naturally exist for the open lamps and was not altogether excluded in the case of those provided with lids, on account of the large openings made to admit the wicks.

Salt was supposed to counteract the excessive heating of the oil or tallow. In the Middle Ages sand was also added to tallow for the same purpose. Thus it is likely that this habit was already practised in antiquity and continued into the Middle Ages. As the lamps were never [1] extinguished, for superstitious reasons, but left till they ceased glimmering and went out, the oil-supply was accurately measured off according to the duration of lighting and so at the same time served for measuring time. The working time in mines, for instance, was ascertained in this way. The wick used to be made of papyrus, pith from rushes, flax, hemp, the leaves

[1] An over-statement. There was an ancient Roman prejudice against doing so, Plutarch, *quaestiones Romanae* 75, *quaest. conuiu.*, p. 702D.—*Trans.*

of *Verbascum Linn.*, parts of the castor-oil plant (said to give forth a particularly good light) and of asbestos, which was frequently imagined to be a sort of flax (*e.g.* Pausanias i, 26, 7, *θρυαλλὶς λίνου Καρπασίου*, *i.e.* from Karpasia in Cyprus).

Candles were used in two forms, one of them resembling the torch, where the fibrous substance predominated, and the other form showing a likeness to modern candles; the mass of the wick was very small compared with that of the combustible matter. According to Niemann, whose statements we are following in our discussion, the wick of the latter kind consisted of the pith of a species of papyrus (*scirpus*), whereas the wick of the former kind, which resembled torches, was twisted together

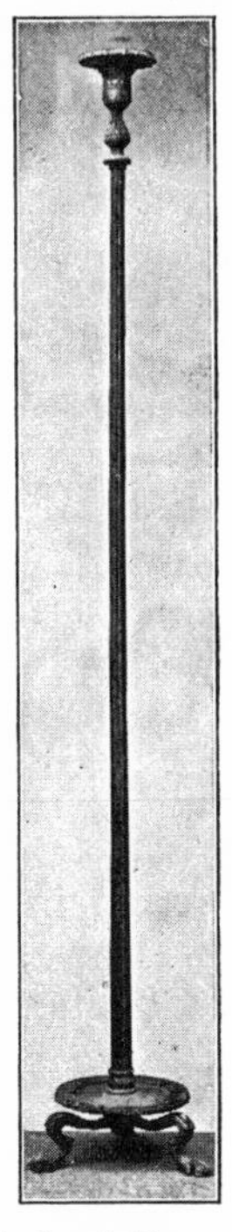

Fig. 319.—Big Greek Bronze Candlestick
Berlin, Altes Museum, Antiquarium

Fig. 320.—Upper part (socket) of a Greek Candlestick, Fig. 319

of the fibres of the papyrus plant, or of other fibres. Wax or tallow was used as combustible matter. Candles were not cast, as is done nowadays. The wick (*θρυαλλίς*, *filum*) was first of all impregnated with sulphur and then repeatedly dipped in liquid tallow or wax, a process designated by the special technical term '*candelas sebare*', which means 'to tallow candles.' Wax used for the making of candles was prepared with special care from honeycombs that had been cleaned in water and dried for three days. Afterwards the wax was pressed out and boiled in water in a bronze or clay vessel. It was then filtered through a texture of rush and boiled once more in the same water mixed with fresh cold water. Finally it was bleached by repeated boiling with sea-water and dried in the open air. Candles were differentiated into tallow candles, wax candles (*candelae sebaceae* and *candelae cereae*), and a special kind with only one wick, the most frequently used, *candelae simplices*. Candles were burned in candlesticks or candelabra, resembling in many ways those of to-day. They were furnished with spikes or sockets and made of clay, bronze or wood (Figs. 319–322). The socket has frequently an aperture to facilitate the

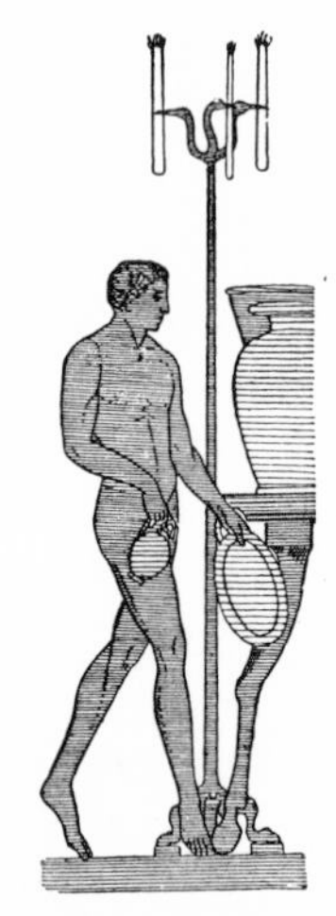

FIG. 321.—Etruscan Candelabrum with horizontal spikes for fixing the candles

FIG. 322. — Boy with Torch. Bronze candelabrum with socket. Pompeii

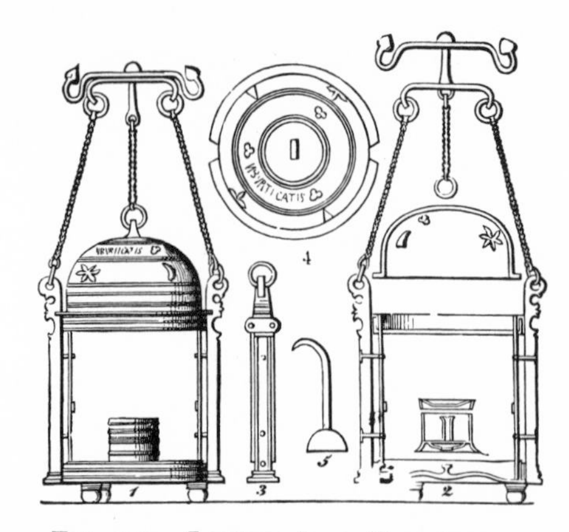

FIG. 323.—Lantern from Herculaneum

Left (1), with closed top. Right (2), cross-section with lifted top. (3) One of the supports on which the top rests, with ring for the chains from which the lantern is suspended. (4) Top from above, showing air-holes which allow the smoke to escape. As (2) shows, the lid of the lamp, added to prevent the oil from spilling, could be taken off. (5) The extinguisher which was placed on the light to put it out

removal of the candle ends. Some candelabra found in the camp at Saalburg are constructed in a particularly practical way, as both ends may be used. They are furnished with sockets of different diameters so that candles of different thickness may be used.

The panes of the lanterns (Fig. 323) consisted either of oiled canvas or of animal bladder, but mostly of horn, which was shaved until the necessary degree of transparency was reached. It was not till A.D. 400 that glass panes were used for lanterns. The origin of the lantern is the woven basket into which the lamp was placed, in order to protect the flame from the rain and wind, as is mentioned by Aristophanes (450–385 B.C.) in his comedy *The Acharnians*.

STREET-LIGHTING

All the above-mentioned methods of lighting were almost exclusively used in the house, for there was no street-lighting in ancient times. Nor was it necessary, as people went to bed very early and, as a rule, got up at dawn. Whoever walked the streets in the dark had to use a servant as torch- or lantern-bearer or carry a light himself, as, for instance, the Roman pupils who started in the dark in order to be at school by sunrise. Streets or single squares were only illuminated for great festivities and that was done with firebrands kindled in basins specially placed there. The substance burned in them was pitch, resin, asphalt, resinous wood, or a mixture of all. Moreover, torches were stuck in the various torch-holes or candelabra. Conditions did not change during the reigns of the Roman emperors; even when the night-life of Rome made considerable progress the streets remained unlighted as before. On the other hand, towards the end of the fourth century A.D. in various towns of the Near East it seems to have become the custom to illuminate the streets at night. Libanius (A.D. 314–393), as well as the Father of the Church, S. Jerome (A.D. 345–420), report that in Antioch in Syria streets were lighted up at night. The illumination of Antioch was effected by oil lamps hung up on ropes over the streets. Also, Caesarea in Cappadocia must have had a similar system of lighting, as is seen from remarks of Basil the Great, in the year A.D. 371.

LIGHTHOUSES

Much more advanced than the system of lighting streets was the illumination in lighthouses, of which a great number were erected in antiquity. It has often been assumed that in the times of Homer fire-stations were established on the coasts (*Odyssey*, X, 30; *Iliad*, XVIII, 207–213, XIX, 375–377), where faggots were burned on special watch-towers to produce the light necessary for safeguarding navigation. According to more recent investigations by Hennig, however, they have to be regarded as beacons for calling up reinforcements or as accidental fires. The question whether there were beacon-fires in the time of Homer—which can be solved only from philological data—does not appear to be sufficiently cleared up at present, but the assumption that beacons were used for assisting navigation in very ancient times seems quite natural, as the idea of indicating in this way the place of landing to sailors overtaken by darkness would very readily suggest itself. In the course of time these watch-towers grew higher and more magnificent. Some of them became world-renowned, such as the lighthouse which was built at Alexandria (299–280 B.C.) at the cost of 800 talents, equivalent to £180,000; it was constructed of white marble and had several stories, on the terraces of which people could easily walk about (Pliny, XXXVI, 12, 83; Caesar, *De bell. civ.* III, 112; Lucan, *Pharsalia*, IX, 1004; Strabo, *Geographica*, XVII, 1, 6). According to Hennig's thorough investigations, the lighthouse of Alexandria served first of all as a day-signal for navigation, and it was not till after A.D. 41 and before A.D. 65 that the Romans turned it into a lighthouse.

The same author regards the lighthouse of Ostia, dating from A.D. 42, as the oldest genuine lighthouse in the world. There are, however, only scant records in existence about the lighting-equipment of these old lighthouses. But in all probability it consisted mostly of open fires burning in the air without a lantern. For instance, the Jewish author Josephus

FIG. 324.—The Lighthouse of Alexandria (reconstructed)

(A.D. 37–95) (*Βίος*, VI, 105) says that on the lighthouse of Alexandria an open wood-fire was kept alight by specially appointed watchmen. According to the same report of Josephus this fire could be seen at a distance of 300 stadia (about 36 miles). The picture of such a fire showing the harbour of Ostia and its lighthouse, constructed by the Emperor Claudius, near the mouth of the Tiber at Ostia, is still preserved in a relief. A high open flame is seen burning on the top landing of the tower, built in several stories with terraces. Probably the fuel was of wood mixed or saturated with tar, resin

FIG. 325.—The Lighthouse of Alexandria on an Alexandrian Medal

The illustration is regarded by Geitel and others as probably correct, at least as regards the exterior of the tower. Above, images of gods

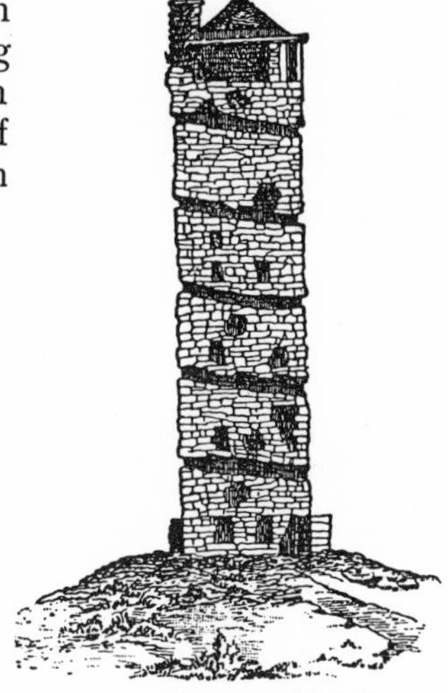

FIG. 326.—Roman Lighthouse: 'Torre di Hercules' at Corunna (Brigantium)

The lighthouse is still in use. Formerly it had an outside spiral staircase, the traces of which are still to be seen in the masonry. It was probably erected in the reign of the Emperor Trajan, about A.D. 100

or asphalt. The lighting power, however, of such open fires, whose light was collected neither by reflectors nor by lenses, can hardly have been as great as Josephus indicates above. Such luminosity can only be attained by modern methods, and even then only by intense sources of light; and at the distance stated by Josephus it is not the source itself that can be seen but only the reflection of the flashes.

HEATING

HEATING MATERIALS

The heating materials used in antiquity were wood, charcoal, coal, a kind of briquettes, and peat. The last three of these and also the dried reeds sometimes used were only of secondary importance. Briquettes, mentioned by Theophrastus (*De ign.* 37), were used only for special technical purposes, particularly for working up metal, and were made by pressing together charcoal, pitch or tar serving as cement. Coal was not employed at all in the countries on the Mediterranean. Like the closely-related lignite, it was burnt only in isolated places (where it happened to be found) such as the districts of the Ruhr and the Sarre, as well as in Great Britain. The same is the case with peat. It was entirely unknown to Southern peoples as fuel, and the Romans must have seen it in use for the first time when they came into contact with the Teutons. Thus Pliny reports of the Chauci on the coast of the North Sea that 'they weave nets with rushes from their swamps, the mud of which they form with their hands and dry it in the wind rather than the sun. They cook their food over a fire made of this mud and warm their limbs, stiffened with the cold of the North'. We shall therefore limit our discussion to the two most important kinds of fuels of antiquity, wood and charcoal. There is little to be said about wood. It was gathered wherever it was found. Whole forests were felled at random for obtaining fuel or for technical purposes without preparing a new supply by reafforestation. Even to-day we find traces of this abuse of forests customary among the Romans. A striking example is met with in the Karst Mountains. This vast expanse was once upon a time thickly covered with forests, but was completely ravaged by the Romans in order to provide fuel or wood for building ships and houses. After the mountain had been cleared the roots of the trees were no longer there to hold the earth together and so it was carried off by the wind or washed away by the rain. And at the present day this extensive tract of land, originally rich in forests, is nothing more than bleak and barren masses of rock. The method of felling and chopping trees has been dealt with above. (See the section on the Procuring of Wood.)

In ancient times charcoal was probably an even more popular fuel than wood. It was already being used at the time of Homer, as is clearly proved by a passage in the *Iliad* (IX, 212):

> 'Then when the fire was burnt down and the flame waned
> He levelled the embers and laid the spits thereover.'

The preparation of charcoal was a very important trade and the community of charcoal-burners was very large and widespread. All kinds of wood were used for charring; the less favoured were some species of oak and the box-tree, because they did not supply a good quality of charcoal. The process was carried out in the same way as to-day, namely in kilns. In order to exclude the air as much as possible from its interior, the kiln was piled up from layers of smooth logs, closely put together, with little space between them for the air. Then the kiln, which was hemispherical in form, was covered with earth and set on fire. During the process of charring, long poles were thrust into the kiln to secure an outlet for the smoke and fumes. It is not known whether the earlier kilns had a vertical channel in the centre, as was often the case in later times. Many kilns were piled up in a special way. They were furnished with a drain at the bottom in order to collect tar from the upper layers of wood by a process of dry distillation. In these upper layers the air supply was even more restricted than in ordinary kilns, so that no oxidation could take place. Wherever the faintest trace of such oxidation was observed, that is as a flame rising from the kiln, it was at once covered and choked with earth. For this purpose—as well as for watching the kiln—some ladders were kept in readiness near by. The tar, being unable to escape upwards, flowed down into a cavity and was collected there. It was then put into coppers and boiled, while vinegar was added in order to prepare 'Bruttian pitch' (Pliny, XVI, 52), a substance used for pitching casks. Pitch was also used for coating the inner side of wine amphorae, for tarring ships, and for painting the roofs in order to render them waterproof; in short, it served in its original form fairly much the same purposes as to-day. For the rest, it was prepared not only in kilns but also in special furnaces probably similar to the 'muffle furnaces', from which they differed in one respect only; they had no waste-pipe to allow the products of dry distillation to escape upwards, but, as mentioned earlier, they probably had a groove into which the tar flowed off.

FIREPLACES: VARIETIES OF HEARTH

Of all the various fireplaces, i.e. places used for burning fuel, the hearth was the oldest and most widespread in antiquity. As is shown by prehistoric finds, it has developed as follows. The fire was a precious possession needing great care and attention, for it could be rekindled only with great difficulty. In order to protect it from rain and particularly from

Figs. 327 and 328.—Oldest forms of the Hearth

Left: Fireplace consisting of a hole dug in the ground without a stone ining. Found at Lobositz on the Elbe. Right: Fireplace of a similar kind with a lining of stones. Found at Platkow on the Oder. Depth of each about 3 ft. Reproduced from models in the Deutsches Museum, Munich

wind, a hole was dug in the ground at the point where the fire was made up. This hole is the oldest form of the hearth (Figs. 327, 328, 329) unless we give precedence to the fact that people frequently contented themselves with protecting the fire by placing stones around it, an arrangement which also made it possible and convenient to roast certain kinds of food, such as meat (Fig. 330). This kind of hearth, which lies on the ground, is still in use among savage tribes. As human civilization progressed, however,

FIG. 329.—Hearth with Seat dug out of the ground

The widening ot the fire-hole (at the bottom of the picture) at the same time provides a seat, and so we see here the origin of the human dwelling. Found at Grossgartach

FIG. 330.—Oldest form of Hearth, consisting of stones placed around the fire

Original in the Landesmuseum, Zürich

FIG. 331.—Hearth consisting of stones placed together and piled one upon the other

Mark Brandenburg. Märkisches Museum, Berlin

and Man gradually gave up his squatting position on the ground to assume a sitting or standing posture, the hearth was correspondingly elevated. Stones were piled up and the fire was kindled on top of them (Figs. 331, 332). This fundamental form of hearth is found in antiquity in numerous modifications. Sometimes it was a simple piece of masonry with a flat top on which the fire was burning, and sometimes it had a raised ledge or

FIG. 332.—Hearth made of piled-up stones
Found at Buch, Mark of Brandenburg. Märkisches Miuseum, Berlin

was merely a pile of stones gathered from the fields and held together by a framework of wooden rafters (Fig. 333).

Just as varied as the forms of fire-places were the devices for supporting the kettle and other cooking vessels over the fire. Sometimes the hearth had a deep groove or pit for the fire. The vessels are either placed on the edge of the pit or on tripods, sometimes they are hung up on hooks; or again, strangely shaped hollow stones of cubic or polygonal form with openings in the side or top are used. The pot for cooking is placed on the hole in the top and is warmed by the flames shooting from outside through the lateral holes up to the bottom of the pot. All the excavations have revealed one or other of these forms of fireplaces, and sometimes several varieties have been found together, as the case in the camp of Saalburg.

FIG. 333.—Hearth made of field-stones, held together by a frame of rafters

All these fireplaces blackened the rooms in which they were situated with smoke, and the principal room in the Roman house, containing the hearth originally, received its name from the smoke (*ater* = black) and was called atrium.

There were no chimneys, not even in Pompeii, although this has often been maintained erroneously. The baker's oven alone had pipes to lead away the fumes. Pipes for getting rid of the smoke came only with central heating. When people wished to prevent their dwellings from getting blackened they used as their fuel not wood but charcoal.

BRAZIERS AND THEIR DERIVED FORMS

However important a rôle the fireplace played in human life it had one great disadvantage: it was immovable. When it was needed for purposes other than cooking food, such as for heating a room, it failed when the habitation consisted of more than one room. For this reason it was replaced by a new device which no longer served the double purpose of heating and cooking, but was used for heating alone. This new article of furniture was the coal-pan or brazier. In antiquity it was widely used as a heating apparatus in many different forms: indeed, it was sometimes an object of great artistic merit. It has, however, the same disadvantage as the hearth: it allows parts of the waste-products of combustion to escape into the rooms, even if there are chimneys specially built for them. But apart from this the brazier must be regarded as a good method of heating, although the consensus of opinion is that its heating power must have been insufficient. Various facts contradict this view—in the first place, the statements of certain people, such as Winckelmann, who became acquainted with the braziers still customary in Southern countries, and spoke highly of their efficiency. Again, certain discoveries such as those made at the tepidarium of the men's baths in the forum of Pompeii prove that braziers of this kind were capable of heating very large rooms. And lastly it has been shown by Krell's thorough investigations that rooms of a considerable size can be heated with comparatively small braziers. Krell writes as follows: 'The brazier found in the tepidarium of the baths in the forum of Pompeii, standing in the place where it was originally used, has a heating surface of 7 ft. 8 in. by 2 ft. 8 in. It is quite sufficient even at the lowest winter temperature to heat a large church with a seating accommodation for over two thousand people, such as the Church of S. Egidius in Nuremberg.' Exhaustive researches have also been carried out as to whether the atmosphere of the rooms became polluted by the use of ancient braziers to a degree injurious to human health. The result may briefly be summarized as follows: The only gas produced in moderately warmed rooms is carbon dioxide. Carbon monoxide only develops at high temperatures, and the quantity increases with the rise in temperature. Starting from these facts, the first problem was to find out whether the content of carbon dioxide could increase to a dangerous limit. According to Krell, this question must be answered in the negative. Even if we assume that a bath-room with a volume of 450 cubic yards is to be heated from 0° C. to 60° C. with a supply of 36,800 units of heat per hour from 11·2 lb. of coal having a heating power of 3,231 units of heat per pound, the air will contain only 2·3 per cent. of carbon dioxide if it is renewed once an hour. It is true that Pettenkofer formerly allowed a much smaller percentage of carbon dioxide in the air used for respiration (namely, one part by volume of carbon dioxide in 1,000 parts by volume of air), but more recent research by Emmerich and Lehmann shows that the effect of 2 per cent. of carbon dioxide is not harmful even if this amount occasionally increases to as much as 6 per cent. or even 12 per cent. For the rest, the difference of 60° in temperature as stated above is much too large. If normal conditions are taken as a basis it is shown that in a room of 336 cubic yards, for instance, the percentage of atmospheric carbon dioxide is 0·47 per cent.; the effect of this amount on human health cannot be detrimental. In Krell's opinion danger can arise only in very small rooms that have been tightly closed. The position is different, however, as regards carbon monoxide. It is true that Eckardt has been able to show the presence of only a trace of this gas in his experiments, which were made with a coal-pan 14 in. long and 10 in. wide and a layer of charcoal 4 to 6 in. thick. But the present author, while engaged on research on the history of poisoning by carbon monoxide, has been able to collect numerous reports of ancient authors themselves about the dangers of using such braziers owing to the possibility of their causing asphyxia. Among the ancient reports worth mentioning are those of Lucretius[1] (96–55 B.C.), Galen (131–200 A.D.), Erasistratos (about 300 A.D.) and of the Emperor Julian the Apostate, who reigned from A.D. 361 to 363. It has been shown that, on the whole, ancient braziers could be regarded as harmless if the

FIGS. 334 and 335.—Chafing-Dishes of bronze for boiling water and keeping food hot
Found at Pompeii

layer of coal burned on them did not exceed a thickness of 6 in., and if the temperature was kept low. Considering the great popularity of these braziers the conclusion may be drawn that the ancients well knew how to manage them, that is, how to regulate the depth of coal and the temperature. On the other hand, it must be concluded that the manifold accounts of poisoning by coal gas due to the use of braziers prove how dangerous they were when handled incorrectly.

The coal-pan had, then, the advantage over the hearth that it could be removed from one room to another. But its disadvantage was that it did not allow food to be cooked on it. For this reason a contrivance was sought which combined those two amenities; so a coal-pan was invented which enabled hot drinks such as the much-favoured mulled wine called *caldum* to be boiled on it, and also served to keep food warm. Braziers of this kind, on which food was heated by means of hot water, were found at Pompeii: they were very artistically executed. Overbeck describes them as follows:

'Like other sorts of coal-pans they consist of a fire-grate or plate bordered by a rim, but this rim was double, closed at the top and formed into a groove around which water could run. It is obvious that the water in it was quickly warmed when the brazier was filled with glowing coals, and the food placed in dishes on the heated rim was thus kept warm. The heat rising from the brazier may have contributed to the same purpose. At the same time the boiling water could be

[1] *de rerum natura*, vi, 802.

drawn from a tap and made use of. This contrivance is shown in all its simplicity in the drawing of Fig. 335, which shows a daintily adorned brazier, and that of Fig. 334, representing a slightly improved specimen. The latter resembles a little fortress crowned with battlements, a form which was particularly popular as an ornament for chafing-dishes. In each of the four corners a crenellated turret rises up covered with a hinged lid. If a lid was opened, as seen on one of the turrets on the figure, a vessel with gravy could be placed directly into the hot water, or the water could be drawn from the tap seen on the left.'

A still more remarkable contrivance was a brazier and hearth com-

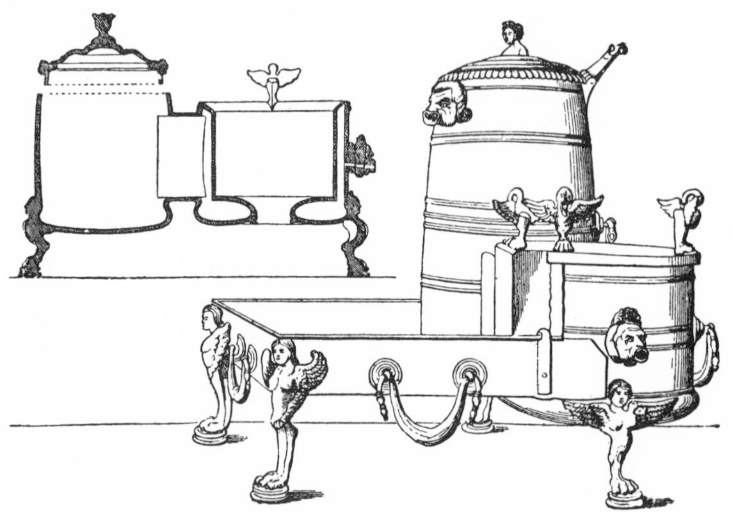

FIG. 336.—Perspective view and vertical section of a compound Brazier
Found at Pompeii

bined. In Fig. 336 one of these is shown in perspective and in cross-section. The plate for firing supports a semicircular coal-pan which is open in the front and has double walls containing hot water. Its upper edge is adorned with three swans on which is placed the kettle for boiling. Thus the coal fire simultaneously heats the water and the contents of the vessel carried by the swans. The heat is concentrated by the specially shaped coal-pan, to which there is easy access by the vertical aperture in the front. The semicircular boiler, which empties through a tap, communicates with a barrel-shaped container provided with a hinged lid and a spout in the form of a mask near the brim. This device made it possible to warm a quantity of water even larger than that in the hollow walls of the semicircular boiler. The spout near the brim allows the steam to escape. *Caldum*, a mixture of wine, honey and water, is prepared in vessels provided with an internal bronze pipe. In order to boil the mixture the bronze pipe is filled with live coals

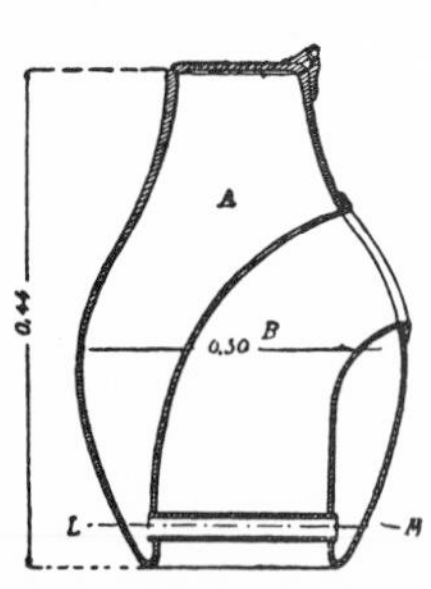

FIG. 337.—Vessel for preparing *caldum*

Space A contains the liquid. B is the bronze pipe filled with glowing coals. L and M, metal pipes of the grate through which the liquid from A circulates. (See Fig. 340.) Found at Pompeii

through a lid. A similar system has recently come into use again in refrigerating machines. Some of the glass vessels employed in these machines closely resemble the Pompeian containers. The pipe, however, is no longer filled with glowing coal nowadays, but with ice.

STOVES

Fixed stoves were unknown to the ancients, but they turned the coal-pan into a kind of portable stove by closing in the fire on all sides. A stove of this description found at Pompeii consists of a metal cylinder with a

FIG. 338.—Pompeian Portable Stove

stove hole and stands on three legs shaped like a lion's paws (Fig. 338). A little over half-way up the metal cylinder there are two apertures masked with lions' heads. They admit the supply of air necessary for maintaining the fire inside. Since the upper part of the stove contains a copper it is obvious that the apparatus was used both for ordinary heating and for boiling water. A model in the Deutsches Museum at Munich represents an ancient Greek portable stove the fragments of which were found in the sea. The original contained a plate pierced with hollows for the fire, that is, a kind of fire-grate, fixed in the upper part of the stove (Fig. 339). The lower section of the cylinder is pierced with numerous holes to ensure a sufficient supply of air for the coal-fire. It also serves as a receptacle for the ashes falling through the grate. Technically speaking it was something intermediate between a brazier and a stove.

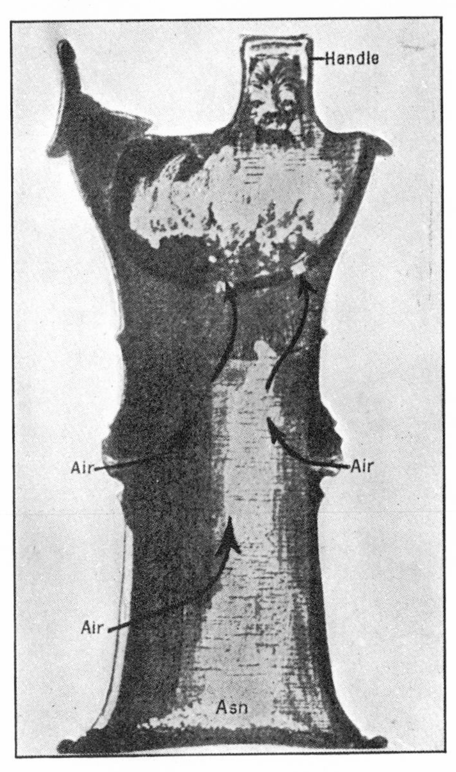

FIG. 339.—Vertical section of an ancient Greek portable Stove

Model in the Deutsches Museum, Munich

A grate is also seen in a Pompeian kettle (Fig. 340) simultaneously used for boiling water and for heating. Since it was not furnished with a tap the water had to be scooped out with a ladle. A comparatively large surface was created for heating by giving the fire-box the shape of a vault. In front it had a stoke-hole, and at the back a small opening which allowed the fumes and gases to escape. It is particularly noteworthy that the bars of the grate consisted of pipes cooled by water flowing to and from the surrounding boiler. This arrangement prevented the bars from being burnt through, as often happens with ordinary grates. Grate bars of this kind are also found in the above-mentioned vessel used for preparing *caldum* (Fig. 337). The fire-funnel of this vessel is turned backwards and thus the *caldum* can be poured off without the coals falling out. The ashes fall through the bars of the grate on to a tray which is supported by an artistic tripod. For the rest, the Germanic tribes seem to have known the grate before the Romans. In any case a stove (Fig. 341) has been found at Oberlahnstein cut in a deposit of clay. According to the reports of Dragendorff and Bodewig it dates from the La Tène period (400–1 B.C.), 'its walls being made of burnt material hard as brick. The vertical cylinder opens out towards the top like a chalice or cup. In its centre there is a pillar 22 in. high and 14 to 16 in. thick with about ten arms at the top forming a kind of grate. The fire-hole is formed like the Roman *praefurnia* (see below).

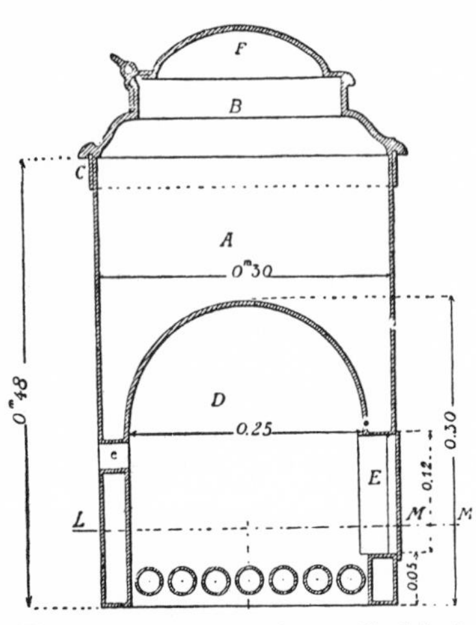

FIG. 340.—Kettle with cylindrical grate bars
Found at Pompeii

The numerous sherds found date from the late La Tène period. The large circular surface could take several vessels simultaneously and the stove thus did the service of a large kitchen range, and so was a great improvement on the earlier fireplaces and crudely-built hearths of stone so far discovered.'

FIG. 341.—Germanic Stove with Grate, dating from the La Tène period
Found at Oberlahnstein

HEATING LARGE MASSES OF WATER

For the heating of large masses of water, such as for baths, peculiar contrivances were used of which those at Pompeii are particularly well preserved. The method of using them and their mode of action is still a controversial matter. We shall therefore first review the various conflicting theories proposed before stating our own opinion, which was arrived at as a result of manifold studies carried out on the very spot. The question at issue is the construction of the boilers used for heating the water in the baths in the women's *caldarium* of the Stabian thermae at Pompeii (Fig. 342). Jacobi says : ' The horizontal boiler, made of bronze plates about ·3 in. thick, riveted together, is vaulted at the top and flat at the bottom, which is over the fire-room. Its height in the vertical section is 22 in., its width 2 ft. 6 in., and its length 5 ft. 10 in. One end of the boiler is closed, the other opens into the front wall of the bath, which is nearly 16 ft. long, 6 ft. 5 in. wide, and just over 2 ft. deep. The flat bottom of the boiler lies 6 in. below the bottom of the bath, causing the water to circulate freely between the bath and the boiler.'

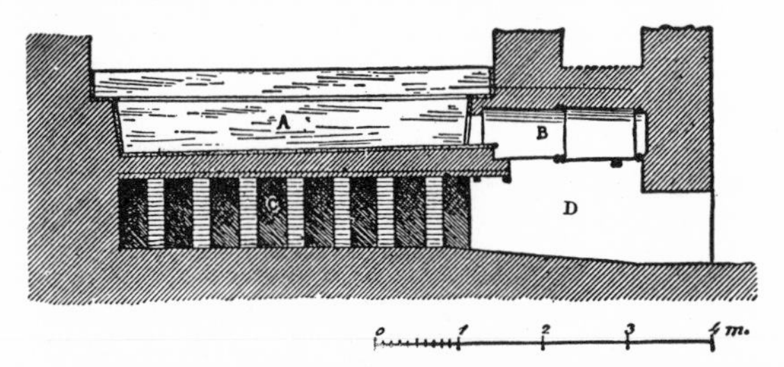

FIG. 342.—Boiler in the Caldarium of the ladies' bath in the Stabian Thermae at Pompeii
A, Bath. B, Boiler. D, Fire-room

' Both, Overbeck and Mau as well as Jacobi,' says Krell, ' are of the opinion that the hot fumes produced by the burning fuel-pan pass underneath the boiler and the stone bath and after that enter the hollow floor, walls and ceiling of the caldarium and tepidarium, and so heat them.'

The objection that Krell raises to these views is that an arrangement of this kind would necessarily have destroyed the basin of the bath, which was lined with white marble ; but it looks quite new even at the present time. In another connection he points out that no firing took place underneath the floor under consideration. What was alleged to be a heating-plant, he says, was merely a contrivance for drying the rooms. Finally he maintains that the heating would have had to be started not less than twenty-four hours before bathing-time, if the water was to be warm. Krell's theory is that the boiler was heated simply by placing glowing charcoal in the fire-space below, that the air was sucked from underneath the bath and from between the walls into the fire-space in order to be dried, and that from this space it streamed into the adjacent fire of the main boiler, which was probably heated with wood.

We pass over sundry other systems of heating baths which are still under discussion, such as the method by which the bath in the Villa Rustica of Boscoreale near Pompeii is heated, and about which investigations are still proceeding. It is useless to quote the various hypotheses put forward, particularly as the study of the pictures is hardly likely to bring the solution of the problem nearer. It is altogether doubtful if the problem can be solved at all, since the excavators have in many cases thoroughly removed all the evidence. If a solution can be obtained at all it will be only, as we shall presently show, by means of an accurate chemical or microscopical investigation, such as has not yet been possible to the required degree.

THE PROBLEM OF CENTRAL HEATING

Ancient central-heating comprises all those contrivances in which one fireplace either served to heat several rooms at the same time or in view of its construction was capable of doing so, even if they were separated from the fire-room. The apparatus for heating will be treated here from the hitherto accepted point of view. It must be borne in mind, however, that the problem involved has not yet been solved. The position is as follows: In many cases the rooms supposedly meant to be heated are built directly over a hollow space. Their floors are supported by columns made of bricks. The walls are also provided with hollow spaces which are obtained by placing together hollow tiles in such a way as to form channels. All these hollows and channels are in communication with the fire-room. Whereas the archaeologists not specially trained in technical science allege that all these constructions are forms of central-heating, Otto Krell, senior, a specialist in this branch of science, points out in his noteworthy descriptions that constructions of the above kind are by no means always apparatus for heating, and particularly not in the case of baths. He admits that there are contrivances of this type which may be claimed as instances of central-heating; they are the so-called hypocausts, some of which are in an excellent state of preservation. As for many others, however, he contends that they cannot have been heated by a fire underneath the floor, because the small columns supporting the floor were frequently made of limestone and plaster, a material which is by no means fire-proof. On the other hand, the floor on them is often of such thickness that it would have been entirely impenetrable to a fire kindled underneath. Lastly, Krell remarks that one would expect to find traces of ashes, soot and the like. He therefore comes to the conclusion that the constructions in question are not examples of central-heating but simply means of drying the rooms above. The present author himself visited some such establishments at Rome, Pompeii, Herculaneum, Fiesole, at Saalburg, at Trèves and Badenweiler and elsewhere, carefully examining separate items in various museums.

These studies lead to the further remark that a fire kindled beneath a thick floor would often have caused it to crack. In view of the slow conduction of heat through such a thick floor there is reason to assume that the excessive heat on the one side and the cold on the other would necessarily have caused tensions in the masonry sufficient to make it crack or break. In addition, traces of carbon, soot and the like ought to have been found, as Krell rightly remarks. But the author has not been able to discover any such traces either ; nor does he feel that particular importance is to be attached to this minor point. The excavators have generally endeavoured to set up the constructions as tidily as possible, and have therefore cleaned the places very thoroughly. If any traces of the above kind had existed at all they are sure to have been removed for good. It has often happened, indeed, in order to obtain as beautiful and clean a specimen as possible excavators took out the tiles, scraped and cleaned them with corrosives, and then built them up once more. On the strength of all these facts the author sums up his views as follows : the construction in question is in all probability intended for drying, and in this respect resembles the modern system of double walls or isolating walls used for protecting buildings from the damp outside. The air circulated between the double walls and so prevented the moisture from invading the main walls, or else led it out. The process of draining off the moisture may have been carried out by a fire to which the air was convected and made to circulate between the walls, as is the case with the Stabian thermae mentioned above.

In any case it would be unwise to reject Krell's views without further discussion, as has been done by Anthes, Brauweiler and others. Fusch, who also studied the problem in all its details, asserts that the hypocaust, originally used only for heating tubs, was subsequently also employed for central-heating in baths and villas. In order to attain absolute certainty, however, the present author maintains that chemical and microscopical investigations would have to be carried out to see whether there are any traces of charcoal-fires in the pores of the brilliantly polished tiles and stones. Substances to be claimed as traces of this kind would be particles of carbon and certain products of the distillation of wood, such as creosote, which are not liable to change. The author hopes soon to be able to give a report on exhaustive investigations carried out along these lines.

HEATING BY HYPOCAUSTS

The system of central heating has been met with only among the Romans, and the oldest form of it is undoubtedly the method of heating by hypocausts, whose inventor is said to have been C. Sergius Orata. The term hypocaust seems first to occur in Statius (*Sil.* i, 5, 59) ; *hypocausis*, a furnace, is found in Vitruvius, who describes this mode of heating in all details in connection with the construction of baths (V, 10) ; this description and its alleged defects have been thoroughly discussed by Krell. The hypocaust consists of a hollow space below the floor of the room to be heated, and in most cases extends the whole length and breadth of the room above. The floor lies some 3 ft. above the ground and is supported by brick pillars whose upper parts widen to a kind of capital. These capitals consist of projecting tiles the uppermost of which sometimes touch the corresponding tiles of the adjacent pillars. These tiles carry the actual floor (Figs. 343 and 344). The fire-chamber lies outside the building and communicates with the above hollow space through a channel which corresponds to the flue or snore-hole in modern industrial establishments for heating. In front of the fire-chamber there

FIG. 343.—Hypocaust in the Roman theatre in Fiesole. The thickness of the floor is striking and makes it doubtful whether it was heated directly. (See page 258)

is a kind of roofless ante-room also sunk into the ground and reached by a few steps.

From this open room, called the *praefurnium*, the fire is kindled and kept up in the fire-chamber, and the daily supply of fuel is piled up here (Fig. 345). The smoke and fumes, passing through the hollow space under the floor, eventually escape through pipes in the sides.

In many cases the walls of a room also contain hollow spaces, which form as it were a continuation of the empty space below the floor. Hollow tiles (*tubuli*) of square cross-section were used for this purpose up to a height of 5 ft. above the floor or as high as the roof, in which case they provide an outlet for the smoke (Fig. 346). Instead of these, other tiles were sometimes used provided with bosses (*tegulae mammatae*) and fixed to the walls with iron

FIG. 344.—Hypocausts at Trèves. The floor is of great thickness and rests upon brick pillars resembling capitals

FIG. 345.—Praefurnium of an ancient Roman heating apparatus

It lies in the open air outside the building. On the right and left of the stoke-hole are implements for heating and cleaning the fire-place. Found at Saalburg Castle

clamps. Occasionally an opening closed with a plate is found in the floor. Through it the hot air contained in the hypocaust was allowed to enter the room after the flue had been closed and the fire had gone out. It is doubtful whether this opening was also used to enter the hypocaust below for purposes of cleaning or repairing, as is assumed by Jacobi (see the description of the hypocaust at Saalburg, given below).

If people did go down that way they must have been obliged to crawl

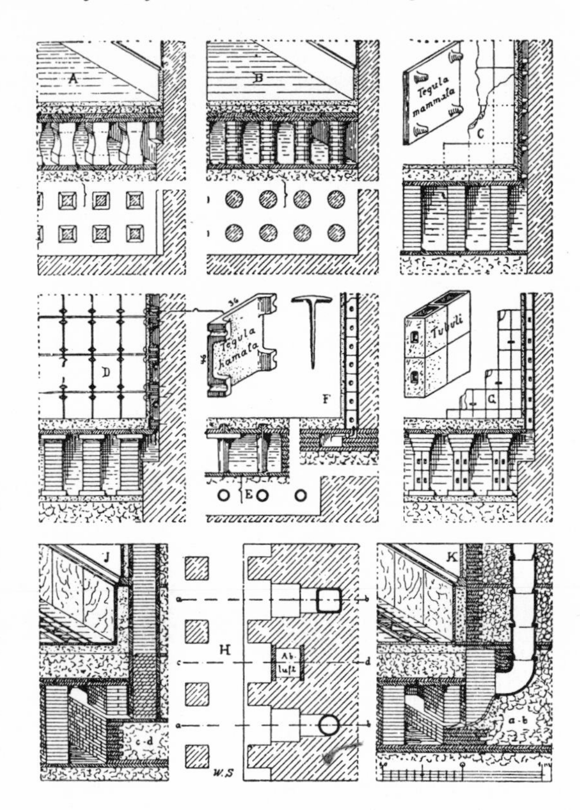

FIG. 346.—Details of construction of the hypocausts and the channelled walls

A, Pillars of ashlar tapering towards the middle so as to form a passage for the waste gases of combustion. The lowest part of the floor consists of two layers of flat bricks. B, Pillars of cylindrical bricks. Lowest part of the floor is the same as in A. C, Brick pillars carrying a floor the lowest part of which consists of a simple layer of large flat bricks. Tiles with bosses (*tegulae mammatae*) are visible in the walls. D, Brick pillars each covered by a large slab in order to counterbalance and uniformly distribute the pressure of the floor above. The lower portion of the floor is made of a simple layer of large flat bricks and is supported by pillars whose capitals consist of a common projecting plate. Hooked tiles (*tegulae hamatae*) are seen in the walls. E, Pillars, each made of two convex or ridge tiles carrying a plate in order to extend the supported surface of the floor. F, The lower portion of the floor consists of reversed roof-tiles laid with the flat side downwards. Above on the right is shown a nail used for fastening the *tegulae hamatae*. A horizontal channel conducting hot air leads along the wall, underneath the floor, into the vertical tubuli-channels of the wall; an arrangement specially built for economizing the heat. G, Tubuli-pillars. The floor is a simple layer of large flat tiles. The walls are provided with tubuli whose lateral holes allow the heated air to spread. H, I, K, Systems of waste-pipes and chimneys, which can be distinguished by the fact that the waste-pipes show no traces of soot. The lower part of the floor in I and J is a double layer of flat tiles.

between the pillars in a very uncomfortable position, the hypocaust being hardly 2 ft. 6 in. in height.

The pipe connecting the fire-chamber and the hollow space under the floor was sometimes provided with lateral orifices admitting fresh air which mixed with the overheated air inside before it entered the rooms above through the openings in the floor.

It is impossible to describe in all detail the numerous systems of hypocausts. Heating apparatus of this class have been found in the course of time in all the parts of the world once inhabited by Romans. At Trèves, Pompeii, Herculaneum, Saalburg and many other places, a great number have been discovered. The best preserved is in the last-mentioned place. It was excavated in the so-called ' civilian settlement ' in front of the *porta decumana*. The author's photographs (Figs.

347, 348, as well as a plan (Fig. 349) of this heating apparatus are seen below. Jacobi describes it as follows :—

FIG. 347.—Hypocaust in the Civilian Settlement near Saalburg

The floor is very thin here compared with the floors in Figs. 343 and 344. Into the wall in the background is let a square tube which allows the fumes to escape

'The front space or praefurnium of the hypocaust is sunk 2 ft. 8 in. in the ground and lies 5 ft. from the building. It is 4 ft. 8 in. long and 4 feet 4 in. wide. Two steps 11 in. high lead down to it. On the opposite side is the mouth of the plant, the stoke-hole some 14 in. high and 8 in. wide (Fig. 349).'

'Behind the stoke-hole are two elliptical bulges shaped like baking-ovens. One of them lies outside the structure and is covered with large basalt stones and earth.'

'In this space, the 'snore-hole,' charcoal was piled up and set on fire. This arrangement proves that the Romans made efforts to protect the brick pillars from direct destructive contact with the red heat radiating from the coal-fire. The hot gases alone were allowed to spread between them.' (Jacobi is wrong here, in the author's opinion, as this space is used in industrial establishments to increase and regulate the air supply for firing.)

'The bottom of the fire-chamber ascends from the stoke-hole to the flues on the opposite sides. The hypocaust proper consists of six rows of eight pillars 2 ft. 6 in. high. The most remarkable of them are those stand-

FIG. 348.—Praefurnium of the hypocaust in Fig. 347

The darkest spot of the picture is the mouth of the fire-chamber, the stoke-hole

ing in a group of nine at the north end marked *m*. They are obviously made of pipes instead of bricks and are filled with fragments of brick and mortar. In order to make them equal in height to the others they have covers at top and bottom, also a few tiles added. The pillars, standing 10 to 14 in. apart, are connected at the top by plates 20 to 24 in. square, and 2 in. in thickness. Their surface is generally grooved in order to offer a firm grip to the plaster of the floor above, which is here 6 in. thick. The plaster covers the whole of the floor and has one hole (*hi*) 20 in. square to allow access to the hypocaust.

FIG. 349.—Plan of the Hypocaust near Saalburg

A, praefurnium; *abc*, the stoke-hole; KI, fire-chamber or outlets for the hot gases; *fg*, ventilating flue; *n*, chimney; *u*B*de*, ventilation

It is closed with a plate of sandstone which is lifted by a stick and a rope fastened to a hole in the centre. Obviously, the only purpose of this entrance was to allow the cleaning to be carried out and perhaps also to allow repairs to be made to the hypocaust. When the work was finished the plate was placed back into the hole, and closed all round with clay or mortar.'

'A tube runs all the way round the hypocaust. It shows a different cross-section from that of the spaces between the pillars owing to the projecting base of the wall. Seven pipes (*r*) sheathed in tiles ascend from this tube. Five of them are $5\frac{1}{2}$ in. square; the two in the back corners are, however, $5\frac{1}{2}$ by 10 in. They rise out slightly above the floor, emitting the hot gases inside directly into the living room. The flue *fg*, in the wall, mentioned above, is divided by a tongue into two shafts. It is still extant about a yard in height, but it seems to have continued through the wall upwards as far as the roof or even farther. It could hardly have been used as a proper chimney for the smoke, as six convex tiles (*n*) on the back wall served this purpose, since they are placed opposite the fire-hole. In the author's opinion the double flue *fg*, provided with an orifice immediately above the floor, can only have been intended to ventilate the room, by sucking up foul air from the floor, or stale air if the room should become overheated.

How much the hypocausts differed in size is seen from a comparison of those at Saalburg with those of the thermae at Trèves. In the latter the praefurnium alone is over 8 ft. high and has the form of a long corridor holding the various fire-chambers. To what extent hypocausts served their purpose cannot be ascertained in spite of the minute calculations of Krell, who worked out their efficiency on the basis of the theory of modern technical science. He confined himself to special cases, whereas an accurate idea would be obtained only from comparative calculations on different types of hypocausts. Even then obstacles would be encountered. The number of such types, preserved sufficiently to safeguard against errors, is not sufficiently large. We do not know whether there was any relation between the fuel consumed and the size of the plant. Neither is the character of the fuel known, nor its heating power.

Hypocausts seem to have afforded a great deal of comfort to the Romans, otherwise they would not have existed in every part of the Roman Empire, particularly in the better sort of dwelling-houses and in the villas of the rich. On the other hand, they must have entailed some inconveniences, judging from the fact that they fell entirely into disuse in the ninth century A.D., after they had been almost universally employed from before the beginning of the Christianera. The people of the Middle Ages made no use of them, although their own heating arrangements were by no means very efficient. For the time being the question as to the real value of the ancient hypocausts must therefore be left open, and it is very doubtful indeed whether it will ever be settled, unless new evidence is brought to light by further excavations.

HEATING BY PIPES

Another mode of heating adopted by the Romans was the one which involved the use of pipes. A pipe conducting the hot gases from the fire-chamber runs along the floor underneath the room intended to be heated. At the edge of the floor it rises vertically through the wall and serves as a flue or chimney (Fig. 350). In many systems it rises gently. Very often several pipes run across below the floor diagonally, their point of intersection being connected with the fire-chamber by a feeding-duct which leads the hot gases to the centre of the floor, whence they are distributed diagonally to the four corners (Figs. 351 and 352). An example of this system is found in one of the boundary towers of Saalburg Camp. In the two corners, opposite to the praefurnium, the orifices of the diagonal tubes are still seen, and in all probability the two other corners had similar outlets.

The Roman system of heating by tubes must be regarded as rather wasteful and unpractical from a technical point of view, since the actual heating surface of the pipe was very small, the room above being heated only by the top surface of the pipe. All the rest of the heat, i.e. the heat radiated or emitted from the bottom or the sides of the tube, was lost, and therefore the calorific value of the fuel was exploited to only a very small degree.

What the fuel used was like is just as little known as in the case

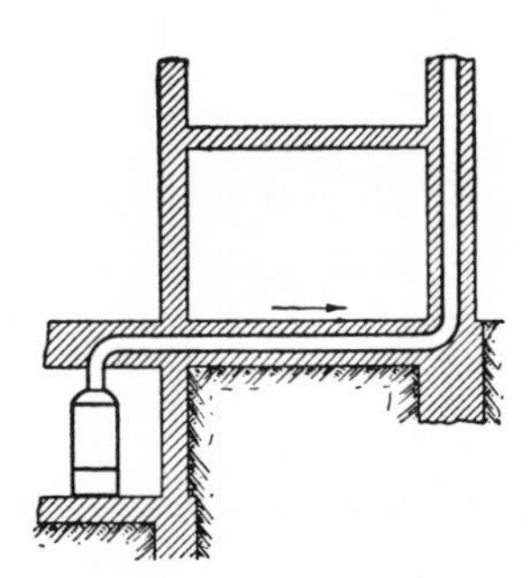

FIG. 350.—Heating by Pipes

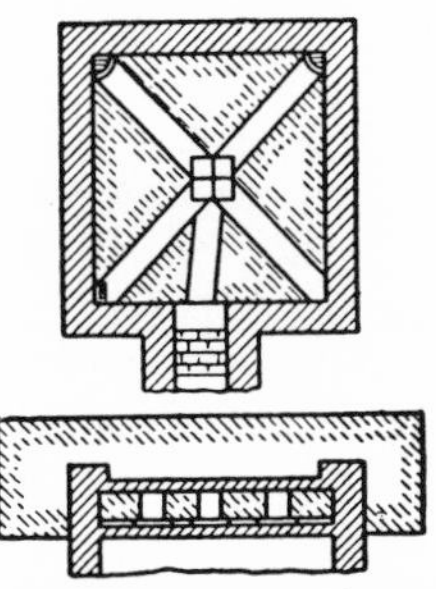

FIGS. 351 and 352.—Cross-section and ground-plan of the system of heating by pipes found in one of the boundary towers at Saalburg

of hypocausts. Jacobi maintains that it was charcoal, whereas Krell assumes it might also have been ordinary wood. The present author made calculations starting from calorific value of the various kinds of wood and charcoal, the size of the fire-chamber and some other points, but he did not succeed in clearing up the problem either.

In Saalburg Camp some further contrivances for heating floors have been found. They are to be regarded as a combination of hypocausts and heating by pipes. Jacobi describes them (Fig. 353) in the following terms:

'In the centre of the room to be heated is a space 6 ft. 7 in. square and 2 ft. 4 in. deep, *abcd* (a hypocaust with pillars). The flue *m* runs into it and seven heating-pipes *n–t* radiate from it. Five of them, *o*, *p*, *q*, *r*, *s*, continuing the flue in a forward direction, strike into the heating pipe *ei*, built in the wall, whereas the two receding pipes (*n* and *t*) end in the two corners on the left and the right of the flue in vertical radiators (K1) which finish on a level with the floor in front of the wall. The five tubes (*o–s*) undoubtedly continued upwards through the walls and led away the smoke. At the same time the thinness of their walls enabled them to heat the room quickly.

'The fire was lighted through the fire-hole S, which is bordered with basalt. The pipes in the floor are merely covered with tiles and a thin coat of plaster. After the fire had gone out and the heat had accumulated in the central hypocaust (*a–d*) and the tubes *n* and *t*, the slides were removed from the radiators K1, and the heat was admitted directly into the apartment. Cold fresh air was also allowed to enter either through the fire-hole specially opened for it or through the chimneys which had been vacated by the smoke in the meantime.' Similar combined systems of heating are also found in various other Roman settlements. They have one advantage over the heating-pipes

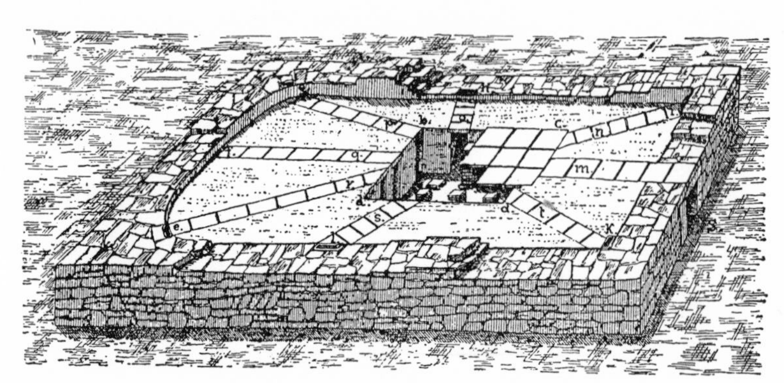

FIG. 353.—System of Hypocaust and Heating-pipes used in combination at Saalburg

in that the heat from the bottom and the sides of the tubes is not altogether lost. It is partly absorbed by the air circulating in the tubes and transmitted to the room intended to be heated. A serious disadvantage, however, must have been incident to either system: the places above the tubes were bound to become heated to such a degree that eventually they could not be stepped upon. For this very reason, so far as we can see, all the better-class houses were provided with hypocausts. Though these were considerably dearer they had the great advantage of heating the whole of the floor uniformly and of allowing the temperature to be regulated.

TOWN PLANNING

THE reasons why towns, that is, settlements on a somewhat large scale, were founded were necessity and expedience. And how very early the planning of towns was taken in hand may be gathered from the fact that in the year 4000 B.C. there were cities of gigantic size. The walls of Babylon enclosed an area twice as large as that of modern London, and some other ancient cities also assumed considerable dimensions. Their population may not have ranked with those of a modern metropolis, but they certainly equalled those of large modern provincial towns. Athens, for instance, at the zenith of its prosperity had some 250,000 inhabitants, Jerusalem about 500,000, Carthage and Alexandria about 750,000, and Rome at least one and a half million. There are only a few cities to-day which surpass ancient Rome in this respect. We are therefore justified in talking of the great cities of antiquity, since cities of that size could have grown only on the basis of a highly developed technical art of town planning.

LAYING OUT TOWNS

Considering the general architectural design of ancient cities, we can divide them into two main groups: the 'natural' cities, which have grown organically, and the cities laid out according to a definite plan. The former arose through the gathering together of an indigenous population in a limited area. With a view to defending themselves against enemies or simplifying the exchange of commodities, people formed settlements which grew as the number of settlers increased. Everyone pleased himself in choosing a suitable site for his house. Consequently a clear premeditated plan is entirely lacking in this kind of town. The streets are narrow and crooked, running irregularly, in all directions. The second group of towns is laid out according to a systematic design. Usually they owe their existence to the will of some autocratic ruler, who ordered them to be built in a place apparently suitable for his purpose. So the 'city architect' proceeds to make plans according to which the town is to be laid out. The fact that the design for a fortification has been found on an alleged statue of Gudea of the year 3100 B.C. conveys some idea of the age of town planning. A city built to a plan displays wide and straight streets, intersecting each other mostly at right angles, markets and other public squares, all laid out according to a definite scheme (see Fig. 365).

In some instances a 'natural' town has changed to a town of the second kind. The old quarters in the centre exhibit all the characteristics of a natural settlement, whereas the later and outer parts show the traces of systematic planning. Athens and Rome both belong to the autochthonous or natural type. Heliopolis in Egypt, on the other hand, was built according to plan as early as 1400 B.C. But it seems that a planned town, the remains of which were excavated some time ago, was founded at Kahun near Lake Moeris even earlier, namely about 2000 B.C. In Italy town planning seems to have been started in the sixth century B.C. when the Etruscans built a regularly laid out city in the district of Marzabotto near Bologna.[1]

The oldest planned towns are found in Mesopotamia, as stated above. The question whether Babylon was laid out according to a plan may be left open. In any case the subsequent extensions were done strictly

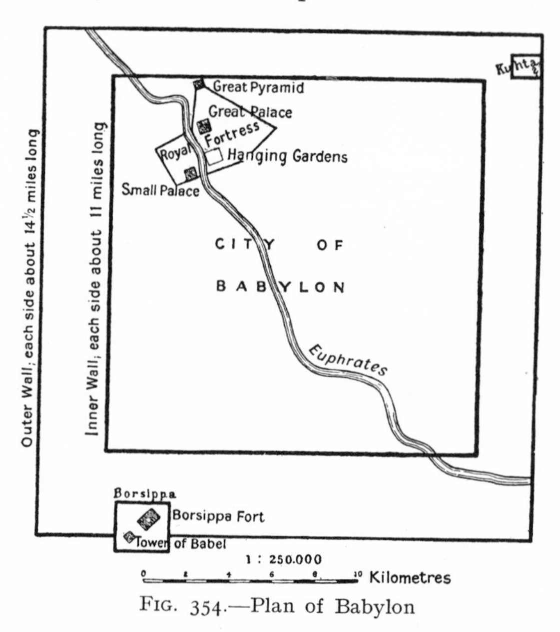

FIG. 354.—Plan of Babylon

according to design, as is clearly seen from the following description given by Herodotus (I, 178–181)[2]:

'Babylon was a city such as I will now describe. It lies in a great plain, and is in shape a square, each side an hundred and twenty furlongs in length; thus four hundred and eighty furlongs make the complete circuit of the city. . . . Round it runs first a fosse deep and wide and full of water, and then a wall of fifty royal cubits thickness and two hundred cubits height. . . . They built first the border of the fosse and then the wall itself in the same fashion. On the top, along the edges of the wall, they built houses, of a single chamber, facing each other, with space enough for the driving of a four-horse chariot. There are an hundred gates in the circle of the wall, all of bronze, with posts and lintels of the same. . . .

'The city is divided into two parts; for it is cut in half by a river named Euphrates, a wide, deep and swift river flowing from Armenia and issuing into the

[1] There is no reason to suppose that Marzabotto was the first Etruscan city to have a regular plan.—*Trans.*

[2] From Godley's translation (The Loeb Classical Library).

Red Sea. The ends of the wall, then, on either side, are built quite down to the river; there they turn, and hence a fence of baked bricks runs along each bank of the stream. The city itself is full of houses, three or four stories high: and the ways which traverse it—those that run crosswise towards the river, and the rest—are all straight. Further, at the end of each road there was a gate in the riverside fence, one gate for each alley; these gates also were of bronze, and these too opened on the river. These walls are the city's outer armour; within them there is another encircling wall, well-nigh as strong as the other, but narrower. In the midmost of one division of the city stands the royal palace, surrounded by a high and strong wall, and in the midmost of the other is still to this day the sacred enclosure of Zeus Belus, a square of two furlongs each way, with gates of bronze.'

A supplement to Herodotus' description is given in graphic terms by Delitzsch:

'Through a gate not very far from the south-east corner of the wall we enter the city proper. Turning to the left we follow a short but wide and apparently well-kept street lying in lonely solemnity. After that we cross the magnificent bridge built over the East canal of Babylon, the Bibil-chegalla (or chigalli), and turning to the right we make for the Euphrates and the vast expanse of houses, the city proper of Babylon. Lost in the maze of streets and alleys we feel bewildered, not owing to any haphazard arrangement of the streets, since they are all straight, both those leading to the Euphrates and the others, but owing to this very regularity, which makes it extremely difficult for a stranger to find his way among the long rows of three- or four-storied houses. The streets throb with the bustle and clamour of city life. But the commotion becomes livelier as we proceed along the straight thoroughfare until we pass one of those little brazen gates let in the brick wall at the end of each road. On the other side of the wall, which stretches along the river, a new sight no less lively is exposed to our gaze. The Euphrates flows along in sublime peacefulness. Its banks are flat, but at the behest of Nebuchadnezzar quays of an extraordinary height and width have been erected on either side of the stream.'

These river-walls called quays have been rediscovered by Ker Porter in his excavations. They are 67 ft. high, and nearly 18 miles in length. The citadel mentioned by Herodotus stood on an artificial terrace. Artificial terraces are very frequently met with in Mesopotamia, having been greatly in favour with every potentate who was fond of display. What a tremendous amount of labour was required for building such terraces has been made clear by Jones, who carried out calculations on two hills near Kujundschik. One of them holds six and a half million tons of earth, the other fourteen million tons. Taking into account the average labour done by one worker, we can calculate that one thousand workers would have required 54 years to build the smaller hill, and 120 years to build the larger one. It is improbable, however, that the building operations lasted as long as that, human lives and labour being of little value at that time. If we assume the work to have lasted 10 years 5,400 people would have been necessary to cart the material for the one hill and 12,000 for the other.

It has been mentioned above that ancient Egypt possessed systematically planned towns at a very early period. It is even likely that the Greeks were the pupils of the Egyptians and the Assyrians in this respect. To begin with they built their towns on the tops of hills with a view to safeguarding them against enemy attacks. Later on they settled on the coasts. In both cases their towns bore the characteristics of settlements built at random, that is, without any system. It was not till the age of Pericles (493–429 B.C.) that the site was divided up according to a definite plan. This is first seen in the Piraeus, the harbour-town, laid out in this way by Hippodamos of Miletus, known as the builder of several towns. Yet he can hardly be claimed as the inventor of this new idea. It is rather probable that he proceeded after Egyptian and particularly after Assyrian models. The advantages of the new method are clearly seen on a comparison of older Greek towns such as Gurnia in Crete with those built later like Soluntum in Sicily, which is also situated on a hill.

Whereas Gurnia covers the hill with an irregular network of streets and narrow little alleys running into the crooked main streets and with stairs built to overcome the gradients, Soluntum, constructed a thousand years later, has parallel streets which lead up the slopes of the hill, and are crossed at right angles by a wide horizontal high-street. These changes are due to the authoritative example set by Hippodamos in the Piraeus.

The plan is very closely adapted to the hilly configuration of the district. The main streets run perpendicularly to one of the two hills, the latter forming a natural termination to the system of streets. Similarly they lie parallel or at right angles to the quay of the harbour. Theatres, temples and other public edifices lean against the hill-sides or form a background to the view along the street, as is the case with the temple of Aphrodite. The naval port and the arsenal are shut off from the town, and the hills are included in the system of the fortifying walls.

The streets are divided into main streets and by-streets, lying at right angles. They are all wide and enclose blocks of houses without any appearance of monotony. Temples, theatres and the castle are arranged in such manner that they all enhance the beauty of the town viewed by anybody sailing into the harbour. The quay is adorned at one end by the temple of Zeus, and at the other by the temple of Aphrodite. The harmony of the aspect is completed by the temple of Pallas Athene. The theatre soars up above the town half-way up the hill which is crowned by the castle. The temples are placed in such a way as to form a termination of the streets. Looked at from the streets the temples always show the front and part of one side. Thus a certain rigidity which invariably accompanies a façade which closes a street at right angles is mitigated or totally avoided (Fig. 355).

The plan of Priene, dating from the fourth century B.C., proves that a highly advanced art of building towns is capable of overcoming great difficulties. Here the conditions are so intricate that even a modern architect would find it very awkward to build a town there. From the plain of the Maeander the rock of the acropolis rises nearly 1,200 ft. A vast and rather steep declivity slopes down from its lower part into the plain. The problem was to construct a town in this very area. It was solved in this way. Parts of the slope were levelled off and made into terraces for the streets and houses. On the elevated artificial level resulting therefrom, six longitudinal streets are laid out, one of which is the main street and is 23 ft. wide. Like a brightly shining band it leads from the west gate in the town-wall directly eastward into the centre of the town, where it crosses the market (ἡ ἀγορά) (Fig. 356). In close proximity to the town-wall are the gymnasium, the shrine of Demeter and the stadium. The main part of the town lies on this, the lowest, terrace. Above it there is a smaller terrace with Pythos' temple of Pallas Athene which dominates the prospect of the town. The difficulties of the ground made it necessary to support the temple by a high retaining wall. The sanctuary is flanked by a theatre, and surrounded by the streets of this upper part of the city, intersecting at right angles. This part has a

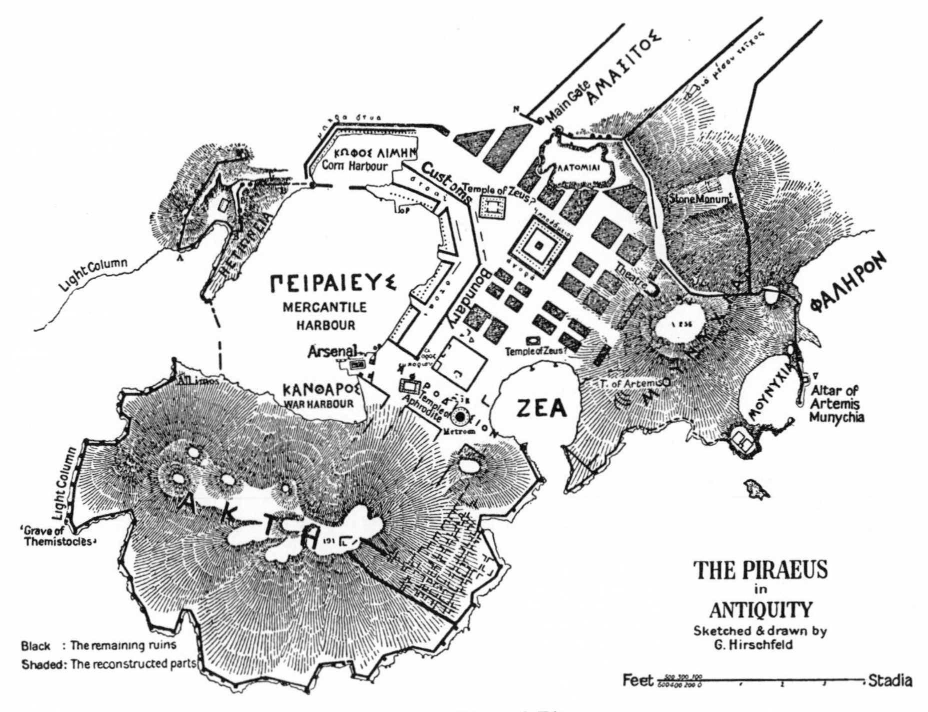

FIG. 355.—Plan of Piraeus

market of its own. In the steep places of the slope, however, the streets are continued in their straight lines by stairs. But the latter are avoided as far as possible. Rather, the streets are extended by landings so as to give them the benefit of height. Lastly a staircase cut in the rock leads several hundred yards high to the acropolis, which stands on a rock rising almost vertically above the city. It must be admitted that in this very instance of Priene the ancient art of building towns has scored one of its greatest triumphs. All the obstructions of the region were overcome without any deviation from the plan drawn after the model of Hippodamos.

In towns lying on the coast streets are usually made to run parallel to the line of the shore. Alexandria, for instance, begun and finished in 331 B.C. after the plan of Deinokrates, has seven streets parallel to the coast and eleven crossing them at right angles each 23 ft. in width. The two main streets were some 46 ft. wide. The island of Pharos with

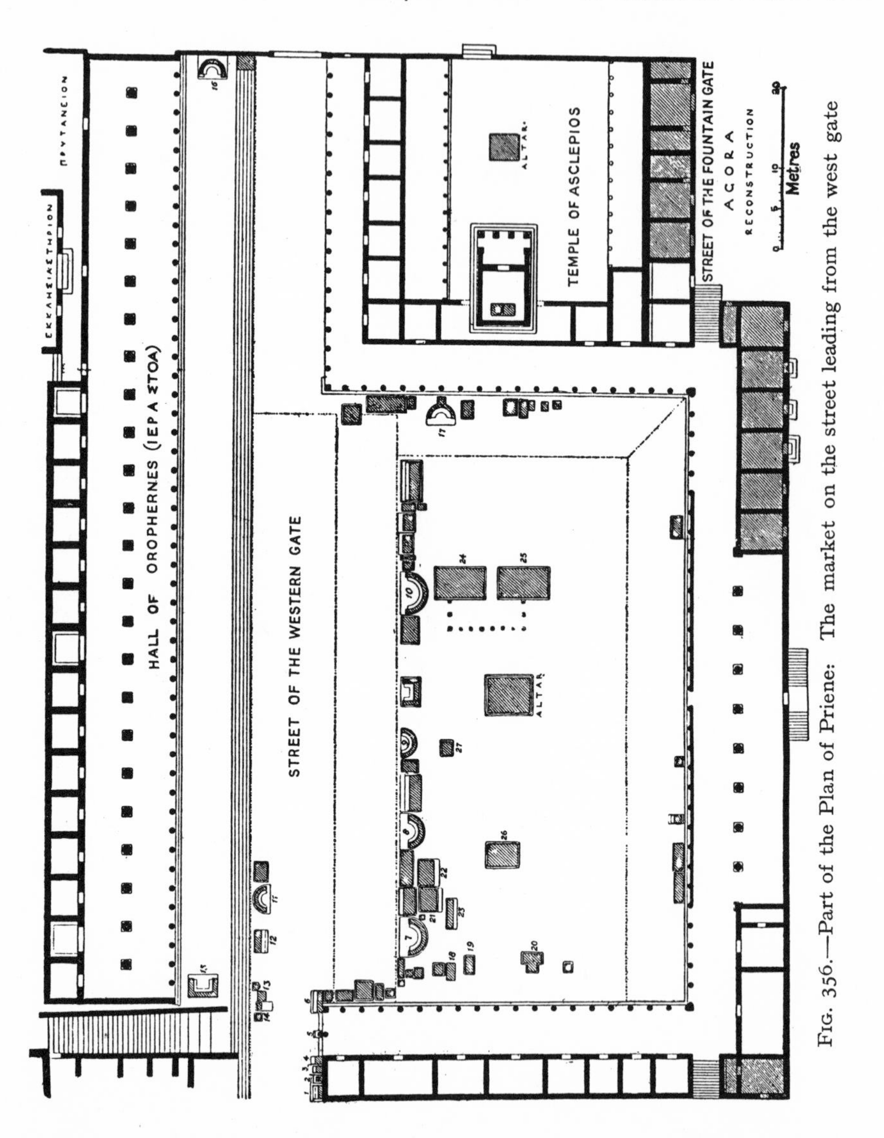

FIG. 356.—Part of the Plan of Priene: The market on the street leading from the west gate

the famous lighthouse (see p. 246) was connected with the city by the Heptastadion, that is, a huge mole 7 stadia or 4,247 ft. in length. The longest street, the Canopic, was not less than 3½ miles long.

Huge artificial terraces, so popular in Mesopotamia, were not less in vogue among the Greeks. They were either made by collecting together or by carting off earth. If necessary, powerful supporting walls were built to resist the pressure of the earth behind and the thrust of the buildings standing on the terraces. The finest example of the art of building terraces among the ancient Greeks is probably found at Pergamon, which was mainly constructed under Eumenes II (197–159 B.C.). The steep slopes of the hill carrying the castle betray no influence of Hippodamos, but they have three long-drawn terraces whose dimensions and technical perfection command our admiration even to-day. The lowest of them was 40 to 47 ft. high and was supported by a wall. On it stood the gymnasium and some massive round towers

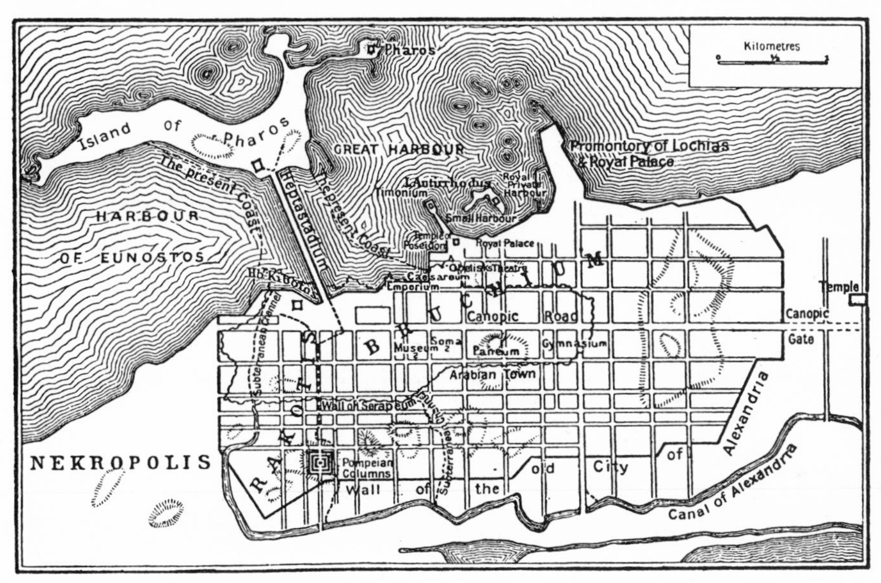

FIG. 357.—Plan of Alexandria

leaning against the breast-walls and the buttresses of the following upper terrace. A special staircase of forty steps, vaulted over, led to the 'Gymnasium of the *epheboi*', standing on the imposing middle terrace where large halls, rooms, temples, and other buildings were also found. The gymnasium on the third or highest terrace comprised a kind of theatre, some halls, bath-rooms and such like. The weight of all these buildings rising on three successive terraces must have been immense, and yet the structure of these breast-walls did not come loose under this load nor under the pressure of the masses of earth and rock inside as long as the town existed. (A diagram of this system of terraces is given in the left-hand part of the plan showing the aqueduct of Pergamon, Fig. 573.)

TOWN PLANNING AMONG THE ROMANS

The Roman methods of building towns was partly based on ancient traditions, and partly influenced by the example of Hippodamos, and again they were determined by the fact that some towns arose out of former Roman fortifications, the castra or camps. The ancient tradition is chiefly evident in the choice of the site. The preference was given to hills or the junction of two valleys forming a promontory upon which the town was built. The number of ancient Roman towns situated on hills is very large. Towns of the second kind, facing two valleys, are Tarquinii and Volterra as well as Coblence. Settlements sprung from Roman camps still show to a certain extent the original plan of the camp in the arrangement of the inner quarters and of the streets leading from them. Instances are Aosta, Turin, Trèves, Cologne, Spalato, Timgad, and Lambaesis (Figs. 358–360).

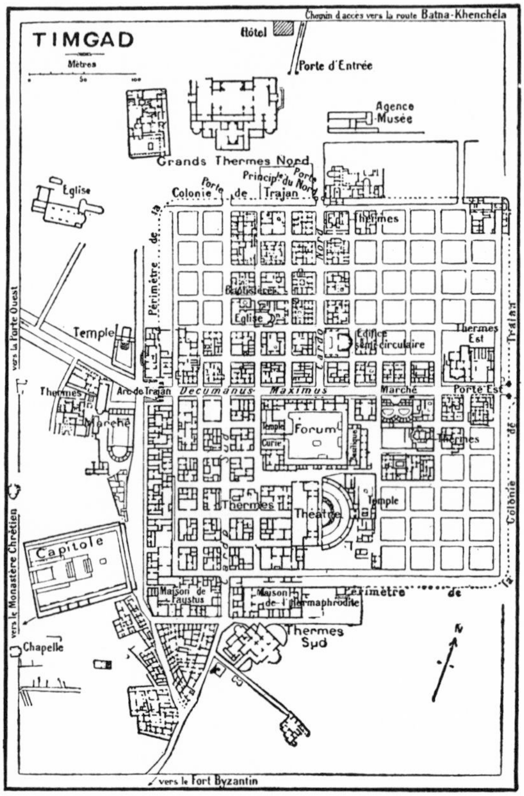

FIG. 358.—Plan of Timgad: a typical example of a Roman town derived from a camp

But the grouping of streets customary in Roman camps is also found in other kinds of towns, and may therefore be regarded as the criterion of the Roman town. As a rule both the town and the camp have two main thoroughfares crossing at right angles in the centre and dividing the settlement into four quarters. One of these main streets was the high-street proper, the *via principalis*. The gates standing at its ends were called the *porta principalis dextra* and the *porta principalis sinistra*. The *via decumana* or simply the *decumanus*, the main street cutting the *via principalis* at right angles, ended in the *porta decumana* and at the other end in a gate called in camps the *porta praetoria*. The main streets were usually marked out according to the four cardinal points, but not with particular accuracy, the directions in which the sun rose and set being ascertained only approximately. For the rest, certain superstitions caused the system to appear turned round in the course of time, so that the North-south street, the *via principalis*, often became the West-east street. Moreover, strategic considerations led to the *porta praetoria* being turned towards the enemy. Details of this kind vary in the different cases, but on the whole the ground-plan of a Roman town is a quadrilateral, mostly an oblong, crossed perpendicularly by two intersecting streets.

According to Merckel, the planning of a town was partly based on

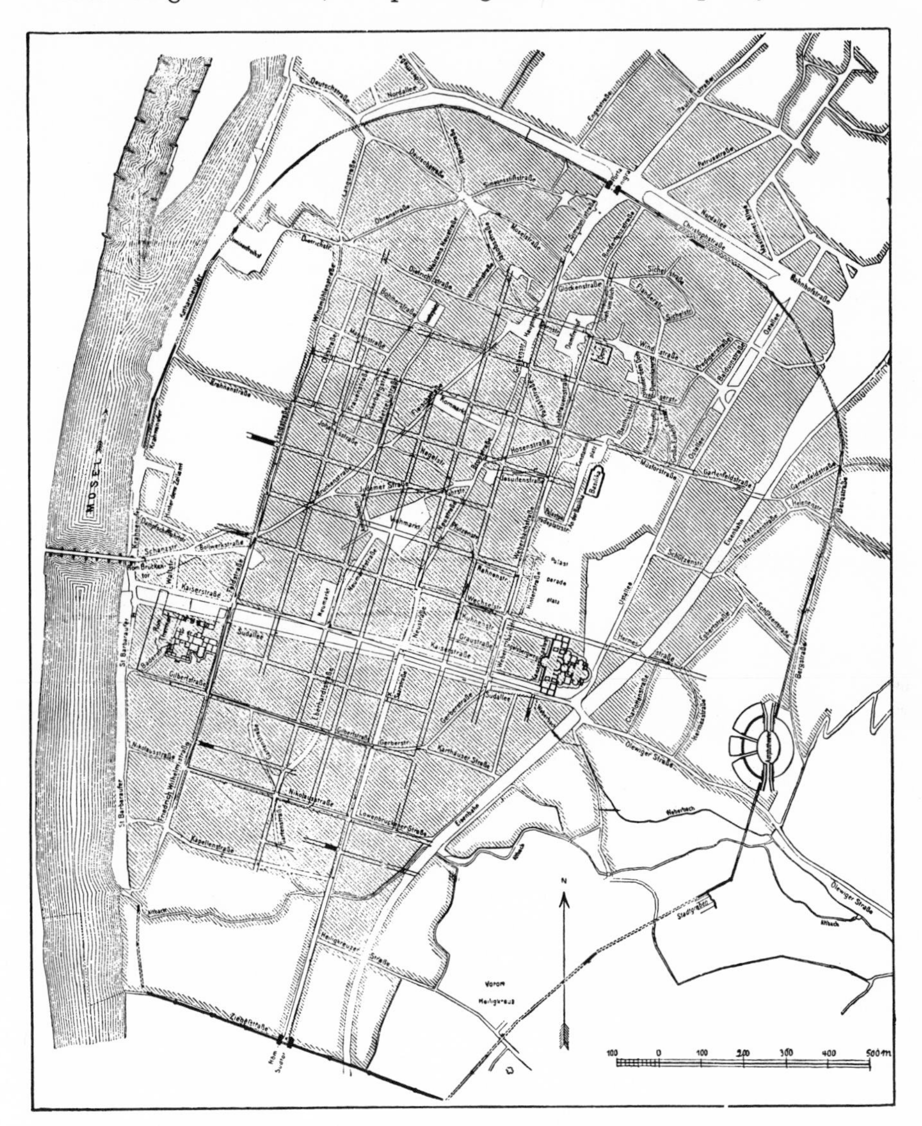

FIG. 359.—Plan of the Roman settlement at Trèves

technical considerations and partly on superstitions and Etruscan traditions. In founding a town or standing camp the rampart was marked out first of all. A plough drawn by two white beasts of different sex was then led along the trace of the future ditch of the town in such a

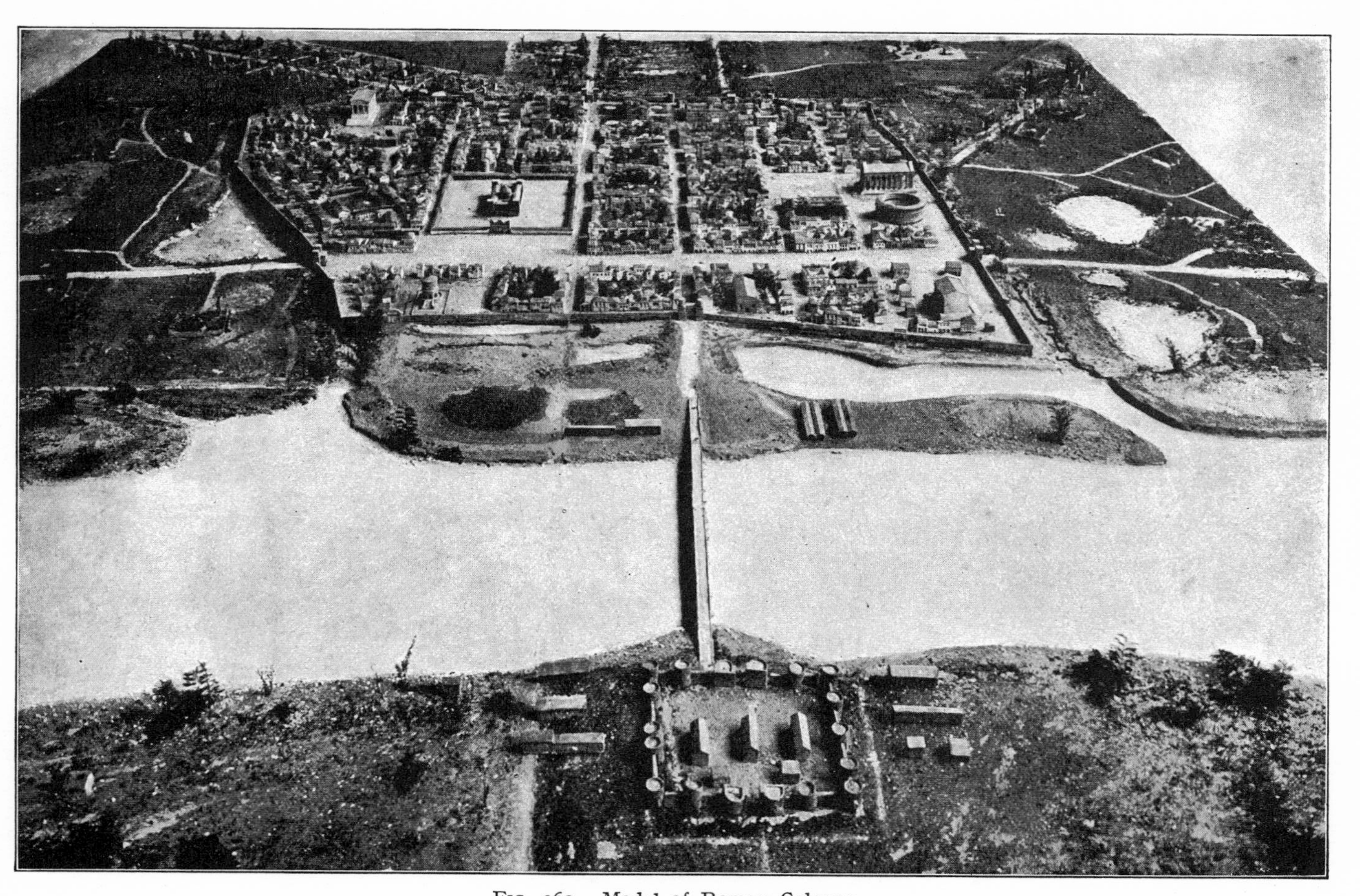

Fig. 360.—Model of Roman Cologne

Above in the centre the original site of the fortified camp and its extent are clearly visible. In the front and on both sides later parts of the settlement with theatres and temples are seen. Below, on the right side of the Rhine, the head of the bridge is laid out in the shape of a Roman castle

way as to turn the sods to the inner side. These sods formed the beginning of the fortification, the rampart. The fathers of the future town always walked round to the left as they accompanied or led the plough. Walking to the right would have brought ill-luck to the town. On the sites of the town-gates no furrow was drawn, the plough was lifted from the ground and carried over the spaces reserved for the future gates. Very often the corners of the town-walls are not pointed but rounded off, the reason of this perhaps being that the plough was not capable of drawing a sharp-pointed angle, but had to be led at the corner from one direction into the other through a curve. It has already been mentioned that the cardinal points were observed.[1]

After all the border-lines had been drawn and the boundary stones been set with all kinds of ceremonies, which we pass over here since they are irrelevant to the art of town planning proper, a map of the future town was drawn. The length and width of the various streets were measured off, the territory of the town outside the walls was accurately drafted, and the whole plan engraved in bronze or marble. The tablet was then fixed and exhibited in a public place where it could be examined at any time. A second drawing made on canvas was sent to Rome and kept there in a special archive corresponding to a modern land-registry office. The maps were elucidated by notes written on wax tablets. They contained the names of the individual land-owners, the numbers of their holdings, which were often distributed by drawing lots, and other such data.

The original system followed in planning is still discernible in some towns like Cologne and Trèves (Figs. 359 and 360). Whereas the Roman provincial towns may thus be called ' modern ' in a certain sense, things were different with autochthonous towns, which were in a very bad condition even at a later time. Rome above all others is an example. A graphic description of it is given by Friedländer :

' When the regal period drew to a close Rome still looked like a country town of to-day in spite of its great extent, which was marked out by the course of the Servian wall. Agricultural work and cattle-rearing were still done in the interior of the city. The houses were built almost entirely of wood and clay, and covered with a thatched roof. People walked in clouds of dust on the unpaved roads when it was summer, and in filth when it was winter.

' The defects in the later design of the city were attributed by the ancients to the fact that the reconstruction after the burning by the Gauls in 390 B.C. was carried out roughly and without a plan. The quarters were laid out irregularly, the streets were narrow and crooked, and in many places the houses stood crowded together. Tiled roofs came into use very slowly, shingles being used for a covering as late as the war with the King Pyrrhus (284 B.C.), a fact which bears witness to Italy's former wealth in forests, which was ruthlessly squandered at a later time when the houses in Rome were time and again burnt down and rebuilt many stories high of timber framework. The paving of streets was started much later. At the same time the city little by little changed its rural aspect. For example, before the year 310 B.C. the wooden stalls of the butchers in the Forum gave way to the banking premises of the money-lenders ; but the general progress towards beauty took place so slowly and sporadically that even in 174 B.C. a party hostile to Rome at the

[1] All relevant passages are collected by Thulin, *Die etruskische Disciplin*, iii, p. 3, *et seqq*.

court of King Philip of Macedonia found cause to scoff at the ugly appearance of Italy's capital which excelled neither in public buildings nor in private residences. Really handsome houses had only begun to be erected a short time previously.'

In spite of the fact that most magnificent and palatial buildings were constructed in Rome from the time of Sulla, the general course of the streets remained unaltered, and even Augustus, who undertook the architectural reorganization of the Roman capital, was unable to remove this defect. The disadvantages of such an arrangement of streets were clearly recognized. In the reign of Tiberius people complained that the houses were so high and the spaces between them so narrow that there was no protection against fire and that it was impossible to escape in any direction in case a house collapsed. The Neronian fire of A.D. 64 owed its vast extent entirely to these shortcomings. Even later on, after the burnt-out quarters had been rebuilt and the lower parts of the houses had been made of fire-proof material such as Alban and Gabinian stone, *peperino* and *sperone*, the original drawbacks of irregular growth continued and made themselves felt in an unheard-of increase in the value of the land. As a consequence of this, people were compelled to extend their houses by adding to their height, as is the case in large cities to-day. According to the account of Juvenal, there were windows in Rome at such a height that objects down below in the streets were seen as though through a mist; and Pliny thought that no other city in the world could compare in size with Rome if the height of her houses was taken into consideration as well as her area and circumference. That her houses were higher than those of an average large modern city is shown in a comparative list by Friedländer. 'Whereas the building regulations of Berlin of the year 1860 allow façades only 40 ft. in height on streets of the same width, and higher ones only on streets which are proportionately wider, the by-laws of Vienna fix the maximum height at 50 ft., or allow four stories, and those of Paris at 70 ft. on roads of the same width, the Emperor Augustus decreed that the front of the houses in Rome should not exceed a height of 70 Roman (about 67 English) feet, *i.e.* six or seven stories, while Trajan is alleged to have limited them to 60 (= 58) feet, *i.e.* five or six stories. But these decrees could hardly have been observed strictly and did not affect the rear part of the houses, which undoubtedly often surpassed the height prescribed for the fronts. Martial writes of a poor wretch who had to ascend 200 steps to reach his bedroom. Conditions were aggravated by the fact that the maximum height was allowed on any street regardless of its width. In this respect Rome was far behind any modern city. In Berlin the average width of the streets comes out at 73 ft., whereas it was only 17 to 21 ft. for the Roman main roads; this is less than the narrowest width (26 ft.) allowed in the Paris regulations of to-day, for which façades not exceeding 40 ft. are permitted. A road even as lively and busy as the Vicus Tuscus, owing to its shops, was only 15 ft. from side to side of its pavement, and the Vicus Iugarius only 18 ft. If the houses of Tyre, according to Strabo's account, were even higher than those in Rome, it must be attributed to its position on a narrow island rock.'

The later roads of Rome were laid out according to plan and were therefore long and straight. The differences between the various quarters are clearly visible in a plan engraved on a marble tablet, fragments of which are preserved in the Capitoline collections. It dates from the third century A.D. and shows how crooked and repeatedly broken roads alternate with straight ones more recently laid down.

As has been mentioned above, in the planning of a town strategic considerations came first and they were followed by the demands of commerce and tradition. Although in general these factors remained in force it was recognized later on that other points had also to be taken into account. The doctrines of Hippodamos, the essence of which is handed down to us by Aristotle (384–322 B.C.) and perhaps added to by him, also became the guiding principle for Rome. According to Aristotle one factor was of vital importance in town planning: that the place of the future town should have fresh air and a sufficient supply of good water. It should face towards the north and west as much as possible in order to admit the winds which were supposed to be refreshing when blowing from these directions. In addition, the site should meet all strategic requirements and facilitate the construction of protective ramparts as well as put the enemy at a disadvantage. Even the form of government should be taken into account. A town with one acropolis was thought to be suitable for a monarchy or oligarchy, a town in a flat district for a democracy, and a town with several citadels for an aristocratic state.

Similar views are put forward by Vitruvius (I, 4):

'In setting out the walls of a city, the choice of a healthy situation is of the first importance: it should be on high ground, neither subject to fogs nor rains; its aspects should be neither violently hot nor intensely cold, but temperate in both respects. The neighbourhood of a marshy place must be avoided, for in such a site the morning air, uniting with the fogs that rise in the neighbourhood, will reach the city with the rising sun; and these fogs and mists, charged with the exhalation of the marshy animals, will diffuse unwholesome effluvia over the bodies of the inhabitants, and render the place pestilent. A city on the sea-side, exposed to the south or west, will be insalubrious; for in summer mornings, a city thus placed would be hot, at noon it would be scorched. A city also with a western aspect would even at sunrise be warm, at noon hot, or in the evening of a burning temperature.' [1]

Further, Vitruvius advises against choosing those districts which emit foul vapours in hot weather. But harm is also done to the human body, in his opinion, by the cool moisture in the air and in winds. If the town walls stand in swamps running parallel to but situated a little above the sea and running in a northerly or north-easterly direction, they have probably been built so intentionally. By digging trenches the water can be drained off to the sea, and at high water the surf of the sea is dashed into the swamps, and with its salt kills the harmful creatures that are apt to occur in swampy regions.

For this reason Vitruvius considers the municipal settlements of Altinum (near Venice), Ravenna and Aquileia as 'incredibly healthy'. When the

[1] From Gwilt's translation.

swamps, however, stagnate and have no outlets either by way of rivers or drains, as is the case with the Pontine marshes, they will putrefy and produce unhealthy vapours. This is why the ancient Apulian town of Salapia was shifted by M. Hostilius, who founded a new Salapia in a healthy district with the permission of the Roman Senate and people. He connected the adjacent lake with the sea so that the former served as a harbour to the new settlement. 'This is why the Salapians now reside in a healthy area 4,000 paces away from their old city.' The reports of Vitruvius, which, by the way, are so utterly redundant and diffuse that we can repeat only the main substance, show that technical and hygienic considerations played a very important rôle in the choice of the site for a new town.

Before the ancients started building a town they found it necessary to provide adequate protection against enemy attacks in order to be able to carry on building operations undisturbed. The site having been marked out in the manner above described, the next step consisted in fortifying the place by erecting walls and towers.

FORTIFICATIONS

THE RAMPARTS

OPEN settlements were comparatively rare in antiquity. It may, indeed, be asserted that during many periods and among many peoples they were the exception. It is true that, later on, houses were built outside the town walls in many places such as Pompeii or Saalburg, but they were connected with the settlement inside in such a way that their occupants could easily retreat in cases of emergency into the area protected by the fortifications. In order to be safe from the enemy preference was usually given to an elevated place for the settlement in order that the approaching hordes might be easily observed and fought against from above. As has been said at the end of the last chapter, the area chosen for settling was in most cases enclosed by the

FIG. 361.—Wendish Earthwork enclosing an oval area in the Zootzen forest near Friesack (Mark of Brandenburg)

fortification proper before the dwellings were built. The oldest and simplest sort of fortification was a sort of parapet consisting of a dike of thrown-up earth. These earthworks as well as the modifications later derived from them varied considerably according to the nature of the ground, for even in their earliest stages the fortifications were built so that certain topographical features were turned to advantage. Labour was economized, for example, by using as a natural stronghold the bed or the winding of a river or the mouth of a tributary; all that was necessary then was to throw up straight or only slightly curved ramparts on the remaining side. Sometimes, however, the bank-fence was drawn right round the settlement or built in close proximity to it in the shape of a ring. In this case it served simply as a retreat (*refugium*). These enveloping earthworks were circular, oval or even rectangular in outline. The method of building them was very simple. The trees of the neighbouring regions were uprooted, and the area inside the future rampart was levelled. The ramparts themselves consisted of piled-up earth, and at a very early date were mixed with stones in order to make them firmer.

On throwing up the earth a ditch was naturally formed, but is by

FIG. 362.—Bank-fence on the Altkönig (Taunus Mountains). The upper of two walls

no means found with all the ramparts now. Sometimes the rampart was made of earth thrown up from inside and outside without a ditch being dug, and in this way a sunken plateau was formed inside, whereas the ground outside merged naturally into the surrounding region. On

FIG. 363.—The lower wall of the same Bank-fence

the other hand, many settlements have two ditches. Very often the tools for making ramparts were extremely primitive, consisting merely of a hoe, which rendered the task of construction very tedious. Frequently also the quantity of loose earth was insufficient, and therefore the ramparts were often made of ordinary stones piled up on top of one another and probably held together originally by wooden rafters. Walls of this kind often enclose an extensive area, as in the case of the Altkönig in the Taunus Mountains, which is encircled not by one row but by several rows of walls. Enormous quantities of stones were piled up to form a huge dike many miles in circumference. The amount of labour spent on it excites our wonder even at the present day.

At a very early date palisades were used for the construction of encircling walls. The paling could easily be made of trees felled and dragged aside, and thus it is quite natural that wood should have been used for fortifications. During the Celtic period wood also served to construct a kind of timber-frame in large walls which were built without mortar (*murus Gallicus alternis trabibus ac saxis*). This method of strengthening ramparts was subsequently taken over by the Romans and used in constructing the Limes, the large boundary dike built in upper Germania against the Teutons.

Technical peculiarities are seen in several such works. Both the

FIG. 364.—Vitrified Wall at Plauen in Voigtland

Heidenmauer on the Odilian Mountain and Frankenburg Castle near Schlettstadt, which date from the La Tène period (400 B.C. to the year of our Lord) consist of huge square blocks of sandstone connected by dovetailed dowels. These dowels have not, however, been preserved. A curious feature is seen in the so-called 'Glasburgen' (glass forts), specimens of which have been found chiefly in Bohemia and Scotland. Whereas the so-called fired walls ('Brandwälle') were only partly glazed by the action of strong fires, the walls of a Glasburg were vitrified all over, and thus became one coherent mass (Fig. 364). As regards the method of producing Glasburgen many theories have been proposed. It seems rather doubtful whether the process of vitrification was done on purpose. It is more probable that it occurred accidentally when a wall of stone, wood and earth was exposed to fire, a theory which is corroborated by the fact that the remains of charcoal or ash have frequently been found near a 'Glasburg'. For the rest, the structures and plans of vitrified walls, such as the wall at Plauen in Voigtland, agree in all details with Celtic walls, described by Caesar (*De bello gallico*, VII, 23).

WALLS, TOWERS AND DITCHES

In the course of time the circular walls developed into the ramparts of real fortifications. This took place at a comparatively late period among many peoples, for example the Greeks of Asia Minor. As late as the sixth century B.C., walls, particularly vertical walls, are met with very rarely. For example, the Wall of Heracles (*Iliad*, VII, 327–347, 435–441) was in all likelihood nothing more than a dike strengthened by a wall. Other walls in the district around Troy will be dealt with more exhaustively later on. In Mesopotamia, on the other hand, fortifications build from very well-thought-out plans were constructed at an earlier date, as is manifested by the design of an ancient Babylonian fortress dating from about 3100 B.C. (Fig. 365). From this we notice that a gate let into the wall is defended by projecting towers, and that its approach becomes narrower towards the inside so as to force its assailants to crowd together in front of it. Penned up in this position the invaders formed a good target for the missiles of the defenders on the flanking towers. The placing of such towers on salients arranged in an echelon, and the erection of other towers on the long front walls, the way in which corners were turned to account, and many other details, bear testimony to the high standard of this early art of fortification. The excavations at Nippur, south-east of Babylon, prove that at that period the inhabitants of Mesopotamia had already progressed from earth-dikes to proper ramparts, the first of which was built during the earliest pre-Semitic period (before 4000 B.C.). On this rampart King Naram-Sin (about 3750 B.C.) erected a high wall of the flat bricks which are typical of his time. The shops of the merchants were built into the wall on the inside; further buildings were added later. The great gate with the three entrances was let into the wall: the central entrance, which was large and low-lying, was for the animals; on each side there was a smaller raised entrance for foot-passengers with steps leading up to them. A particularly good adaptation to the conditions of the environment is exhibited by the fortifications of Kujundschik. These fortifications had a kind of tower-like forts raised on the hills which lay in front of the city-wall. Behind them stood the rampart, the ditches and two other walls, one of which was as high as the outer main wall. Diodorus says that the walls [1] were 300 ft. high and wide enough for six chariots to drive side by side on the top. The inner walls were built of stone and brick, whereas the outer ones seem to have consisted of earth, loose pebbles and large stones. The latter were taken from the ditches which at the expense of tremendous efforts were hewn out of the solid conglomerate rock. The excavations have shown the substructure of the walls to be of stone with a superstructure of sun-dried bricks. The upper edge of the stone wall was ornamented by cornices. In some places the wall extended to the river, which formed a natural moat filled with water. Where this arrangement was impossible, the wall was protected by a canal which was supplied with water from the river. On the north side the canal was made to pass into a deep ditch.

[1] *Sc.*, of Babylon, not Nippur. The reference is to Diod. Sic. ii, 7, 3 *seqq.*—*Trans.*

The art of fortifying reached a particularly high stage in Egypt; this is to be expected since this country is entirely flat and unaided by Nature in its defence against the inroads of enemies. Therefore, not only were isolated towns fortified, but all along the frontiers a number of strongholds were built, some of which were called 'walls of the king'. Of others mention is made in the hieroglyphics, which state that they stood against the 'gates of the barbarians'. As far as possible the plan of these forts was adapted to the configuration of the country. A long valley extends from the eastern part of the Delta of the Nile far into the middle of the country. From this valley hostile hordes could easily penetrate into the interior. This danger was obviated by strong fortifications headed by a wide canal which drew its water from some neighbouring lakes. A bridge was raised across the canal and its head was surrounded by several forts which were permanently occupied by troops. In the south of the kingdom strongholds were likewise built in places important from a strategic point of view, advantage being taken of the peculiarities of the landscape. An Egyptian king, probably Usertesen III[1] (about 2300 B.C.) according to Lepsius, had a huge fortress built near Semneh in Nubia, where the Nile breaks through a wall of rocks. It was constructed of bricks and provided with ditches, earthworks and walls. Opposite the river stood a high wall which, by virtue of its position on the river and its height, could be regarded as safe from all assaults. The wall was continued inland, and it followed the undulations of the land to such an extent that its height varied from 50 ft. on rising ground to 83 ft. in depressions. At the bottom it was 26 to 30 ft. thick and at the top some 13 ft. The upper part had a deep slope to prevent its being scaled with ladders. The ladder could not be propped against the upper slope. If it was placed on the lower edge the scalers found it impossible to proceed from the top rung of the ladder on to the steeply ascending slope. The wall was strengthened by twelve or thirteen buttresses which were about 7 ft. thick and projected like bastions. Every corner had a double tower from which missiles could be hurled upon the approaching enemy. The ditch in front of the wall had the extraordinary width of 100 to 130 ft. Its embankments were faced with carefully polished stones intended to make the assailants lose their footing on them and to slip into the ditch, the edge of which was also faced with stones. The glacis bordering the ditch was paved in a similar way. On it the defenders

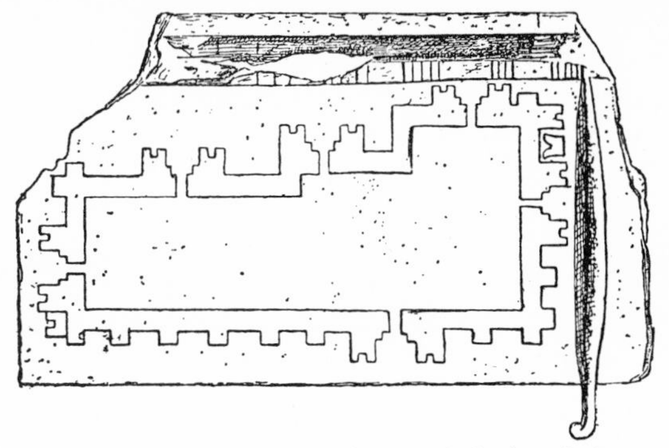

FIG. 365.—Plan of an ancient Babylonian fortress (From a statue of the King Gudea.) About 3100 B.C.

[1] = Senwosri.

awaited the onslaught of the enemy, as is still done in the case of modern fortresses. In war time the walls were especially equipped. Their pinnacles were furnished with timber frames, conning-towers and projecting scaffolds. On them the defenders took their positions and hurled stones and other missiles, or when the invaders came near enough, poured boiling oil over them. The fortresses in Syria may have been constructed in a similar way. In any case conclusions to this effect may be drawn from the mural paintings in the Ramesseum depicting the conquest of the country by Ramses II about 1300 B.C. It cannot be ascertained, however, whether the Egyptian artist who painted these battles had seen the fortresses himself or had copied Egyptian models. That the Scythians had similar fortifications is more or less proved by the paintings at Thebes bearing witness both to their capture by Ramses II and to the fact that the conditions of the ground were turned to account. The Scythian fortification was surrounded by a double ditch filled with water from a neighbouring river and crossed by two bridges. In front of the ditch and the bridges the defenders stood on what appeared to be a kind of glacis which was also within the range of arrows shot from the towers. The towers were higher than the walls, in order to enable the defenders to continue fighting the assailants who had stormed the wall and to oust them from the battlements.

THE ART OF FORTIFICATION AMONG THE GREEKS

The art of fortification reached a particularly high stage among the Greeks. Here the earth-dike had also originally been the customary mode of fortifying a place. For instance, the wall of the camp at Troy built by the Greeks near the sea-shore was made of earth strengthened by tree-trunks and stones which were driven into it (*Iliad*, XII, 28, 29). In front of it there was a deep ditch (*Iliad*, VII, 327–347, 435–441). The wall was provided with towers through which or beside which gates led into the camp (*Iliad*, XII, 35, 36; VII, 338, 339). The wall and towers had battlements (*ἐπάλξεις*) rising from the wall like steps (*κρόσσαι*). The wall was strengthened by buttresses (*στῆλαι προβλῆτες*), probably a kind of beams or planking supported by rafters which were intended to prevent the earthwork from sliding. A particular passage often mentioned in the *Iliad* (IX, 67, 87; XII, 64–66, 145; XVIII, 25, 228; XX, 49) ran between the wall and the ditch. In it the Greeks used to sit and cook their meals. The passage and the wall were cut off from the ditch and protected by palisades rammed into the elevated side of the ditch (Schliemann). The *Iliad* contains a description, not only of the Greek wall, giving full particulars, but also of the Trojan wall, the technical details of which have, moreover, been exposed by Schliemann's excavations. According to the *Iliad* (XXII, 3, 145; XVI, 700) this wall had parapets and towers and was easily accessible in one place only (*Iliad*, VI, 435–437). Although Schliemann's excavations have shown that the different towns of Troy had different kinds of walls, the wall of the third town on the whole conveys a clear idea of the Trojan art of fortification. It is characteristic, for instance, that the Cyclopean wall of the second town rests on the revetment made of smaller stones which belonged to the first town. It probably also served as retaining-wall to the hill. The wall of the first town (A in Fig. 366) was built exactly like the walls of the houses of the first or lowest town, namely in such a way that the joints of two stones were overlaid by a third stone. The wall of the second town, the Cyclopean wall (B in Fig. 366), consists of large blocks connected up by small stones. A further wall was afterwards discovered which was made of large blocks cemented together with clay.

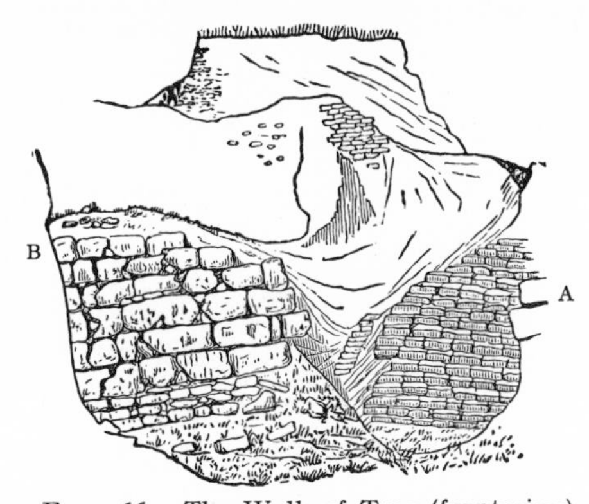

FIG. 366.—The Walls of Troy (front view)

Wall B belongs to the second town. The leaning position of the layers of stones seems due to a subsidence of the soil. Wall A is older, being that of the first town. It is a breast-wall for strengthening the slope of the hill and at the same time a revetment for the wall B

On the strength of all his excavations and researches Schliemann makes the following statements about the second wall (B):

'It is 10 ft. high, 6½ ft. thick, and is built in so-called Cyclopean masonry, i.e., in regular layers of large and rough square blocks of limestone joined together by small stones. Its vertex lies exactly 34 ft. below the surface of the ground. As is shown by the strata of debris running in a slanting direction underneath, it was originally constructed on the steep slope of a hill. A large quantity of similar blocks lying beside the wall seem to indicate that it used to be considerably higher. When I first laid it bare at the end of July 1872 it was much longer. In February 1873 I partly cleared it away in order to uncover the curious revetment A described above. It stands under the wall B at an angle of 45° and is 6 ft. high; it served originally as retaining wall to an isolated sand-mound which seems to be 20 ft. high with its ridge lying 20 ft. below the surface of the hill. It is fairly certain that the revetment belonged to the first town, as I have explained above.

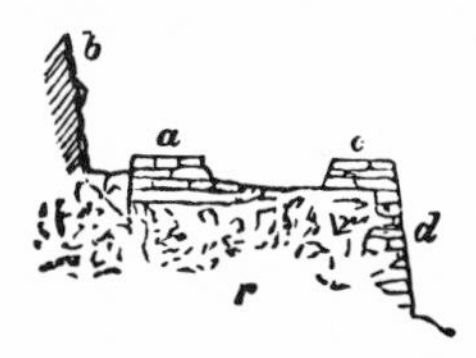

FIG. 367.—The larger inner and outer Walls of Troy

'The large inner wall marked *a* in Fig. 367 and *c* in Fig. 368 must in all probability be ascribed to the inhabitants of the second town. It also consists of large stone blocks and leads south at an angle of 45°. But it is only the south side that consists of solid masonry. On the north side it is built of stone not more than four or five courses deep, and is here supported by a wide dike (*r*) of loose stones and debris, the same material which was used for the greater part of the interior of the wall. Directly south of this large wall there stands another of the same size (*cd* in Fig. 367 and *b* in Fig. 368) which was obviously built by the third generation of settlers. It will be discussed below. The large inner wall runs eastward for some distance and then diminishes in width, becoming a wall some 11¾ ft. high, 6 ft. wide at the top and 12 ft. at the bottom. Finally it abruptly turns to the north-north-west. It is made of solid stone. Its builders did not take the trouble to clear the earth from the rocky ground, for the wall stands on a layer of earth which covers the rock to a depth of 2 ft. The inhabitants of the second town seem to have built the gate too, and the paved road which runs south-west down into the plain, for the lower portion of the gateway and the walls which I have laid bare by clearing away some stones of the pavement prove that they were built of equal-sized large blocks of white limestone. The observant eye of my

FIG. 368.—The Walls of Troy

a, Road to Troy. *b*, Outer wall. *c*, Inner wall. *d*, Projecting outer wall. *e*, Earthen pitchers. *f*, Ruins of the marble temple of Athene. *g*, Hellenic walls. *h*, Heaps of debris outside Troy. *k*, Entrance to the excavations

friend Professor Sayce discovered at once that this road was laid out by the second generation of settlers in such a way that they heaped up a rampart of debris on the then ascending ground. The walls crossing the road under its pavement can have served only to fortify this protecting rampart.'

Finally, the wall of the third town reveals the features of a most singular construction. To the new settlers the wall (marked *c* in Fig. 368) did not seem to be a sufficient protection, for it could easily be ascended, its angle of slope being only 45°. For this reason, in the very front of it, the large wall *b* was built facing towards the south at an angle of 15°, but perpendicular to the wall *c* on the north side. Thus, between the two walls a large triangular space emerged which was filled up with earth completely free from debris, as is proved by the excavations. Like wall *c*, the second wall *b* does not consist of solid masonry, but of two walls standing some 7 ft. apart. That which faces south slopes up at an angle of 75°. The space between the two walls of *b* was filled with loose stones. As a revetment for these stones the southern wall would hardly have been able to resist the tremendous pressure in a vertical position; this accounts for its slope. Both walls are made of small stones cemented with loam, and apparently contain not a single hewn block. The stones were placed with the flat side outwards in order to make the face of the wall as smooth as possible. The crest of wall *b* as well as that of wall *c* was topped with larger stones. Since the walls *b* and *c* were equal in height, a wide platform was obtained by filling the space between them with earth. The further part of wall *b* is constructed merely of a few courses of large blocks of stone placed on the debris of the second town. Upon these blocks brick walls were raised. As they appeared too weak, however, for this weight, a kind of clay cake was placed between them; the use of this clay cake for making walls was peculiar to the builders of the third town of Troy. It is true that it also occurs in the first two towns, but it does not form a part of the constructional system. The reason which led the Trojans to employ these clay cakes is discussed by Burnouf as follows:

'The new settlers started by levelling the debris over the ruins of the second town. They filled up the hollows and cavities with stones and other material such as ash or clay, and in order to consolidate the ground they laid clay cakes (*galettes*) into the interstices.'

As regards the brick wall standing on clay cakes Burnouf gives the following information:

'In A (Fig. 369) there are sixteen courses of brick cemented together with a material which was prepared from crushed bricks. These courses extend almost up to the Hellenic wall (C). They are inclined outwards. The layer of clay cake (B) on which they rest is some 6 ft. thick. It is separated from it by a layer of blocks of limestone. B lies upon the large wall D which encircles the citadel. At a later period the town spread over the area covered by the debris which had been thrown over the walls. R designates one of these accumulations of debris; it contains a layer of black ashes N. M is the wall of a house which leans against the Hellenic wall C.'

On the north side the brick wall does not rest on a stone wall but on a course of large stone plates. It consists of two parallel walls with the intervening space filled with broken bricks. But it also shows traces of white plaster.

The *Iliad* mentions a watch-tower (XXII, 145), and another

tower (XVI, 700), which proves that in the art of fortification a distinction between watch-towers proper and towers belonging strictly to the defence system was drawn at a very early date. The ordinary watch-towers did not project beyond the wall, either in ancient or in mediaeval fortification. The towers, however, which joined part of the fortification, did project and so enabled the defenders to cover the walls and the ditch in front with arrows or other missiles. The distances between these towers varied between 165 and 330 ft. according to the range of the weapons and ballistae used. Sometimes the towers stand out at right angles from the 'curtain', i.e. the wall between them, and sometimes their sides form a kind of nook with the curtain so that one edge is turned towards the assailants. This arrangement renders the climbing of the curtain more difficult, and for this reason the tower is often placed in an angle of the curtain, or the curtain is built on a broken line between the towers. Instead of the above-mentioned funnel-shaped gate entrance between two flanking towers, as was customary in Mesopotamia (see page 284), hexagonal towers came into use later on for flanking the gates; by this arrangement the same result was achieved. Round towers were comparatively rare, though they occurred in isolated cases such as at Messene.

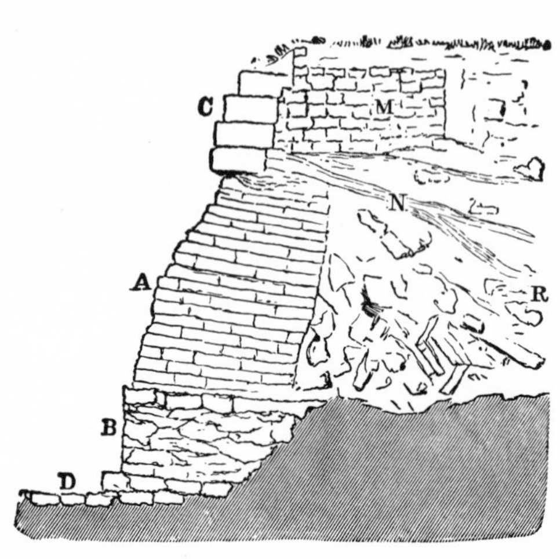

FIG. 369.—The Brick Wall of Troy which rests on clay cakes

GATEWAYS

Particular care was bestowed on the entrance gate of fortifications. Apart from strong flanking towers (Fig. 370) special salients were built with the wall for hiding the gates. This gate was approached by a road which was protected in many ways. For instance, it turned at a sharp angle and caused stoppages amongst the advancing assailants or exposed portions of itself to the missiles of the defenders. Or, again, it helped the defenders to reach the area in front of the fortress without being wounded during a sally. Inside the gate there is often a yard closed towards the town by a second gate. In this yard the troops were drawn up, inspected, relieved or assembled for sallies; or the enemy who had managed to enter through the outer gate could be checked and prevented from advancing further by shutting the inner gate and could under certain circumstances be annihilated. Specimens of particularly well-built gates are found in the citadels of Tiryns and Mycenae. The walls of Tiryns contain stone blocks 6 to 10 ft. in length, 3 ft. wide and 3 to 6 ft. thick. The weight of some pieces amounts to 20 tons. The walls are not sloping but rise vertically to an imposing height. The main wall of Tiryns runs round a hill which is some 330 ft. wide and about 1,000 ft. long, and falls into three sections. On the highest of them stood the old royal palace. The middle section contained the dwellings of vassals and servants, and the lowest part constituted the town proper. The walls of the various sections were very different in thickness. Whereas some are only 23 to 26 ft. thick, others are not less than 53 ft. thick. The ramp forming the ascent to the citadel is constructed in such a way that a man approaching the gate held his left hand, which carried the shield, on the other side. The right hand was turned towards the wall of the citadel. In this way he was from the outset rendered defenceless on account of his position, for he was unable to protect himself with the shield on the wall side and to throw javelins or other missiles upwards. The gate had a width of 6 to 10 ft. and could be locked by a sliding bolt, the grooves of which may still be seen in the wall. The gate was no folding-gate but a swing-gate, as is seen from the traces left in the threshold and the ruined lintel. It was provided with pivots forming the continuation of the longitudinal axle and swung round in pans lying in the middle of the threshold and the lintel. When the door was open one half was turned inwards and the other outwards. An enemy, unfamiliar with this peculiarity, who pressed against both halves of the gate thus kept them steady by his own act, and was thus stopped and exposed to missiles from the wall for a longer time. Behind the gate there was an additional defence, a passage protected by walls.

FIG. 370.—Gateway with projecting flanking Towers
Reconstruction of the gate of the palace of Sargon

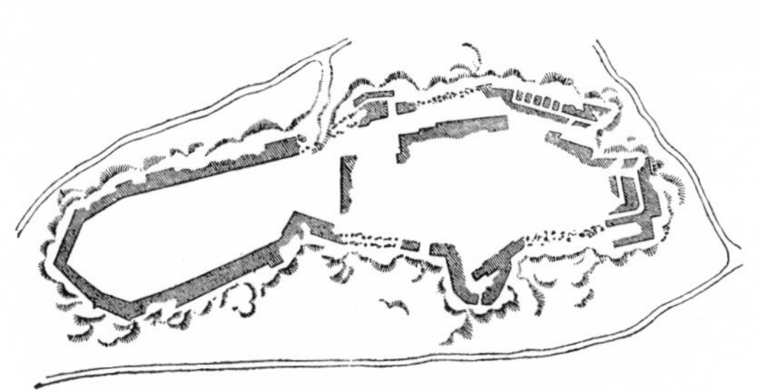

FIG. 371.—Fortification of the citadel at Tiryns

A well-fortified tower contained a cistern, which was of vital importance for providing the garrison with drinking water ; it is specially protected in many ancient fortifications. A double gate comes next behind which the passage continues further between high walls. On both sides of the entrance are the casemates carrying vaults in the shape of pointed arches, the oldest specimens of their kind. We shall recur to the construction of these pointed arches in the sequel. (See page 274.) How scientifically the builder planned everything can be seen from the fact that only the exterior walls and part of the foundations were constructed of those huge blocks of stone mentioned earlier. All the constructions and the masonry of the interior consist of brick, clay and wood.

FIG. 372.—Part of the Town Wall of Athens, constructed by Themistocles 479 B.C.

The citadel of Mycenae was built in a similar way. In front of and behind the entrance—the famous 'Lion Gate'—runs the passage between massive walls, from which the enemy who was advancing or had even entered the gate could successfully be fought. Whereas the fortifications of Tiryns consist entirely of crude Cyclopean masonry, those of Mycenae also contain artistically hewn and carefully joined square blocks. But here, too, the use of masonry of such size and resistivity is limited to the defence works and the substructures. The same is the case with the citadel of Knossos, in the island of Crete. The further buildings, except the sepulchral vaults, which are made of stone, are constructed of easily perishable materials such as brick or clay. If defensive works of this kind had to be prepared in a hurry, the same principle, of using only the best material, was observed. In the year 479 B.C. Themistocles hurriedly changed Athens into a fortress and in spite of the disapproval of the Spartans he connected it with the Piraeus, which had also been fortified. As we are told by various authors (Thucydides, I, 90 ; Cornelius Nepos, *Themistocles*, 6), tombstones, which are still to be found in the remains of this wall at the Dipylon, were used in this hasty construction. Their quantity being insufficient and the transportation of further stone material

FIG. 373.—Another section of Themistocles' Wall

from a distance requiring too much time, the superstructure of Themistocles' wall was made of clay tiles. The construction of the gates also shows that they were planned with great care, and in some cases a fair amount of technical knowledge is manifested. The gates of fortifications reached a particularly high degree of technical development because some parts had to support excessively heavy loads as a consequence of the material used. The most primitive gates were constructed in the following way. The lintel was simply placed across the top of the jambs and then the rectangle formed by these parts and the threshold was let directly into the wall. In order to obtain a large-sized gate the lintel had to be made of greater width ; it thus became heavier, consequently demanding a greater bearing power in the jambs. This difficulty was overcome by placing the jambs obliquely, that is by making the doorway narrower towards the lintel. The result was that the width of the gate at the top and with it the lintel were kept small even with a wide opening at the bottom. A narrow lintel was less liable to break under pressure than a wide one lying on vertical posts. Later on, a further expedient was discovered for relieving the strain on the lintel and preventing its collapse. According to Reber, whose account we are following, the 'Lion Gate' at Mycenae is a classical instance of the new method of procedure. An aperture, a sort of upper doorway, was made above the lintel with both sides narrowing towards the top, so that the weight over the gate was reduced. Thus

FIG. 374.—The Lion Gate of Mycenae

FIG. 375.—Gate at Messene (restored)

the lintel was no longer pressed down by the weight of the superincumbent wall, and a free opening was formed which was either triangular, quadrilateral or polygonal, and was either left vacant—as in the gate of Messene—or filled with some lighter masonry embellished by plastic ornaments as in the case of the Lion Gate at Mycenae.

FIG. 376.—Gate at Missolonghi

FIG. 377.—Gate of Thorikos

If we now imagine a gate of the kind just described with an upper aperture but with the lintel and jambs removed we should have a form of gate such as is actually found in ancient fortifications, for example, in

FIG. 378.—Gate of Phigalia

FIG. 379.—Gate at Samos

Messene (Fig. 375). The wall itself forms the perpendicular sides of the entrance, which is triangular at the top. If the sloping parts on each side are slightly curved, they form a gate with a pointed arch, such as the gate of Ephesus. If the sides slope up all the way from the threshold they will form a regular triangular gate (as at Missolonghi, Fig. 376). And if they are curved, in addition, the gate will be a simple pointed arch like the gate of Thorikos (Fig. 377). If the sides of the entrance are vertical at the bottom but slant towards the top, space is left for the insertion of a lintel, which, however, can be of only small dimensions. (Cf. the gates of Phigalia, Fig. 378, and of Amphissa.) Again, the corbelling blocks of the sides may be oblique, as is seen in the gates of Samos (Fig. 379), Abae and Samothrace. A useful method of relieving the lintel, applied, for example, in pyramids and other Egyptian works of architecture, was as follows. The lintel was cut in two beforehand, and the two pieces were leaned against each other with their lower ends standing on buttresses or on the wall where it bounds the gate. In this way the pressure of the masonry above the lintel was transferred from the two halves of the lintel to the buttresses or the lateral parts of the wall, as is often the case with bridges. An example of this construction is found in the gate at Delos.

ROMAN FORTIFICATIONS

In general the fortifications of the Romans are very much like those of the Greeks. Sometimes they exhibit ancient Greek peculiarities so distinctly that their origin is beyond all doubt. The fortified camp on the Bay of Verudella near Pola, for instance, recalls the above-described fortifications of Tiryns and Mycenae, as regards its plan and the construction of its entrance (Fig. 380).

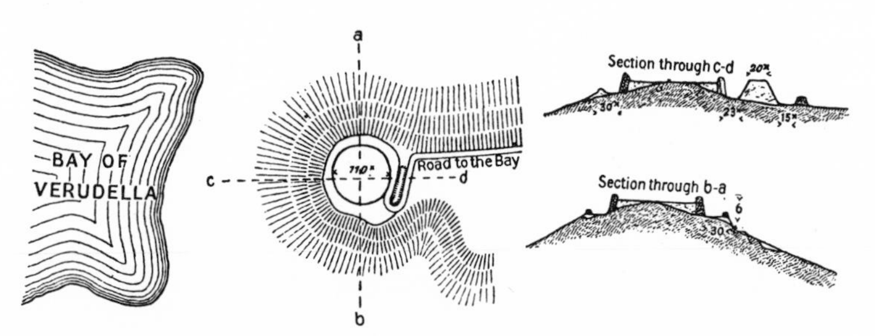

Fig. 380.—The Fortified Camp on the Bay of Verudella

Anthes describes it in the following terms:

> 'A retaining wall, made of blocks and quarry stone without mortar, was constructed round the summit of the hill, and the intervening space was filled up. A fortified plateau 100 paces in diameter and 165 ft. above sea-level was thus obtained. Parallel to the wall, and at a distance of 10 to 20 ft., there runs a terre-pleine which varies in width from 60 to 180 ft., and is bordered on the outer side against the declivity of the hill by another rampart made of stone. The approach to the camp lies along the north side of a ridge which gives the fort a land connection with other ranges of hills. Near the camp this road is continuously flanked on both sides by walls, and thus a defile is created which is the only mode of access of the assailants to the weak parts of the plateau. Immediately after meeting the rampart tangentially the road runs for more than 300 ft. along a kind of bulwark which compels the attackers to expose their right sides to the defenders.'

Even in Vitruvius' description of the construction of walls and towers (I, 5) practically nothing is found which suggests features distinctive from those of Mesopotamian, Egyptian or Greek fortifications. Vitruvius, too, maintains that the entrance should have a position which compels the enemy to turn outwards the side which is covered by his shield. He vetoes building towns either as plain quadrangles or with three-cornered salients, but advises that the latter should be curved, 'to give a view of the enemy from many points. Defence is difficult where there are salient angles because angles protect the enemy rather than the inhabitants.' Vitruvius seems to be trying to explain a traditional peculiarity of Roman fortifications, the origin of which we attempted to make clear above (page 277), but he is not convincing, for the salient is still to be found in fortifications of the later Middle Ages and of the following centuries. Further, it seems more expedient to avoid the angle by constructing a tower rather than by rounding it off. Besides, in many Roman fortifications the rounded corner is protected by being sloped or by specially constructed outer works placed in front of it (for example, the fort of Niederbieber, in the '*Novus vicus*' at Heddernheim). Vitruvius recommends round or polygonal towers, the square ones being more easily destroyed because the impulsive blows of the battering rams break the corners, 'but in the case of round towers they can do no harm, being

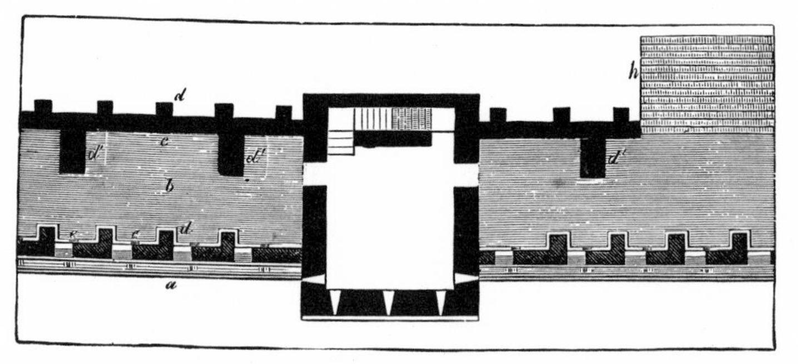

FIG. 381.—Ground-plan of the town-walls of Pompeii

engaged, as it were, in driving wedges to the centre'. There are many Roman walls still extant which show how accurately the theories of Vitruvius or the earlier traditions derived from the ancient East by way of Greece were followed. Vitruvius maintains that the strongest walls were obtained by making the ditches around the site of the future works as deep and wide as possible, and that the earth thrown up in this way should be heaped up as a rampart between an inner and an outer wall. If the rampart were then battered down sufficiently hard to stand by itself it would be, he says, practically impregnable to battering rams, mines or any other contrivances, even if a breach should be made in the outer walls. All the important features of Vitruvius' statement are found in the fortification at Pompeii, apart from the outer ditch, which is missing probably because it was levelled out later on, when Pompeii was made an open city. As to its walls, Overbeck says:

'If we examine their ground-plan we find the rampart or *agger b*, raised between the outer wall or escarp *a* and the inner wall or counterscarp *c*, both of which are supported by strong buttresses which stand on the inner side. In addition to the ordinary buttresses *d*, projecting towards the inner side of the agger, the counterscarp has some larger ones (*d′*) catching into the agger at certain intervals, possibly in order to strengthen it. The outer wall does not rise vertically on the outside, but slopes inwards, becoming nearly 2 ft. narrower towards the top. The outer

FIG. 382.—Cross-section of the Town-wall of Pompeii

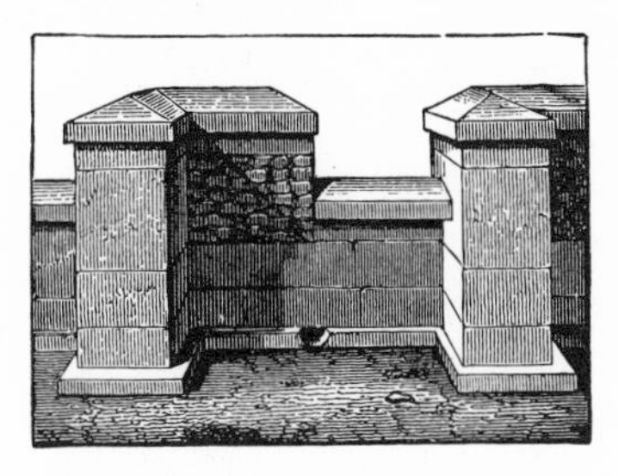

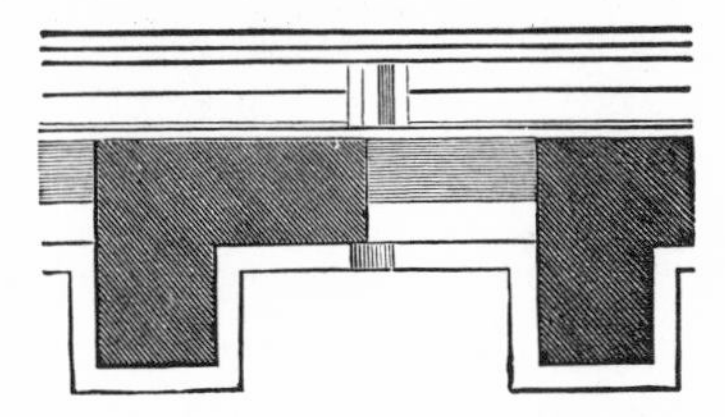

FIGS. 383 and 384.—The Breastworks of the walls of Pompeii

wall and the earthwork behind are on an average 26 to 28 ft. high, neglecting some irregularities due to the conformation of the ground, and the earthwork measured between the parapet of the front wall and the inner wall, which is higher,

FIG. 385.—Tower on the City Wall of Pompeii (side-view)

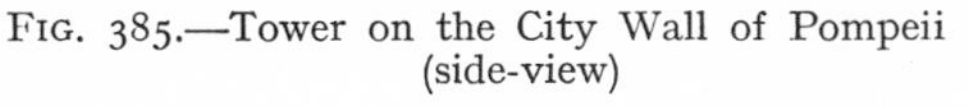

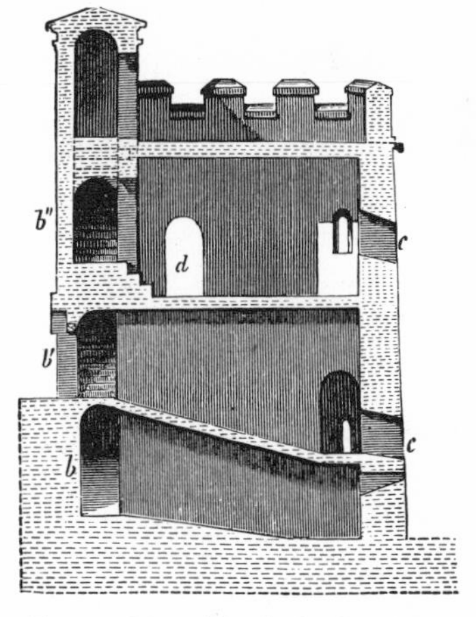

FIG. 386.—Vertical Section through a tower on the City Wall of Pompeii (see also Figs. 387–89)

is 18 ft. thick. The upper surface of the earthwork slants slightly outwards in order to allow the rain water to flow off through the escape pipes of stone provided at intervals of 9 ft. underneath the crenellation. The breastwork of the outer wall rises some 4 ft. above the stone-slabs of the rampart and is pierced by embrasures over 2 ft. wide and 2 ft. deep, through which the missiles were thrown. Several embrasures have been blocked up or left out altogether. As is seen from the interior view and the small ground-plan (Figs. 383 and 384), these embrasures have the form of a carpenter's square and project perpendicularly inwards for a distance of 3 ft. 2 in.: they are at the same height as the parapet. In this way they formed a stone shield on both sides for the soldier behind, who had only to move to the loophole on the right for a moment in order to throw his javelin. He could at once resume his place of shelter behind the breastwork, from where he had an uninterrupted view of the assailants. The inner wall rises some 18 ft. above the plateau and increases the total average height to about 43 ft., sufficient to ward off any missiles thrown by ballistae or other machines.'

As regards the construction of the towers in the walls, ample informa-

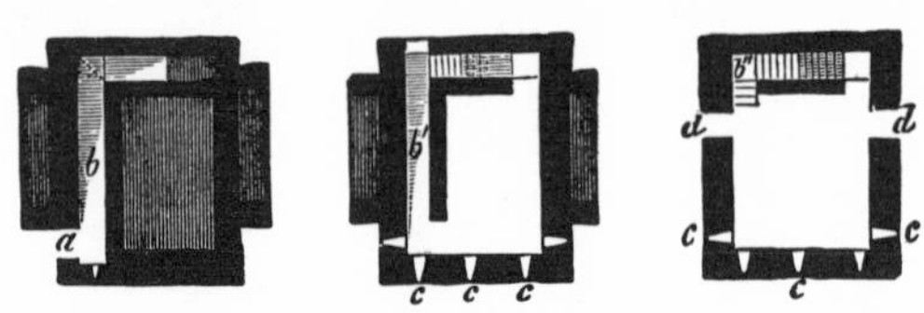

FIGS. 387–389.—The three Stories of the tower on the wall of Pompeii

a, Sally-port (which may be closed by a portcullis); *b*, ascending corridors leading to the first floor; *b'* and *b''*, stairs leading to the second floor or terrace; *c*, *c*, loop-holes; *d*, doors opening on to the rampart (cf., Fig. 386)

tion can be gathered from Figs. 385 to 389. Special care was taken by the Romans in constructing the gateways, the upper parts of which, especially in later times, were almost always arched. They often have several entrances and sometimes attain to the standard of monumental works of art. The arch itself seems to have been taken over from the East, where it had been used in ancient times in the shape of arched roofings over

FIG. 390.—Porta Nigra at Trèves. (View from within)

street crossings (*tetrapyla*). Many of these arches allow themselves to be crossed in all four directions (*quadrifons*). The Roman fortified gateway reaches the highest stage of elaboration when it develops into a kind of stronghold. A striking example of this type is the 'porta nigra' of Trèves (Figs. 390, 391). The ground-floor has no windows. The same is the case with the small square watch-towers standing at equal intervals on the *limes*, the Roman boundary wall in Germania. The lower parts, which were exposed to the assailants, are merely bare walls devoid of any

FIG. 391.—As Fig. 390. View from the outside

weak points of which the enemy might have taken advantage (Figs. 392 and 393). Over the ditch (now vanished) in front of the *porta nigra* a bridge led to two circularly arched entrances. The assailant approaching them was very much exposed to missiles projected from the double rows of windows above and the three-storied flanking towers. If, having succeeded, however, in capturing the bridge and the strongly bolted gates, and in forcing the portcullis behind, he rushed through the gateway in the delusion of having the city in his hands, destruction lay in wait for him. He entered a courtyard which led into the city and which had its inner gates bolted and barred. On to this space the windows of the fortified gateway also opened, from which the defender dispatched his javelins (*pila*) in large numbers. Trèves has yet another peculiarity of the Roman art of fortification to show. The amphitheatre, the place of pleasure and merriment, was built

FIG. 392.—Roman Watch- .ower on the *Limes*
Model in Saalburg

into the system of encircling walls in such a way as to make it also a means of defence. The wall was not led around the amphitheatre but

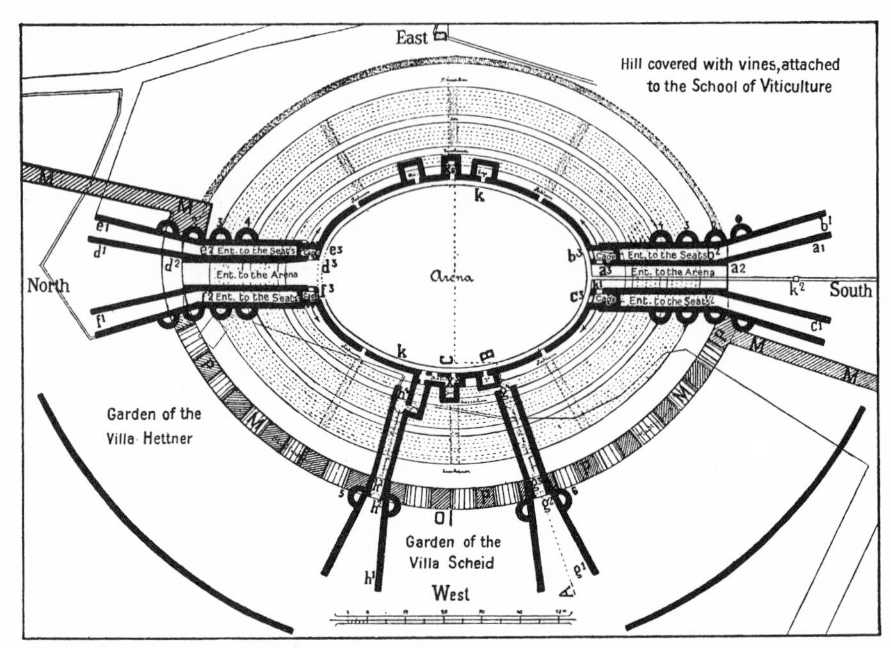

Fig. 393.—Plan of the Amphitheatre of Trèves

MMPP, Roman town-wall. P, Pillars. M, arches

made to bridge its northern entrances and then drawn in a regular curve around the long arc of the elliptical arena in the west, i.e.

Fig. 394.—Porta Herculanea at Pompeii

The gateway in the middle has the form of a double gate; when the enemy had penetrated into the inner court, it could be shut off by a portcullis and doors from the by-ways intended for pedestrians and could be commanded from the ramparts

around the side nearer the city. The foundations of the arena were laid in a hill which had been artificially raised to hold the tiers. Before the wall reaches the south side of the arena it turns to the right and resumes its original north-south direction. The idea of this arrangement is clear. The deeply sunk arena lay in front of the wall and formed a huge moat, a kind of pitfall, in which the enemy who had penetrated into it could effectively be pelted with missiles (Fig. 393).

There are also fortified gateways in various parts of Pompeii, of which a particularly good example is the Porta Herculanea (cf. Fig. 394).

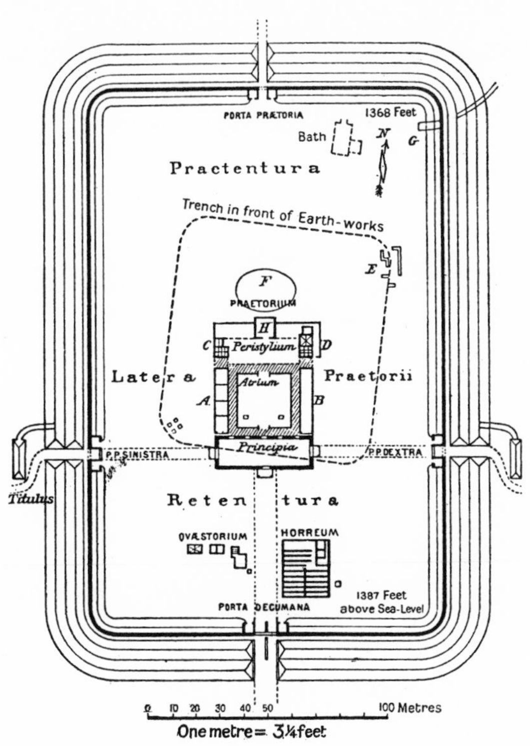

FIG. 395.—Ground-plan of the Camp at Saalburg

The ditch of the original camp, as well as the double ditches in front of the ramparts, the *via sagularis*, and other details, are clearly visible

The camps or *castra*, in spite of their varying sizes and their stereotyped oblong form with rounded corners, exhibit all the above characteristics of the ancient Roman art of fortifying (Figs. 395–400). The outside consists of a strong crenellated wall, as is clearly seen at Saalburg. The crenellations are built in the form of niches, as in Pompeii. A paved road, the *via sagularis* (Fig. 397) ran round the camp along the inner side of the terre-pleine. In front of the rampart there is a path about 3 ft. wide similar to that of Troy, with two ditches in front, having the characteristic wedge-shape of Roman ditches. Farther outside there is another rampart. The camp had the two familiar main cross-roads of Roman settlements and four gates with rounded arches, of which the *porta decumana* was developed as a double gate (Figs. 398 and 399). The gates are flanked by low towers, and the ditches in their vicinity are partly interrupted and partly bridged over. There are no lateral and no corner towers. The double ditch and also the *limes*, which was 335 miles long, was fortified with stakes, each being separately rammed down by a hammer, after it had been pointed and charred or tipped with iron

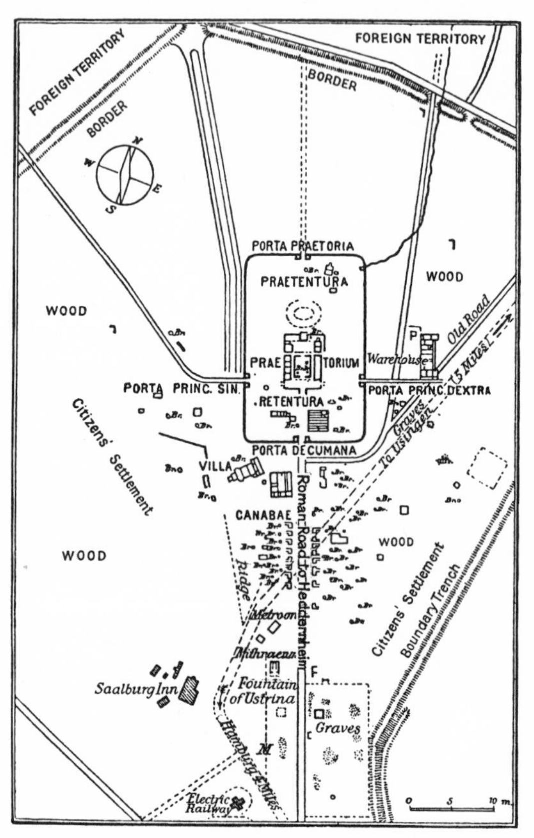

FIG. 396.—Plan of the site of Saalburg Camp and environment

to protect it from putrefaction. The stakes, about as thick as a man's arm, were driven in some 3 ft. deep, and then connected up by a hurdle-work of rods of a finger's breadth. This wall of fascines was strengthened on the inside by strong supports. Afterwards a 3 ft. deep ditch was dug at a distance of about 18 in. and the earth thrown against the hurdle-work to give it great power of resistance. In order to protect the soldiers working in the ditch in close proximity to the enemy, sheds were built, and platforms for the archers raised within the inner circle of the fortification. It was not till this ditch was finished that the rampart was begun. It was made of earth, turf and stones held together by three rows of rough stakes connected by cross-beams, as is exemplified at Saalburg. A wooden wall was then

Fig. 397.—Gateway of Saalburg Camp (*porta sinistra*)
Interior view. On the left, niches of embrasures, and the *via sagularis*

built, consisting of stakes, the gaps between which were blocked up with

Exterior view showing the bridge, double ditch, wall with crenellations.

Interior view showing the double gate and other details

Figs. 398 and 399.—*Porta decumana* of Saalburg Camp

hurdle-work. Next, the construction of a stone wall was taken in hand :

two parallel walls, each 2 ft. 8 in. thick, were erected, and the space between them filled with earth. In order to make them safe from the

FIG. 400.—Parallel triangular Ditch with Wall (Saalburg)

outward pressure of the earth they were held together by rafters. A terre-pleine of hurdle-work was arranged on the scarp, and finally the

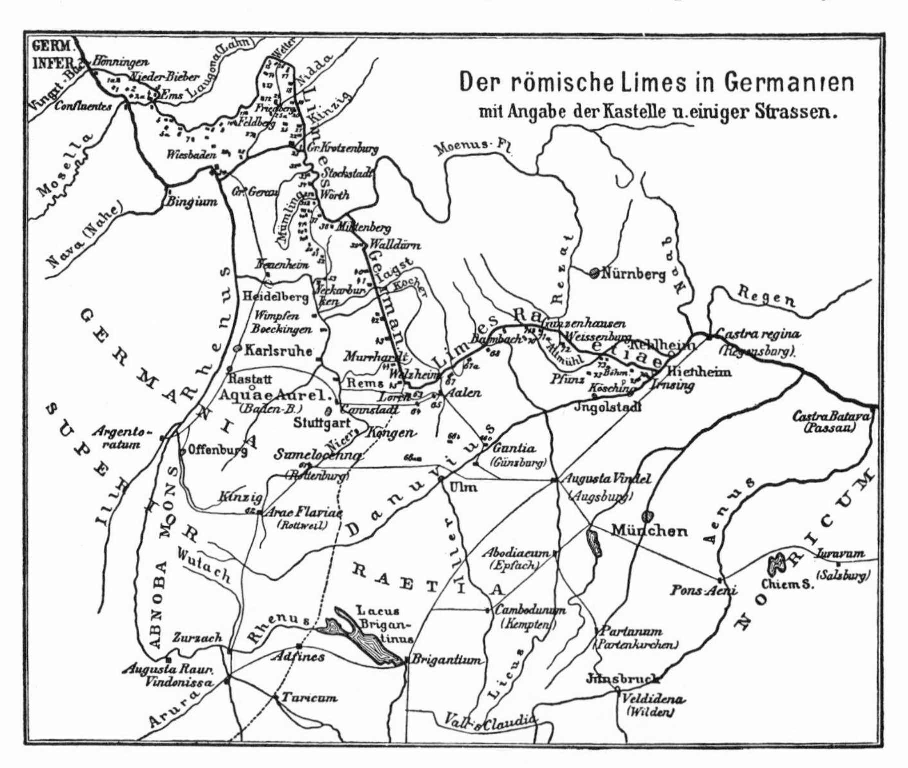

FIG. 401.—The Roman *Limes* in Germania, with the attached camps

stone wall (since reconstructed) was raised and the ditch doubled, but not filled with water. It was intended only to check the advancing enemy and to throw him into disorder.

TOWN STREETS AND SQUARES

THE streets and squares were laid out more or less in the same way in all the cities of antiquity. In most cases there was one ornamental street or more, usually paved. These branched off into a system of by-streets, which were paved less carefully or not at all. The origin of pavements is lost in the obscurity of prehistoric times. Wherever we come across towns, whether in Babylon, Egypt or Greece, we find pavements. Besides paving proper there was a sort of macadam : the ballast—that is, the small broken stones—was battered down into a base. When the ballast had become reduced to powder by the traffic, it was covered with a fresh layer. It may thus be rightly maintained that almost every kind of pavement known to-day was used in antiquity except perhaps wood-pavements, for even asphalt was used to pave the sidewalks at Pompeii. The stone-paving might be slabs or cobbles.

The ancients also knew how to level irregularities in the surface of the streets by filling rubble and sand into the depressions and stamping it in wherever necessary. They also knew how to camber the road-surface to allow the water to flow off to the sides. As in the case of fortifications, the art of road-making was highly developed in the East and in Asia Minor, whence it spread to all parts of the world. This is proved not only by excavations at Babylon, Nineveh and other places, but also by investigations made at Palmyra which, according to legend, was founded by Solomon and used to be the capital of the Syrian province Palmyrene. The magnificent gateway (Fig. 402) which stands to this day at the head of the long colonnade has a triangular ground-plan ; this proves that even ancient builders knew how to utilize corners to produce monumental effects. The gate joins the famous colonnade that consists of four avenues of columns : this form of street is often met with in antiquity ; for example, in Alexandria, Antioch, Seleucia, Ephesus and Gerasa. The Greek colonnade was imitated by the Romans, as at Timgad, Lambaesis, Dugga and Tebessa. The colonnade of Palmyra (Fig. 403) consisted of a 37 ft. wide causeway for vehicles and two 18 ft. wide covered sidewalks for pedestrians. It was about a mile in length and had 1,500 columns, each of which was some 57 ft. high. The highly perfected art of cutting stones is still shown by a column 37 ft. high which consists of a single block of blue speckled granite. According to a theory, the truth of which is often doubted, a gallery extended over the side-walks from which the lively coming and going in the street below could be observed.

A model of this kind was bound to give a new impetus to road-making.

But this holds good only for the ornamental main streets (Fig. 405); it did not affect the by-streets, which were, on the whole, left with their dreary

Fig. 402.—Ornamental Gate at Palmyra

appearance, as the private houses in them had only few or no windows towards the street and practically no architectural pretensions. But in general we know very little of them. The best examples of ordinary thoroughfares in ancient towns have been preserved in Pompeii. In that city the façades of the houses have some ornamentation even in by-streets, which are also enlivened by shops built on the ground floor, by small works of sculpture and paintings. As a rule the streets were narrow, for this was considered healthier on account of the shade (Tacitus, *Annals*, XV,

Fig. 403.—The Great Colonnade at Palmyra

43). Pompeii's widest street measured only some 26 ft. across from house to house, including the sidewalks. Many streets were 13 ft., others only 8 to 10 ft. wide. The streets having sidewalks, the track for vehicles in the middle was often so narrow as to make it impossible for two carriages coming from opposite directions to pass each other. If one was in the street, any that met it had to wait till it had left. Many streets were blocked to traffic altogether. For this purpose some big stones were fixed at their entrances across the causeway or some larger blocks

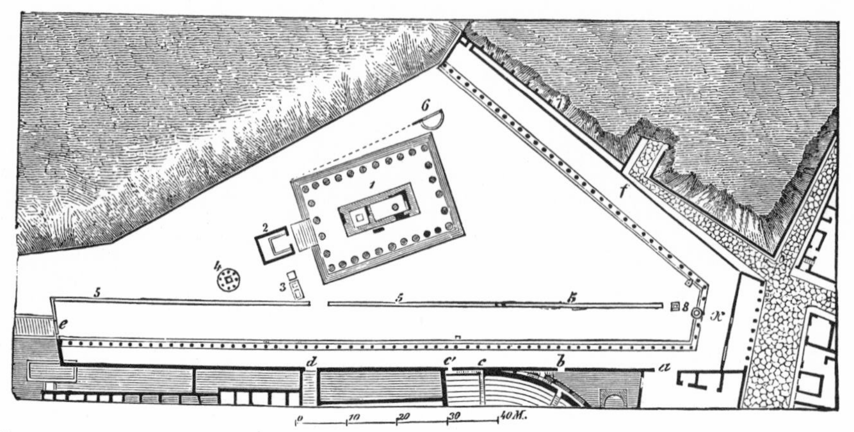

FIG. 404.—Plan of a Roman Ornamental Public Place: the *Forum Triangulare* at Pompeii

The triangular space was entered through doors at *x*. On two sides it is bordered by a colonnade 16 ft. wide and some 670 ft. long, consisting of 100 columns. The third side is open

1, Greek temple; 2, probably the wall of an altar for burnt-offerings; 3, altars; 4, wells (?); 5, low walls, shutting off the temple without hindering the view; 6, seat with sun-dial; 7, drains for the rain-water

FIG. 405.—Roman Ornamental Street: The *Forum Civile* at Pompeii

placed longitudinally in such a way as to project from the pavement (Fig. 407).

The streets were slightly cambered. The pavement consists of lava blocks. This material being very soft, the cart-wheels gradually wore ruts into it, which are still visible. (The theory that these ruts had been

FIG. 406.—Pompeian Street

In the centre the pavement, consisting of polygonal lava blocks. On the left and right are seen elevated sidewalks with kerbstones ; in the houses, shops with counters (visible on the left)

cut purposely after the pavement had been laid down is wrong.) From them it can be ascertained that the distance between the cart-wheels in those days was 3 ft. (Fig. 408). The lava-tiles used for paving were

FIG. 407.—Street blocked to traffic. (Strada del Tempio di Augusto at Pompeii)

The original well-worn rut was probably made before the kerbstones were laid, which cover the site of the second rut. Certain irregularities in the rut suggest that the stones originally lay on the sides. Afterwards the ruts *b b* were made, and finally the street was barred to vehicles by means of the large stones lying at the level marked *a*

joined as tightly as possible. For this purpose they were cut specially at the corners.

The paving-stones were joined very accurately, but as corners and edges broke off easily a general loosening took place in the course of time, and the pavement had to be mended. For this purpose small stones were inserted or iron wedges rammed into the pavement (Fig. 409). The sidewalks were kerbed with cut stones (Figs. 406, 408, 411) which were often bored through. These borings served to fasten the awnings with which the shopkeepers protected their shops and the goods displayed in front of them from the sun-rays and the rain. Some larger blocks —usually three in a line— were made to project from the pavement of the causeway. They were intended to be used by the pedestrians as stepping-stones in violent rains (Figs. 408, 410). The materials used for making the sidewalks varied according to the house-owner who was responsible for the repair and upkeep of the section. On the hard battered earth there lay a cover of tiles or mosaic (*opus signinum*) slabs, marble or asphalt. At the corners of the streets there were guard-stones, and along the sidewalks gutters with drain-pipes through which the rain-water flowed into the sewers (Figs. 412–415).

FIG. 408.—Street in Pompeii
In the foreground there are seen two cart-ruts and behind them three stepping-stones used by pedestrians in wet weather

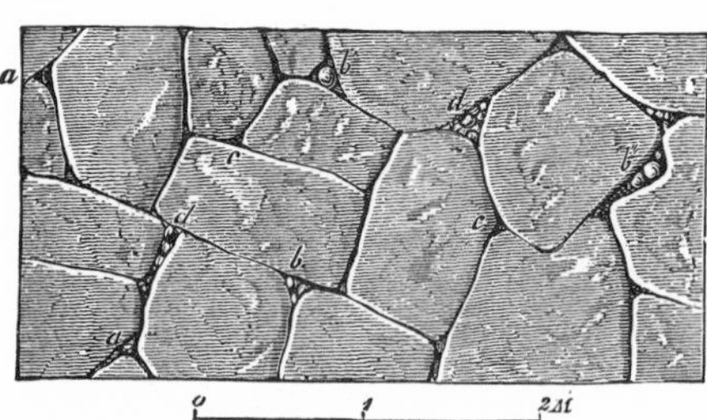

FIG. 409.—Mended Pavement in Pompeii
a, Iron; *b*, granite; *c*, marble; *d*, gravel.

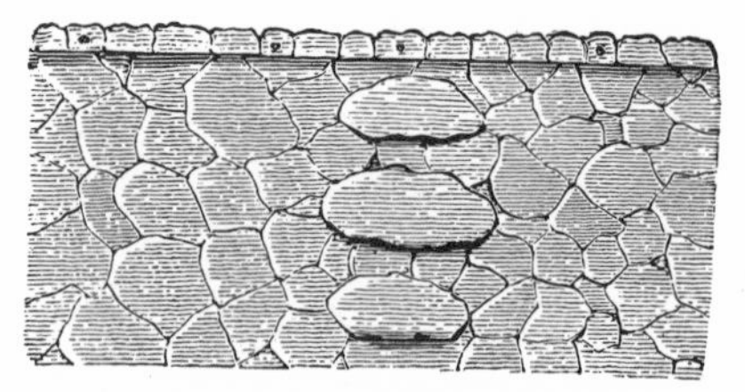

FIG. 410.—Pavement with Stepping-stones for pedestrians.

Hence, the art of road-making practised by the Romans was excellent and suited the requirements of the traffic of that age perfectly. It must be borne in mind, however, that the traffic was chiefly effected on foot. Heavy vehicles for goods were not allowed in the streets except early in the morning. Even riding and driving were uncommon. On this

FIG. 411.—Street in Pompeii
Sidewalk with irregular kerbstones. Behind, a shop with counter, showing openings for holding vessels

account no stables have been found in Pompeian houses, and only one doorway for carriages has been discovered. Besides, the elevated side-

FIG. 412.—Street in Pompeii, with Sidewalk and Gutter for the rain-water

walks, the stone steps and the thresholds would have been sufficient to hinder the circulation of vehicles. The reason is that riding and driving was regarded as undemocratic.

Suetonius reports the decree of the emperor Claudius which prohibited travellers to pass through Italian towns otherwise than on foot or in sedan-chairs (*Claud.* 25). Of Marcus Aurelius we are told (*Hist. Aug.* iv, 23, 8) that he forbade horse-

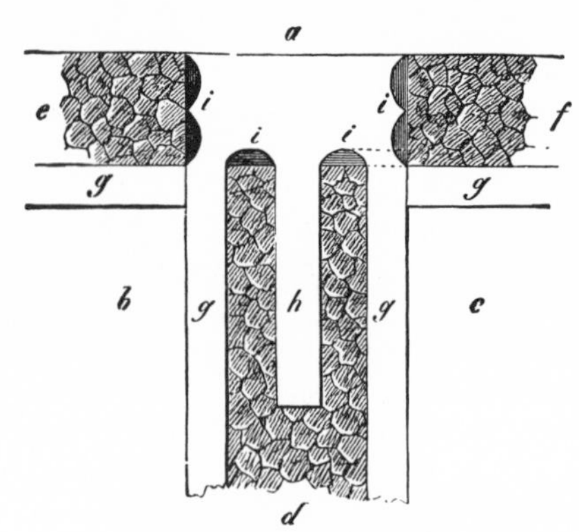

FIG. 414.—System of Gutters at Pompeii for draining off the rain-water

a, b, c, houses; *d, e, f,* streets (*d,* Street of Fortuna); *g, g,* sidewalks; *h,* ascending ramp under which the conduit lies; *i, i, i, i,* outlets for the rain-water coming from three different streets. These outlets lie perpendicular to the pavement above which they rise. (Cf. Fig. 415)

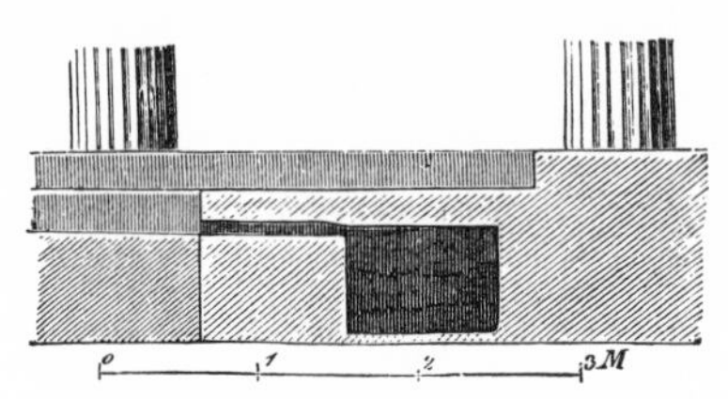

FIG. 413.—Sewer in the Forum at Pompeii, receiving the water from the pavement

The connection with the main sewer was effected by small lateral drains

back riding, but apparently not driving, in towns. As a rule, if people wanted to ride for their pleasure, they used high-roads or places outside the towns, or sometimes covered colonnades (Juv., *Sat.* vii, 181).

FIG. 415.—Outlets for the rain-water in a street at Pompeii

The diversion of rain-water was not the only problem of sanitation. It was just as necessary to remove the refuse and dust from the houses and the waste from the workshops. All these were carted away to special places outside the towns. Places of this kind (*κοπρίαι* or *κοπρῶνες*) have been found near Alexandria, Arsinoë and ancient Cairo. Other questions of hygiene were considered as much as possible, 'hygiene', however, being here understood in the sense of the ancients. Vitruvius, for instance (I, 6), maintains that the winds should be kept off as far as possible from the towns because they convey an unpleasant sensation if they are cold, and make people ill if they are warm. As regards the laying-out of the inner parts of the towns, he advises that the sites of temples, markets and other establishments devoted to public purposes ought to be fixed immediately after the marking-out of lanes and streets; that temples should be erected to the various deities, as well as a gymnasium, amphitheatres, etc. He asserts that the size of public squares should be in accordance with the size of the population; that the length and the width of the *forum civile*, the main square, should be laid out in the ratio 3 : 2; and that the basilicas should be built in warm quarters in order to keep merchants warm in winter (cf. page 376).

As to the horticultural embellishment of public squares, the ancients do not seem to have made use of it any more than the southern countries to-day. Green lawns and shrubs would be ill-suited to their architecture and they would only spoil the general effect of a public square.

HABITATIONS

THE ORIENTAL HOUSE

OF the appearance, the ground-plan and the internal arrangement of ancient oriental houses we have practically no record. None of the numerous excavations that have otherwise furnished such very valuable information on monumental buildings, arts, and many branches of industry, has been able to shed light on the art of building houses in the ancient East. This defect may be due to all the results of investigations and excavations having been used chiefly to explain their relevance to the history of the fine arts. Thus there is a vast and rich field open to technical science which it may take decades to explore. As far as can be ascertained to-day, the ancient oriental house, especially in Mesopotamia, evolved from the tent of the nomads. Its original form may have been a four-cornered or round space sheltered with a skin or mat. In the middle of this primitive roofing there was an aperture to admit the daylight, and to allow the smoke rising from the hearth to escape. Gradually the space became subdivided. Probably to begin with, cattle, which originally lived with the people, were separated from the living-room proper. There are certain indications that these dwellings were originally built against rocks. In any case statements relating to the original primitive habitations are based on hypothesis. What the Eastern dwellings which developed from them looked like, we do not know.[1]

THE EGYPTIAN HOUSE

More trustworthy information is available about the dwelling-houses of ancient Egypt, deficient as our knowledge still remains on the whole. Diverse models of Egyptian houses have been found in tombs. Dwellings are also shown on paintings, and lastly, some light is thrown on them by various isolated finds. These representations of houses combine a proper ground-plan with the design of various rooms, the contents of which are also drawn in minute detail. This peculiar method of showing houses with strange representations of doors and other details makes it rather difficult for people of to-day to obtain a clear idea of the ground-plan of these habitations. Nevertheless, attempts have been made to transpose these designs into the form of modern plans, and so it has been possible to draw some conclusions about distribution of rooms in large houses. It must be understood that all these pictures merely show the residences of the wealthy, or of high dignitaries. As to the houses of the lower

[1] The excavations at Ur have thrown some light on this problem.—*Trans.*

classes, we can make inferences only from the few preserved models and other important data.

The models exhibited in various museums show a rectangular court enclosed by a wall. On one of the sides there is a house whose ground plan is a long narrow rectangle, that is, it is fairly wide, but not very deep. A flight of stairs leads from the court on to the flat roof of the house, which has obviously only one story. The roof is surrounded by a parapet, which is higher on the outer side than against the court, and thus allows all sorts of articles to be passed or thrown down into the court below. On one side of the roof there is a narrow cabin with the open side turned inwards. It may have served as a kind of bower in which people were protected from the sun's rays and could gaze on the neighbourhood, or oversee work done in the court. Three rooms, probably the living-rooms, are to be seen on the ground floor. Although they are filled with grains of corn in the model at the British Museum, this does not justify the conclusion that they had actually been filled with corn in Egyptian houses, the above model being simply a toy-like imitation on a small scale, such as is used for a money-box or as a dainty receptacle for all sorts of trinkets.

In Abydos, ground-plans of houses were found that showed great differences. In some a long narrow corridor runs through the house with rooms on both sides. In another the rooms are arranged along the four sides of an open court into which their doors open. Some rooms are built like porticoes. No far-reaching conclusions, however, can be drawn from these ground-plans, as it cannot be determined whether all their parts belong to the same early period. Large houses represented in the reliefs of tombs frequently exhibit a considerable number of rooms. From the entrance, near which the doorkeeper's lodge usually stands, a long corridor leads into the interior court, one or more sides of which have the character of porticoes. Houses often have several courts and halls which may have been pillared. A peculiar feature of the Egyptian dwelling seems to have been the form revealed by the horizontal section, namely, a perfect square, or an almost exact rectangle. Residential houses, —at least, larger ones—do not appear to have been made of an elongated shape. In this respect the ancient Egyptian house differed widely from the Greek—which nearly always had unequal sides. For the rest, the deciding factors seem to have been the same as with us. Men had their houses built according to their economic circumstances, their requirements and their tastes. It is improbable that the Egyptian dwellings were constructed on a more uniform principle than ours, at least with respect to the distribution of rooms. Similarly, the laying-out of gardens, which are often found attached to Egyptian homes, was obviously a matter of personal taste, but not so in the case of the external appearance, which must have been practically the same for all houses, irrespective of the pecuniary condition of their owners. The houses were mostly low and consisted only of a ground floor, which was sheltered by a flat roof on which there probably were isolated superstructures. The windows were but few, and there was probably only one outside door, the frame of which gave ample opportunity for ornamentation. Apart from the decoration of the door, the windows, and the well-known hollow moulding, the façade was plain. Smaller dwellings were usually built together, and the streets consisted, therefore, of unbroken rows of houses. Large houses, however, seem usually to have stood alone or in gardens. The court was probably paved, and contained some open rooms and a well or fountain. Smaller properties lay round a common court. Large residences sometimes had a pillared vestibule in front of the chief entrance. Near the main gate of palaces, which served as a doorway for the vehicles, there were some smaller gates for foot-passengers. The gates were closed with doors turning on pivots, which were fixed in pairs in the lintel and the threshold. If the door was made of bronze, the pivots were cast with the door in one piece (Fig. 69). In doors of other materials bronze mountings were nailed into them which ended in pivots. Doors were fastened by bolts or by locks with keys ; they will be discussed in detail below.

THE GREEK HOUSE

The Greek dwelling, too, evolved from the cottage, which had been built after the nomadic period at the foot of a hill on which the citadel stood. It must be assumed that these cottages were originally round. But in very early times the influence of palace buildings exerted itself on the ground-plan of ordinary houses. Their ground-plan, which seems to be an imitation of the Mycenaean palaces, becomes rectangular and elongated. In the fifth century B.C. the middle-class house at Athens, built on this plan, was extremely simple. It consisted of a small court, next to which was the main room, surrounded by smaller apartments. The reason for this extreme simplicity is to be sought in the fact that in ancient Greece life was enacted in public ; people worked in the streets and frequented the market or tribunal (Courts of Justice). The private house was entered comparatively rarely, as it was only used for sleeping, cooking and storing provisions. It was no place of comfort, business or social intercourse. Consequently the furniture was very primitive and consisted only of the most necessary things. A change took place in the fourth century B.C. Demosthenes (383–322 B.C.) complained that the good old times had gone in which the dwellings of Themistocles, Miltiades and Aristides did not differ in any way from those of their neighbours—while only temples and public buildings were magnificent. The development which began at that time can easily be followed. In a more ancient dwelling, dating from the fourth century B.C. at Priene, we find the same parts as in the Palace of Tiryns from which it is derived. In neither case does the door in the wall which surrounds the building lead into the house but into a large court where we face the front of the main building, the *megaron*, which has the appearance of a temple owing to the portico and columns in front. The temple-like façade consists of two antae, two columns standing between them, and the frieze and pediment above. Through this vestibule we enter the largest room of the house, which, like the Palace of Tiryns, contains the hearth, the centre of all home life. On one side of the megaron and the court there is a long corridor. Along the whole length of the court, it is covered by a roof resting on columns. On the opposite side of the court there are bedrooms and rooms for the servants. Another covered building stands near the door which leads from the street into the court. In it were presumably kept implements, waggons and other articles. Later on this building developed into a more luxurious one, having

FIG. 416.—Ancient Greek House at Priene, of the second century B.C.
Reconstruction of Thiersch, according to the excavations of H. Schrader and H. Wiegand. Model in the Deutsches Museum, Munich

a peristyle. It is characterized by the absence of the hall (the prostas which opens on the court) and by the fact that a colonnade surrounds the court —naturally there are transitional stages between houses with the prostas and houses with the peristyle, that is, there are houses which still have the prostas, but at the same time are bordered along the court by a colonnade (Fig. 418). As the sun is fairly high at midday in Greece and the sun-rays fall almost vertically, the house with a prostas as well as that with a peristyle had to be constructed accordingly. The prostas as well as the colonnade which superseded it always opens towards the south. Both of them stood between the hot sunny court and the principal room of the house, the *oikos*, which lay far back in the shade and was moreover shut off from the heat by a door. The interior of the *oikos* was faced with marble slabs or marble stucco, bordered along the top by a cornice, on which were placed household utensils, small works of art and statuettes of gods. The upper part of the wall, particularly the frieze, was painted. The court was paved or inlaid with mosaic. The mural paintings simulated walls of coloured marble or architectural details such as brackets, and, at a later period, figures.

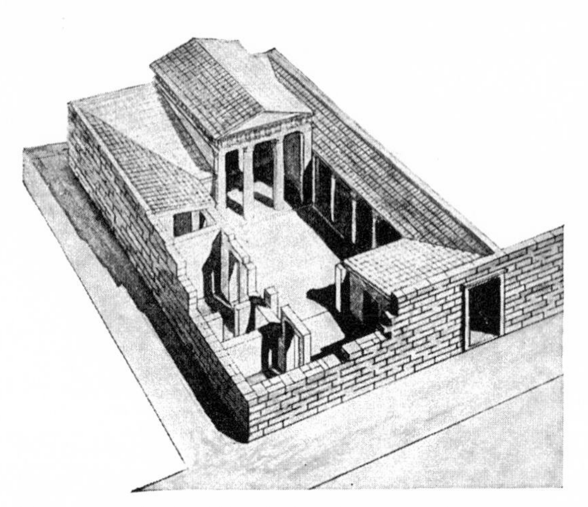

FIG. 417.—Ancient Greek Dwelling in Priene of the fourth century B.C.

After a model in the Deutsches Museum, Munich

As paintings, however, grew more elaborate, houses became more luxurious ; further stories were added to the ground floor of the megaron, and afterwards also to other buildings situated round the court. In isolated cases this had been done earlier, as the excavations in the Palace of Minos at Knossos in Crete have shown. In the hall of the upper terrace a large mosaic was found representing some forty houses, which are obviously built partly of wood and partly of stone. Some are three-storied and have windows with panes. They may have been palaces or simply exceptions to the rule, as the house of several floors did not appear till later. In the second century B.C. they occurred fairly frequently. A loggia opening between columns into the court was built above the prostas or peristyle (Fig. 416). The upper floor served as a ladies' apartment. When houses were enlarged two were joined together to form a large block with shops facing the street, rooms for practical purposes on the two longer sides of the court and living-rooms on the court opposite the entrance. The living-rooms are distinguished by different names : there are the common room of the family, the men's apartment (*andronitis*), and

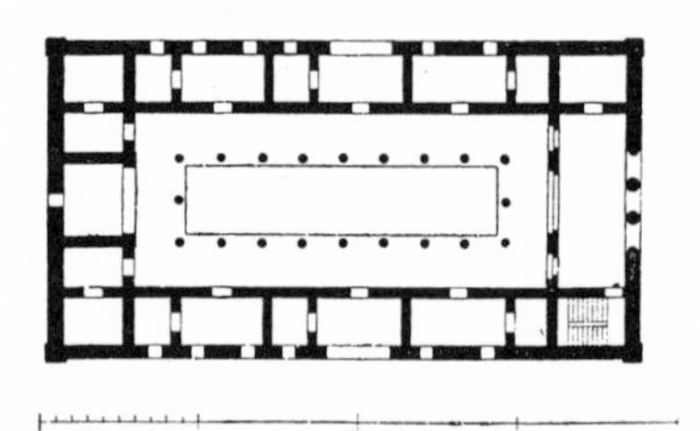

FIG. 418.—So-called 'House of Hyrcanus' (a court surrounded by a colonnade)

the ladies' rooms (*gynaikonitis*), which mostly lay at the rear or on the upper floor, and lastly, working-rooms for maidservants. For the rest, it is clearly seen from references by Homer in the *Odyssey* (XXI, 381) that even at that period the working-room for female servants lay behind the megaron. Extensive literature has gradually accumulated on this subject. As is further seen from Homer, houses had an upper floor which served as the ladies' habitation. These facts, as well as that the megaron was lighted by two windows (*ὀπαί*, *Odyssey*, I, 320), are beyond doubt. It has often been assumed that the back-rooms were subdivided into two or three parts and that the megaron had either one or two doors leading into these rooms. But this point is so irrelevant as regards the technicalities of the essential parts of the ancient Greek house that we can pass it over.

THE ROMAN HOUSE

Although the houses at Pompeii have many details in common with those of Greece described above, and seem also to be related to those of Priene, Thera, Delos and Pergamon, the Greek influence on house-building in Italy did not make itself felt till a later period. The original Italian dwelling had nothing in common with the original Greek house: the two, in their most essential features, differ from each other. Even the Homeric home exhibits one strange peculiarity of the Greek dwelling—it was a kind of stronghold. The various parts of it were situated round a court and enclosed by a protecting wall which went right round the estate. When the Greek was at home he was entirely separated from the outside world. The windows were intended only to admit the light, not to satisfy people's curiosity about things outside. In Italy it was different. How the Greek home developed we do not know. Apart from what we can glean from Homer, the only trustworthy information we have is about houses dating from after Alexander the Great; nor is it possible to trace the growth of building from the earliest beginnings in the case of Italian houses. We do know, however, that the mode of living was different in the two countries at a very early period. In Greece houses stood alone, whereas in Italy they had *parietes communes*—that is, they were built together. Owing to the rain which collected in the partitions and damaged the woodwork, every house had to provide its own arrangement to drain off the rain-water. This caused people to set up a kind of funnel on the roof through which the rain-water entered the house, where it was collected in a special basin. This arrangement, indeed, gave the Roman house, which is derived from the Etruscans, its characteristic form, whereas in the Greek house the central court is not roofed at all. The central hall, the *atrium*, round which are grouped the various rooms, was completely covered by a roof with a funnel-shaped aperture (the *compluvium*) through which the rain-water flowed into the atrium, where it was collected in a basin, the *impluvium;* it was then generally passed into a cistern for domestic use. Like the court of the Greek house, the atrium is surrounded by rooms, the most important of which is the master's room, the *tablinum*, adjacent to the atrium. The entrance hall, which is characteristic of the chief apartment of the Greek house, namely the megaron, is completely absent here. The entrance door (*ianua*) opposite to the tablinum leads the visitor into a corridor adjacent to the atrium. The *parietes communes* were very convenient for the laying-out of streets, and since the latter were favourite resorts for business transactions, shops were built at a very early date on both sides of the street-entrance and of the corridor behind. As a rule they were not connected with the interior of the house in any other way and were accessible only from the street. In the atrium, behind the impluvium, stood the hearth (*focus*), which gave its name to the hall, because it filled the whole room with smoke and made it black. The Latin *ater* means black or dark (Fig. 419).

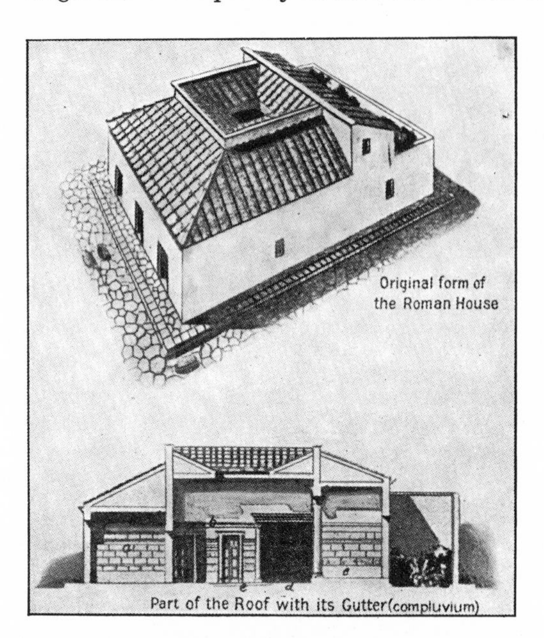

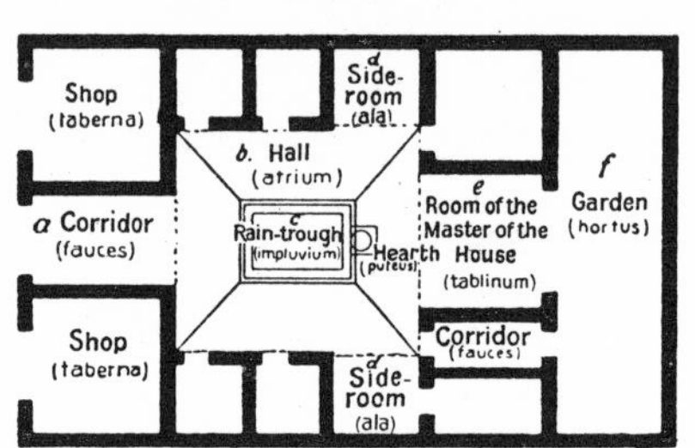

FIG. 419.—Oldest known form of Roman House
After a model in the Deutsches Museum, Munich

Influenced by all sorts of models, the most important of which were Greek, the original form of Roman house developed into a new type in the course of time—which was a combination of the Italian and Greek dwelling. Properly speaking the new type consisted of two houses—a Roman one in front containing the compluvium, atrium, and tablinum, with a corridor shortened by bringing the street door further inside. By this process a narrow exterior entrance hall, a *vestibulum*, was created. At the back this Roman house led into a Greek one characterized by the peristyle court, with its surrounding columns. Since here, as in Greece, two houses were combined into one, it was quite natural that this house, like the ancient Greek, should be divided into men's apartments and women's apartments. The latter were contained in the Greek part, that having a peristyle. Both houses were encircled by a common wall with only a few small windows. Inside rooms received their light from the court. As in the Greek house, the outer world was effectually cut off by the wall;

the privacy was undisturbed by the presence of the shops—in many cases, however, there were none (Fig. 420).

Owing to the fact that light did not enter through windows, but from the court or compluvium, mural paintings had to be done in rather glaring colours, in order to make them visible (Fig. 421). The roofing of the peristyle shut out the best part of the light. The rest, falling on the paintings, was mostly reflected by the slabs of the court or the atrium. The colouring would appear too gaudy on the upper floors of our houses, lit up by windows, but is very well suited to the peculiar conditions of illumination in Roman houses. Sometimes special architectural contrivances were used to put the paintings in a suitable light. In the so-called 'House of the Silver Wedding' at Pompeii, for example, there is a peristyle, similar to those found in Rhodes. The columnated wall on the south is higher than the three other sides. The lower columnated court is entered from the elevated atrium by the tablinum. Through this technical peculiarity of the peristyle the sun's rays are more freely admitted in winter. Moreover, the colours were adapted to the conditions of lighting—darker or lighter shades being chosen accordingly.

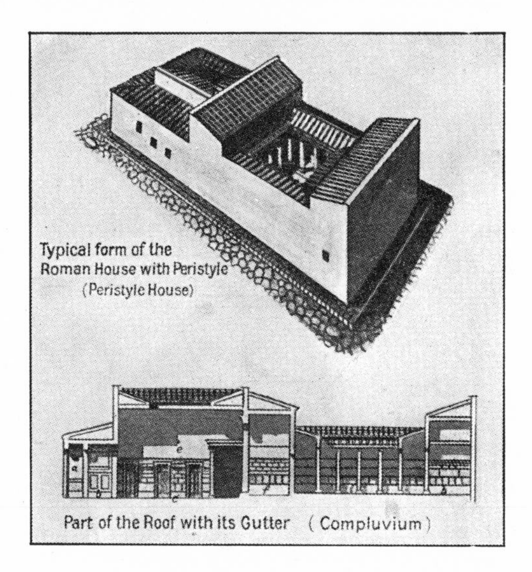

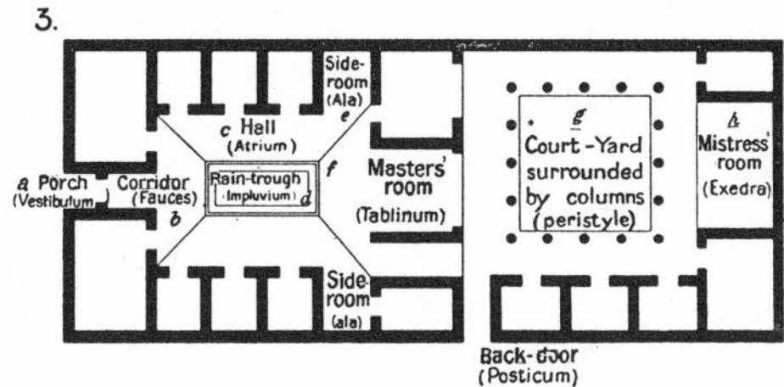

FIG. 420.—Roman house with Peristyle Court
After a model in the Deutsches Museum, Munich

By degrees this type of Roman house—the most original form of which frequently possessed a small garden adjacent to the tablinum—underwent many changes, which were chiefly due to the increasing luxury, to the want of space in the cities (see Vitruvius ii, 8, 17), and the consequent rise in the price of land. How the last-mentioned process reacted on the further extension of Rome has been graphically described by Friedländer, who bases his remarks partly on Seneca: 'The contractors not only economized the building land by putting up as many stories as possible, but more so by narrowing and decreasing the rooms of individual dwellings to the utmost limit, reducing, at the same time, the cost of building to a minimum.' But this method also increased the danger of fires.

The walls of these flats were piled on top of each other and consisted of wood or wood and brick; being very thin, they afforded no protection from heat or cold. A favourite pattern for walls was so-called net work,

Fig. 421.—Mural Painting in mosaic style (Landscape on the Nile, Rome)

opus reticulatum (see the section 'Building in Stone'). Speculative jerry-builders favoured the handsome design for the sake of appearance. The result was often a lack of stability of the structure, as walls built in this form cracked very easily.

Friedländer continues: ' " A part of our fears," says Seneca, " are our roofs; people flee from the halls of large palaces, adorned with paintings, as soon as they hear a creaking." A large number of tenement houses were in a dilapidated state, the most necessary repairs being neglected or done insufficiently. If a landlord

FIG. 422.—Roman Floor made of large slabs (Trèves)

"had strengthened the tottering walls by a support and covered over an old chink, he would assure his tenants that they might sleep safely, although a collapse was imminent." The collapsing of houses and the prevalence of fires were two of the evils characteristic of Rome even during the last years of the Republic.'

FIG. 423.—Roman Floor restored

FIG. 424.—Roman Floor made of stones of different colours

It stands to reason that in these circumstances it was impossible to adhere to any one uniform type of house. But uniformity of design was gradually abandoned in the case of the more luxurious residences, which increased in number towards the end of the Republic. For a long time changes had been in progress due to the gradual increase in the size of houses. The tablinum, for example, originally the private room of the master of the house, was left open on both sides towards the atrium as well as towards the peristyle, or,

FIG. 425.—The House of the Vettii at Pompeii

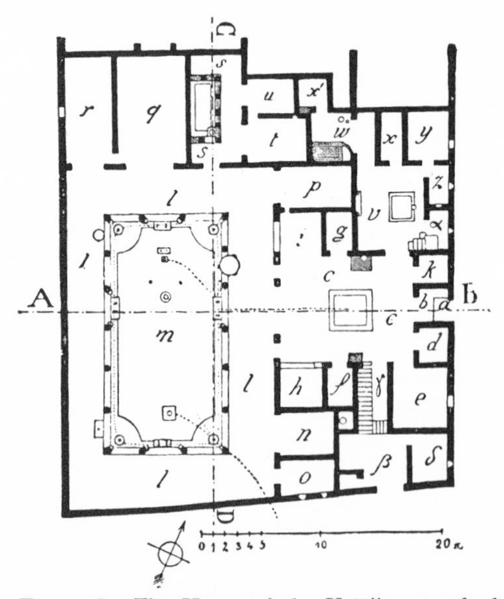

FIG. 426.—The House of the Vettii, ground plan

B, door; *a*, vestibulum, shut off from *b* by the street door; *b*, short corridor (fauces); *c*, atrium; *h*, *i*, alae; *l*, large peristyle; *m*, garden; *s*, second peristyle, smaller; *n*, *o*, *p*, *q*, *r*, rooms; *v*, second atrium with altar dedicated to the Lares; *u*, bedroom; *w*, kitchen; *x*, cook's chamber

when the latter was missing, towards the garden. In this way a room was created which offered a pleasant coolness without otherwise serving a special purpose of domestic life. Moreover, the last two rooms on the two long sides of the house were left completely open on both sides. In this way two wings evolved (*alae*, Figs. 426, 437, 443) which were marked off from the atrium, as luxury increased, by pilasters or adorned with columns between *antae*. The alae themselves were provided with a specially handsome floor and other ornamentation (Figs. 422–424). It was here that the portraits of the

FIG. 427.—Pillared Hall with Garden in the house of the Vettii at Pompeii (Fig. 426, *l* and *m*)

ancestors were kept and the master of the house received his visitors. A second, smaller atrium, containing the altar of the Lares (as in the house of the Vettii at Pompeii) and a second peristyle were added later. Gradually the atrium lost its original character as a common room for the family which contained the money chest, and in earliest times, even the master's bed and other articles of daily use, and where the wife sat spinning. It also in later times often became a reception room. In order to avoid any disturbance in the tablinum, which served for social entertainment, one or two corridors (*fauces*) were built near the tablinum for people going from the atrium to the garden. The ground-plan of the

Roman house thus changed more and more. Yet its original features were still to be recognized in the luxurious residences of a later period (Figs. 428–431).

But it was completely lost sight of when the Romans began to equip the large villas in the neighbourhood of the greater cities with more and more magnificence. Pliny the Younger says of his two villas that one was provided with an open swimming-bath and that a sojourn there was made pleasant by large rooms with two windows, gardens, and fountains. But such a villa was nothing compared with the gigantic and palatial buildings that arose during the time of the Caesars, to which the ruins of Hadrian's villa near Tivoli still bear witness to-day. This was no longer a house but

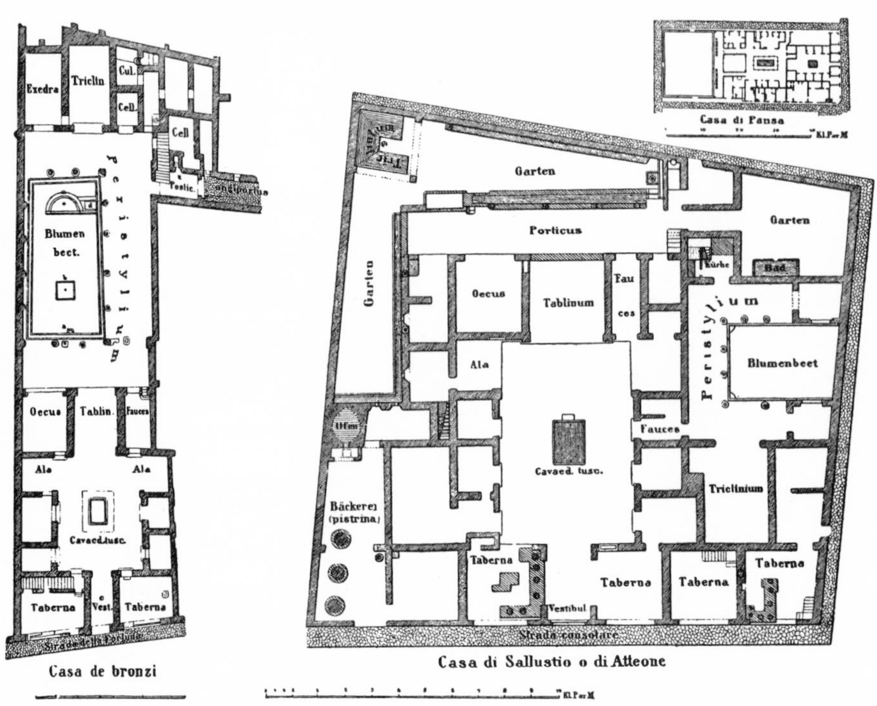

FIGS. 428–430.—Plans of Pompeian House

a multitude of buildings scattered over an extensive stretch of land (Fig. 432). It was no longer planned according to a definite technical tradition but entirely adapted to the special features of the ground and the caprice of the builder.

Pliny had placed the couch in his villa at Laurentum in such a position that he had the sea at his feet; Diomedes at Pompeii had a semicircular bedroom built with three immense windows, and placed his bed in a recess from which he had a view of the whole environment (Fig. 431, No. 14). Hadrian, however, ordered a stupendous wall of nearly 700 ft. in length to be built, stretching from east to west, so that one side always lay in the sun and the other in the shade; this allowed people to take a walk in either sun or shade at any hour of the day (Figs. 433–435).

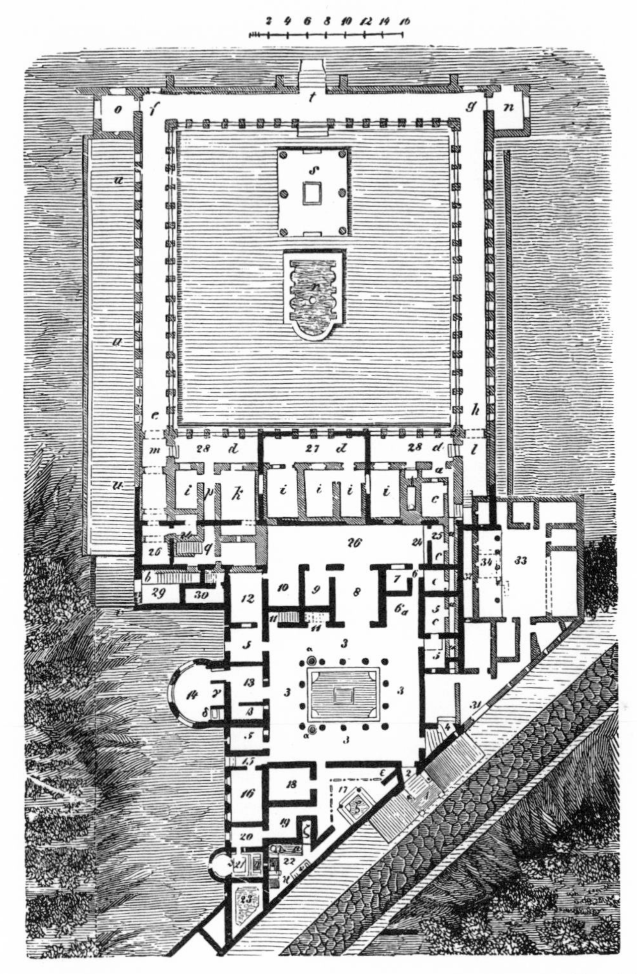

FIG. 431.—Ground plan of a Pompeian country house (so-called ' Villa of M. Arrius Diomedes ')

The house stands on an incline and has several stories. Parts lying on a level with the road are in black and are marked with figures; those lower than the road are lighter and have small letters. 1, outside stairs leading to the front door; 2, small vestibulum; 3, peristyle with impluvium with two troughs at its sides; 4, staircase leading to the lower rooms; *aaa*, corridor leading into the court and gardens; 5, sleeping-room with bedsteads of masonry; 6*a*, anteroom; 6, corridor; 7, room; 8, tablinum; 9, room; 10, exedra; 11, staircase leading upwards; 12, triclinium; 13, antechamber; 14, large sleeping-room—β,γ, alcoves; δ, washstand; 15, passage to the garden; 16, cloak-room ?; 17, small court; ϵ, hearth; ζ, cold bath; 18, 19, rooms; 20, tepidarium; 21, caldarium; η, hot-water trough; θ niche with bath; 22, hypocaust; 23, water tank; 26, gallery; 25, 27, rooms; 28, terraces; 29, 30, small rooms; 31, entrance to the steward's department; 32, passages to the steward's rooms, which are separated from the rest because of the danger arising from fire; 33, atrium-like court; 34, portico; *b*, staircase; *c*, storerooms; *ddd*, corridor; *efgh*, garden (335 sq. ft.); *i*, *i*, rooms; *k*, triclinium used in summer; *l*, *m*, *n*, *o*, closets; *p*, corridor; *q*, stairs leading to cellar; *v*, fish-basin with fountain; *s*, pillared hall; *t*, back door; *u*, corridor; *v*, stairs to garden

If we enter into the technical details of the interior of Roman houses we are struck by the smallness of the individual rooms as compared with those of modern times. The House of Pansa at Pompeii is 110 ft. wide and 20 ft. deep (Fig. 429). A modern builder would perhaps fit 15 to 20 rooms into this space. But Pansa's house contains no fewer than 60 chambers. The same applies to almost any Roman house. Even in Hadrian's vast and luxuriously equipped villa the guest-chambers are nothing more than small and rather dark rooms (Fig. 525).

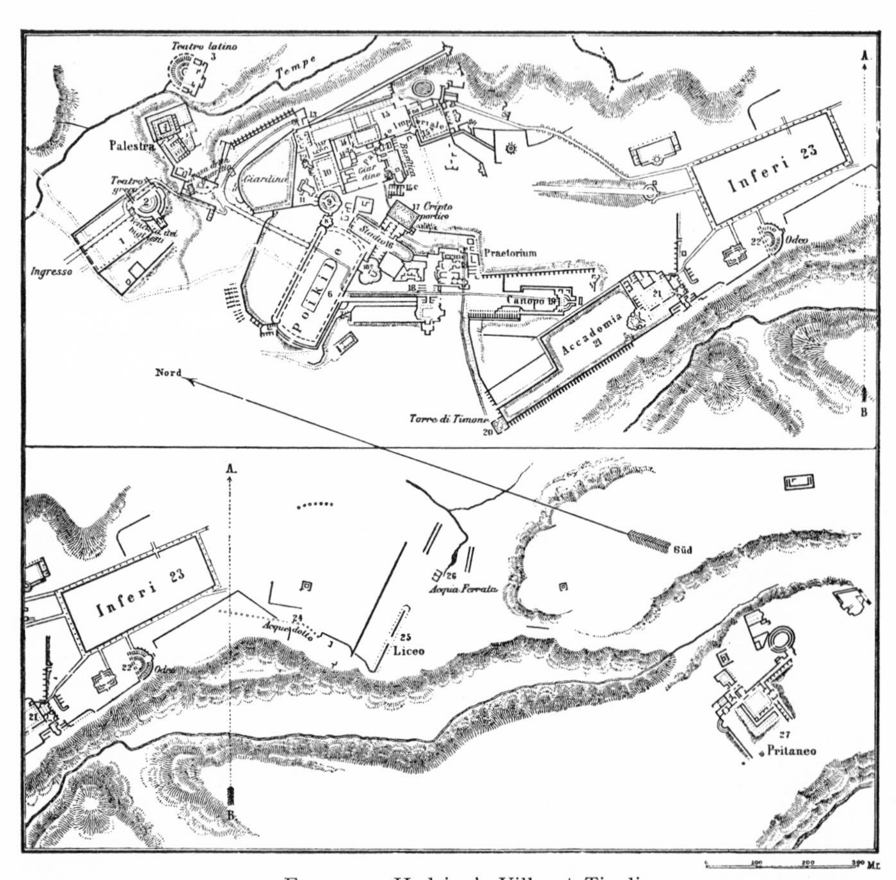

FIG. 432.—Hadrian's Villa at Tivoli

1, Open space; 2, Greek theatre; 3, Latin theatre; 4, ground for athletics; 5, nymphaeum, ladies' bath; 6, pillared hall; 7, chambers of the body-guard; 8, school; 9, swimming-bath; 10, court of the library; 11, Latin library; 12, Greek library; 13, triclinium; 14, Doric peristyle; 15, the Emperor's palace; 16, the stadium; 17, subterranean passage; 18, thermae; 19, Valley of Canopus (artificial valley); 20, Timon's tower; 21, so-called Academy (dwelling-house); 22, Odeon (theatre)

This peculiarity is due to the predilection of the Southerner for spending as much time as possible in the open air. This same tendency left its traces in the curious development of the roof, which was often made flat in order that people might promenade there and enjoy the sunshine during the cool hours of the day or in chilly weather. That is why it was called *solarium*. But sometimes people also wished to be cool or to have shade in the solarium ; for this reason they constructed bowers or airy cabins, *pergulae,* a favourite haunt for taking meals. When a second story was added to the building, the upper chambers partly served this purpose and were therefore called *cenacula.* The vestibulum was closed towards the street (Figs. 426, 428, 430, and 431). In poorer quarters it was entirely absent or very small. It increased in size with the wealth of its owner. In many houses it became a kind of hall with colonnade, ornamented with statues and other works of art.

FIG. 433.—Part of Hadrian's Villa at Tivoli (in the background the long wall)

In houses let to several families the staircase often led from it to the upper floor. The vestibulum was closed to the ground floor by the front door, which in most cases opened inwards. Only owners of high standing were allowed to have a door opening on to the street. (Concerning the door itself, cf. p. 335.) Inside the door we see the inner part of the corridor, the *ostium,* in which there was often a lodge for the doorkeeper (Fig. 442) who kept watch with his dog. This explains why the warning *cave canem* has often been found painted on the floor there or inlaid as a mosaic.

FIG. 434.—The 'Promenade-wall' in Hadrian's Villa at Tivoli

The ostium, when it occurs, leads into the atrium. Vitruvius (VI, 3) distinguishes five kinds of atria, which, according to their form, are called

Tuscan, Corinthian, tetrastyle (four columns), displuviate (without eaves), and testudinate (covered). Of these only the *atrium testudinatum* was entirely covered; all the others were partly open. The Tuscan atrium is a simple quadrangle with its roof shelving inwards. The roof was supported by two main rafters whose ends lay in the walls, and by two auxiliary

FIG. 435.—Part of the 'Promenade-wall' of Hadrian's Villa

rafters fastened to the other two. Mazois has reconstructed this kind of atrium (Figs. 438, 439) as follows: '*a*, the walls; *b*, the main rafters (*trabes*); *c*, auxiliary rafters (*tigilli* or *trabeculae*) fitted into the main rafters, thus forming the quadrangular opening; *d*, mid-beams (*interpensivae*) which kept the whole beam-work on the same level; *e*, the inclined supports

FIG. 436.—Ruins of a Roman House (Sallust's villa), excavated in Pompeii
Model in the Deutsches Museum, Munich

(*tigni colliciarum*); *f*, the laths (*capreoli*). The roof was covered by two kinds of tiles: flat tiles (*imbrices*), and hollow tiles (*tegulae*) which were laid over the joins of the flat tiles to cover the gaps. A third kind of tiles are the hollow tiles which cover the junction of the two sides of the roof (*tegulae colliciarum*).' All these kinds of tiles were found in 1852 at Pompeii in the Casa di Sirico. They all belonged originally to the roof of the peristyle, which unfortunately collapsed (Fig. 440): 'A, flat tiles; B, hollow tiles inverted over the joints of the former; C, curious hollow tiles covering the junction of two adjacent sides of the roof, obviously an excellent arrangement for draining off the rain-water quickly; it also made the roof water-proof at points where the rain flowed on it from two sloping sides. Some of the ordinary tiles (1, 2, 3) are provided with special apertures of varying forms for admitting the daylight into the rooms below. In order to keep off the rain at the same time they may have been closed with some transparent material; no traces of it, however, have been found and the point is still open to dispute. Fig. 440 shows the various forms of tiles on a larger scale and marked with the same letters and numbers as in the main drawing. C is a side view of the recently discovered corner tiles exhibiting the curvature and upturned edges over which the hollow tiles were inverted' (Overbeck).

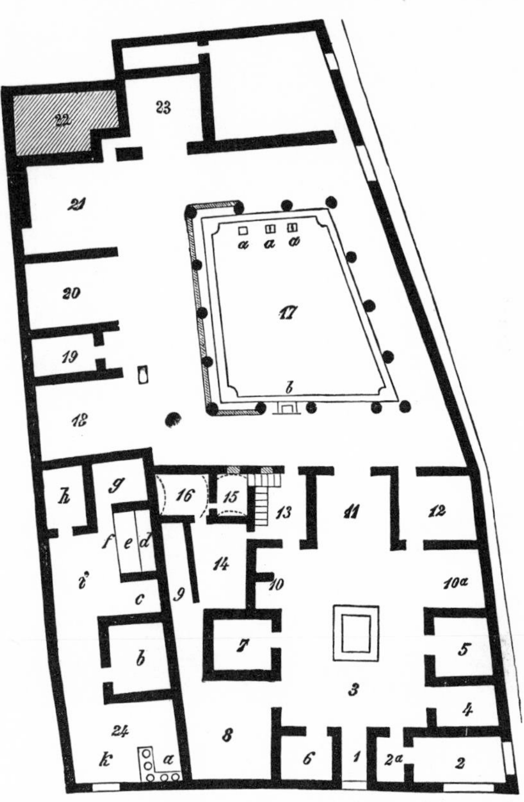

FIG. 437.—House with Tuscan Atrium. (House of M. Nonius in Pompeii)

1, Ostium; 2, 2*a*, shop with back room; 3, atrium; 4, 5, 6, 7, sleeping-rooms; 8, front yard; 9, corridor; 10, 10*a*, alae; 11, tablinum; 12, oecus; 13, front yard; 14, kitchen; 15, tepidarium; 16, caldarium; 17, colonnade; 18, exedra (reception-room with settees along the walls); 19, sleeping-room; 20, oecus; 21, summer-triclinium; 22 and 23, uncertain, buried under débris; 24, shop

The Corinthian atrium and the atrium with four columns were fundamentally like the Tuscan with the exception of one detail in the four-column atrium, in that the main rafters are supported by columns at the four points at which they are connected with the auxiliary rafters. The Corinthian atrium has more than four columns and a larger opening for the compluvium, as there must be sufficient space for the extra columns. The rafters only reach from the walls to the epistyle or architrave of the columns. As for the *atrium displuviatum,* the roofs slope outwards, that is, the rain does not flow into the impluvium, but is collected in the eaves fastened to the outer edge, from which it flows into the cistern. According to Vitruvius this kind of atrium offers great advantages in winter dwellings because the roofs are turned upwards and thus do not keep off the light from the dining-rooms. The drawback, however, is the frequency with which they have to be repaired, because the eaves often flow over, causing damage to the walls and the woodwork of the building.

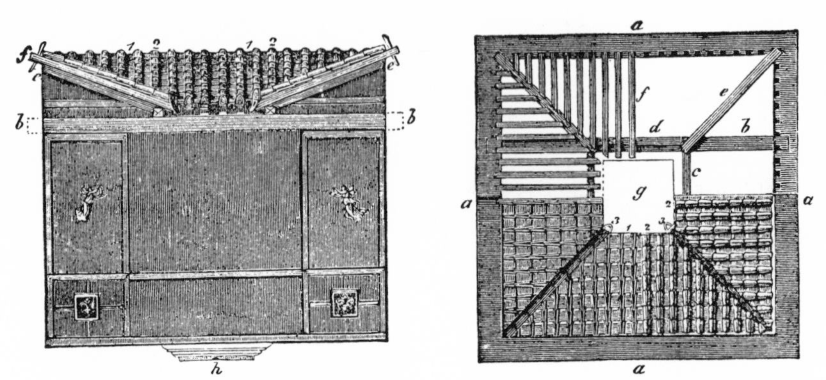

FIGS. 438 and 439.—Tuscan Atrium (ground-plan and cross-section)

But the *atrium displuviatum* had also an inner aperture which is missing in the *atrium testudinatum*. Although the latter had received its name from the tortoise (*testudo*) it bore no resemblance to it. The roof was not vaulted but shaped like a pyramid. Vitruvius recommends it wherever spacious living-rooms are to be built on the upper floor.

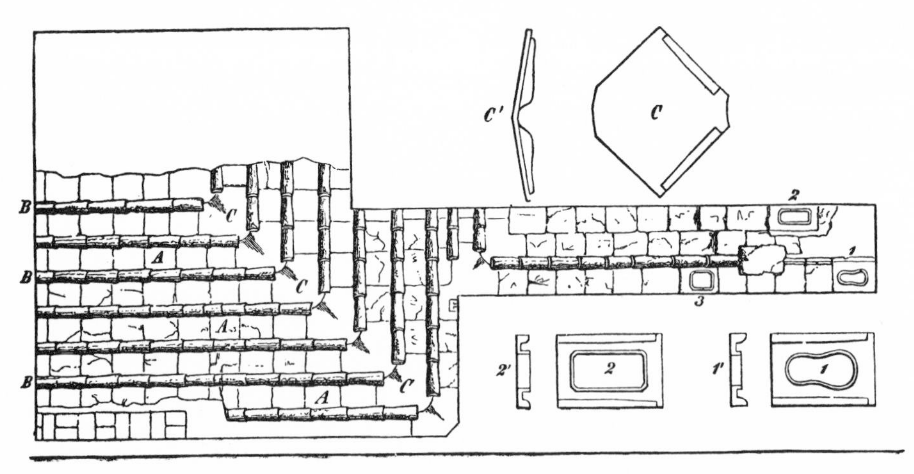

FIG. 440.—Tiled roof of the Casa di Sirico in Pompeii

Ancient houses also had cellars, the *hypogaeae*, though not as frequently as modern houses. The light entered them from the court or peristyle. The ceiling was sometimes vaulted. The windows were smaller than ours, taken in proportion to the total surface of the house.

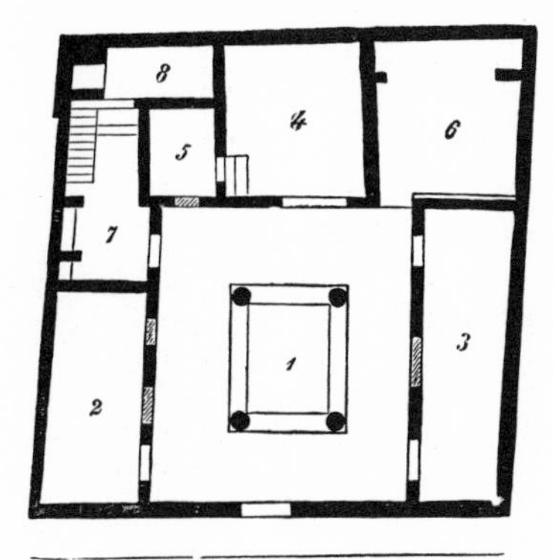

FIG. 441.—Tetrastylum (Atrium with four columns) of a small Pompeian house

The street-door leads directly into the atrium (1), the ostium being missing; 2 and 3, working-rooms?; (4), tablinum; 5, sleeping-room; 6 (?); 7, kitchen with hearth, sink, and a staircase leading to the upper floor

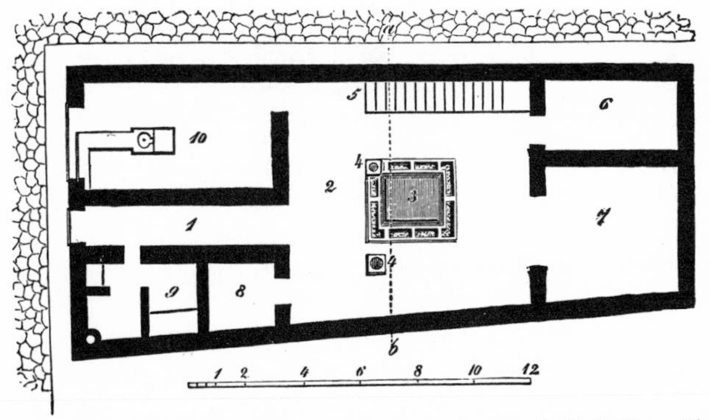

FIG. 442.—Pompeian House with Atrium Displuviatum (called Casa di Modesto)

In 3 the basin of the impluvium is missing. On the other hand, the double wall suggests that flowers had been planted there instead. Next to this pseudo-impluvium there are the openings of cisterns (in 4) into which was conducted the rain-water from the pipes and from the roof, which sloped outwards. 1, Ostium; 2, atrium; 3, pseudo-impluvium; 4, openings of the cisterns; 5, stairs leading to two apartments on the upper floor; 6 and 7, apartments; 8, room of the doorkeeper; 9, kitchen; 10, shop with counter, directly connected with the interior of the house

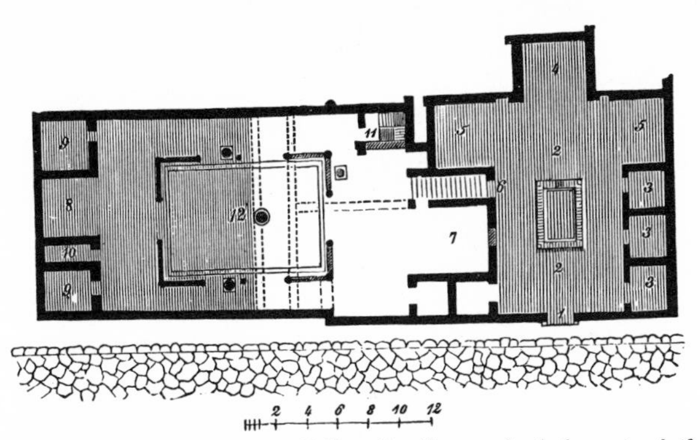

FIG. 443.—Pompeian House with a Cellar (in the unshaded part of the drawing)

1, Door without a vestibule; 2, atrium; 3 and 9, sleeping-rooms; 4, tablinum; 5, alae; 6, stairs; 7, triclinium; 8, exedra; 10, stairs leading to the upper floor; 11, stairs leading into the cellar

The shops occasionally had some further rooms at the rear (Figs. 437, 444) and sometimes they were connected with sleeping-rooms on the upper floor.

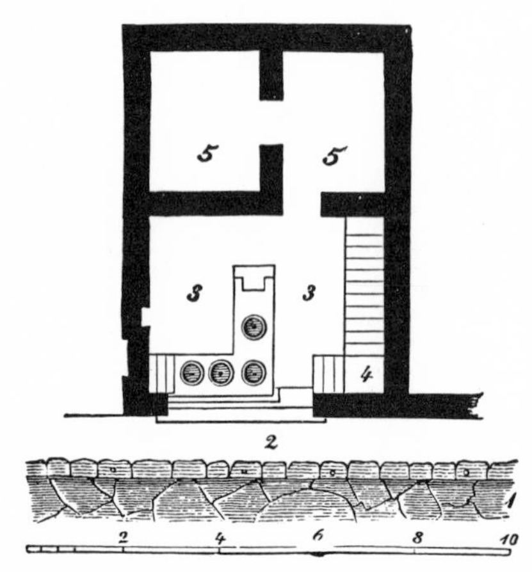

FIG. 444.—Plan of a Shop

3, Shop proper, with counter, bent at a right angle. The counter contains openings for vessels. At its end a small stove (provisions, including cooked food, were sold here). Shelves along the walls. 4, Staircase leading to rooms above; 5, back rooms; 1, causeway; 2, sidewalk

FIG. 445.—Front view of a Shop in Pompeii (Reconstruction)

On the street-front was the counter, past which people could walk directly into the house. The counter often had openings into which goods or vessels could be placed (Figs. 444, 445, and 411). The door-step in front of the shop was provided for about three-quarters of its length with a narrow groove. Narrow planks with overlapping edges could be pushed sideways into this groove when the shop was to be shut up.

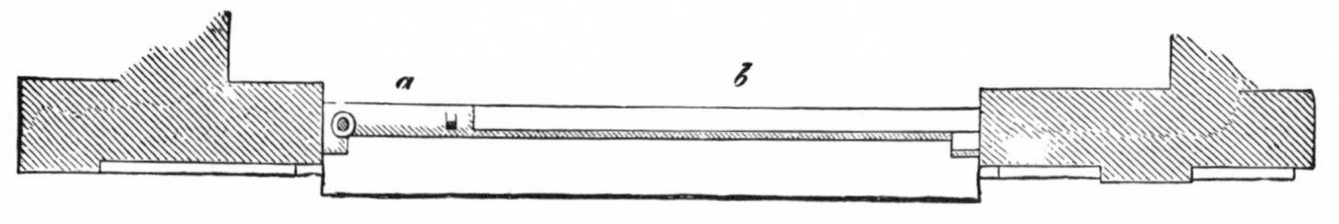

FIG. 446.—Entrance of a Roman Shop

a, Device for locking the door; *b*, groove cut in the doorstep

A movable door turning on hinges was placed on the threshold at the point where the groove ended. In the daytime it was thrown back; at night it was pushed forward and firmly fastened to the adjoining plank of the shutter with a lock. In this way the shop was entirely closed, the planks reaching as a rule to the upper transverse beam, as is shown by the grooves there (Figs. 446–448).

FIGS. 447 and 448.—Shutter of a Shop

a, Device for locking the door; *b*, boards with overlapping edges

DOORS

The various apartments of a house were shut off from each other by means of doors, or often simply by curtains. Like the street-doors, these interior doors were made of wood, preferably of the cypress, oak or deal. Hard wood, such as box-tree, oak, olive, or elm-tree, was used for the pivots and the bolts. The wood had to be well seasoned, and was often left in the press for years after having been glued, in order to prevent it from warping. The doors of the rich were veneered and adorned with bronze, ivory and other ornaments. In order to counteract the warping of the wood, the doors were not constructed of boards but were provided with panels (*paginae:* Pliny, XVI, 225). These panels were let in below the surface, and the angle between the frame and panels was filled in by a moulded fillet. Ancient doors did not turn on hinges like those of our day but swung round on pivots (*στρόφιγγες, cardines, scapi cardinales*) fixed in the threshold and the lintel. It has been mentioned above that these pivots were made of hard wood, but more frequently they were cast in bronze. Sometimes the doors had special timbers (*ἄξονες*; that is, axles), the top and bottom of which projected as tenons. These tenons moved in mortises or bronze bearings which were let into the threshold and the lintel. More often, however, the bronze caps were directly fastened to the pivots, or the pivots as well as the mortises were protected by bronze shoes. Later, the bronze shoes were provided with a point underneath, to give the door firmness, and to ensure the stability of the mechanism. The door was fastened by means of bolts (*pessuli*) which slid into the lintel and the threshold, or by means of transverse beams which lay across the door and fitted into holes in the door-posts. A curious way of fastening the door from the inside was to plant a rafter firmly at an angle against it, the lower end being held in position by a stone which was fastened into the ground and left projecting. Beside these contrivances, however, locks were used during the whole of antiquity.

LOCKS AND KEYS

Locks and keys are already referred to in Homer's *Odyssey* (XXI, 5, 42). The genesis of the key is to be explained as follows: a door was fastened originally by a bolt which fitted into a hole in the door-post, or in the case of folding doors, into a clamp nailed to one of its wings. As this contrivance could easily be undone, an obstacle was created in the form of a notch made for one or more pegs in the bolt. In order to open the bolt the pegs had first to be removed from the notch. This could easily be done from the inside, but from the outside a special instrument had to be applied. This led to the invention of the key, the earliest form of which

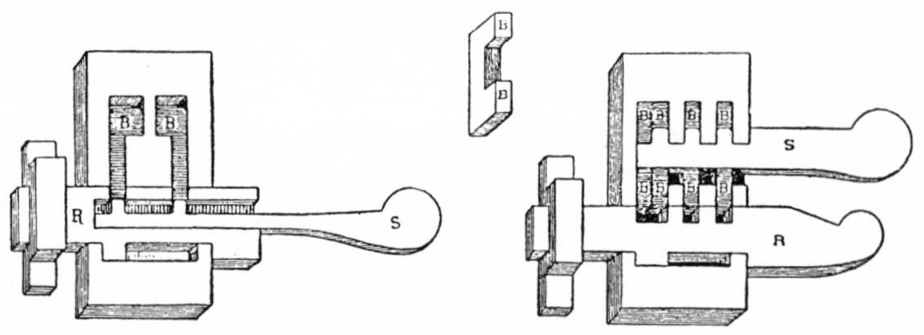

FIGS. 449–451.—Models of Roman Keys

was a rod with pinnacle-like projections. When necessary, the part of the rod with these projections was bent in such a way that the bolts could easily be reached through a hole in the door, the keyhole. Keys of this kind were used very long ago in ancient Egypt. The parts of the lock described above were originally made of wood, and so, probably, was the key with which it was necessary to be able to exert the required pressure. Later it was made of bone, and finally of metal. In isolated cases locks were made of metal, even in Egypt. The ancient Egyptian locks known to us from the age of Ramses II (1292–1225 B.C.) were also used by the Greeks and Romans, and still continue in use in the East. According to the explanations given by Diels and the reconstructions made by Jacobi, they were made in the following manner. For simplicity we shall assume that the lock lies in such a position that a straight key may be used, though it makes no difference if the position of the lock renders it necessary to use a bent key, examples of which have been found in Egypt. The key may have any desired number of prongs or teeth. It can be introduced either into the incision made specially in the bolt R, or into the case above (Figs. 449–451). When it has entered the bolt it is pressed a little upwards, by which action the plugs or pegs B that had previously fallen into the notches of the bolt are lifted. The teeth of the key will then take the place previously occupied by the pegs in the openings of the upper part of the bolt which reach down to the keyhole. It is then easy to pull out the bolt towards the outer end of the keyhole. Only one hand is needed for this kind of lock ; but if the key is inserted into a lock of the second kind the small pegs are lifted so much by the pressure of one hand that they leave the notches in the bolt. The bolt itself can then be pulled out by the other hand. The fact that these pegs are called *βάλανοι*, that is, acorns, gives rise to the name balanos-lock. Its mechanism has served as the basis of the locks of many modern safes, such as the Yale lock, in which the teeth of the key are of different lengths and have to fit most accurately into the wards filed into the lamella-shaped plugs. Otherwise the latter cannot be lifted high enough to fasten the lock. The ancient Greek lock mentioned by Homer chiefly consisted of a wooden bolt which was fastened to the inside of the door (Figs. 452 and 453).

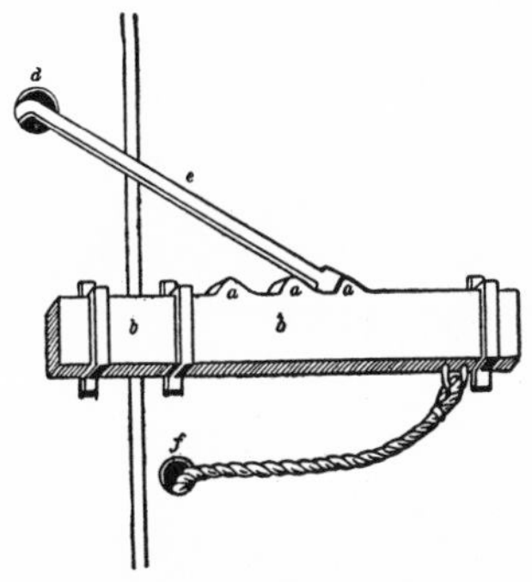

FIG. 452.—Homeric Lock. The original form had only one protuberance

The above model by Brinkmann (see Figs. 449–51) corresponds to a type which was probably also used by the ancients; as it has three protuberances wider play of the bolt is obtained

FIG. 453.—The Unlocking of a Homeric Lock, on a Greek vase

Berlin Altes Museum, Antiquarium. For explanation, see the text, which is based on Diels' description

By means of a narrow thong the bolt was pulled from the outside into the clamp and thus fastened the door. The strap was then tied into a knot. If the door was to be re-opened from the outside, the knot was untied and the bolt pushed backwards by a long hooked key. What the key looked like is seen from pictures (Figs. 453 and 454) and above all from a key found in the temple of Artemis at Lusoi in Arcadia. As Brinkmann suggests, the key probably had several protuberances (*a*) by which the bolt could be pushed back by the key (Fig. 452). This contrivance was not absolutely trustworthy. That is why the ' prudent ' Penelope ties the strap into quite a special knot. During the post-Homeric period this kind of lock was more and more perfected ; Schliemann found, during his excavations at Mycenae and Troy, iron keys with wards or three teeth as well as a ring for suspending them (Fig. 455). The metal, and particularly the iron, lock was not really developed until the Roman period. The whole make-up of the Roman lock proves clearly that it evolved from the ancient wooden lock. The essential improvement was brought about by the use of a spring which pressed the small pegs into the notches of the bolt and made it more difficult to raise them. More pressure had to be applied to lift them and so it was found necessary to make the key of metal. In addition, the position of the pegs was altered in such a way that they could be moved only by certain keys. Thus the key-bit varied in different cases and often showed a very complicated form (Fig. 456). It catches in the cell-like gaps of the bolts and displaces

Fig. 454.—Female Servant with Key (Attic relief on a grave)

the pegs. In the meantime the pegs altered. They became straight pins which often glided in grooves and were pressed down by a spring, which enabled the bolt to be moved forwards or backwards. The mechanism is thus the same as that of the hair-trigger-lock of fireproof money chests (Figs. 457 and 458). The keyhole of Roman locks (Fig. 459) was con-

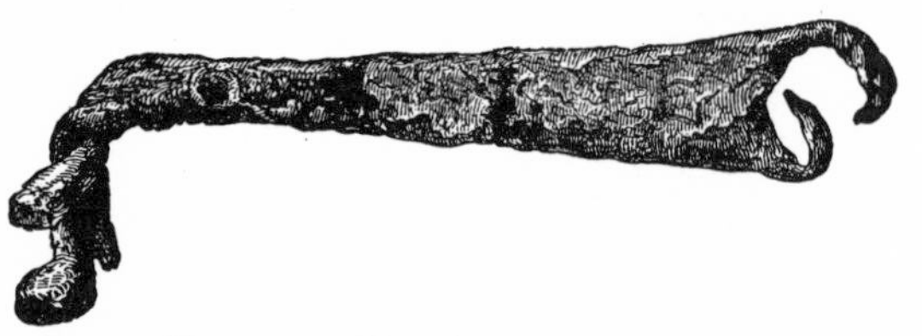

Fig. 455.—Key from Ilium (Troy)

Fig. 456.—Roman Key

structed in such a way that the key was not thrust in straight but hooked in diagonally to the left, then placed at right angles and lifted a little in order to fit the key-bit into the notchcs of the bolt. The bit then displaced the pins, which were wedged into the notches and pressed down by the spring. The bolt was next moved to the right by the key and the lock was opened. In the older locks the key could not be withdrawn as long as the bolt was not shot. But later Roman locks have devices which allow the key to be removed.

A very frequent form of key was the 'finger-ring key'; it was originally made of bronze, and later of silver and gold. It was worn by the head

FIGS. 457 and 458.—Roman Trigger-lock with spring, pegs moving in grooves, and a key (Same principle as the Yale lock.) Model in the Deutsches Museum, Munich

of the family on the middle finger of the left hand as a sign of authority. At a subsequent period this sort of key was worn by elegant Roman ladies as an ornament.

FIG. 459.—Roman Keyhole and Key
Model in the Deutsches Museum, Munich

Even padlocks were known to the Romans. They consisted of two parts that fitted together. A double spring pressed

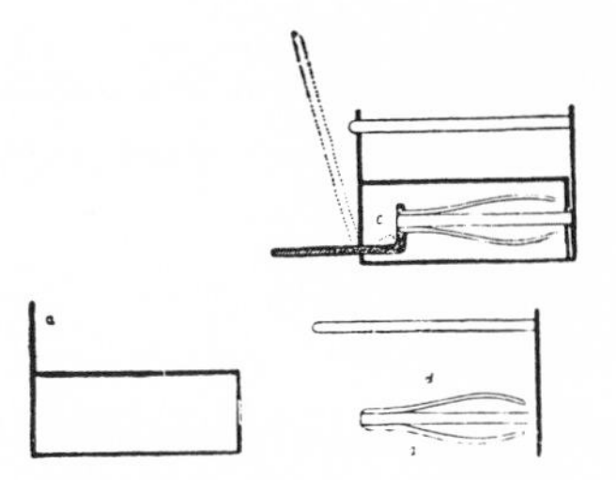

FIG. 460.—Roman Padlock

against the opening and prevented unlocking. If the lock was to be opened this spring had to be compressed by means of the key (Fig. 460).

MONUMENTAL AND PUBLIC EDIFICES

ANTIQUITY produced a great number of monuments and public buildings, often of truly colossal dimensions. Many of them are even superior to anything constructed by the highly developed technical science of our time. The gigantic mass of material used to build them has often led to the belief that the ancients must have had at their command special technical devices which were more efficient than our modern means but have been lost and forgotten. Nothing can be more fallacious. The technical resources were altogether very simple, as has been shown in the chapter on 'Technical Mechanics and Machines'. The prodigious achievements of the ancients were entirely due to the fact that both human labour and time had a low value, and could be supplied on a lavish scale quite foreign to our present-day standards.

But on the whole little remains to be said about the general technical criteria of monumental and public buildings that is not treated in detail in other sections of this book, such as the section on 'Building Implements'. Generally speaking, the ancients erected them according to the conventional principles of their time, which were also applied to the construction of houses and fortifications. Yet some of these buildings exhibit technical characteristics which are peculiar to themselves alone, and the purpose of the following pages is to discuss these peculiarities more closely. If any particular monumental edifice is ignored this is is to be taken as signifying that it lacks these peculiarities, and that it was built according to the general methods and with the means dealt with in other chapters. The size of a building, taken alone, is not a technical peculiarity.

THE PYRAMIDS

Among the monumental edifices distinguished by a special technique the pyramids occupy the foremost rank. There are in Egypt some eighty royal tombs of pyramidal form and in a state of complete or partial preservation. The largest and most important of all is that of Cheops. The lower part of this pyramid as well as the subterranean sepulchral vault hewn in the living rock was built by Cheops (Khufu) II (about 2600 B.C.) and the gigantic work was completed ultimately by Chabryes (Khofra), the fourth king of the Fourth Dynasty, who had a magnificent sepulchral chamber constructed in the upper part of the pyramid.[1] The subterranean vault remained a crude unfinished cavity. The length of the base-lines of the edifice amounts to about 775 ft. and the height to 493 ft.

[1] This statement is far from certain, see Flinders Petrie, *History of Egypt*, i, p. 56 *et seqq*.

Over two and a half million cubic metres of masonry were necessary to build it. The material used was nummulitic, limestone obtained from the large quarries in the Mokattam mountains near Cairo.

What is most remarkable about this pyramid is the way in which mathematics enters into its technical construction. Sir Isaac Newton in the seventeenth century studied this aspect, but it was not till the nineteenth century that the majority of the underlying problems was solved. The mathematical relationships show what astounding knowledge of mathematics and astronomy the ancient Egyptians possessed, and how well they knew the way to apply it to their most striking monumental works. The four sides of the pyramid accurately coincide with the four cardinal points, and this fact has led Biot and others to believe that they were intended to ascertain the dates of the equinoxes in the following way: the day was noted on which the centre of the rising or setting sun coincided with the northern or southern base-line of the pyramid. Similarly the eastern and western amplitudes were determined for any day of the year by measuring the angle T which has a maximum value of 27° there (Figs. 461 and 462). But there were also astronomical observations that could be carried out by means of the pyramid, as the sections made through its apex from north to south and from east to west coincide with the meridian planes and the prime vertical respectively, and the Pharaoh, according to the view of the Egyptians, was the luminous pole about which the world revolved. This idea was expressed in the technical proportion of the pyramid in that the adit leading down into the subterranean sepulchre had an inclination of exactly 27°. As the earth's axis is not fixed, but, on account of precession, describes a circular cone of angle $23\frac{1}{2}°$ in about 26,000 years around the poles of the ecliptic, any star lying in the neighbourhood of that circle becomes a pole star once in this time. At present this position is held by the star α of the Little Bear. In the time of Cheops, however, according to the calculations of Flammarion and Ule, the star α of the Dragon (Draco) was the pole star, which at that time stood nearly 3° away from the north pole. Accordingly the height of its upper culmination was $30° + 3° = 33°$, and the height of its lower culmination $30° - 3° = 27°$ (strictly speaking, 26° 18′ 10″). As the adits leading to the sepulchral vault showed the same inclination, the rays of the polar star when at its lower culmination must have fallen directly on the dead Pharaoh, the deceased centre of the contemporary world. Herschel, who also studied the astronomical problems of the Cheops pyramid, conjectured that the lower culmination of the contemporary pole star was chosen because in 2160 B.C. the star Alcyone in the Pleiades, which was so familiar to the ancients, and is now the star η of Taurus, happened to cross the meridian above the pole at the very point where the star α of the Dragon had its lower culmination.

This was a coincidence of two astronomical events that repeats itself only after 25,827 years. For this reason Herschel attributes a great significance to the year 2160 B.C. in the history of the construction of the pyramid. To judge from a theory put forth by several investigators, the periodic cycle of 25,827 years which is due to the precession of the equinoxes has also received expression in the pyramid, inasmuch as its circumference at the height of the floor of the upper royal vault amounts to 25,827 pyramid units (see below).

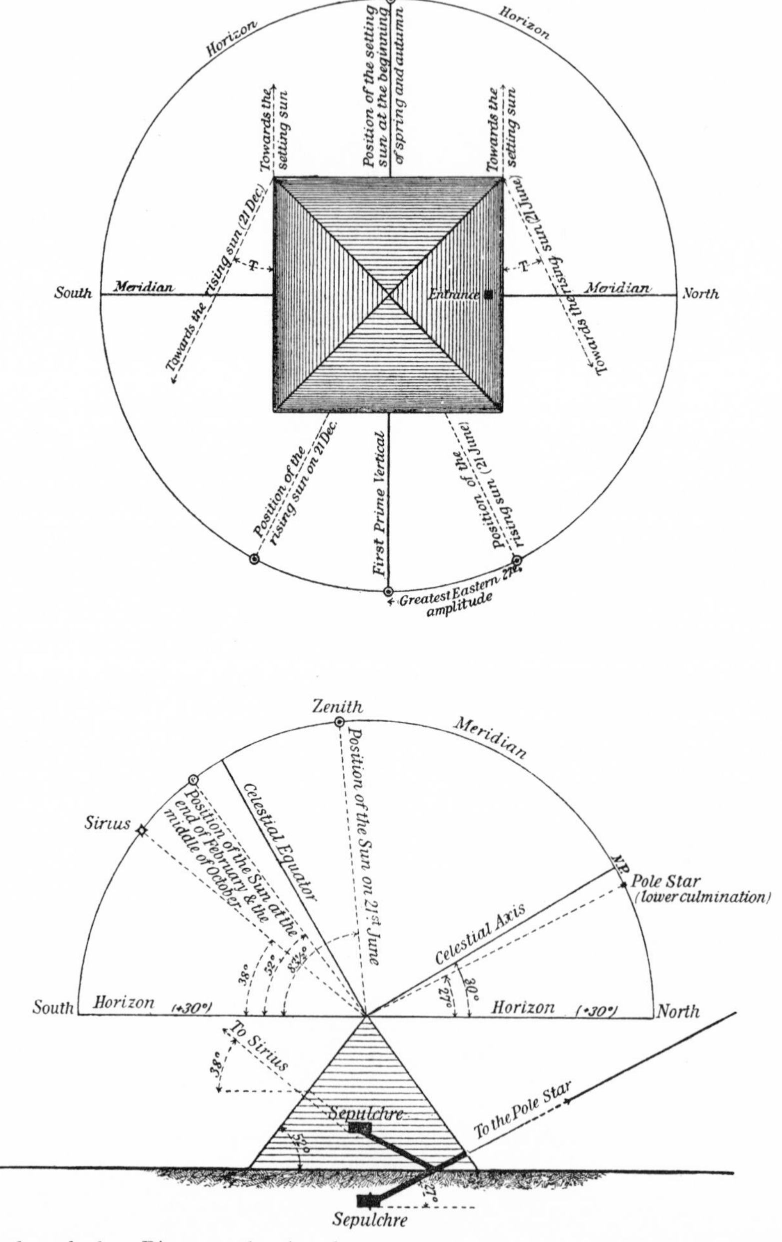

FIGS. 461 and 462.—Diagrams showing the astronomic relations of the Pyramid of Cheops

But this is not all. The brightly shining star Sirius, which the Egyptians called Sothis, in the southern sky was the object of special worship, because to them it was the embodiment of the goddess Isis. By means of this star they fixed their years and important dates. From the sepulchral vault ventilating shafts led towards the outside. The four planes of the pyramid were inclined in such a way that the rays of Sirius when culminating fell on the southern plane, hit it exactly at right angles, and passed straight through the ventilating shafts, which also met the plane of the pyramid perpendicularly, into the sepulchral vault, lighting up the sarcophagus of the dead Pharaoh. At the time of Cheops Sirius culminated in Egypt at an altitude of nearly 38°. Consequently the planes of the pyramid had to be given an inclination of $90° - 38° \approx 52°$ (strictly speaking, 51° 51′ 14·3″). Before discussing another correlation of this figure with the pyramid we wish to point out that a result of this inclination of 52° was that at midday the sun lit up the pyramid in such a manner as to produce no shadow from the last days of February to the middle of October. This again is symbolical. From Nature's awakening at midday in spring till the beginning of her autumnal decline, Ra, the God of the Sun, pours the full lustre of his rays on to the resting-place of the Pharaoh. Moreover, Schoy points out that the pyramid, on account of its orientation and the inclination of its planes, could well serve as a gnomon (hand of a sun-dial), for it was possible to ascertain fairly accurately the beginning of the four seasons by the distribution of light on the planes, the possible error being less than 24 hours for the equinoxes and less than 42 hours for the solstices.

The same angle of 51° 51′ 14·3″ occurs in the facing-stones that, centuries ago, were removed from the pyramid to Cairo and used for building houses. To-day the pyramid appears as a structure rising in steps. But this is only the core. When originally covered with the facing-stones the surface of the pyramid was so smooth that it was impossible to ascend it. In 1837 two of these facing-stones were discovered by Howard Vyse. Since then Dow Covington has found other traces of the facing on the northern base-line. The facing-stones astonish us with the precise workmanship of their surfaces, corners and edges. They must have fitted together extraordinarily well. If we calculate from the mathematical proportions of the pyramid such as it was when covered with the facing-stone, we come to the surprising conclusion, according to Piazzi Smyth, that the perimeter of the quadrangular base (3,095 ft. 6 in.) is equal to the circumference of a circle of radius equal to the height of the pyramid, namely 492 ft. 3 in. Or circumference equals 2×492 ft. 3 in. $\times \pi = 3095$ ft. 6 in.

As this can hardly be pure chance, we must assume that the builders of the pyramid knew the famous ratio $\pi = 3{\cdot}14159$ of the circumference of a circle to its diameter thousands of years ago; moreover, they applied it in their mechanical arts; it was not rediscovered in later times till the Dutch mathematician Ludolf van Ceulen calculated it in the sixteenth century.

The solar year of our earth has 365·2422 days. If we divide a base-line of the pyramid by this figure the result is a unit which recurs so often in the dimensions of the vaults and galleries that Smyth has called it the pyramid-metre (0·635 m. or 2 ft. 22 in.). Strange to say, this unit is exactly the ten-millionth part of half the polar axis of the globe. If the pyramid-metre is divided into 25 equal parts, a new unit will be obtained,the ' pyramid-inch ', which was probably used by the builders of the pyramid, for it seems to be represented on a plate of granite found in front of the entrance to the royal chamber. The perimeter of the base of the pyramid is 3,6524·2 pyramid-inches, being the figures which represent the solar year of the earth. The axis of the earth has a length of $5 \cdot 10^7$ pyramid-inches. The distance between the sun and the earth amounts to 10^9 times the height of the pyramid, another striking fact which surely

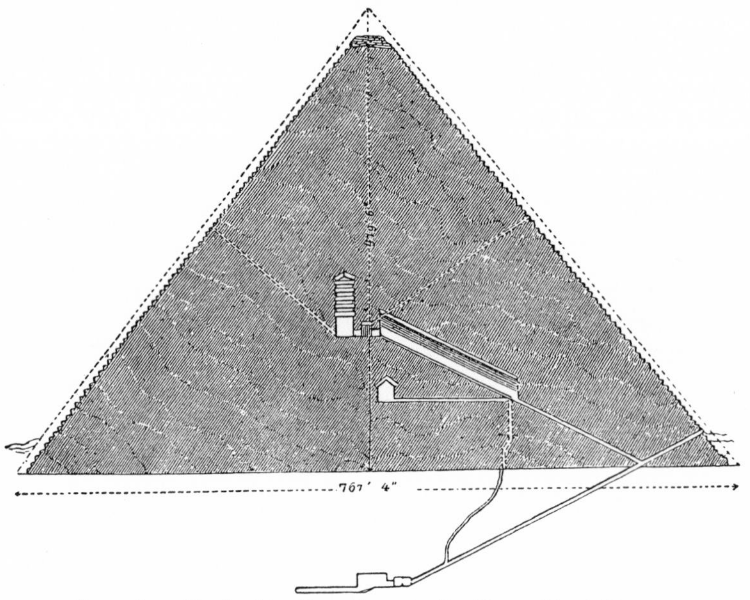

FIG. 463.—Vertical section through the Pyramid of Cheops

cannot be a whim of chance. Rather it gives us an insight into the amazing astronomical knowledge of the ancient Egyptians, or at least of their priests. For the rest, the figures 10 and 9, which certainly do not occur as accidental expressions of the ratio between the sun and the pyramid, are also found in the external dimensions : the height of the pyramid is to half the diagonal of its base as 9 is to 10.

These remarks show on what wonderful mathematical calculations and astronomical relations the dimensions, planes and angles of the pyramid are based, and what secrets and problems it contains, of which perhaps only a part have been unfolded. On the other hand, the investigations of Dow Covington have revealed what a great technical feat was accomplished in constructing this miraculous work. One hundred thousand workers piled up stones for twenty years (Herodotus, II, 124) and arranged not less than 2,300,000 blocks in 210 successive layers. The facing was made of white limestone, so that the pyramid must originally have presented to the onlooker a truly dazzling aspect in the bright rays of the Egyptian sun. After the southern ventilating shaft mentioned earlier, as well as another facing the north, had been cleared, it was found that the air streaming through them produced musical sounds resembling those of an Aeolian harp. These sounds were different for each shaft, but if heard together they were all in harmony. The royal chamber is made of polished granite, being composed of exactly one hundred blocks. Above it there are five more chambers, which were first discovered by Davidson in 1763. They are constructed in such a way that the ceiling of one forms the floor of the next above. The granite slabs of the ceiling are carefully polished, whereas those of the floors are left rough and uneven. What purpose these chambers served has remained a secret till the present day. Nor has it ever been explained how the empty and lidless royal sarcophagus was conveyed into the sepulchral vault, all the galleries, shafts and adits being much too narrow to let it pass. So many questions arise in the case of the large pyramid that doubts have been entertained whether it is a royal tomb at all. From time to time the theory has been proposed that it served only to fix for ever the standard measure of the Egyptians, the pyramid-metre, just as the standard measure of the metric system is nowadays preserved in a vault of the International Bureau for Weights and Measures at St. Cloud near Paris, safe from fire, thieves and shocks ; it is the standard metre, which is made of an alloy of platinum and iridium, this metal being humanly speaking unchangeable for all time. Moreover, starting from the false assumption that the length of the axis of the earth is invariable, its inventors referred the length of the metre to the dimensions of the earth in order that the standard metre may be reconstructed at any time in case it should get lost. Perhaps the Egyptians had a similar object in view. But these are mere conjectures, although put forward by technical experts. Nevertheless it is striking that the pyramid of Cheops is the only one to exhibit the above mathematical and astronomical relations. All the other pyramids are deficient in them ; they are not even orientated towards the four cardinal points. For the present the theory must be accepted that the large pyramid of Cheops, like other pyramids, was the burial-place of the Egyptian king.

SPHINXES

Among the masterpieces of ancient Egyptian monuments we must also count the sphinxes, which excite our astonishment not only on account of their size but equally much on account of their consummate execution. We admire the dying lion of Lucerne, cut out of the rock by Thorwaldsen. But if we consider only its dimensions and not its artistic value, what does it signify in comparison with the great sphinx situated near the pyramids of Gizeh ? They are both made of one block, but the sphinx is no less than 77 ft. high and 190 ft. long. What must have been the size of the block out of which this overwhelming masterpiece was sculptured with a skill that does not cease to inspire the deepest admiration!

But this is not the only sphinx. There are a great number of others, all of which are, however, monoliths in spite of the fact that the material of which they are composed was by no means always easy to work. Sometimes sandstone was used, but more often porphyry; mostly, however, granite of such hardness that the very best modern steel chisels rapidly blunt themselves on it. Many of these sphinxes were probably polished like a mirror; but how was this achieved, by what means, and how long did it take to polish surfaces of such colossal dimensions?

All these are problems which may perhaps never reach solution. The sphinxes are usually found placed in front of temples. In front of smaller temples we find thirty to forty, but hundreds have often been found near large temples. In spite of this great number not a single sphinx has been discovered in a good state of preservation. In the course of time they have all been worn away by the sand of the desert or destroyed by human hands. We now know that the sphinxes are representations of Egyptian kings, though in the shape of animals. The largest of all known sphinxes lies in front of the pyramids at Gizeh, where it was buried in the sand of the desert till 1817. In that year it was excavated at the request of the European consuls, when it was at once found to be cut out of the bed rock of the earth. A magnificent staircase was found leading up to the monument, and between its forelegs a carefully paved terrace was laid bare which led to a shrine built against the breast of the colossus. The entrance to the shrine was near the right fore-paw. The face of the sphinx looks directly towards the east. The excavation of the monument cost a great sum and twenty years later everything that had been brought to light was again buried in the sands whirled up by the winds. In 1843 a second excavation was organized by Lepsius, the German Egyptologist, a third by Marietta in 1853, and a fourth by Maspero in 1886. They all led to the conviction that the sphinx had been covered up at least 3,400 years ago and laid bare again by King Thothmes IV in 1533 B.C. Some time or other it must have been buried with intention, for in certain places layers of sand with strata of small stones one foot high have been discovered piled up round the sphinx and cemented so well as to make it possible to cut steps. The colossus has been excavated again recently, and in spite of the damage it has suffered, it has proved possible, by repeated investigations, to obtain a true conception of its original appearance. The ancient Egyptian stonemasons showed great discrimination in choosing a rock, part of which projected sufficiently far to make it well suited for the head of a monument. Fig. 464 conveys an idea of the appearance of this sphinx which was created some 6,000 years ago. It is certainly more than 5,600 years old. The face bears the features of a king, probably of Amenemhat III of the Twelfth Dynasty. But it is not out of the question that it is the face of the God of the Sun. The former assumption, however, seems confirmed by the strangely folded kerchief which, in this form, belongs to the symbols of royal rank, as also the uraeus on the forehead of the colossus. Under its chin there is to be seen the strange artificial beard worn by the ancient Egyptians on festive occasions, when it was fixed to the chin by means of a string. In front of the breast between the fore-paws of the sphinx a large tablet is seen which reports in the form of a dialogue that King Thothmes IV, mentioned above, soon after his accession in 1533 B.C. ordered the colossus to be freed from the sands of the desert.

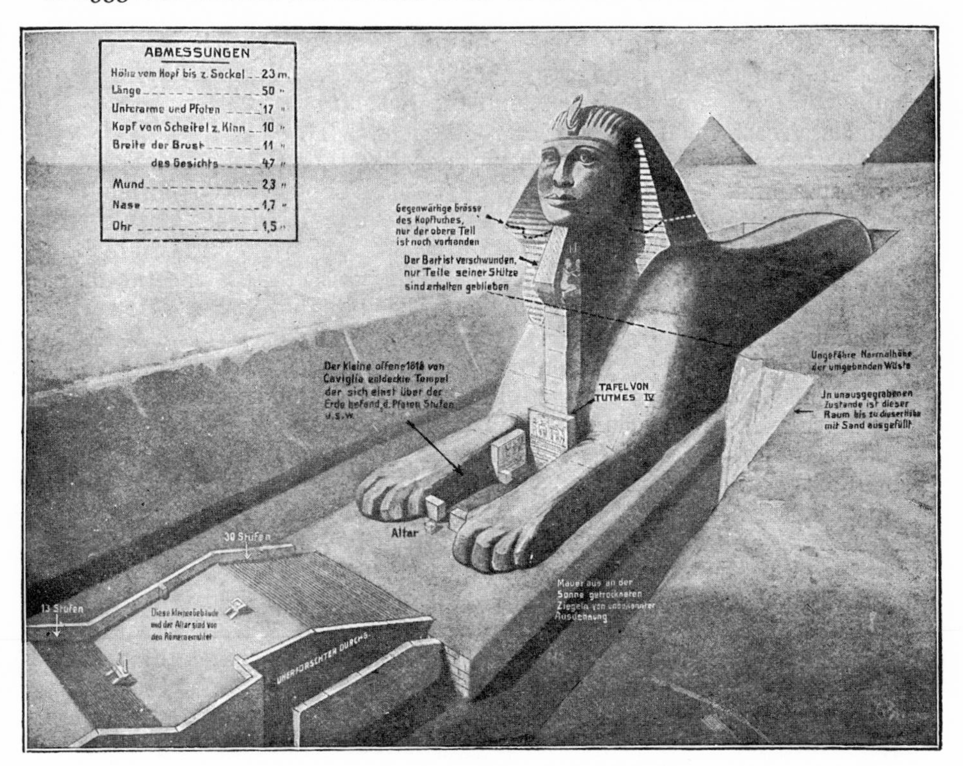

FIG. 464.—Reconstruction of the Sphinx

Next to the tablet, near the right fore-paw, there is the entrance of the temple, which has also been referred to above. Opposite to the sphinx there is the gigantic staircase leading down to the temple. A point worthy of particular notice is that the creators of the monument are very unlikely to have worked from a model, as the dimensions of the colossus under construction rendered futile any effort to compare measurements with a model of ordinary size.

TEMPLES

Of the temple buildings of antiquity that erected by King Solomon about 990 B.C. is fairly accurately described in the Bible (First Book of Kings v.–vii., Second Book of Kings xxv., Jeremiah lii., Second Book of Chronicles ii.–iv.), but among the details given there are none of interest from the point of view of the mechanical arts, except the fact that the temple proper was surrounded by lateral rooms which lay three stories high on top of each other. The Babylonian temples had one outstanding feature: the towers rose in terraces like steps, seven in number—corresponding to the sacredness of the number seven. These towers, called 'ziggurat', were famous throughout antiquity. Their outer walls were enamelled; the succession of colours from below upwards was: white, black, purple, blue, cinnabar, silver and gold. The ziggurat of Khorsobad near Nineveh is fairly well preserved. Its lowest terrace is 143 ft. long and as many wide, and is 20 ft. high. A ramp 8 ft. in width and 2,666 ft. in length winds round the tower up to the top. It is the spiral staircase mentioned by Herodotus (I, 181).

The temples of the ancient Egyptians, like those of the Babylonians, were surrounded by walls of vast extent. These always formed an elongated rectangle, and had neither windows nor pillars. Within this wall lay the temple proper. Its roof was always horizontal, and the façade characterized by the hollow moulding which ran along the roof; like the sides of the temple and the walls, the roof was covered with numerous coloured designs. An avenue of sphinxes or crio-sphinxes led up to the temple. The entrance was very narrow and lay between two pylons (see below). Several outer courts followed upon the entrance, and further inside there lay the main hall whose roof consisted of massive cross-pieces of stone resting on close columns. The remaining rooms are small and narrow; among them is the cella, in which the image of the deity is enshrined. The columns of the Egyptian temples are remarkable for their form as well as for their capitals, but technically there is nothing worthy of particular remark. The attention of technical experts has, on the other hand, been the more attracted by the pylons. As early as the fifteenth century B.C. the Egyptians were in the habit of arranging their temples in such a way that their entrance was formed by a large gateway, the 'pylon', which was flanked by obelisks and images of gods, kings and other objects of worship; it was protected by two tall towers which resembled the towers of a fortress. On close examination it is found that they are provided with two grooves running from top to bottom. Some ancient drawings disclose that these grooves served to hold high masts, to the top of which flags of various colours were hoisted. Some of these masts reached a considerable height; that of the temple at Edfu, for example, was 100 ft. high. At first sight they seem to have been merely ornamental. But there are now reasons for believing that they served as lightning-conductors. For instance, an ancient inscription dating from the time of the Ptolemies (323–30 B.C.) describes the masts of the temple at Edfu in detail, stating that they were intended to conduct the lightning. Translated from the German version of Brugsch, it reads as follows: 'This is the high pylon of the god of Edfu at the throne of Horus, the light-bringer; masts are arranged in pairs in order to cleave the thunderstorm in the heights of the heavens.' Another inscription says that the mast had in many cases been 'covered with copper of the country' in order to make them more effective. Masts of this kind must, indeed, have been excellent lightning-conductors. Other inscriptions also state that in order to make obelisks serve as lightning-conductors the little pyramids placed on them, called 'pyramidions', were covered with pure copper or gilt copper.

The Hebrews, too, seem to have possessed contrivances for protecting themselves from the dangers of lightning. The spikes on the roofs of their temple were connected with chains and these were fixed to the capitals of two bronze columns standing near the entrance of the hall. The capitals ended in a water-container (First Book of Kings vii. 17, Second Book of Chronicles iii. 17). Another document which seems to prove that the ancients were acquainted with lightning-conductors is found in Numbers xxi. 4–9: 'And they journeyed from mount Hor by the way of the Red Sea, to compass the land of Edom . . . and the Lord sent fiery serpents among the people, and they bit the people; and much people of Israel died . . . and Moses made a serpent of brass, and put it upon a pole.' Further evidence is given in the First Book of Kings vii. 13–22: 'And king Solomon sent and fetched Hiram out of Tyre . . . and his father was a man of Tyre, a worker in brass: and he was filled with wisdom, and understanding, and cunning to work all works in brass. And he came to king Solomon, and wrought all his work. For he cast two pillars of brass, of eighteen cubits high apiece: and a line of twelve cubits did compass either of them about. And he made two chapiters of molten brass, to set upon the tops of the pillars: the height of the one chapiter was five cubits and the height of the other chapiter was five cubits. . . . And upon the top of the pillars was lily work.' This seems to justify the conjecture that the metallic points on top of the columns are being referred to as conductors. These pillars are also mentioned in the Second Book of Chronicles iii. 15, but the height ascribed to them is nearly double. 'Also he made before the house two pillars of thirty and five cubits high, and the chapiter that was on the top of each of them was five cubits.' It is obvious that columns of that height must have been highly efficient conductors. The two above passages in the Bible also contain an accurate description of the water-vessel which formed the earth-contact, and an instruction given in Exodus xxvii. 17 reads: 'All the pillars round about the court shall be filleted with silver; their hooks shall be of silver, and their sockets of brass.'

The above Scriptural passages, taken in conjunction with some others (Leviticus x. 2, Numbers iii. 4, First Book of Chronicles xiii. 9 and 10, and others), makes it evident that the ancients must have found out by accident that lightning is conducted by metal rods or that the danger of lightning is obviated by metallic contrivances. It is not at all necessary to know the electric nature of lightning to discover a fact of this kind. It is true that Martin and von Urbanitsky, as also Hennig, deny the possibility of such contrivances having been used before Franklin: they maintain that the texts relevant to this question have been wrongly interpreted. But Hennig is obliged to admit that the ancient facts and customs and the literary passages which suggest the existence of lightning-conductors among the ancients (unless they are wrongly interpreted or belong to the realm of meteorological superstitions), 'are to be explained as an accidental and unconsciously correct application of Franklin's laws concerning lightning conductors'. (He is referring in particular to the Temple of Jerusalem.) In our opinion there

FIGS. 465 and 466.—Original forms of Greek Temples

is no doubt that the ancients, without knowing the nature of lightning, used protective measures against it, which they had found out to be effective by experience.

FIG. 467.—Ground-plan of the original Greek Temple

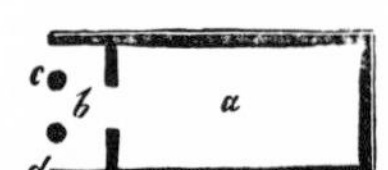

FIG. 468.—Templum in antis: *a*, cella (naos); *b*, vestibule (pronaos); *c*, columns; *d*, antae

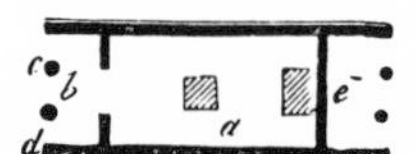

FIG. 469. — Templum in antis with back vestibule: *e*, opisthodomus

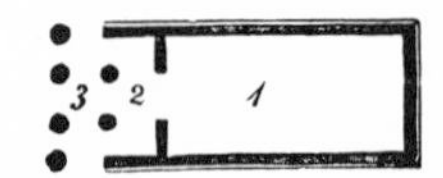

FIG. 470. — Ground-plan of the Prostyle Temple

The Greek, and later on, also the Roman temples are remarkable for the technical development of the columns; this applies also to the ground-plan, which was influenced by the way in which the columns were placed.

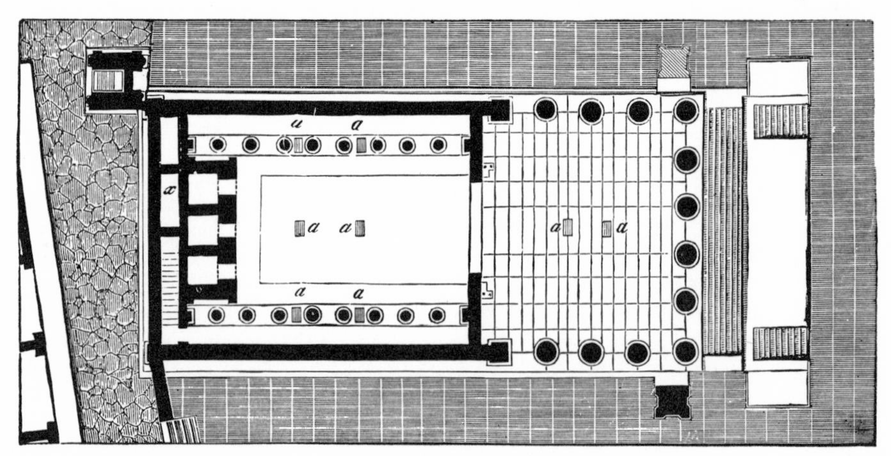

FIG. 471.—Plan of a Prostyle Temple. The temple of Jupiter at Pompeii. *aa*, apertures for admitting light into the cellar below the temple

The oldest known temple in Olympia and in Hellas is the Heraion, the temple of Hera. Its columns exhibit such differences that they must be assumed to have consisted originally of wood and to have been gradually replaced by columns of stone at a later period. This assumption is con-

Fig. 472.—Peripteral Temple

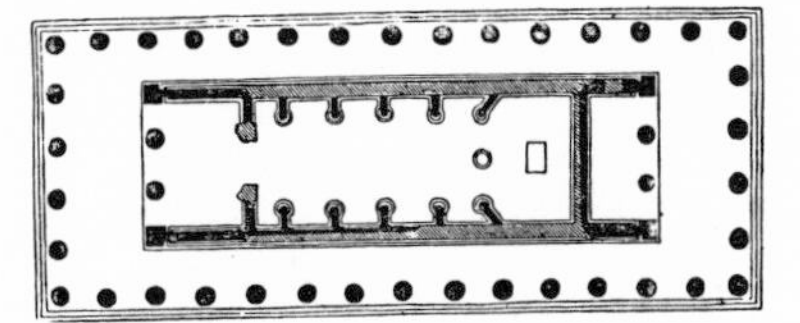

Fig. 473.—Plan of the Temple of Apollo at Bassae: example of a peripteral temple

firmed by Pausanias (V, 16, 1), who at as late a time as the second century B.C. observed that certain ancient columns and even whole temples consisted of wood (VIII, 10, 2). Pliny also mentions temples with wooden

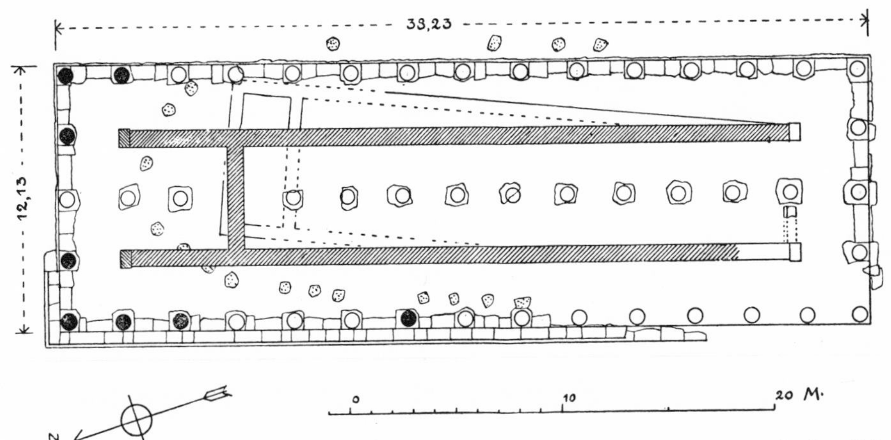

Fig. 474.—Peripteral Temple with five frontal columns. (Temple at Thermos in Aetolia)
In most cases the peripteral temples have six frontal columns and double that number on the sides, including the columns in the corners. Figs. 473 and 474 are exceptions to this rule

columns (XIV, 9). In point of fact the stone column evolved from the vertically placed wooden post which was originally used to support the roof. Probably it first appeared as a column of the Doric type, a supposition which seems confirmed by the above-mentioned temple of Hera.

We shall not follow the further developments of these columns from the artistic point of view, but shall simply consider their technical aspects, regarding them as the supporting elements of buildings, particularly of temples. We first notice that temples in their oldest forms could entirely dispense with columns. They consisted only of the simple cella, which contained nothing but the image of the deity and the sacrificial table on the altar for incense (Figs. 465, 466, and 467). In the next stage the lateral walls of the cella were extended in a forward direction and closed by frontal columns (*antae, parastas*). The elongated lateral walls were covered by a roof, which was further supported by columns standing between the antae. In this way an open vestibule, called *pronaos*, was created in front of the temple (Fig. 468). The ground-plan of the temple assumed a new characteristic form (templum in antis, the temple with antae). To make it possible to enter the cella from the back, the rear part of the temple was provided with a similar vestibule; so the ground-plan became further transformed, being characterized by the back vestibule, the *opisthodomos* (Fig. 469). The next stage of development is the prostyle temple, in which the vestibule is no longer carried by walls and antae but entirely by columns (Figs. 470 and 471).

FIG. 475.—Special form of the Peripteral Temple in which the columns are connected with the lateral walls of the cella by low walls, thus producing little chapels for receiving votive offerings

The *prostyle* or pillared vestibule may be combined with a simple rectangular cella or a temple in antis. If another prostyle is added to the back of the temple a new form arises called 'amphiprostyle'. If a colonnade is built right round the cella so as to form an open walk on all

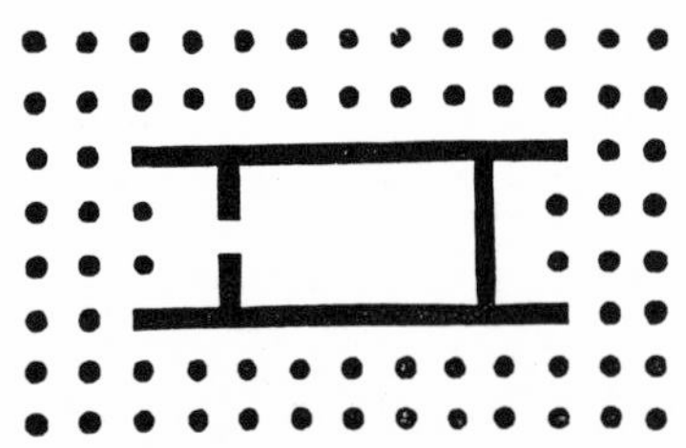

FIG. 476.—Dipteral Temple

FIG. 477.—Pseudo-dipteral Temple

four sides the result will be the peripteros (Figs. 472–475), whose name is due to the lateral colonnades being called 'wings' (πτερά, *e.g.* the

FIG. 478.—Ruins of a Pseudo-dipteral Temple (the *forum triangulare* at Pompeii)

The remains of the columns and the intervals between them allowed the type of the temple to be ascertained with accuracy. The substructure is surrounded by a flight of steps, a characteristic feature of Greek temples

Parthenon). A special form of the peripteral temple, the 'pseudo-peripteros', was developed by the Romans. In it the columns no longer serve to support the roof of the colonnade, but simply to simulate a peripteros from the front. For this purpose they are attached to the lateral walls as semi-columns.

FIG. 479.—Circular Roman Temple (Monopteros), the 'Temple of the Sibyl' at Tivoli

If the row of columns in the peripteral temple is doubled in such a way that two parallel colonnades or galleries are formed, a new type arises which is called *dipteros* or dipteral temple (Fig. 476), which may again give rise to the *pseudodipteros* (Fig. 477) in which the inner row of columns is left out. But in this case the empty space between the walls of the cella and the outer columns is as large as in a dipteral temple. This form is exemplified in the *forum triangulare* at Pompeii (Fig. 478). The Greek temple was orientated in an east-west direction in such a way that it was entered from the east, the image of the deity being placed in the western part. Roman temples show no such orientation; they were placed in any direction. Whereas the base of the cella of the Greek temple always has the form of an elongated rectangle, the Roman cella originally covered one-half of a square, the other half being occupied by the vestibule. This division into two sections was still retained at a later age when the square was enlarged into an oblong. In Roman temples the threshold of the cella invariably coincided with the bisecting line of the ground-plan. Finally the Greek temples were bordered all round by a series of steps leading up to them, whereas the Roman temples stood on a substructure which was ascended by steps from the front only.

THEATRES

Among the public buildings of the ancients the theatres held a very important place. Apart from the circuses and stadia, which are of little technical interest, there are two main kinds of theatres, namely the theatres proper or playhouses, and the amphitheatres in which not only plays but all sorts of other performances, such as gladiatorial combats, fights with animals, or naval battles, were also enacted. The playhouses in particular were objects of great veneration in ancient Greece. They, together with the temples, were regarded as the noblest buildings, and the drama had the importance of a divine service; it culminated in the Dionysiac cult. The oldest form of the theatre must have been something resembling an amusements park in the open air, that is, an enclosed lawn in which the performances took place, the spectators standing round.

FIG. 480.—The Theatre of Pergamon

It gives a clear picture of all parts of a Greek theatre. The acclivity of the hill served as a foundation for the auditorium. On the terrace at the foot of the hill the orchestra is seen; behind it we observe the skene (σκηνή)

Later on a wooden platform was raised on which the representations took place. In order to make it easier for the spectators to follow the proceedings, the circular or semicircular stage, called the orchestra, was placed at the foot of a hill on the slopes of which the spectators stationed themselves. For the comfort of the spectators seating accommodation was provided by digging terraces, one above another, out of the side of the hill so that the spectators were arranged in rows. From this stage it was but a step to construct the auditorium of stone. Even the oldest ruins of theatres preserved at Knossos show that the theatre was divided into two parts: a space for performing the plays (the *orchestra*) and a space for the spectators (*theatron*). Later a third part was added, the *skene*; it was a wooden booth from which the actors made their entrances, and into

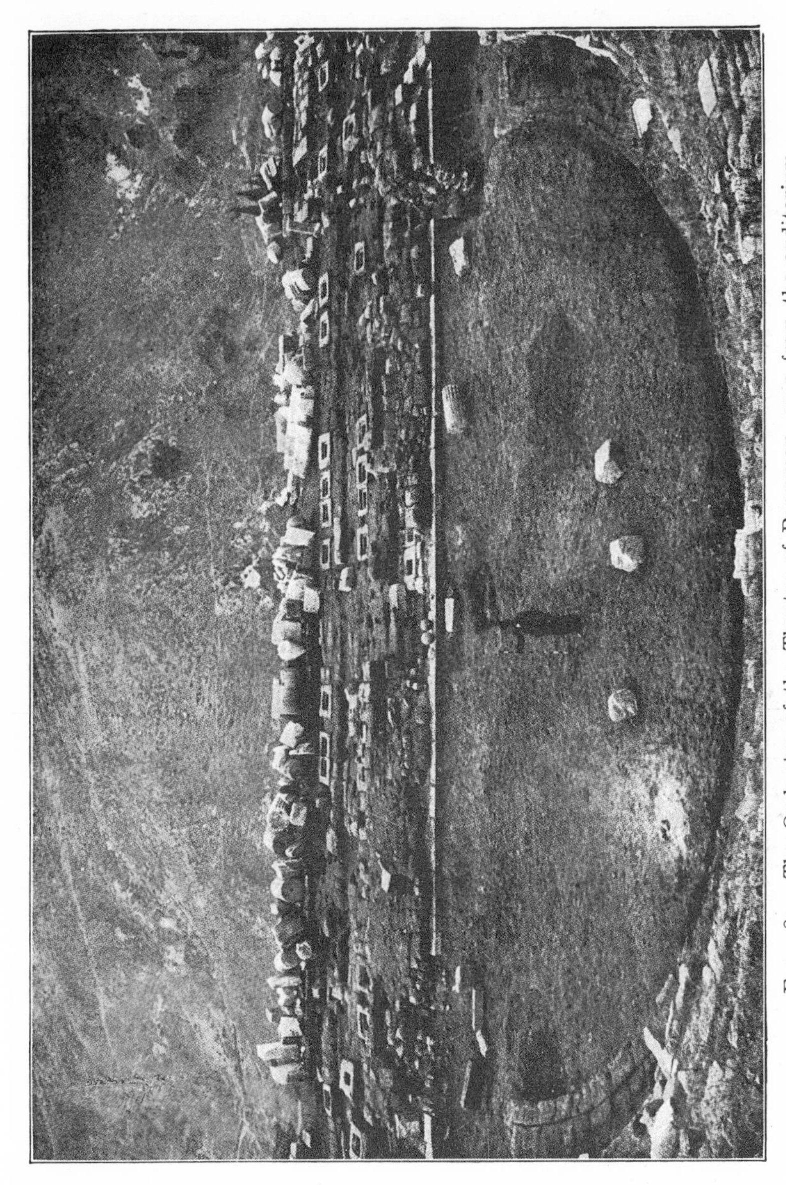

FIG. 481.—The Orchestra of the Theatre of Pergamon, seen from the auditorium

The dark depression in the middle contained the *thymele* in front of the skene. The posts of the skene were fixed in holes which are in an excellent state of preservation. On the left- and right-hand sides of the skene are the *parodoi*, whose exits lead into the orchestra. Near these exits are gaps in the front wall of the skene which were formerly entrances to the skene. On the right and left in the front part of the skene there are elevations which are the remains of the *parascenia*

which they made their exits after their scenes. The theatre at Athens, dating from the fourth century B.C., was built of stone except the *skene*, whose floor was still laid on wooden scaffoldings. The orchestra, however, had in isolated instances been constructed of stone at an earlier period. The theatre lay at the foot of the Acropolis, part of the rock being used as a back wall and a foundation. But also in other parts of Greece there was a predilection for building theatres in rocks or against hills in such a way that the slopes formed a natural back wall, and at the same time the groundwork (Fig. 480). Generally speaking the Greek theatre was arranged as follows (Fig. 482) : the circular orchestra was the centre round which all the other parts were grouped. At about the year 400 B.C. the floor of the orchestra was made of earth, and in the middle of it was an altar, the *thymele,* round which the chorus moved. The orchestra was partly surrounded by the auditorium, which rose in the form of a horseshoe on the slope of a hill or on an artificial foundation made of walls of different height, the intervening spaces being filled with earth. Opposite to the auditorium stood the skene, which derives its name from its originally unimposing appearance (σκηνή = hut, tent) ; in most cases it had an odd number of doors, of which the middle one was called the king's door. Later on the stage space (*logeion*), in which the drama was mainly enacted, was usually closed not only at the back but also on both sides by the structure of the skene, which was occasionally three stories high. Projecting parts on both sides of the skene, the *paraskenia,* served to hold between them a painted wall, the *proskeniom.* Subsequently the background could be opened out by a special contrivance, the *exostra* or *ekkyklema,* which allowed the spectator to see what was happening inside the building. The theatre was entered by the *parodoi,* two spaces intervening between the skene and the auditorium. These parodoi also gave access to the orchestra. The stage had entrances at the rear and others at the sides of the skene. The stage could also be mounted from the front, but not by means of stairs as was erroneously assumed formerly, for the orchestra was level with the stage [1] (Dörpfeld and Reisch). The theatre was provided with various machinery which served not only to open up the back of the stage but also to work traps or to shift various pieces of scenery. Theatres even had wings of a kind, the *periacts* ; they were triangular wooden prisms, which turned on pivots near the paraskenia. The three sides were painted with different views which were turned towards the auditorium according to the demands of the play. Possibly the pictures could even be removed from the sides of the periacts and so give place to still more scenes. The auditorium was divided into a number of blocks of tiers, *kerkides,* by a wide corridor, the *diazoma,* sometimes by several such corridors running parallel with the outer circular walls, and by stairs ascending radially from the orchestra to the circumference. The best seats were those nearest the orchestra or the diazoma ; they were reserved for the priests and persons of rank, and others to whom this honorary privilege, the *proedria,* was granted.

The stage of the Roman theatre, like that of the Greek, was originally a planked scaffolding with the onlookers standing in front. Wooden tiers for them were not built till after the year 145 B.C.[2] The first theatre

[1] This theory is now generally abandoned.—*Trans.*

[2] A mistake ; they had been in use earlier, but had been temporarily done away with.—*Trans.*

to consist of stone was erected by Pompey in 55 B.C. In 13 B.C. the Theatre of Marcellus was built, of which some ruins are still preserved. The Roman theatre resembled the Greek, being divided into three parts, namely, the space for the spectators, called *cavea* in Latin, the *orchestra*, and the stage, called *scaena*. There is practically no essential structural difference between the Greek and the Roman theatres. This similarity is even seen in the dimensions of the stage, which is comparatively wide but not deep, so that its ruins show a long, narrow, rectangular ground-plan. The orchestra of the Roman theatre has, however, no altar, the reason for this being that with the Romans the drama had lost its religious quality. But there are some further differences : the Roman orchestra was covered

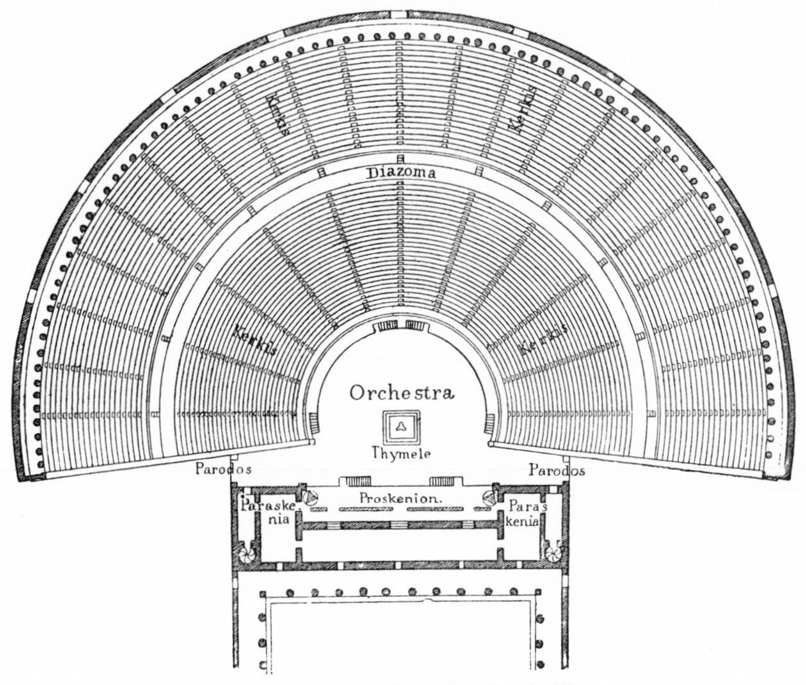

FIG. 482.—Ground-plan of a Greek Theatre

with rows of seats for the spectators of noble rank (*podium*) and was thus very much reduced in size. As the orchestra and the stage proper were on a level in the Greek theatre it was difficult for the spectators on the orchestra to overlook the skene or the place from which the actors were talking. This place, the *pulpitum*, was therefore deepened. In addition the Roman stage was furnished with a curtain, the *aulaeum*, and the cavea with an awning in order to protect the spectators from the sun. In the Greek theatre only the skene had been covered over and possibly also the topmost circular gallery which ran along the outer fringe of the auditorium. All the rest of the theatre was left uncovered.

The ancient theatres were extremely large, some holding as many as 20,000 people. The acoustics of these buildings was therefore a matter of great importance. Not only did the builders endeavour to make a theatre a satisfactory resonance chamber as a whole, they also placed special bronze vessels, called *echeia* (see Vitruvius, V, 5, 1 *sqq.*), in recesses; these were intended to magnify the sound. Moreover, the masks of the actors were shaped in such a way as to strengthen the sound. The

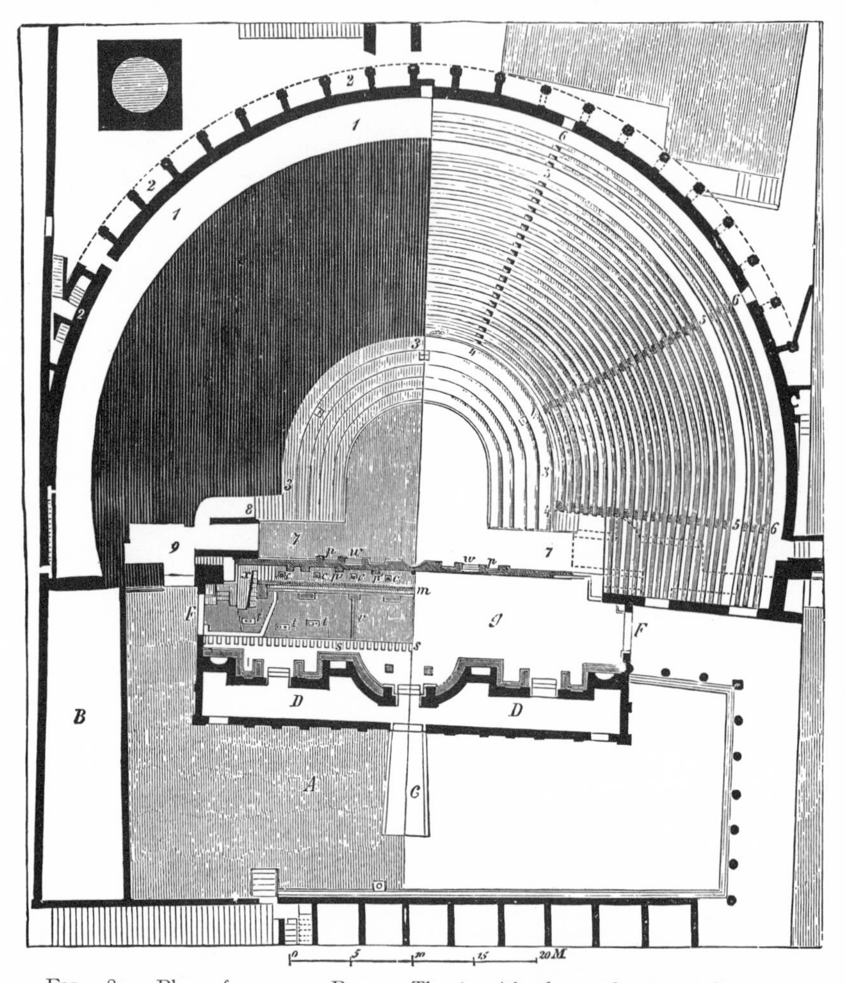

FIG. 483.—Plan of an open Roman Theatre (the large theatre at Pompeii)

On the right, part of the tiers, the stage and the floor. On the left, by removing the floor we get a view of the stairs, the corridors and the substructure of the stage. 1, Circular vaulted gallery; 2, corridor; 3, gallery; 4 stairs; 5, exit; 7, entrances of the orchestra; 8, doors; A, court in which the chorus assembled; B, property-room; C, ramp; D, the actors' rooms; *s*, stone rings for attaching the awning; *p*, room in which the curtain was folded *x*, staircase leading to the rooms below

point has been frequently raised how it was that these masks, which were after all a hindrance to the actors, continued in use for such a long time instead of being replaced by natural facial expression. If we consider the colossal size and the openness of the ancient theatres it is obvious that great demands were made on the human voice. No actor would have

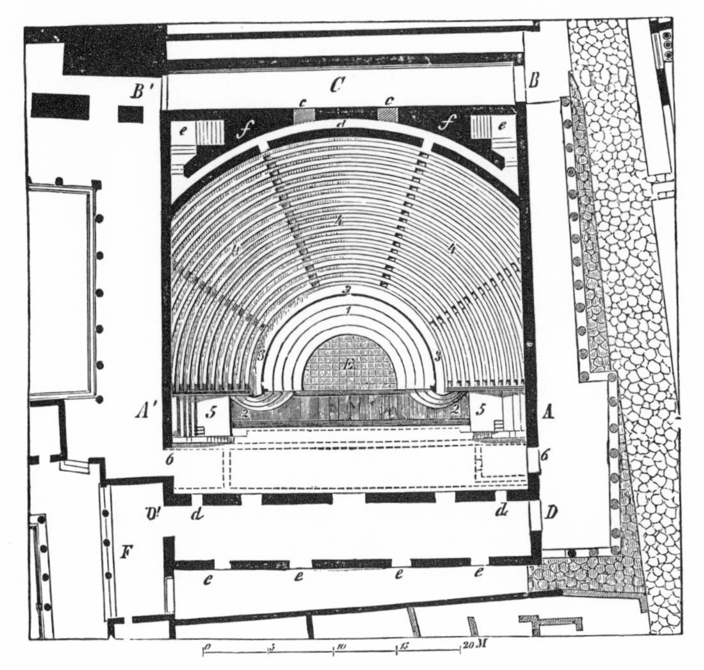

FIG. 484.—Plan of a roofed Roman Theatre (the small theatre at Pompeii)

This theatre is encircled by walls which probably supported columns, carrying a wooden roof constructed so that daylight was yet able to enter into the interior. A', A, Entrances to the orchestra; B', B, entrances of the vaulted corridor; C, D, entrances to the boxes; 5, 5, byway to the stage; D', entrance to the barracks of the gladiators; F, vestibule; 1, seats for spectators of rank; 2, stairs; 3, small gallery; 4, tiers

FIG. 485.—Roman Theatre at Fiesole

View from the stage of the auditorium (cavea), built into a hill. On the left, entrances to the orchestra and the stage

been able to shout through a leading part and sustain a tone which could be heard all over the theatre. It was soon discovered that the opened mouth of a mask could easily be formed into a sort of speaking-tube.

Fig. 486.—Reconstruction of a Roman theatre (theatre of Ostia)

The mouths of all ancient stage-masks are shaped in a most peculiar fashion. Following a suggestion by Castex, replicas of such masks were made for special acoustic experiments in which both actors and singers with voices of different pitches, that is, basses, sopranos and others participated. A number of spectators were also engaged in order that the action of these masks should be thoroughly tested in every direction. The very first experiments with masks revealed that to the hearers the intensity of the human voice appeared strikingly increased. Words spoken in a low voice without a mask were found to be unintelligible to the audience, but when a mask was applied the words were easily understood in all parts without the speaker increasing his efforts. Further, the voice became more distinct. This result was considerably more marked in the case of tones of higher pitch. The tone was neither blurred nor did it acquire a nasal quality through the mask. The peculiar formation of its mouth caused the sound to be conveyed with increased intensity not only towards the front but also towards the sides of the auditorium. The actor at once felt in his voice a sensation of increased carrying power. He found the simple face-masks to be acoustically superior to the animal masks which covered the whole head and which caused a buzzing sensation. The result of these experiments all point to the conclusion that the actors of antiquity were well aware of the advantages gained by the use of the mask.

AMPHITHEATRES

The amphitheatre consists of two theatres placed together, or we may regard it as an orchestra entirely surrounded by tiers for the spectators.

FIG. 487.—The Colosseum in Rome (seen from the outside)

Since a circular orchestra, such as the ring of a modern circus, gives only limited freedom of movement, an oval shape, as long as possible, was

FIG. 488.—The Colosseum in Rome (general view of the interior and some parts of the cellars)

FIG. 489.—The Amphitheatre at Trèves. (Inside view. On the left it is partly built against a hill)

adopted. This led to the characteristic ground-plan of the amphitheatre, which, on account of its shape, could not always be built against a hill (cf. Figs. 393, 489 and 490).

FIG. 490.—Section of the Amphitheatre at Trèves (built against the slope of a hill

The auditorium was therefore supported on pillars and walls, and in this way extensive corridors running around the building were formed

FIG. 491.—View of the Amphitheatre of Verona

below; these pillars frequently reached a considerable height (Figs. 487, 492, and 493). Cages for the wild animals were fixed underneath the lowest seats, or in annexes. The lowest circle of seats was generally separated from the arena by a wall which was insurmountable by the wild

Fig. 492.—Surrounding Wall of the Amphitheatre at Verona

Fig. 493.—Corridor and Buttress underneath the Auditorium of the Amphitheatre at Verona

animals and which sometimes carried a railing in addition. In many amphitheatres the arena was undermined by a number of cellars which

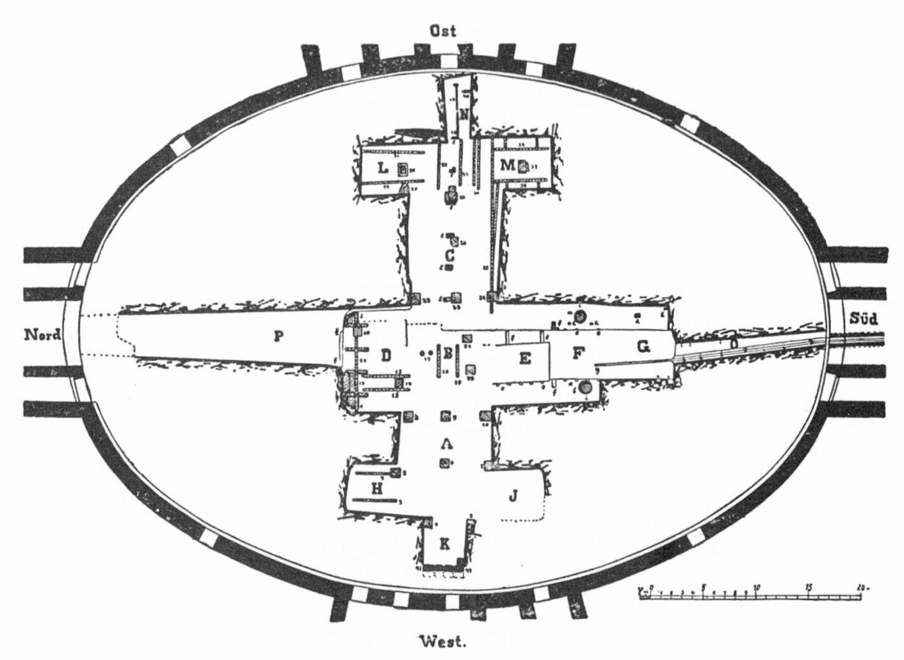

Fig. 494.—Plan of the Cellars and the Machinery of the Amphitheatre at Trèves

D, B, E, F, G, Main room for the machinery. In D and F large round holes for holding posts. In D, remains of the machinery, consisting of beams and cross-pieces. In front of them a wooden lifting device. In the corridor O, chambers for draining the cellars enabled the whole or part of it to be placed under water for aquatic displays (Colosseum at Rome). The cellars were made either by sinking

Fig. 495.—Cellar (den ?) underneath the Amphitheatre at Trèves

shafts into the soil (Metz) or by cutting them laboriously out of the solid rock, as was the case at Trèves, where some of the cellars are as deep as 15 ft. (Figs. 494 and 495).

Fig. 496.—Details of the Masonry surrounding the Amphitheatre at Verona

The ceiling, on which the arena rested, was supported by strong wooden posts. Special arrangements were provided in the amphitheatre for draining off the water which had been used during the performances. At Trèves a canal 330 ft. long and 7 ft. deep leads into the Olewig brook. In most cases the amphitheatres also had special rooms for the machinery which lay underneath the arena and was used for working the traps opening the water-containers and for other purposes no longer exactly known (Fig. 494). The gigantic size of those amphitheatres is common knowledge ; the Colosseum at Rome held some 45,000–50,000 spectators.

BATHS

As regards dimensions and grandeur of conception the baths which are likewise to be found in practically all the Roman settlements are hardly second to the amphitheatres. At the time of greatest luxury these baths

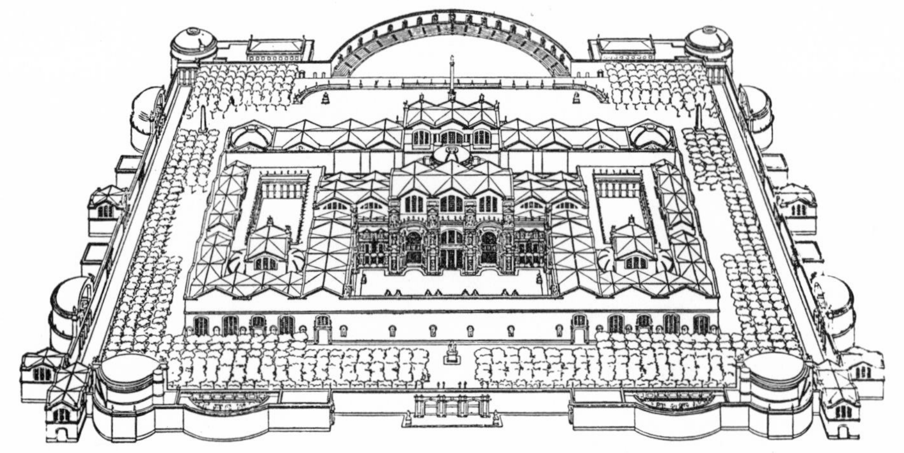

FIG. 497.—Reconstruction of the Thermae of Diocletian

or thermae formed a whole group of buildings containing a great number of rooms whose exact uses can in many cases hardly be ascertained nowadays (Figs. 497–511). But the essential parts, alike in these and in the smaller baths, of earlier date or in provincial towns, are as follows : the undressing-room or *apodyterium*, the cold bath or *frigidarium*, the steam-bath or *caldarium*, *sudatorium*, and a tepid room, the *tepidarium*, in which the bathers stayed on coming from the hot room. Other essential parts are the arrangements for heating, which have been discussed in the section on ' Lighting and Heating '. None of these rooms showed technical peculiarities except in smaller practical details. For example, the bathers could easily catch cold from any draught in the baths. For this reason the door-posts of the thermae at Pompeii are inclined in order that doors left open may close automatically by their own weight and so obviate draughts and make it impossible for the heat to escape from the caldarium. In the hot-room the seats were made of wood, as stone benches would have conducted away too much heat. No paintings have been found anywhere in the thermae ; this proves that the Romans rightly distrusted the durability and covering power of the paint in the damp heat.

Concerning the uniform distribution of heat in the hot-room and the method of regulating it, Vitruvius makes the following statements (V, 10) :

' The sweating-baths must adjoin the tepid room, and their height to the bottom of the curved dome should be equal to their width. Let an aperture be left in the middle of the dome with a bronze disc hanging from it by chains. By raising and lowering it, the temperature of the sweating-bath can be regulated. The chamber itself ought, as it seems, to be circular, so that the force of the fire and heat may spread evenly from the centre all round the circumference.'

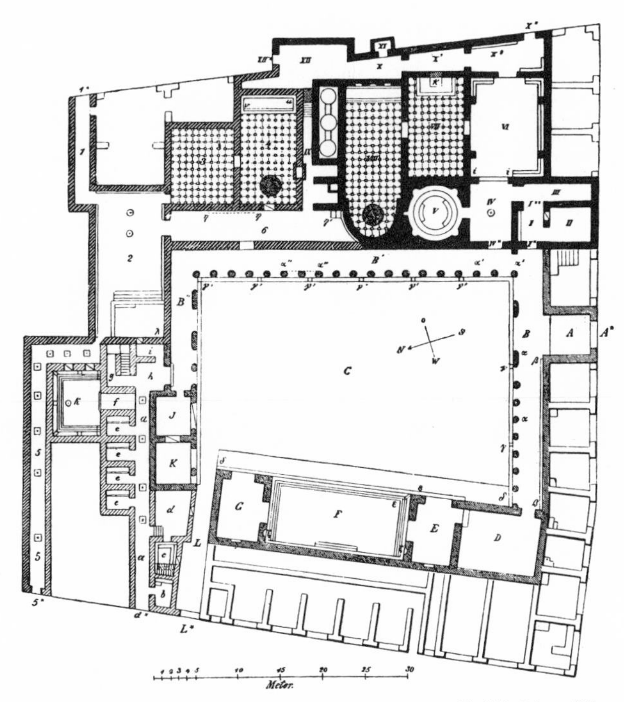

FIG. 498.—Plan of the large Thermae at Pompeii (Stabian Thermae)

A'', Main entrance ; A, vestibule ; BB'B'', colonnade running round the palaestra ; C, the court for physical exercise ; D, apodyterium ; E, room ; F, frigidarium; G, room ; VI, apodyterium ; VII, tepidarium ; VIII, caldarium ; IX, heating apparatus

On the whole the arrangement of these thermae is comparatively simple, like that of the ' Small Thermae '. Compare them with the great Roman thermae built by Agrippa, Diocletian, Caracalla and Titus (Figs. 497, 504, 506–511), which exhibit such grandeur of conception and magnificence of design

Fig. 499.—Apodyterium of the Stabian Thermae at Pompeii

FIG. 500.—The Palaestra of the Stabian Thermae

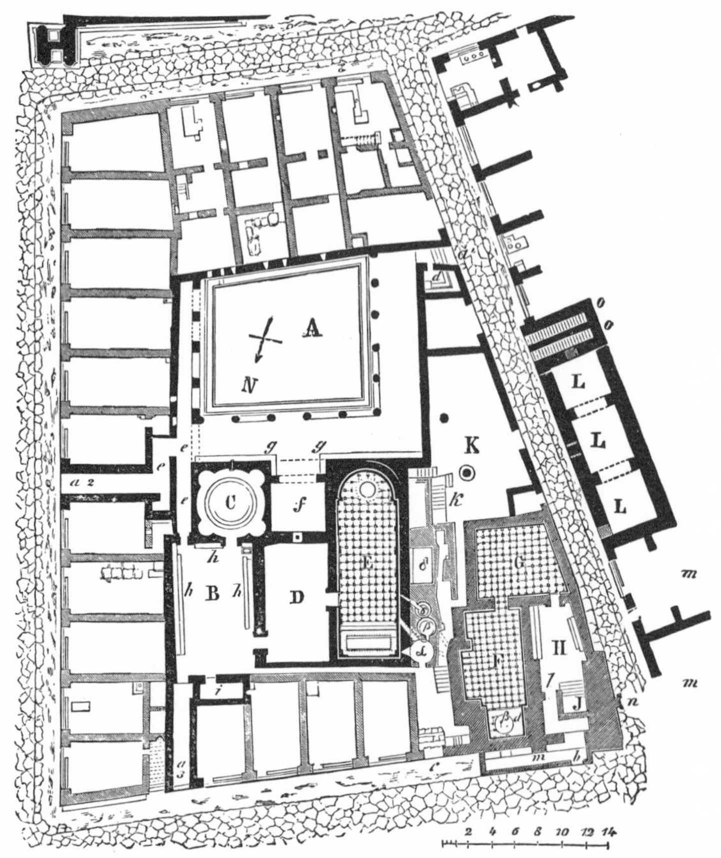

FIG. 501.—Plan of the 'Small Thermae' at Pompeii

A–E, men's baths ; F–J, women's baths ; *a*, 1, 2, 3, entrances to men's baths ; A, internal court ; *d*, lavatory ; *c*, corridor ; B, undressing room (apodyterium) ; *f*, exedra (resting-room with benches) ; C, cold bath (frigidarium) ; D, tepidarium ; E, caldarium ; F, caldarium ; G, tepidarium ; H, apodyterium ; J, frigidarium ; K, court ; L cisterns

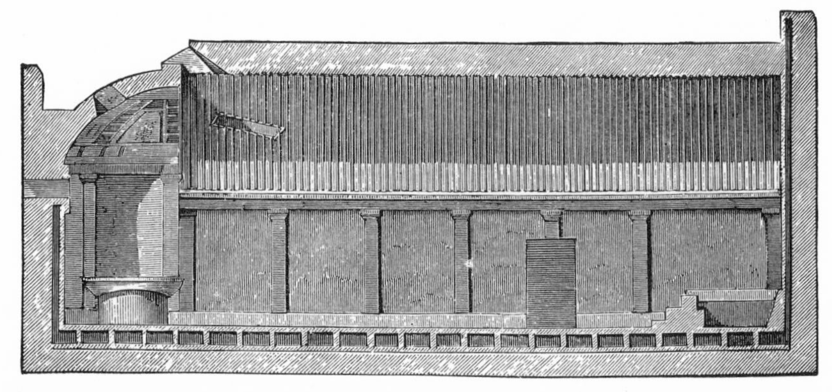

FIG. 502.—Vertical section through the Caldarium of the men's baths in the 'Small Thermae' at Pompeii

FIG. 503.—Inside view of the Caldarium of Fig. 502

FIG. 504.—The Frigidarium of the same baths (men's part)

FIG. 505.—The Tepidarium of the same

FIG. 506.—Ruins of the Thermae of Titus

Fig. 507.—Reconstruction of the Thermae of Agrippa in Rome (cf. Fig. 511)

The front view and the ground-plan of the reconstruction exhibit the clear design and imposing grandeur of the buildings

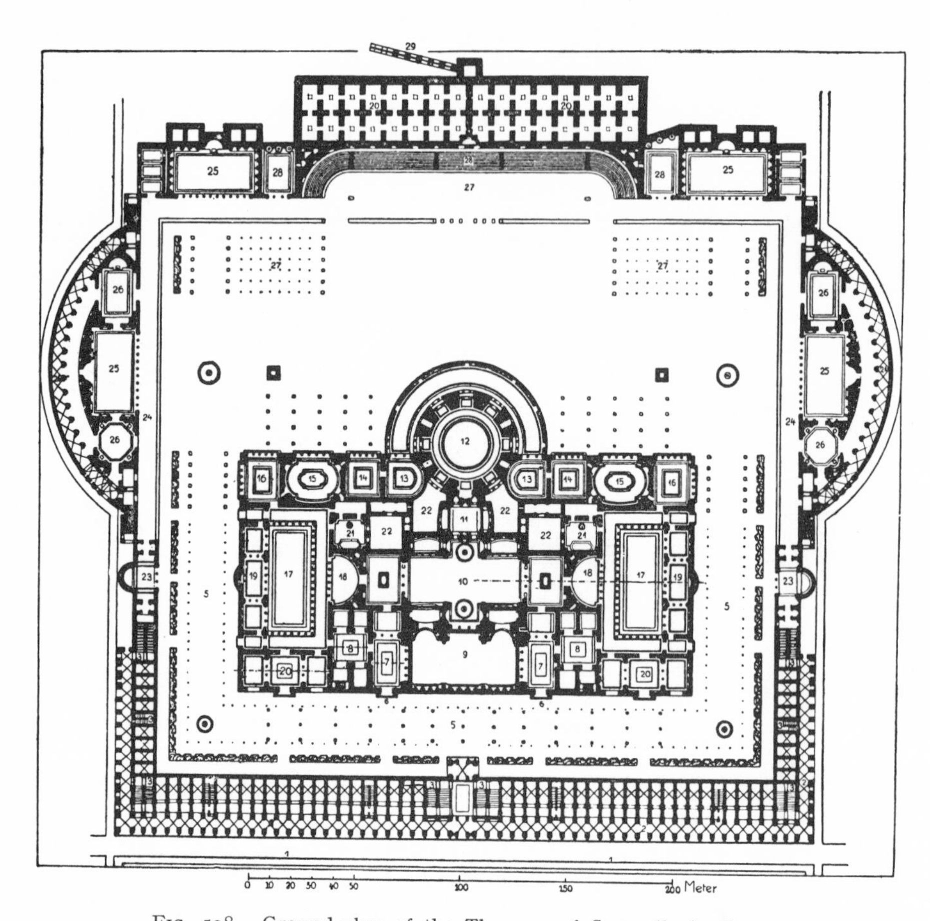

FIG. 508.—Ground-plan of the Thermae of Caracalla in Rome

The ground-plan reveals the complex yet well-balanced design of the main building. The thermae represent a little city in themselves, covering an area of about 27 acres. The purpose of the individual rooms has not been established with certainty. Nevertheless all the essential features characteristic of Roman thermae have been found, viz. : opposite the entrances, situated on both sides at 23, there is a palaestra (47), (wrestling-school), a large caldarium (12), a frigidarium also of great size, besides numerous dressing-rooms and a large tepidarium (this last has been questioned). The functions to be assigned to the other parts of this great construction have been discussed on various occasions, but no definite conclusions have been arrived at which are worth mentioning here. The thermae had accommodation for 1,600 bathers and were most luxuriously equipped. Even at the present day their ruins (Figs. 509, 510) make a deep impression on the beholder and still allow us to recognize among other things the profusion of domed vaulting, the numerous arches, and the lavish use of marble and other costly building materials. A great many works of art have been found there. The whole was surrounded by a wall which also enclosed numerous other buildings such as a stadium and a swimming-bath. The construction of the Thermae of Caracalla was begun in A.D. 212

FIG. 509.—Ruins of the Thermae of Caracalla

FIG. 510.—Another view of the Thermae of Caracalla

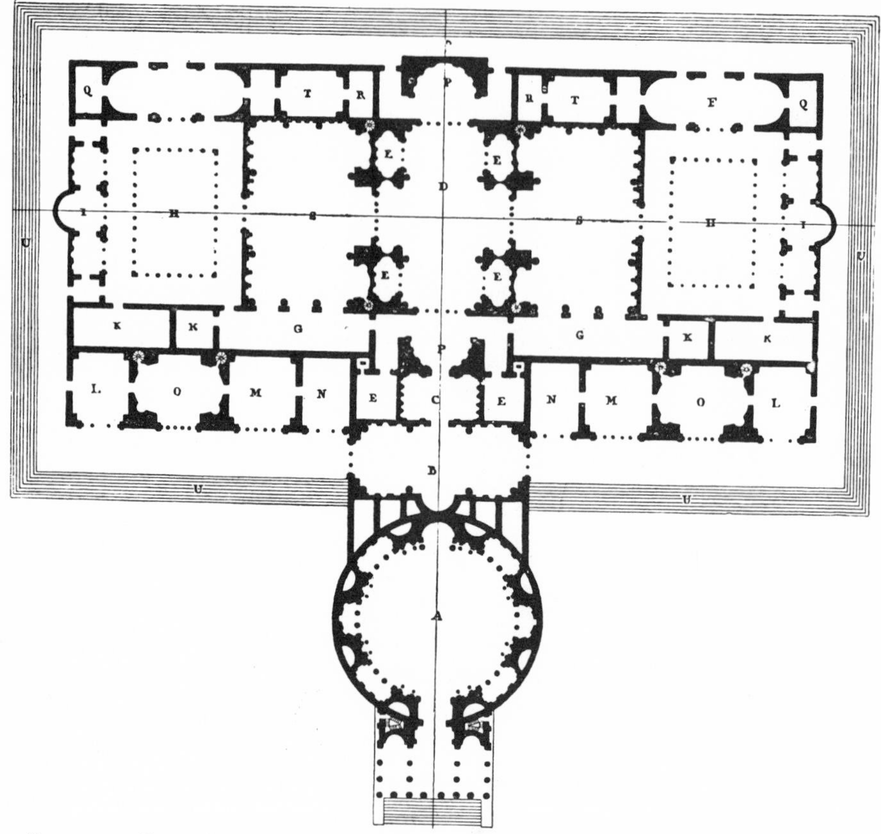

FIG. 511.—Ground-plan of the Thermae of Agrippa (Reconstruction, cf. Fig. 507)

BASILICAS

Basilicas must also be classified as public buildings. Their name is derived from βασιλεύς, which means 'king'. In Greece the original meaning was 'royal hall'. In Rome the basilicas did not appear till a later period, when the first building of this kind was erected by M. Porcius Cato in 184 B.C. The basilicas were not always used for the same purpose. Originally they may have been a simple sort of market-hall or exchange, but later on they became places of assembly and judgment-halls. A special section was partitioned off for the tribunal, or raised or built on in the form of an apse. The Romans seem to have been very fond of visiting the basilicas or loitering about in their neighbourhood. Some evidence of this propensity is given by figures used in a board game which have been found scratched on the steps of Roman basilicas and probably date from ancient Roman times; this is further supported by Vitruvius' advice that basilicas should be built in the warmest place of the forum. Rome, Pompeii and many other cities possessed several basilicas, of which only comparatively scanty ruins remain, besides, we are by no means sure that all

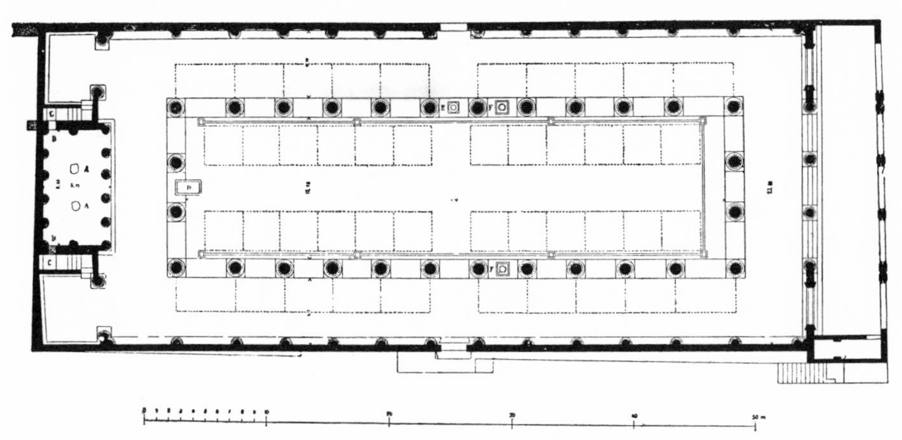

FIG. 512.—Ground-plan of the Basilica of Pompeii

A, a platform 7 ft. high representing the tribunal; B, doors; C, stairs leading down into the room below, which is lighted by two apertures (AA) in the floor of the platform; D, foundation for a monument

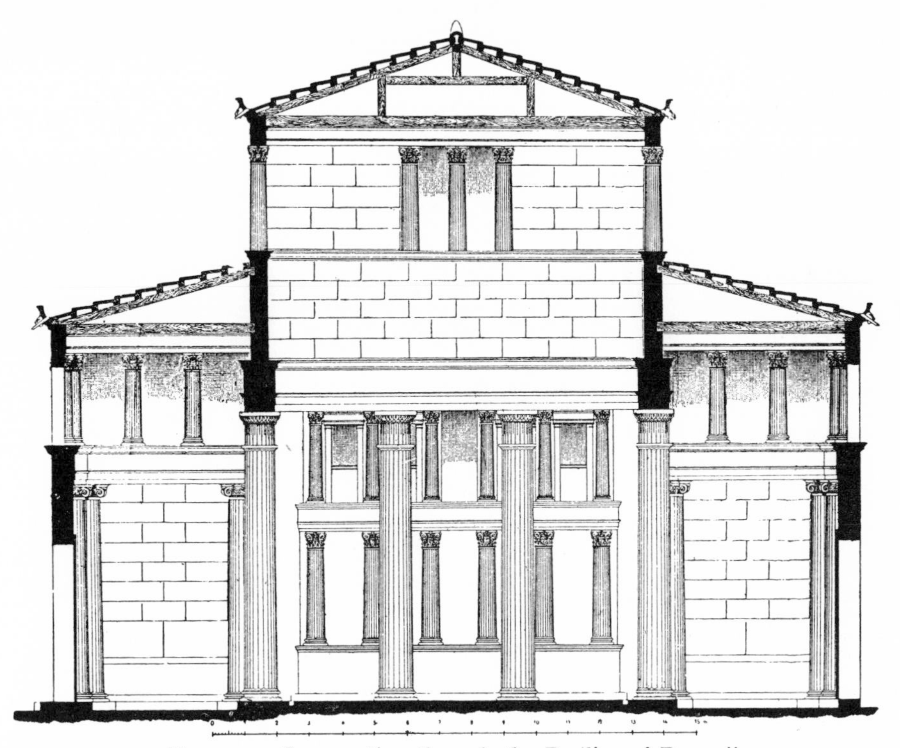

FIG. 513.—Cross-section through the Basilica of Pompeii

the buildings supposed nowadays to have been basilicas actually belonged to that category. Concerning the construction of basilicas we are entirely dependent on their ruins and the description by Vitruvius. Besides giving his opinion on the most favourable position for basilicas mentioned above, he states that they should be oblong in shape and of certain dimensions. 'In breadth they should be not less than one third, nor more than one half of their length' (V, 1, 4). The interior should have two rows of columns one above the other; the lower, supporting the side galleries, should be larger than the columns of the upper row. The basilica should be constructed in such a way that people standing in the galleries cannot be seen from below, and that people near the tribunal, which is placed on one of the narrow sides, do not disturb those in other parts of the building. All these and other requirements have been complied with in the basilica of Pompeii, further details of which are to be seen in a reconstruction by Lange, and in the ground-plan (Figs. 512–515).

FIG. 514.—Probable appearance of the Basilica of Pompeii

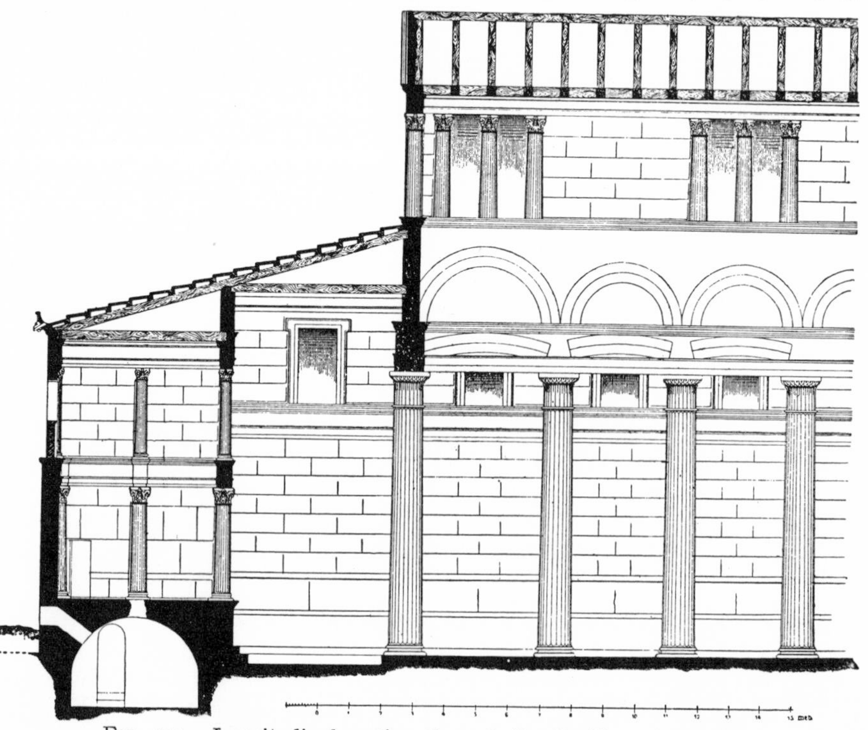

FIG. 515.—Longitudinal section through the Basilica of Pompeii

METHODS OF BUILDING

ORIGINAL METHODS

IN the earliest times the various ways of building were intimately connected with the stage of advancement of the human dwelling, and it was not till considerable progress had been made in construction that the methods practised in the case of large buildings became dissociated from those used for houses. In all probability the first dwelling was a round tent made of animal skins. Out of it arose the first fixed abode, the hut, which was likewise circular. With a view to dividing its interior into several rooms the base of the hut was gradually extended, assuming an oval form, and from this the rectangular form finally evolved. This course of development determined the character of the buildings and the methods of construction. The work was at first carried out in such a way and with such materials as were required for a round building. Twigs and straw, rushes, or field-stones simply piled up could easily be adapted to the circular form. Similarly clay could be used alone or in combination with the above materials for circular or oval structures. When civilization had progressed as far as the stage of the rectangular hut, new kinds of edifices appeared, namely the log-hut and the house with timber-framing, that is, with nogging or baywork, which gradually led to structures of stone and similar material.

No trustworthy record has reached us about the most primitive dwellings of prehistoric times, that is, of the huts built of reed, straw or rushes. We can only infer, from the similarly built dwellings of the primitive tribes of our own times, that the blades of the long-stalked plants above mentioned were woven together, stiffened by means of palings and coated with clay in order to make the walls impenetrable to wind and rain.

Willow wands, twigs and such like were also used instead of long blades. To give the clay greater consistency it was mixed with chopped straw, awns of cereals, or pine needles ; if no clay was to be had moss was packed into the hurdle-work. Foundations were unknown, and the supporting stakes were simply rammed into the ground.

TIMBER-WORK

As the form of human dwellings changed, endeavours were made to render them firmer and more lasting. This aim was achieved by reducing the hurdle-work and increasing the supports ; the stakes became more and more numerous and the relative area of rushwork became progressively smaller. Thus the log hut gradually evolved ; its mode of construction allowed an entrance that could be made more solid by the introduction of a proper door-frame and a threshold. As the stakes standing directly in the ground rotted in the course of time and so entailed a general loosening of the structure, the builders began to avoid fixing them in this way or erecting the houses directly on the ground, which was often damp. A solid layer of dry stones, the foundation, was interposed between the ground and the building. In this way the log-dwelling arose, which possessed practically all the essential components of the later house ; it had windows and even woodwork for carrying the roof, which was made of straw, reed, turf or small thin laths (shingles). At first the rafters were round and hollowed out only at the joints. Later on they were cut square, so that the structure acquired rigidity, and irregularities of the joints were averted. The separate parts of the building were connected simply by their own weight, or by notches in the beams or by binding. The roof may have been weighted with stones. Nails did not appear till later, perhaps only when baywork came into existence. The first nails were made of wood.

If we consider that even at the present day, in our age of highly developed technical science, there are still huge log-houses with shingled roofs weighted by stones in Upper Bavaria, the Tyrol and in Switzerland, there can be no doubt that this form of dwelling must have been used by many ancient peoples throughout their history. Traces of them have mostly disappeared, the wood having rotted in the course of time, but post-holes in the ground filled with rotten wood or coloured brown by it, as well as other remains, still bear witness to the actual existence of primitive or more elaborate wooden buildings in bygone ages.

It is also possible to form a conception of ancient timber-work from other sporadic accounts. It appears that the Jews above all other peoples erected wooden buildings in large numbers and succeeded in making them of great architectural beauty. In the Bible the carpenter is called the man 'who builds the house' and a great many Biblical similes relate to carpentry. Even apart from Noah's Ark, which was completely made of deal, it is to be assumed that Solomon's Temple, according to the descriptions given in the Bible (First Book of Kings vi.–vii., Second Book of Chronicles ii.–iv., Jeremiah xv., and so forth), was built of wood of the most precious kinds. Only the foundations were of stone, as is seen from the First Book of Kings v. 17 : 'And the king commanded, and they brought great stones, costly stones, and hewed stones, to lay the foundation of the house.' Similarly the foundation of the inner court seems to have been of the same material : 'And he built the inner court with three rows of hewed stone and a row of cedar beams' (1 Kings vi. 36). On the inside the walls were specially lined with boards, that is, they were wainscoted (1 Kings vi. 9, 15). The roof was made of rafters : 'and covered the house with beams and boards of cedar. . . . and he built the walls of the house within with boards of cedar, both the floor of the house, and the walls of the ceiling : and he covered them on the inside with wood, and covered the floor of the house with planks of fir'. Surveying these facts we can hardly be wrong in assuming from the Biblical descriptions that Solomon's temple was a supreme example of ancient Jewish architecture in wood, for the construction of which an immense quantity of timber was used—in all probability a huge log-house made of hewn timbers, wainscoted on the inside and richly decorated with carving. Even the supporting columns, which stood on a foundation of stone, seem to have consisted of wood. The Tabernacle of the Lord, which we may regard as a model of the Jewish dwelling, was also a wooden structure reminiscent of the tents used in nomadic times. The walls of the Tabernacle were 50 by 17 ft. and 17 by 17 ft. They consisted of vertical boards each of which stood on two silver feet and was joined to its neighbours by mortises. Each board being 2 ft. 6 in. wide, twenty boards were needed for a side-wall and six for the back wall of the sanctum. In the corners there were pairs of posts, clamped together at the top and bottom, to which these boards were attached, and five horizontal rafters were dovetailed into these corner-posts. These rails were passed through golden rings which were screwed into the boards. The material used was gilt wood from the locust-tree. For the rest, it appears that the shortage of wood which occurred very early in Palestine put an end to the ancient Jewish custom of constructing wooden buildings, for even Solomon, who for the last time followed the ancient tradition in its most elaborate form, had to import the wood for his Temple from great distances. His own palace, however, he ordered to be built of stone (First Book of Kings vii.).

FRAME BUILDINGS

Whether it was also the shortage of wood or simply technical considerations which led man to abandon the log-house in favour of the house with timber framing, or whether both reasons were involved, may be left an open question. At any rate the ancients must have observed that the stability of a building did not depend so much on the number of beams used as on the way in which they were joined, and the door-frame must have taught them that a solid timber frame capable of standing severe strains is formed by the combination of a horizontal threshold, upright posts and a lintel placed on top of them. Whether a frame of this kind is afterwards filled with loam, hurdle-work, woodwork, brick or stone is irrelevant. Thus it was due to a simple technical observation or perhaps to a shortage of wood and the subsequent endeavour to economize in this material that the frame-building came into being ; its essential characteristics were the same in antiquity as to-day. The threshold, the lowest course of rafters, serves also as the foundation of the whole building. Other wooden rafters, the stays or props, rise up vertically from it ; they are joined together by horizontal beams, the ' rails ', and by oblique struts, the ' dragon-beams '. In this way isolated panes or bays of rectangular shape are formed, which are filled in with some weaker material. Another important new feature of the frame-building is the complete separation of the roof from the walls, each becoming an independent part of the structure.

If we leave aside monuments, public buildings, and the residences of the rich, and if we leave out of account districts in which the shortage of wood or an abundance of suitable stone caused people to erect buildings only of stone, we come to the conclusion that the timber-frame house is the most widespread kind of building in antiquity. At the time of the Empire it was still extremely popular in Rome, according to Friedländer, and although stone buildings are fairly common in the south it is unlikely that they predominated over frame houses. In the north, however, the frame construction was naturally adopted, as all the necessary material, wood and loam, were at hand in superabundance. Roman forts were mostly built in this way, sometimes on a stone foundation. This is almost certainly true of the houses in cities like Trèves and Cologne, apart from the foundations, as before. Moreover, architectural buildings like temples were originally constructed with framework, when the building in wood alone had been superseded. The Heraion at Olympia, the most ancient Greek temple, mentioned above, was made partly of wood and partly of baywork with clay tiles. At Tiryns only the surrounding walls and foundations consisted of stone. For buildings which stood in the interior of fortifications and were not directly exposed to enemy attacks, baywork or brickwork was preferred. But attempts were made at a very early period to give the baywork the appearance of stone by coating it with loam or limestone, and ornamenting it elaborately on the outside. Decorating frame-buildings was very popular in Greece, as is seen from the ancient temple of Thermos in Aetolia, which is constructed of timber-work and clay tiles, and is decorated with painted clay slabs which add to its stability. ‘Above the epistylium, the beam that lies over the columns,’ says Lamer, ‘clay-slabs were placed as metopes, separated by vertically grooved triglyphs. Above them lies the gutter. The typical ancient painting on the left of Fig. 516 represents Perseus with winged shoes, and the metope on the right represents goddesses on their thrones.’ It was stated above (p. 351), that the column originated in timber, the first being the Doric column. The Heraion at Olympia is not the only evidence in support of this. To judge from the form of the capital even the Egyptian column seems to have evolved gradually from the carved wooden beam.

FIG. 516.—Timber-work in the Temple of Thermos in Aetolia, faced with clay slabs

ROOFINGS

Like the columns, so the roofs in their later form seem to have been a result of the practice of building in wood. Originally the roof was conical like the tent covering from which it had developed. Its various parts rested on a scaffolding of poles or rafters which were tied together at a point vertically over the centre of the base. The scaffolding itself lay on the circular wall of the dwelling. When the ground-plan of the hut became rectangular, the roof also changed its circular form into that of a rectangle, the tent-form being preserved while the cone became a sort of pyramid with a ridge-piece to which all the laths of the scaffold converged. But the timber-frame building later allowed the construction of gabled roofs. As the walls were entirely independent there was no difficulty in keeping the front and back walls low, while raising the side-walls right up to the edge of the gable. The triangular gables became the carriers of

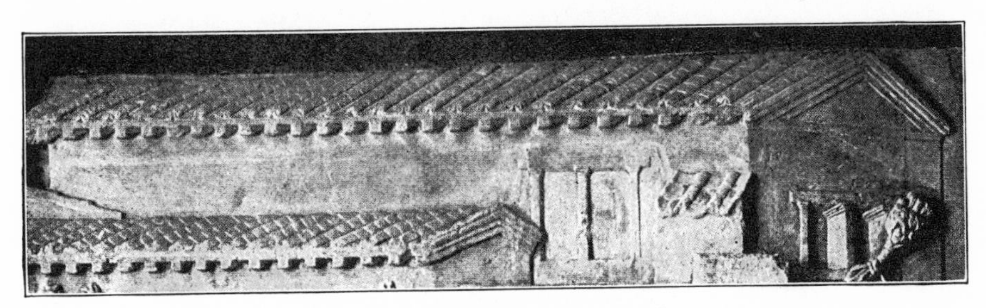

FIG. 517.—Greek Gabled Roof
From a votive relief dedicated to Dionysos (Museo Nazionale at Naples)

the roof and formed an integral part of the frame-construction. Yet, in spite of its simplicity, the gabled roof did not occur as frequently in antiquity as might be expected. Both in Greece and in Rome roofs were mostly flat or pyramidal, like tents, the reason being that the gabled roof was with few exceptions a privilege reserved for the residences of the gods. Assyrian temples as well as King Solomon's temple were crowned with gabled roofs ; they were also an ornamental feature of Greek and Roman temples. The building regulations were so strict that even during the last years of the Roman republic a special senatorial decree was necessary to grant Julius Caesar the honour of having a gabled roof. The structure of the Greek gabled roofs, of which the timber frame has in no case withstood complete decay, is clearly delineated on a votive relief dedicated to Dionysos in a group called ' Dionysos visiting Ikarios', which is kept at the *Museo Nazionale* at Naples. The gables are bordered by ledges. On the long sides the lower ends of the square rafters are seen projecting from the wall. These rafters carry woodwork on which the tiles rest (Fig. 517).

Two kinds of tiles are to be distinguished : the flat tiles which were simple plates with both sides turned upwards, and the capping tiles which were either semi-cylindrical or of a gable shape. When the flat tiles were laid close to each other on the wooden frame of the roof with their crockets hooked on to the transverse laths and with the joints formed by their upturned edges covered by capping tiles, a roofing was formed which was

Fig. 518.—Eaves, Mouldings and Ridge of the Treasury at Gela

absolutely rain-proof. The water flowed over the capping tiles into the grooves formed by the flat tiles. Instead of fastening the tiles by means of crockets the transverse laths of the roof were sometimes covered with boards, and the boards were coated with a layer of loam on which the tiles were laid (Figs. 419 and 440). The oldest known frame building of the Greeks, the Heraion at Olympia, was covered with a tiled roof. The timber-work of the roof did not always project from the walls. Remains of the eaves-mouldings on the treasury at Gela show that in certain cases the rafters of the roof terminated in specially elaborated mouldings ornamented with terra cotta or otherwise (Fig. 518). The ridge of the roof was supported by a massive transverse beam. In order to protect this beam and the laths ending upon it, the ridge was covered all along with a series of capping-like tiles which were often artistically worked. The Roman gabled roof was very much like the Greek, and Vitruvius has therefore nothing new to tell us in his lengthy description (IV, 2) apart from a few details about the props of the timber-work.

STONE BUILDINGS

Whereas the wooden building steadily evolved from a lattice-work of rushes to a structure with a timber frame, no similar development can be traced in stone buildings. Formerly it was held that the Cyclopean walls discussed below were older than the walls which consist of horizontal courses, but no convincing evidence of this has been adduced. Nor are the arguments sound which are based on the differences in the joints of the masonry, in the measurements of the blocks, and the rôle played by the horizontal line. When the stone within easy reach split off in parallel strata the masonry constructed with it naturally would not be Cyclopean, but would consist of horizontal layers; in the same way, walls with polygonal blocks were built simultaneously with walls of square blocks. The walls of the ruined citadel of Mycenae, for example, are of Cyclopean masonry, whereas parts of the wall in the neighbourhood of the Lion-gate are of another construction and the corners of the encircling wall are again different. At any rate the Cyclopean masonry ranks among the oldest kind of walls. It was made by placing crude unhewn blocks beside and on top of each other without using cement. The intervening spaces were filled up with smaller stones. Walls of this kind, often constructed of enormous blocks, aroused the astonishment even of the ancients at a time when they were no longer made. This was the case with the walls of Tiryns, which resemble towering masses of rock; they are mentioned by Homer and Hesiod. Pausanias (second century A.D.), filled with the greatest wonder at the sight of them, writes: 'The wall, all that is left of the ruins of the city, is a work of the Cyclopes and built of unhewn stones, each of which is so large that a yoke of mules would be incapable of moving even the smallest of them in the least. In bygone times small stones had been placed in the gaps between them in order to connect them as far as possible' (II, 25, 8). Concerning the way in which such walls were raised, we are entirely left to conjectures. It is probable that the inclined plane played a part in the work of construction. With the aid of such an arrangement, a kind of ramp, or possibly also slides manipulated by an enormous number of workmen, these rocks may have been piled up on the walls. Various investigators, who have attempted to solve the problem of these walls, have suggested the use of the strangest devices, involving levers and lifting contrivances, and have given directions for building, but there is no evidence to support any of them and they all seem highly impossible. Judging from the facts actually known to us concerning ancient craftsmanship, we are bound to arrive at the same conclusion as was stated in the chapter on 'Technical Mechanics and Machines', namely that these gigantic tasks were accomplished with the simplest of mechanical means, but with the expenditure of an immense amount of human labour and time.

Polygonal Masonry is characterized by the form of the stones used. The sides of crude stones were superficially hewn in such a way that the original shape was more or less preserved, the result being irregular polygons of unequal sides. These blocks were then placed beside each other in such a way that their joins fitted as close as possible. Practically no mortar was used, the structure holding together by the weight of the stones. Polygonal masonry has been found in numerous places in the ruins of Corinth, Mycenae and Ostia, in Epirus, Oiniadai in Akarnania and others. Some of these walls seem to have been executed with such care and industry that no trace of horizontal courses is observable. In others again, such as the huge walls at Norba, polygonal blocks were used, but they were all arranged in horizontal layers, or in such a way that the polygonal network was interrupted by horizontal lines, separating the layers.

A third kind of masonry is produced by using *ashlar* (square-hewn stones); which have the advantage of giving absolute stability irrespective of the dimensions of the stones used. The stability is due to the carrying surface being very large and fully utilized. Although a great many instances of ancient ashlar masonry are only preserved in ruins, the reason for this is not due to a lack of resisting power. Structures of this kind would have endured unaltered till our day in all the regions which have not suffered from earthquakes, if their stones had not been removed and used for new buildings. In many districts, above all in Rome, ancient ashlar structures served as quarries from which the building material was extracted during the Middle Ages. Like Cyclopean masonry, walls composed of ashlar were made without cement—they consisted simply of piled-up blocks of stone, sometimes fastened with cramp-irons. For this purpose incisions were made in the contiguous surfaces of the blocks, into which iron bars were inserted; the gaps left were then filled up with molten lead. In addition to these horizontal cramps vertical iron dowels were used by the Greeks for consolidating walls and preventing a lateral shearing of the courses. The dowel was fixed with lead into a hole which had been cut into the centre of the upper surface of the lower stones; it projected vertically from the surface and fitted loosely into the corresponding hole in the centre of the lower surface of the next stone above. The upper hole was not sealed with lead. Two neighbouring stones were clasped horizontally by means of cramp-irons as follows: a deep horizontal groove was chiselled into the communicating upper surfaces and a double T-shaped cramp-iron laid into it. A rim of clay was then placed round the edge of the groove and in this way a kind of trough was formed, which was filled with liquid lead so as to cover completely the iron cramp. The clay rim was then removed and the block of lead projecting from the stones reduced in such a way that it filled into a corresponding groove in the lower surface of the stones above. Numerous ancient structures still extant prove that walls consolidated in this way have been able to survive thousands of years. The successive tambours of large columns were fastened in a similar way, i.e. with iron and lead. In many Attic buildings these are grappled with a wooden dowel, which is fixed into cedar plugs of which one belongs to an upper and one to a lower surface. Frequently the dowel is so weak that its purpose can only have been to connect two tambours of a column so as to make them fit together accurately. In this case the tambours could be made to rotate around their dowel. Otherwise the parts were joined by means of peculiar iron plugs fixed with lead into holes in the tambours of the columns. The plug became narrower towards the middle, so as to project wedge-like on both sides from the lead stopper. First the plug was fixed into the upper tambour, which was then placed on the tambour below. The latter had been provided with a hole, for receiving the thole projecting from the periphery of the column to the hole. The groove widened as it approached the hole. A clay funnel was then introduced into the groove between the two tambours, and lead was poured through it into the hole around the plug.

FIG. 519.—*Pseudo-isodomum*. Section of the masonry in the cellar of one of the buildings in Saalburg

A well-preserved example of this kind of treenailing is seen in the 'Juppiter-column' in the Römisch-Germanisches Museum at Mayence. Ashlar masonry, however, as well as brickwork, was sometimes cemented, the material being mortar (see section 'Building Materials').

Ashlaring was accomplished either by using blocks of equal size with regularly alternating joints—this kind of masonry was called *isodomum*: examples are seen on the left of Fig. 520 and in the two bottom rows of Fig. 539—or the blocks differed in size, making courses of unequal height (*pseudo-isodomum*, Figs. 519, 521, 523, 527, also the substructure of Fig. 541).

The thicker walls were frequently made of some cheaper

material such as brick, which was then faced with ashlar. The

FIG. 520.—Roman Wall, consisting of brickwork inside (seen on the right) and ashlar facing (*isodomum*, on the right) shortened by means of bond-stones
Casale Rotondo on the Appian Way

brickwork and the facing were combined to form a whole by prismatic

FIG. 521.—Corner of a House made of hewn stone (Saalburg)

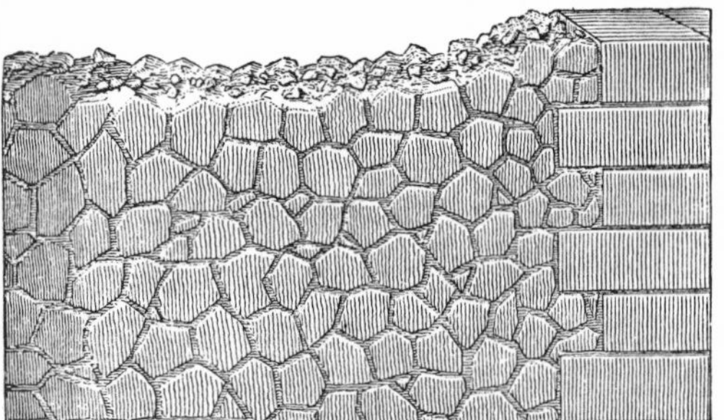

FIG. 522.—*Opus incertum* or *antiquum*

bond-stones whose heads lay in the outer surface of the wall, whereas the

FIG. 523.—'Cast' Masonry in the Forum Civile at Pompeii
The front wall shows *opus pseudo-isodomum* and *reticulatum*

bodies entered the wall perpendicularly to the facing (Fig. 520). Ashlar was further used for constructing the corners of buildings (Figs. 521 and 522) or for making insertions in isolated parts of a structure.

A special kind of masonry is the *opus incertum*, also called *antiquum* (Fig. 522) according to Vitruvius (II, 8, 1). It is met with especially in Roman buildings, of which it is characteristic. It is very durable, though it is apt to crack (Vitruvius). The method of production was very simple. A box was made of boards to exactly the same dimensions as the wall to be erected. Mortar and broken stones of all sizes were then battered into it. As soon as the whole had become hard the boards were removed and the new wall was embellished with plaster. Traces of the boards are still recognizable in places where the plaster has fallen away from the *opus incertum*.

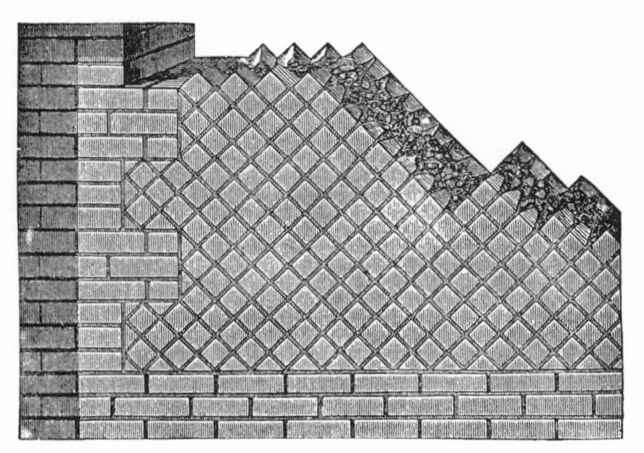

FIG. 524.—*Opus reticulatum*

FIG. 525.—*Opus reticulatum*
The guest-rooms in Hadrian's Villa at Tivoli

Apart from the material used this method is very much like the modern way of making concrete. In order to render the *opus incertum* more durable, permanent outer walls of ashlar, brick or marble were made instead of the boards; they served as lining walls, into the gaps between which the mixture of stones and mortar (Fig. 523) was then cast. Finally these lining walls were grappled with braces which

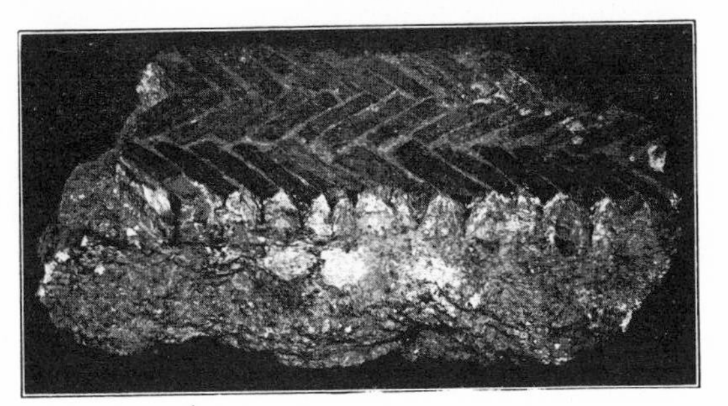

FIG. 526.—*Opus spicatum*
From a Roman tiled floor in the Deutsches Museum at Munich

thus connected all three constituent parts of the wall, namely, the two retaining walls and the packing.

As the *opus incertum* had not a very handsome appearance unless it was hidden behind the lining walls, a new kind of cheap masonry, the *opus reticulatum* or 'network' (Figs. 524 and 525) was introduced, wherever ashlaring would have been too expensive. Small cubical stones were joined in such a way that they did not rest on one of their sides but were supported on an edge at the lowest parts. Comparatively large gliding planes, however, were thus created with a distinct tendency to give way under the oblique pressure from above. For this reason the *opus reticulatum* with all its handsome and attractive design was not very lasting. Another kind of Roman masonry was the *opus spicatum*, a variety of the *reticulatum*. In this the individual courses of stones were placed upon each other like the grains in an ear of corn (Figs. 526 and 527).

FIG. 527.—*Opus spicatum* (on the left) and *pseudo-isodomum* (on the right) at Saalburg (outer settlement)

BRICKWORK

In the ancient art of building *brickwork* played a very important part and is found among practically all the peoples of antiquity, either in the form of pure brick buildings or associated with other methods of building. The Romans above all achieved great results in this field of work. They succeeded in constructing with nothing but brick huge vaults which seem likely to last for ever. Even at the present day the craftsmanship of the Roman builders in this field is attested by the cupola of the Pantheon, the colossal vaultings of the basilica of Constantine in Rome, the thermae of Diocletian and many other structures. Strong spandrel-bracketings of beams and planks were used, over which the bricks were built in regular layers. The greatness of the achievement, however, does not consist in the use of these cradlings, but in the correct calculation of the vaulting and the uniform distribution of the pressure acting on the vaults and the walls carrying them.

FIG. 528.—Masonry consisting of Stone with binding courses of Brick

On the right at the back the masonry has been replaced by darker courses of brick

THE CONSTRUCTION OF VAULTS

The art of constructing vaults was known to the Assyrians and Babylonians as early as 4000 B.C. This is shown by the excavations which were promoted by the University of Chicago. But despite the fact that the knowledge of the art spread to other peoples, it seems to have been lost in the course of time. The early Greeks did not know it; they built only horizontal ceilings. If wide openings had to be roofed over they were covered with horizontal beams of wood or stone, on top of which was placed the ceiling or roof proper. This primitive method naturally restricted the size of the rooms that could be built. The desire to build large halls led to the use of an increasing number of uprights for supporting the roof-beams; as a result, however, the cover-space was again reduced. The Hall of the Mysteries at Eleusis, for example, contains seven rows of six columns each; in the municipal hall at Megalopolis the columns were arranged radially. When the Greeks first started building cupolas they constructed pseudo-vaults: a typical example is the so-called treasury of Atreus at Mycenae, which was apparently the antechamber of a king's tomb (Fig. 529). A cupola-shaped space 50 ft. high and 50 ft. in diameter was created in the following way: 33 horizontal layers of stone were piled up in concentric circles upon the impost of the cupola and made to corbel out till they met in the centre of the topmost course. Similar pseudo-vaults have also been discovered in the East, for instance in Chaldaean tombs such as the sepulchral vault at Mugheir, in which the walls are slightly inclined outwards, and carry at the top the pseudo-vault, which is covered in its narrowest parts by brick-plates (Fig. 530).

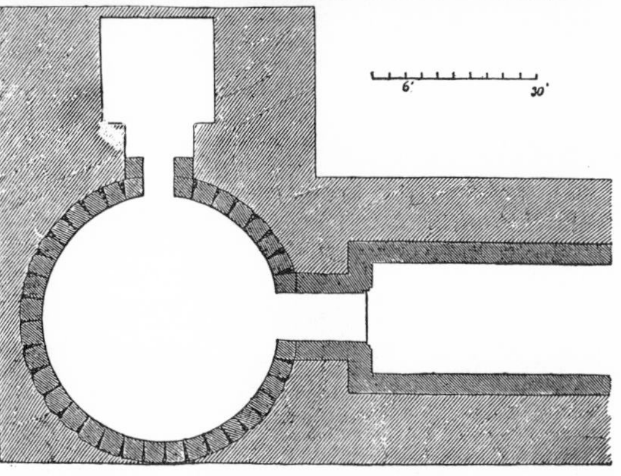

FIG. 529.—Pseudo-vault at Mycenae, called the Treasure-house of Atreus

FIG. 530. — Chaldean Pseudo-vault in the Sepulchre at Mugheir

In Greece the real art of constructing vaults is first exemplified by the erection of the arches over the Acarnanian town-gates. An early archway

FIG. 531.—Vault made of wedge-shaped Stones

Supposed to be a heating gallery. From the small Roman theatre at Verona

FIG. 532.—Vaulted Ceiling, consisting of several layers, in the imperial palace at Trèves

of this kind is the gate of the Holy Road at Palaeros. It is a joint-cut vault made of stones which are wedge-shaped. They are not all entirely alike, but they yield a structure which is of sufficient stability to carry the weight of the partly preserved ceiling even to-day. The difficulty seems to have been to connect the cuneiform stones with the neighbouring stones of the wall. But it was overcome by a very irregular joint-cut and by inserting polygonal stones. Even some of the wedge-shaped stones are polygonal at the top. The arched gate at Palaeros is likely to have been built in the fifth century B.C.

FIG. 533.—Barrel-vault made of irregular Stones

Corridor in the cellars of the Thermae at Trèves. The joints of the vault and the lateral walls are worthy of particular note

Among the buildings of the ancient Romans there are arches and vaults of every description. Besides those made of wedge-shaped stones (Fig. 531) there are frequently to be found vaulted ceilings consisting of several parallel arches lying one above another, as is seen from vertical sections (Fig. 532). Often the stones used, and the layers made with them, are very irregular, particularly where they join the lateral walls (Fig. 533). A very remarkable feature of Roman buildings commonly met with is the superposition of arches one above another such as in amphitheatres (Fig. 487, 492), aqueducts, in the imperial palace at Trèves (Fig. 534), and many other places. They disclose too the extensive knowledge of the Romans concerning the bearing-power and the distribution of stresses in masonry.

By a gradual widening of the arch the simplest form of true vaults originated, namely, the cylindrical or barrel-vault, which is repeatedly met with in Greek masonry and still more in Roman triumphal arches. The heavy weight of barrel-vaults constructed of ashlar does not allow of great width. In order to create wide spans the arch-piers had to be very strong and massive, which not only made them look clumsy and out of proportion but occasioned great expense. A way out of the difficulty was furnished by the brickwork structure; this made the vaulting lighter and consequently allowed the supporting walls also to be made lighter. Brickwork also led to a greater freedom of design in vaultings in general; cross-arched vaults and domed vaults came about, whose further development, however, demands attention more from an architectural than from a technical point of view; they will therefore not be discussed here.

Fig. 534.—Superposed Roman Arches (imperial palace at Trèves)

It has been said before that vaults were usually constructed with the aid of a special scaffold, the spandrel bracketing or cradling. But whereas nowadays such cradlings are usually placed on the ground or on the foundation, the ancients, at any rate the Romans, apparently placed them on the masonry of the piers or other walls adjacent to the future vaults. Numerous offsets or projections found on the inside and the outside of the piers served as carriers and abutments for the cradlings used during the construction of the vaults. Examples of such offsets are met with in the ruins of the ancient Roman bridge at Narni in Umbria, in the aqueduct called 'Pont du Gard' near Nîmes, and in many other buildings. If they are missing nowadays, the reason probably is that they were knocked off or chiselled away at a later period. Sometimes these offsets are seen only for a short distance inside the vault, the reason being that those further inside had been chiselled off, or the cradlings had been placed only partly on such offsets, and partly on the ground. But there is no doubt that in some cases the cradlings rested entirely on the ground, although they were more often supported on offsets.

BUILDING IMPLEMENTS

Concerning details of instruments used in building, particularly windlasses, blocks and pulleys and other apparatus of this kind, the reader

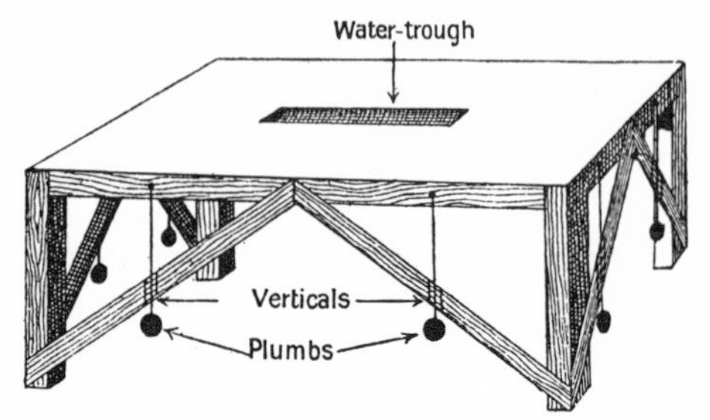

FIG. 535.—Chorobates (reconstructed by Neuburger)

is referred to the section on 'Technical Mechanics and Machines'. In order to make the list complete a number of special contrivances and implements will be discussed here which were utilized in the constructional work. Above all there is the group of *levelling instruments* which

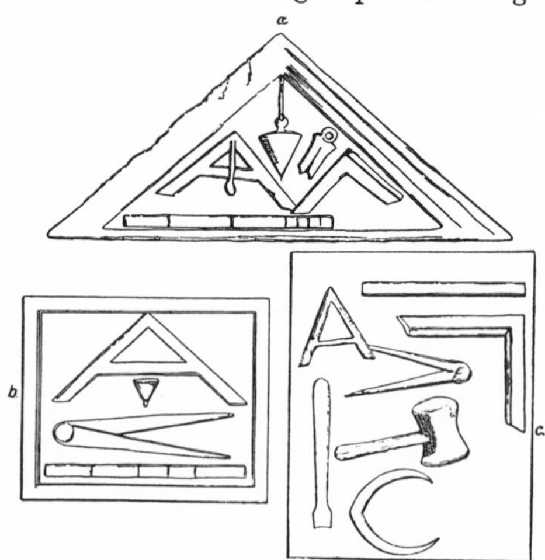

FIG. 536.—Tools of Roman Masons (from tombstones and doorplates)
a, Plummet (at the top); plumbline (on the left); compass (on the right at the top); set-square (on the right, below); ruler (at the bottom). *b*, Plumbline, plummet, compass and ruler. *c*, Jointing-rule (on the right above); level, set-square, compass, chisel, hammer and calipers. (Deutsches Museum, Munich)

served to determine the horizontal direction and were used in erecting houses as well as in laying out roads or constructing aqueducts. On the whole they were used in the same way as nowadays. The simplest of all ancient levelling instruments was the *groma*, which was the chief implement of the Roman surveyors. Remains of an ancient Roman groma have been found at Pfünz, near Eichstädt. It is identical with the cross described by Heron of Alexandria, which consisted of two arms placed at right angles in a horizontal plane. From the ends of the arms were suspended plummets. Heron draws attention to the errors caused by the arms of the instrument being placed otherwise than horizontally or by the winds. An advance on the groma is to be recognized in the *chorobates*, which is described by Vitruvius in the following words (VIII, 5):

FIG. 537.—Mason smoothing the Plastering on a Wall (mural painting at Pompeii)

The picture shows the scaffolding, the tool and the way in which it was used, two vessels and possibly the working clothes worn by masons

'The chorobates is a straight edge about twenty feet long. At the extremity it has legs made exactly alike and jointed on perpendiculars to the extremities of the straight-edge, and also cross-pieces, fastened by tenons, connecting the straight-edge and the legs. These cross-pieces have vertical lines drawn upon them, and there are plumblines hanging from the straight-edge over each of the lines. When the straight-edge is in position, and the plumblines strike both the lines alike and at the same time, they show that the instrument stands level. But if the wind interposes, and constant motion prevents any definite indication by the lines, then have a groove on the upper side, five feet long, one digit wide, and a digit and a half deep, and pour water into it. If the water comes up uniformly to the rims of the groove it will be known that the instrument is level. When the level is thus found by means of the chorobates, the amount of fall will also be known.'

(The last remark of Vitruvius is to be understood as a reference to the levelling of an aqueduct which he is describing.) The chorobates was thus nothing but a stool whose legs were connected with the seat by inclined struts (Fig. 535). The latter were provided with marks showing whether the plummets suspended from the edge of the board were vertical, in which case the surface of the levelling implement lay horizontal. Any deviations from the horizontal line could easily be ascertained. But the chorobates also allowed itself to be used as a water-level. From further remarks by Vitruvius, however, it is clear that the ordinary water-level, that is, a glass tube which is filled with water and contains an air-bubble, was also known and used as a levelling instrument.

There was yet another implement for sighting known to the ancients, namely the *diopter*, mentioned by Vitruvius and described by Heron of Alexandria. H. Schoene, with the help of an engineer, J. Neumann, has recently reconstructed it. Heron's diopter was a water-level, a well-known contrivance based on the principle of transmission of pressure in fluids by communicating vessels. It was however constructed in the form of a theodolite which allows a large or a small movement about a horizontal and a vertical axis. The diopter or dioptric rule was 6 ft. 2 in. long and was provided at both ends with an objective, an eye-piece and two pointers. For levelling purposes the dioptric rule was connected with a water-level. By means of this instrument and a system of rectangular co-ordinates, Heron mathematically solved the problem of 'piercing a mountain with a straight tunnel when the two entrances have been given.' Confident of success, Heron also promised that the workers advancing from both ends would meet in the middle of the mountain. But the example of the aqueduct at Samos (Fig. 572) shows that the instruments were not sufficiently accurate to allow the promise to be fulfilled; but it has not been proved that Eupalinos, the builder of the aqueduct, actually used the contrivance described by Heron.

FIG. 538.—The Tools of a Mason (from a Roman cinerary chest)

Trowel, plumb-level, carving chisel and a rake (below). Provincial Museum at Trèves

Other surveying instruments used by the ancient builders were the *plummet* and the *set-square*, both of which very much resemble the modern tools that serve the same purpose. The same is true of the mason's tools. The tombstones and doorplates (*insignia*) of ancient masons show the rake, the trowel, the brush, the plummet, the calipers and many other implements, all of which are very much like those used by modern bricklayers (Figs. 536, 537 and 538).

BUILDING MATERIALS

WOOD

OF the building materials of the ancients wood was the most important in the earliest times—as is clear from the statements of the last section. Almost all the sorts of wood were used that are still employed nowadays. Convenience often determined the choice. For example, for producing frames, particularly in Roman times, fir-wood was apparently used only because it happened to be more easily accessible than oak, which had to be fetched from a greater distance. Further, nobler sorts of wood were used for superior buildings as well as for panelling. Apart from this there is nothing further of importance to be said about wood as a building material. Concerning the manner of felling and working the wood, details are given in an earlier section. The Romans were among the first to use for their building wood that was impregnated so as to be fireproof. Aulus Gellius (about 150 A.D.) narrates in his *Attic Nights*, XV,[1] that when he was one day accompanying the orator Antonius Julianus home together with other members of his audience they passed a burning house. This led Julianus to refer in the course of conversation to the passage in the chronicles of Claudius Quadrigarius, in which Claudius relates that in the year 86 B.C. Athens was hard-pressed by Sulla in the struggle with Mithridates. Archelaus, the commander of Mithridates, in order to protect the Piraeus had a wooden tower built which, in spite of all attempts of the Romans to light it, would not burn. Archelaus had made it fireproof by saturating all the wood with alum (*ita Archelaus omnem materiam obleverat alumine*).

The ancients also knew how to provide against dry-rot, which, as we now know, results from an infection of the wood. They never seem to have been clear about its being connected with the wooden parts of the structure. Measures for countering it are contained in Chapter 14 of Leviticus. Since they are to be regarded as expedient, however, even from the view of our present-day knowledge, and since they can refer only to dry-rot, we shall quote the passage in question here. If in the land of Canaan a house bore the sign of 'leprosy', the priest had first to view the house.

> 'And he shall look on the plague, and, behold, if the plague be in the walls of the house with hollow strakes, greenish or reddish, and the appearance thereof be lower than the wall; then the priest shall go out of the house to the door of the house, and shut up the house seven days: and the priest shall come again the seventh day, and shall look: and, behold, if the plague be spread in the walls of the house; then the priest shall command that they take out the stones in which

---

[1] The story proves nothing for *Roman* use of this device, indeed the remarks of Julianus (*ibid.*) imply that it was not generally known.—*Trans.*

the plague is and cast them into an unclean place without the city: and he shall cause the house to be scraped within round about, and they shall pour out the mortar that they scrape off without the city into an unclean place.'

STONES

Stones formed the most important building material of antiquity—they were first probably collected singly wherever found; later, they were probably obtained from stone quarries in the manner described in the section on mining. The rule that material was in general collected

FIG. 539.—Gigantic Stone which has been transported for building purposes
(From the base of the Temple of Juppiter at Baalbek)

from whatever place in the vicinity it happened to occur, whereas definite sorts for particular purposes were fetched from greater distances, applies also to buildings of stone. For example, Tiryns was built from the limestone that occurs in its neighbourhood. In Rome there are stones from all parts of the Italian peninsula, but the majority are from quarries situated near by. In other places again sandstone is used. Everywhere the tendency to derive the stone from the nearest source is manifest. Even in ancient times the stones were burst apart and separated into smaller and larger ones by making lines of holes in them and placing wooden wedges into the holes; these wedges were made to swell by having water poured on them. Dörpfeld found such holes still in existence in the rocks at Tiryns. This primitive technique sufficed to break off stone blocks 2 to 3 yards long, 1 to 2 yds. in thickness and 1 yd. wide, which were used for building the town walls. The weight of some of these massive blocks amounts to nearly 20 tons. But they are by no means the largest produced by ancient craftsmen. The base of the temple of Juppiter at Baalbek contains stones of truly gigantic size. In the quarries situated in the vicinity shaped stones from the second century A.D. have been found; they are about 14 ft. wide, over 15 ft. in thickness, and no less than 23 yds. in length. Their weight amounts to nearly 1,000 tons (Figs. 539 and 540).

It would seem almost impossible to explain how such stones were moved away and raised to their height in the buildings if we did not

FIG. 540.—Shaped Stone in the Quarry of Baalbek
Length 23 yds., width 14 ft., thickness 15 ft., weight about 1,000 tons. After a photograph in the Deutsches Museum, Munich

know that at that time the work was performed by vast numbers of workmen far in excess of those employed in modern industry, in which the tendency is to replace human labour by machine work. In some cases huge blocks of stones of this kind were transported over wide stretches of land. In Ravenna we still see the grave of Theodoric, which was probably built about A.D. 520. It is covered by an enormous

FIG. 541.—The Tomb of Theodoric in Ravenna

cupola no less than 36 ft. in diameter (Fig. 541), made from a single stone. This stone was not extracted from the vicinity, but was probably transported from Istria by water. Thus it appears to have travelled long distances, in spite of its stupendous weight, before it arrived at its destination, where it again required the labour of many men, as well as the use of high platform-like structures, to enable it to be drawn up to its present position. Pillars 36 ft. high produced from one block are to be found in the remains of the avenue of pillars of Palmyra, and so we find everywhere traces of an antique art of working stones which was undaunted by the most gigantic tasks.

This art may be traced back to pre-history; it made use of very simple tools. Besides being broken up by the insertion of wooden pegs in holes, as mentioned above, the stones were also split by means of knives or blades, which in the beginning were made of wood, bone or horn. On account of their softness they were not sufficient to cut through the stone unaided, since they simply wore flat. For this purpose moist sand was strewn between them and the stone surface that was to be worked. Later on tools made of bronze were used, and, later again, tools made of hardened bronze, iron and steel. According to Flinders Petrie the ancient Egyptians were supposed to have used saw-blades whose edges were studded with jewels. There is no evidence of the use of such jewelled saws among the Romans, but there are indications that in dealing with very hard stone, such as granite, not only sand, but also steel-sand, that is, a mixture of sand and steel-filings, was strewn under the teeth of the slightly curved saw-blades.

FIG. 542.—The great Sea of Stone on the rocky mount of the Odenwald (granite)

FIG. 543.—Granite worked by the Romans at the 'Pyramid' in the Odenwald

We find evidence against the use of jewelled saws in the very narrow incision of half-finished stones that are still found; they lead us to conclude that a narrow saw-blade was used. The application of ordinary sand is also mentioned by Vitruvius (II, 7, 1) and Pliny (XXXVI, 51), while the remarks of Vitruvius make it clear that saw-blades without teeth were used for hard stones, while toothed saws were used for soft ones. Blümner also points out that Pliny mentions the use of sand, the best variety being supposed to come from Ethiopia. Indian sand, as well as sand from Naxos and Koptos, was too soft and therefore made the cutting much rougher.

FIG. 544.—The 'Altar-stone'. Front view
Lateral holes for the insertion of wedges

FIG. 545.—The Altar-stone. View from above
Saw-cuts and wedge-incisions in granite

The saws were first manipulated by hand, and later saw-mills were used, which were driven by water-power. The Gallic-Roman poet Decimus Magnus Ausonius (A.D. 310–396) in his poem 'Mosella', verse 359, sings the praises of the saw-mills situated in the valley of the Ruiver, in which the stone slabs for the buildings of the Imperial city of Trèves were cut out.

FIG. 546.—Huge block of granite, worked. In the vast collection of stones in the Odenwald

FIG. 547.—'Giant Pillar' on the stone mountain in the Odenwald
Roman work in granite

The slopes of the Odenwald, particularly the rocky hill about 1,700 ft. high, give us an exceptionally clear insight into the Roman art of working stone. They are covered with fragments of rock, from which the Roman masons procured their building material for the towns of Oppenheim, Mannheim, Mainz, Trèves, Wiesbaden and Aix-la-Chapelle. This source of stones was later deserted. The more or less completed stone slabs which we find lying around in these places to-day (Figs. 542–57) allow us to recognize important details in the ancient Roman method of working stone. The blocks are to be found in all stages of treatment. There is, for example, the 'Pyramid', which was split into three huge pieces by means of two horizontal rows of holes for the insertion of wedges. Then there is the 'Altar-stone', from which two blocks have already been removed for pillars. From the technical point of view

FIG. 548.—Egyptians working in Stone.
Using chisels and a stone, as a hammer. Smoothing with polishing stones and so forth

this one is the most interesting of all. Its length varies from 3 to 5 yards, its height is nearly 6 ft. Deep incisions cut with admirable accuracy by a saw indicate the intention of detaching still more blocks of 20 to 24 in. thickness. The saw-cuts were supplemented by holes into which wedges were inserted to split off the desired piece.

In this process the surface of fracture itself assumed a somewhat curved form which could be used to advantage when greater curvature was required. The saw-blade used for this purpose must have had a length of at least 15 ft., and have produced cuts only one-sixth of an inch wide, that is, not wider than the most modern frame-saw. Many other granite blocks show signs of having been worked. The so-called 'Giant Pillar' (Fig. 547), which lies at the higher end of the great multitude of stone on the way to the village of Reichenbach, is also very striking. Its length measures 30 ft., its thickness at the lower end 5 ft. 1 in., and at the upper, 4 ft. 1 in.; the volume is therefore well over 9 cubic yards and the weight about 15 tons. A second pillar, of nearly the same dimensions, but less finished, lies a short distance from it. In breaking off the pillars, the procedure consisted in marking the length of the pillar by means of deep incisions. Then a half of the pillar was worked to a state of completion. Along the sides of this half-column a deep furrow was chiselled in the block and numerous wedge-holes were made in the furrow. After inserting and saturating the wedges with water the back part of the pillar broke off in a convex shape, caused by the semicircular course of the lines of pressure due to the swollen wedges. This process was practised by the Egyptians and later by the Romans. As a rule the Greeks did not make their columns of monoliths but by superposing blocks in the form of discs, a method also applied by the Romans in some cases (for example, the Juppiter Column in Mainz).

When the blocks had been broken off and prepared in the manner described, the fine work was begun; that is, they were cut down to the right size, smoothed off and polished by exactly the same methods and with the same tools as we still use in general nowadays (Fig. 548).

BRICKS, ARTIFICIAL STONE AND ARTIFICIAL MATERIALS

Bricks used in ancient times were in many cases only dried in the sun or slightly burned. As a rule only the glazed bricks show signs of having been more intensively burned. Their colour varies within wide limits according to the clay used; almost all shades of colour occur from light yellow to dark red. All further details about their production are mentioned in the section on 'Ceramics'. The brick of antiquity has either a square form or the shape of a long rectangle, resembling those we make nowadays. The size varies greatly. As the art of building in bricks attained to a high degree of perfection, particularly among the Romans, great attention was naturally also given to the preparation of the bricks. Vitruvius (II, 3) describes in detail the properties which a good brick should have and also the forms in which it is best prepared. He points out that clay used for making bricks should be neither sandy nor stony nor gritty. It should be capable of being kneaded easily. The best materials are white chalky clay, red earth, or 'male', i.e. very firm and hard, sand. The bricks made from them are light and at the same time solid. He recommends spring or autumn as the time for making bricks, for then the drying out takes place slowly and uniformly. Care must be taken that the outer layer does not dry up while the interior is still wet. A good brick should dry for two years. If undried bricks are used for building they contract in the wall and work themselves loose from the plaster, which falls off. In those days the people of Utica (near Carthage) obtained official certification that their bricks had dried out for five years. Vitruvius knows of other kinds of bricks, of which one variety, the 'Lydian', was particularly used in Rome. The other two forms were usual in Greece. Vitruvius further mentions bricks that float on water, because the earth out of which they were made was a variety of pumice-stone.

The usual Roman brick is broader and flatter than ours and varies greatly in size. Its dimensions certainly do not keep within the limits of 18 in. length and 12 in. breadth given by Vitruvius. Most of the ancient Roman bricks are smaller. They are, however, more durable than the machine-made bricks of our day ; this is probably due to the fact that they were made by hand, and another reason is the dexterity of the brick-moulder. As a rule Roman bricks carry a stamp, either the mark of the manufacturer or the number of the legion whose soldiers had produced the bricks (Fig. 194). As it was necessary to keep the Roman army occupied in times of peace, in order that idleness would not lead to revolts and revolutions, soldiers who were not fighting were made to mould bricks or build roads or perform other works. (Further details of making bricks are given under the heading 'Ceramics'.)

Besides freestone and bricks the ancients in isolated cases also used artificial stone and other artificial material. Such stones have been found in the ruins of ancient Babylon. According to the analysis carried out by Rathgen they consist of 94 per cent. of quartz and are cemented together by a mixture of quartz, lime and magnesia into a sort of 'magma'. A further artificial substance was also known to the ancients which corresponds to our modern concrete or beton. It was especially used by the Romans. The basic substance for its production was the pozzolana which occurs at Puteoli [1] in the bay of Naples ; it is a volcanic clay consisting of clay and gravel, which, with the addition of burnt lime, could resist the action of water. For building in water, it was customary to mix two parts by weight of pozzolana with one part of ordinary mortar. The actual building was carried out by a process resembling that in use nowadays ; namely, the beton-mass (to which in some circumstances sand and chips of stone were added) was poured or stamped under moulds made of boards and there allowed to harden. Such beton was used for making conduit-pipes, parts of aqueducts, harbour works and so forth. The concrete or beton was used both in the form of ballast and in the form of hardened blocks which could be joined together. In the reign of Caligula a mole was built at Naples from such blocks. In the case of vaults made from freestone, concrete was used instead of pure mortar as a cement. It was poured into the gaps left in between the stones.

MORTARS AND CEMENTS

The mortars and other cements used in antiquity were of very diverse kinds. Herodotus knew of two methods that were used even by the old Babylonians to hold together stones in buildings. The first (II, 186) has already been mentioned several times and represents the method of forming junctions by means of iron and lead described in detail on page 386 ; the other (II, 179) consists of hot bitumen, that is, of asphalt. The excavations of Layard at the ruins of Nineveh and Babylon prove that the stones joined by asphalt have remained fixed together through thousands of years. This strong connection is due to the asphalt, having been applied hot to the stones, penetrating into

[1] Now called Pozzuoli.

them and so providing protection from weather influences. The asphalt used by the Babylonians was derived from the oil-wells on the Is, a tributary of the Euphrates. The more easily volatile constituents of the crude petroleum were allowed to vapourize so that the bitumen used in Babylonian buildings remained as a residue. The use of asphalt in Babylonian structures was known to the Romans; it is described, for example, by Pliny (XXXV, 178). Vitruvius (VIII, 3, 8) also describes asphalt and Pliny mentions it in another passage (V, 72). But in spite of this knowledge the Romans no longer used it as a cement.

On the other hand, it was still used in isolated instances by the Egyptians, who, however, for the great majority of their buildings, used the two principal cements of antiquity, gypsum and lime, as well as mixtures of both. As is clear from the discussion of the Egyptian drain-constructions (p. 439) a cement was used for fixing in the drain pipe; it consisted of 45·54 per cent. of gypsum and 41·36 per cent. of carbonate of lime, and contained, besides, 13·10 per cent. of insoluble components, mostly sharp-edged transparent particles of quartz and particles of siliceous substances. Lucas, on the basis of his analyses, has raised the question whether the ancient Egyptians were acquainted with a lime-cement mixed with sand, or whether they used only gypsum-mortar which contained lime carbonate as an impurity to varying degrees. Analyses of the gypsums obtained nowadays in Helwan favour the second suggestion, which receives further support from the fact that gypsum and lime regularly occur together in Egypt.

Other analyses of samples of mortars are available, which were taken some decades ago by Lepsius from the pyramids of Khofra (Chefren). Rathgen makes the following statements about these analyses, which he supplements with deductions of his own.

'Mortar from the pyramid of Khofra, index No. 1334. Gypsum mortar containing little lime, pieces of crystalline gypsum often 1 cm. long, and a few quartz particles mostly rounded off.

'Mortar from the pyramid of Khofra, index No. 1334. Lime mortar with many pieces of limestone and with very few sharp-edged particles of quartz and isolated fragments of crystalline gypsum.

'Mortar from the pyramid of Khofra, index No. 1342. Mixture of gypsum- and lime-mortar with pieces of crystalline gypsum and small amounts of particles of limestone and of quartz, mostly rounded off. The composition of this mortar from the pyramid of Khofra is quite similar to that of the mortar from the drain of the mortuary temple of Sahura (see page 440) and of the mortar from the Sphinx' (see page 346).

In the light of all this we may say that the Ancient Egyptians in general used gypsum as a mortar, of which the content of lime carbonate, when derived from quicklime, was mostly accidental, but that the use of gypsum containing lime may have caused them often to add further lime purposely to the gypsum before burning, and that under certain circumstances they even burned limestone alone. As a thinning agent they used small fragments of unburned gypsum and pieces of limestone, mostly probably in the form of grit from their workshops, which explains the small and varying amount of insoluble matter contained in the mortar.

The composition of Greek mortars is also known to us from analyses which show us that lime-mortars were chiefly used. For example, the stones of the orators' tribune built about 400 B.C. on the Pnyx, the meeting-place of the Athenian Assembly, were cemented together with a lime-mortar to which sand had been added. According to analysis this lime-mortar consisted of:

45·7 per cent. burnt lime,
37·0 per cent. carbonic acid,
12·0 per cent. sand,

and contined admixtures of magnesia, aluminium acetate and iron oxide which came from the lime and sand used. In the course of time the sand content of the mortar continually increased (see, for example, the prescriptions of Vitruvius below). Particularly noteworthy are Rathgen's researches on mortar from ancient Pergamon; this incidentally proves that the mortar is about 1,700 years old. The peculiarity of this mortar is that as a thinning agency for the lime there was added, besides the usual substances so used, that is, sand and gravel, also shells of mussels, a species of *murex*. As these shells also consisted of lime, the question naturally arises whether the basic substance of the mortar, the burnt lime, was not also obtained by burning these shells, or whether it was obtained in the usual way by burning lime. Since the shells also contained phosphoric acid, only its presence in the mortar could prove the assumption that shells were used. Analysis disclosed that the mortar contained some phosphoric acid, but to a somewhat higher percentage than the shells. This excess of phosphoric acid can be explained only by assuming that it is derived from the bodies of living mussels. From these results we may therefore infer that the lime for making the Pergamene mortar was obtained by collecting and burning the shells of mussels, among them being some which still contained the living or dead bodies. To the burnt lime there were added as thinning agents, besides sand and gravel, further shells from shell-fish which again partly contained the animal bodies. The phosphoric acid contained in these bodies then likewise became mixed with the mortar so that its percentage of phosphoric acid was greater than that of the shells used in its production.

Roman mortars were similarly lime-mortars in the main. Concerning their production Vitruvius (II, 51) states that good lime should be made by burning white building-stone or flint. That made from dense and hard stone was advantageous for the brickwork, that made from porous stone was better for the outer coating or plaster. The mixture of lime with sand was to be in the ratio of three parts of sand to one of lime in the case of pit-sand, whereas in that of river- or sea-sand a third part of powdered and sifted shells was to be added, and the proportion of sand and lime to be as two to one.

The burning of the lime took place in limekilns, which, according to Cato (*de agri cult.* XXXVIII, 1), were to be underground in pits specially dug, to exclude the wind. If the hollow could not be made deep enough (the kiln was to be 20 (Roman) ft. high, 10 ft. wide at the bottom, and 3 ft. at the top; 1 Roman foot = 11¾ in.), a border of bricks or ashlar was placed on top, which was pointed with clay. One or two fire-holes could be made. We are here again dealing with a type of oven still extant in distant regions which once stood under Roman rule or in neighbouring parts. They have remained preserved in a

FIG. 549

FIG. 550

FIG. 551

FIGS. 549–551.—Lime-kiln in the Val di Gardena (Fig. 549, from the front; Fig. 550, from the side; Fig. 551, from above)

The limekiln (see Fig. 551), built into the foot of a hill, consists of rough stones arranged in layers to a small height. It is filled with wood or wood-charcoal, and then ignited. Flames come out at the top. After being fired, the burnt lime is removed through the front aperture

particularly typical form, for example, in the Val di Gardena, where we encounter besides the language many other relics of ancient Roman civilization (Figs. 549–551).

The slaking of the lime, that is, the mixing of the mortar, took place in special pits with the help of a kind of rake (*ascia*) which resembled that still used nowadays. To apply it a trowel was used, likewise resembling the modern form. (See the Figs. on pp. 395 and 396).

Besides lime-mortar the Romans also used hydraulic mortars or cements, that is, mortars that harden under water. Their most important hydraulic mortar was the pozzolana, already mentioned above (p. 404). But they were also acquainted with Babylonian cement from the plain stretching out west of the Euphrates; the Babylonians had early used this cement with an admixture of ashes for building their wells. But in other parts of the world, too, builders had an expert eye for discerning the kinds of stone from which hydraulic mortar could be produced. Stone of this sort they found, for example, in the trasses of the Eifel, the Moselle, the Nette and the Brohl valleys, as well as in the Ries district near Nördlingen. The trasses of the Eifel played an important part in the magnificent waterworks of Cologne built in the reigns of the emperors Trajan (A.D. 98–117) and Hadrian (A.D. 117–138); they ended where the Cologne Cathedral now stands, and served to supply various Roman fortifications with water besides Cologne (*Colonia Agrippinensis*). The mortar of this Roman canal is of a wonderful hardness and rigidity. As proved by blasting operations it is even harder than the natural rock. This rigidity has given rise to all sorts of foolish ideas, such as, for example, that the Romans had special secrets about making mortar, and that they used white sugar, wine, common salt and like substances as additional ingredients! Recently, numerous analyses of the mortar from the Eifel canal of the Romans have been carried out by the Prussian Testing Department for Materials (Materialprüfungsamt), by Lüttgen, Hambloch, Kiepenheuer, and others. The trass was prepared for the production of mortar by simply grinding the tufa from the Eifel. At other points of the long aqueduct, which were too far for transporting the trass, a calcareous marl was used for preparing the hydraulic mortar; this marl contained silicon dioxide and argillaceous earth as water-resisting constituents, which entered into combination with limestone, forming a compound which, like the trass, hardened in water. The hydraulic mortar obtained from lime-marl, the so-called 'water-lime of the Eifel', was produced by mixing one part of this water-lime with 3 to $4\frac{1}{2}$ parts of coarse sand. The red outer coating consists of water-lime from the Eifel with brick-dust and fragments of brick admixed. It was applied to a thickness varying from $\frac{4}{50}$ to $\frac{4}{10}$ of an inch.

In general the Romans seem not to have used gypsum as a mortar.

WATER-SUPPLY

LIKE the animals, so also Man had once upon a time to set out in quest of water to satisfy his thirst. Streams, lakes and springs were at his disposal. They have the common failing, however, of drying up at times. This gave rise to the most primitive method of water-supply, scraping to reach the precious moisture that had filtered away. Haberlandt has proved that the digging up of sand represents a method still practised nowadays by the aboriginals of Australia for obtaining water artificially. By a development of these 'soakages' in the sub-soil of dried-up beds of rivers the wells dug out of sand or soft stone arose. In soil particularly poor in its water-content there is a further technical development, according to Haberlandt's researches in Australia; it is the suction-tube, which, however, occurs here in a very simple form: a hole is made by driving a spear deep into the ground, a clump of dried grass is inserted into the hole to serve as a protective covering, through the middle of which a hollow reed is thrust; the water is then sucked up through this reed. As Haberlandt has proved that similar devices are in use among the Hottentots and the Bushmen of South Africa, and also among the inhabitants of Tierra del Fuego, and since according to a generally accepted theory the stages of development of mankind in its first beginnings resemble those of the present-day primitive races, we may also assume that in the case of water-supply, soak-holes were followed by wells, and that suction-pipes were a still later development.

WATER-SUPPLY IN THE EAST

In proportion as settlement increased the demands for improved methods of water-supply became more pressing. The importance of water was recognized and efforts were made to conduct it to settlements by means of special constructions in cases where great natural sources were not at hand. So the first aqueducts arose, which consisted of artificially constructed trenches, more or less inclined; these were at first uncovered at the top and conducted the water to the desired spot. Water was then simply scooped out as required. To facilitate this, special basins were made in the watercourse.

An ancient aqueduct of this kind, consisting of a trench with scooping basins, was discovered by Layard in his researches in ancient Assyria: it is situated in a gorge at Bavian. Layard writes: 'Higher up in the gorge I also had the earth removed and I found a row of water-basins hewn out of the rock, which led in steps down to the river.

The water had originally been conducted from one basin to the next by little gutters; at the mouth of the lowest basin two lions rampant in relief had been erected as ornaments (Fig. 552). We cleaned out the choked gutters, poured water into the uppermost basin, and so restored the water-service to what it had been in the time of the Assyrians.' Water was also supplied to Nineveh by means of open canals, which first collected the water from many places, and then conducted it to the town, where they again branched off along the different streets. Apparently no indisputable relics of this construction have been established, but an inscription concerning them which is contained in one of the rock-pictures at Bavian, and has been translated by Hincks, gives us some information about them. It states that these waterworks were constructed by Sennacherib, that is, about the turn of the eighth and seventh centuries B.C. 'From eighteen districts or villages', it says, 'he led eighteen canals to the Ussur or Khusur, in which he collected their water. He also dug a canal from the boundaries of the town or of the district of Kisri as far as Nineveh, conducted the water through it and called it the canal of Sennacherib.' We frequently find similar constructions in the ancient East. How extensive these trench-systems were commonly made is related by Herodotus (II, 188 *et seq.*), who says that Cyrus, during his march to Babylon, had three hundred and sixty trenches dug out leading from the River Gyndes, in order, so it is alleged, to revenge himself on this stream which had swept away his horse. The rest of Herodotus' description, however, makes it clear that Cyrus was only waiting for the more favourable season in order to advance on Babylon and that he probably had a water-system constructed there for his army, which was encamped in that neighbourhood for nearly a year, according to the same account. Further, an old relief in the British Museum derived from the Palace of Kujundschik[1] shows us how the water is distributed through these trenches. It appears that this water-system served to supply the needs of the palace, and after its passage was used to water the gardens. The side-canals branch off at a fairly acute angle from the main canal.

FIG. 552.—Lowest Water-basin of the ancient Assyrian aqueduct in the gorge at Bavian

The trenches were not always dug out of the ground but were also cut out of rock, as, for example, in the case of the River Zāb and its tributary Ghâzit. The canal is 28 miles long and 44 ft. deep in places, and has been hewn out of hard shell-limestone. Sometimes channels were built up with masonry. One of these is to be found at Damascus. It cannot, however, be stated with certainty that it belongs to antiquity. In view of the high degree of perfection attained in ceramics in Mesopo-

[1] Also written Kuyunyik.

tamia (see the section on Ceramics) it is rather surprising that clay-pipes have not been found more often as water-pipes. But, as pointed out by Merckel, in isolated instances, for example, at Senjirli, such tubes have been found having a length of 12 in., diameter of $4\frac{1}{2}$ in., and a wall $\frac{4}{5}$ in. thick. On the one side they had a rabbet, on the other a cusp 2 in. long which had been thrust into the rabbet to prevent relative change of position. At the points of contact the pipes are joined tightly with clay. A particularly noteworthy feature of this water-system is the fact that it rises vertically at one point, and then descends again. At the time of construction, then (probably about the sixth or fifth century B.C.), it must have been known in the country which we now call Kurdistan, that the pressure of water was able to overcome differences of level. Besides water-systems, there are in Mesopotamia also wells, often of considerable depth, which, however, exhibit no technical characteristics worthy of comment. Water was drawn from them by means of buckets with the use of blocks and pulleys (Merckel).

The systems of water-supply organized by the Jews are of unusual interest; among them is that of King Solomon (1018–978 B.C.), which has recently been partly restored, and, as once upon a time, supplies a part of Jerusalem with water. The great reservoirs which King Solomon had constructed in the hills of Judah are to be counted among the greatest of all the technical achievements of antiquity, and manifest a definite knowledge of the laws of water-pressure. Like the above-mentioned ancient Babylonian aqueduct they served a double purpose: water-supply and irrigation. This is clear from the Bible; for in Ecclesiastes (ii. 6) we read: 'I made me pools of water, to water therewith the wood that bringeth forth trees.'

The source of Solomon's water-system lies to the south-west of Jerusalem and is a little higher than the city. The water here collected was led into three great artificial reservoirs situated one above the other, which had been built in a hollow of the valley. The highest was rectangular in form and almost square; the middle one showed the form of an elongated trapezium; the lowest, which was divided into two parts by a transverse wall, was an elongated rectangle. The reservoirs are large and, in comparison with their length of 120 to 160 yds., rather shallow basins, whose depths however vary between 27 and 63 ft. The water comes partly from the source mentioned just above, and partly from the four springs at the reservoirs themselves, which had all been enclosed. At first only the springs appear to have served to supply Jerusalem with water; their contents were stored in the reservoir and drawn off according to requirements. When the supply was no longer sufficient, further steps were taken, and the water from the source to the south-west of Jerusalem was fed into the reservoirs. On the side of the uppermost reservoir there is a water-chamber or water-tower, that is, an overhead cistern for collecting the water. This cistern was fed by one spring. It could either be emptied directly into the aqueduct leading into the town or used to fill the highest reservoir. Between this reservoir and the tower there is a structure which served to regulate the inflow of water. In it the water from a second spring collected; it was led in by a subterranean channel. This water could also be emptied either directly into the main water-channel or into the reservoir above. From the last-mentioned spring ('Ain-es-Sâleh), however, there is a branch channel to the lower reservoir, which is fed by a spring ('Ain-Farûjeh) underneath it. The water from 'Ain-es-Sâleh, together with that from 'Ain-Farûjeh, and also from a third spring ('Ain 'Atan), first flows into a basin built into the massive dam-weir that forms the end of the lower reservoir. From here the 'lower water-system' leads to Jerusalem, Bethlehem, and the ancient Herodium,[1] which were thus all supplied by these reservoirs (Fig. 553–565).

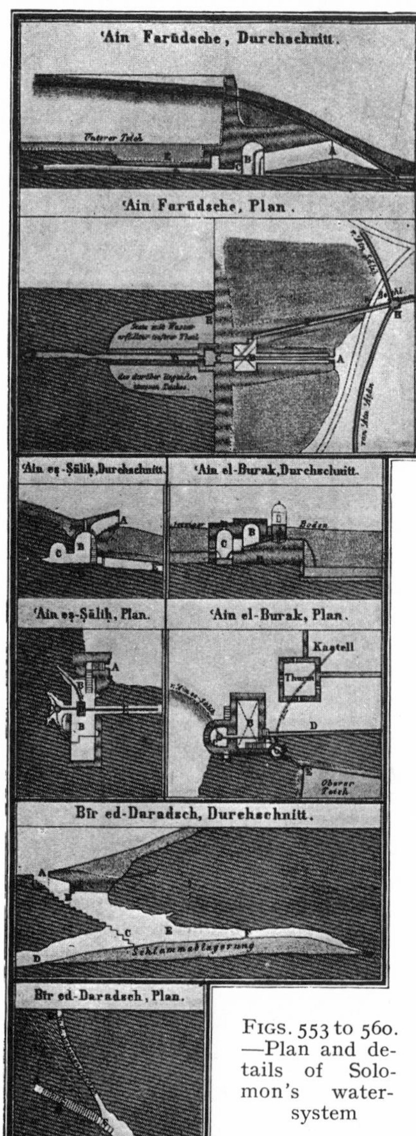

FIGS. 553 to 560. —Plan and details of Solomon's water-system

Whereas the springs, as we see, poured their waters into the immediately adjacent reservoirs, subterranean channels being used throughout this process, special aqueducts had to be constructed to admit the water from the other local sources. There are two of these, of which the one comes from the valley Wady el-Biyar, whereas the other serves to conduct the water from the valley Wady el 'Arrub. The former, which has a fairly straight course, is worthy of remark because it is partially constructed as a tunnel. The channel, which is up to 2 ft. wide and fairly deep, passes under the ridge of a hill. It is provided at the top with nine air-shafts leading to the surface. This proves that it had already been recognized at that early date that all spring water contains air. The air collects in the interior of the conduits in the form of large bubbles and has to be removed by special air-removing contrivances. If this is not done, various interruptions in the conduction as well as in the drawing off of the water may occur. The constructions made

[1] Now Jebel Fereidis, Frank Mountain. For this and other places mentioned in this section see *Atlas of the Historical Geography of the Holy Land* (Hodder & Stoughton).

here for this purpose are probably the oldest that we know. It appears, however, that—at least in the time of King Solomon—men were averse from building tunnels; later, under King Hezekiah, things changed. At any rate tunnels were deliberately avoided in the water-system leading from the valley of Wady el 'Arrub, and the builders preferred to conduct the pipes around all the hills and along the valleys, instead of piercing them. In the aqueduct of Wady el 'Arrub there is only one tunnel; it has three ventilation holes and passes through the hill Sahl-Tekoa. In consequence of this absence of tunnels the aqueduct is very long and circuitous. The bed of the channel is sometimes constructed of masonry and sometimes hewn out of the solid rock; at one point it is supported on a bridge.

Like the water from the springs, so the water from these aqueducts could be conducted either directly to the town or fed into the reservoirs, the distribution being such that the aqueduct from Wady el-Biyar led to the uppermost reservoir, and that from Wady el 'Arrub to the two lower reservoirs. If we survey the whole system, we see that the water could either be conducted straight to the towns to be supplied or could be filled into one or more reservoirs whence it could be drawn at will. The whole construction permitted the water to be regulated and distributed over a wide area.

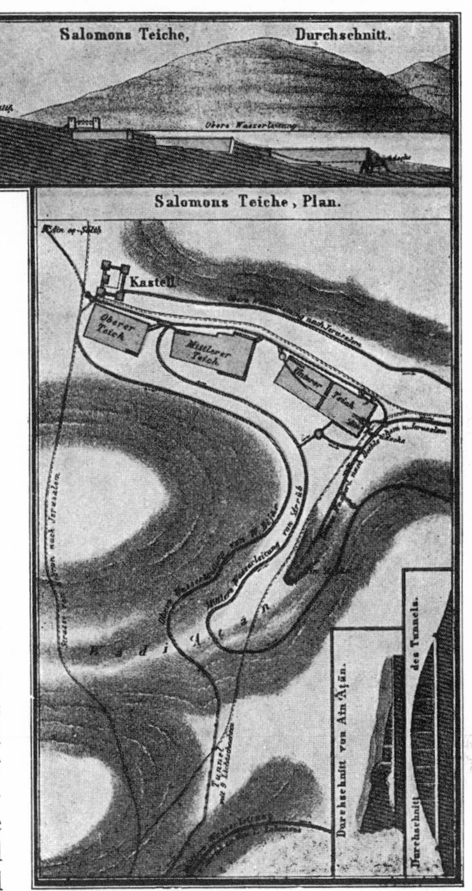

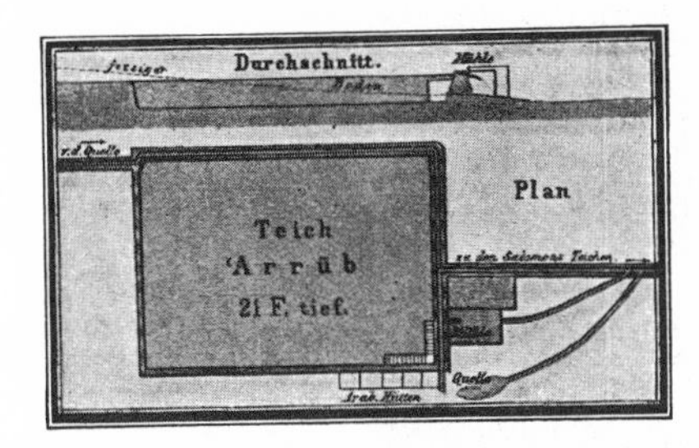

FIGS. 561 to 565.—Plan and details of Solomon's Water-system

More recently, as reported by Huntemüller, further aqueducts have been discovered, namely those of 'Ain Khurwa'ah (to a length of over half a mile) and of Wady

FIG. 566.—Solomon's Water-system
Stone reservoir in Wady el 'Arrub

FIG. 567.—The Water-supply of Jerusalem
Wady Artâs. Bethlehem in the background. View of Solomon's aqueduct and the elevated conduits

ed-Deir; they are of Roman origin, and the former shows a Roman water-chamber. These water-channels also conducted their water, which had been derived from a common aqueduct, to the old reservoirs of Solomon. There are also numerous traces of Roman works in the other valleys and, indeed, in the course of time more and more springs were exploited to supply Jerusalem with water (Figs. 553–569).

Fig. 568.—The Water-supply of Jerusalem
Water-conduit in Wadi el Choch (with Bedouins' tents alongside)

The members of the Palestine Exploration Fund have been foremost in showing that three massively built aqueducts led from these reservoirs to Jerusalem, Bethlehem and Herodium, one of which was completely hidden. The so-called 'lower' of the two other aqueducts was constructed by Herod (37–4 B.C.). The so-called 'high' one is noteworthy because of its being constructed in part of stone pipes. These pipes were made from blocks of stone and had a bore of nearly 2 in. At the points of contact each block had a groove into which a projection from the next block fitted. By this device the pipes were held together and kept in their respective positions. The junctions were coated with clay. Since the aqueduct passes over the ridge of a hill, the builders already knew how to make use of the pressure of water to overcome such obstacles. The 'lower' conduit conducted water through tunnels at two places. Later, when improvements were made, it was conducted through clay pipes.

FIG. 569.—Jerusalem's Water-system
Ancient Roman aqueduct just below the reservoir-dam at Wady el-Biyar

The water used in the town was drained off by channels whose course has not yet, however, been fully laid bare.

The ancient aqueduct of Solomon has been restored by the Greek engineer Franghia; it was found possible to use considerable parts of the old system, in particular the conduit of pipes. They end in the mosque of Omar, which stands to-day on the site of Solomon's temple, into the front porch of which the two old aqueducts led. Besides providing the fountain of the mosque of Omar with water, which may be used only by Mohammedans, this most ancient of all water-systems, still in action, also feeds a second fountain which is for the use of people of other creeds.

Much credit is also due to King Hezekiah for his efforts to supply Jerusalem with water; in particular, he built a tunnel which nowadays still reçeives the water of the Siloah spring. This tunnel is 1,776 ft. long, and has a curved shape approximately like a capital **S**. In 1888 some children who were bathing there discovered an ancient Hebrew inscription, which may be rendered thus:

> 'When three cubits were still left to be pierced the voice of one was heard calling to another; for there was a cleft in the rock from the south side. And on the day on which the boring was finished, the stone-cutters struck one towards the other, pick against pick. Thereupon the waters flowed from the entrance to the reservoir, 1,200 cubits away. And the height of the rock above the heads of the stone-cutters was 100 cubits.'

It has not been found possible to decipher all the parts of this inscription. Apart from the sentences just quoted only a few words of the remainder can be made out, which seem to indicate that, among other tools, chisels were also used in making the tunnel. The tunnel itself is 24 to 32 in. wide; it is 2 yds. wide at the north exit and decreases to 18 in. in the middle. Towards the south side it increases to over 3 yds. The fall of the water is very slight, being only 12 in. The peculiar shape of the tunnel and other traces allow us still to determine where the workmen who advanced from opposite sides must have encountered one another (Fig. 570). It must certainly be regarded as a masterly achievement of technical science at that time to have started a tunnel of such length and of a curvilinear shape from opposite ends and to have directed the workmen in such a way that the two sections exactly met. A task of this kind would present certain difficulties even in our day. Unfortunately we do not know how the problem of getting the right direction for the two parts was solved.

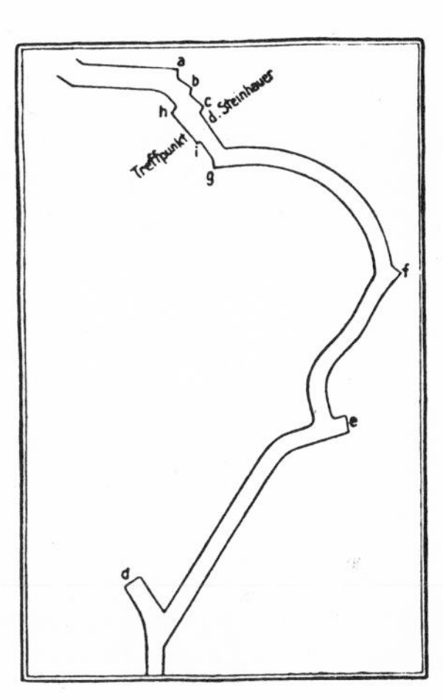

FIG. 570.—The Siloah Tunnel and the 'Meeting-point'

At the meeting-point it is seen that the course was wrong on several occasions but that it was soon given up and the error was improved upon, until finally, probably guided by sound, the workmen made the ends meet exactly

The water from these ancient systems of the East was not distributed among the houses of the town but was conducted to public fountains from which the desired water was fetched. The nature of these fountains is not precisely known.

WATER-SUPPLY AMONG THE EGYPTIANS

In consequence of the character of their country, the Egyptians had in the first place no choice but to construct wells, as there were various obstacles in the way of building aqueducts, namely the poor supply of springs and watercourses with sufficiently strong gradients, and the flatness of the ground. Even at an early date, therefore, wells were dug, particularly in the oases of the deserts, and were continued down to water-level; to provide against collapse the inner walls were lined with wood along the length that passed through the desert sand. The woodwork thus extended to a depth of 20 to 30 yards. The lower part of the well was less wide and was cut through the underlying rock often to a depth of 160-180 yards. Some of these wells are very deep; they were so famous in antiquity that they are mentioned by many writers, for example, by Strabo, but technical details are not given.

FIG. 571.—Egyptian Sakia with a Windlass

In the course of time water-systems were built by which Nile water was conducted to the towns. An aqueduct of this sort was built in Alexandria, for example, not by the Egyptians, however, but by the Greeks. As the water-level of the Nile lay deeper than the towns to be supplied, the water could be conducted to the towns only at the times when the Nile was in flood. The locks of the canals leading to them were then opened and the water flowed into the cisterns in the centre of the town and filled them. Alexandria had 360 such cisterns, many being four stories high. From them the water flowed into the wells, from which it was drawn at will. If water was required at other times when the Nile stood at a low level, it was raised by artificial means with the help of the sakia, as is still done nowadays. The sakia, of which we have also a description by Vitruvius (X, 4, 3), consisted of a vertical wheel over which ran ropes made of palm bast with buckets attached. When the wheel was turned the empty dippers on the one side descended into the water, while those on the other side ascended full and emptied their contents into a drain. The wheel was turned by a winch (see the section on 'Technical Mechanics and Machines'); it was kept in motion by an ox or a camel which walked in a circle day and night (Fig. 571). This device for scooping and raising water was in practice in ancient times, and has remained in use unchanged up to the present day, but it now serves only purposes of irrigation, as the transport of water for the water-system is performed with the help of steam pumps.

(Concerning another means of raising water, the *shadooff*, used by the Egyptians, see p. 203.)

WATER-SUPPLY AMONG THE GREEKS

Among all the peoples of antiquity the Greeks appear to have been the first to recognize the value and far-reaching importance of a good water-supply, and especially of a distributing centre that served the whole life of a community. Even in the most ancient seats of their civilization, as at Mycenae, we find traces of ancient water-systems. In all the towns there are numerous fountains, often of very artistic design, which proves with what religious respect the Greeks treated their water-supply. The hygienic value of water had also been estimated at its true value, and Aristotle refers to the great importance of a good supply of drinking water for public health. From ancient times the traditional feeling had been passed down that water to be used for human consumption was not to be polluted in any way, and was therefore not to be used for other purposes. The reverence with which springs were generally regarded is expressed in an emphatic form by the fact that the washing of clothes in them was considered a serious offence. The fountains were specially guarded and their use was regulated by special laws.

Before the system of a central supply was adopted, that is before water-mains were constructed to provide water for whole cities and communities, it was probably the usual custom for individuals to look after the various supplies. This was not universal, however, as not every section of land had water on it. For those inhabitants who did not strike water even at a given depth the use of public wells was allowed by a law made by Solon in the sixth century B.C. These wells were at first either merely dug out of the ground or were cisterns or tapped springs. Above many of an early date we find spring-houses of which the purpose was to prevent dust, dirt, and so forth from falling in. There are no special technical features in these primitive constructions.

The oldest known water-system of Greece is that of Mycenae, already mentioned above. Its whole mode of construction shows that the Greeks of that time did not yet know how to turn water-pressure to advantage. The system was to supply the fort of Mycenae with water. It was also, however, to remain concealed from the enemy, whose existence played a determining part in the planning of many such systems in antiquity, as every effort had to be made to deprive him of the possibility of cutting off or poisoning the supply of water. That is why many ancient water-mains are underground. That of Mycenae also runs underground where it goes beyond the walls and conducts the water from a spring into the well, which can be reached by the fort also by a subterranean channel. How the water could be conducted up to the fort was not yet understood.

Among the water-systems of antiquity that of Samos was particularly famous. It was probably constructed at the time of Polykrates (535–522 B.C.) by Eupalinos of Megara ; it was distinguished by the fact that the water passed below the bottom of a tunnel driven through a hill, which was over half a mile long. From here pipes branched off to the town. Recently this ancient construction has been more carefully investigated and it has become clear how competently the work was done. Between ancient and modern water-systems there is a fundamental difference with respect to the distribution of the water. Nowadays we have a reservoir from which the water is conducted to the town by a main. From this main there are branches to the individual streets and again subsidiary branches from these to the individual houses. The antique water-systems also had reservoirs, but no mains. Rather, the water flowed from the collecting centre, the water-tower (see below : the water-systems of the Romans), along individual aqueducts in approximately radial directions to the different parts of the town. At the end of each of these aqueducts there was another container as a rule, from which another set of aqueducts radiated out to the places of supply, that is to fountains and so forth. If, therefore, a water-system was to be constructed at Samos or in other towns, it was necessary to choose as the radiating centre of the distributing network a point from which the aqueducts could conveniently branch off to the individual parts of the town. Such a point lay on the heights of the southern side of a hill which surrounded the town. This formed the southern end of the tunnel. For the northern point another spot was chosen which made it possible conveniently to get rid of the great quantities of rubbish that accumulated in building the tunnel. A suitable point for this purpose was found on a rocky slope down which the dirt and fragments of stone could easily be thrown. In this way the two directional points for the tunnel were fixed. The next problem was to connect it with the source in such a way that an enemy threatening the town would observe no sign of the presence of the aqueduct. The aqueduct was therefore constructed underground and was even made to pass underneath the bed of a rivulet. This particular aqueduct is curved and is 920 yds. long. It starts from a reservoir in which spring water was collected. The reservoir is covered by a shed having a roof which is supported by fifteen pillars. The connection between the reservoir-shed and the entrance to the tunnel was made by the above-mentioned subterranean passage, which was about $5\frac{1}{2}$ ft. high and $1\frac{1}{2}$ ft. wide. The water flows along the bottom of this channel in a gutter covered with stone plates. In the tunnel itself the water was probably conducted along clay pipes ; at least such have been discovered. It is not, however, certain whether they were used in the actual construction of the tunnel or only afterwards. These pipes are partly circular and partly square in cross-section ; when square, they probably served merely to line the gutter. They were then probably covered by stone or clay plates. Of the circular pipes every second one was perforated at the top, probably in order to furnish a means of ventilation (Fig. 572).

The tunnel appears to have been started, like that of Siloah, from both ends simultaneously. We are led to this conclusion by a very uneven part in the middle of it, which shows that the junction was effected closely enough but not quite so accurately as in the case of the tunnel of Siloah. The northern section came up so high that it made its appearance above the roof of the southern section of the tunnel, the difference of level being over three feet. The floor of the northern section was therefore deepened to smooth out the passage. In order to proceed as rapidly as possible with the work the soil and fragments of stone were not removed through the tunnel itself, but special shafts were sunk for the purpose. In the walls of the tunnel there are niches in which the oil-lamps of the workmen were placed during their work. Whenever the solidity of the natural stone was not trusted the tunnel was lined with masonry.

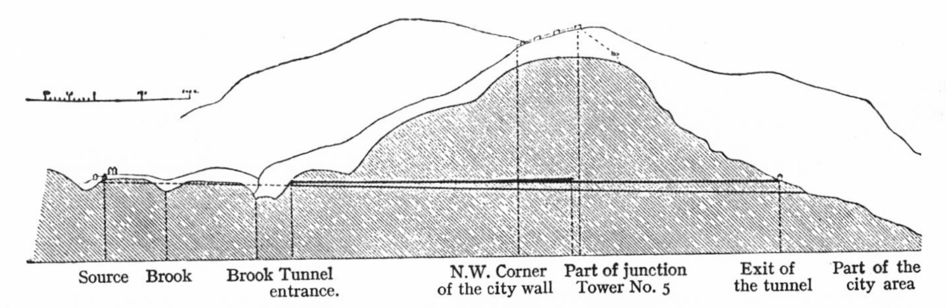

FIG. 572.—The Aqueduct of Samos

In the interior the water ran into a pit which lay below the floor of the tunnel. It entered the tunnel through a subterranean passage and was also conducted on to the town in the same way. The pit was connected with the tunnel by shafts. At certain distances it had a special covering of stone slabs and was then filled up to the floor of the tunnel, so that by filling the pit in this way the trouble of removing the dirt from the tunnel could be saved. This pit has the remarkable property of lying only a little over 6 ft. below the floor of the tunnel at its commencement, whereas in the vicinity of the opening of the tunnel towards the town its depth is 25 ft. below the floor. Thus the pit loses in height with respect to the tunnel to the extent of about 19 ft. This is probably due to the inability to determine with sufficient accuracy the level of the points chosen for the ends of the tunnel. When the tunnel was finished, then, the gradient was too small. Therefore the pit was constructed under its floor with a steeper gradient and served as the true aqueduct. Herodotus (III, 30) gives the following description of the water-service of Samos, which enjoyed great fame in antiquity :

'I have written thus at length of the Samians, because they are the makers of the three greatest works to be seen in any Greek land. First of these is the double-mouthed channel pierced for an hundred and fifty fathoms through the base of a high hill; the whole channel is seven furlongs long, eight feet high and eight feet wide; and throughout the whole of its length there runs another channel twenty cubits deep and three feet wide, wherethrough the water coming from an abundant spring is carried by its pipes to the city of Samos. The designer of this work was Eupalinus, son of Naustrophus, a Megarian.' [1]

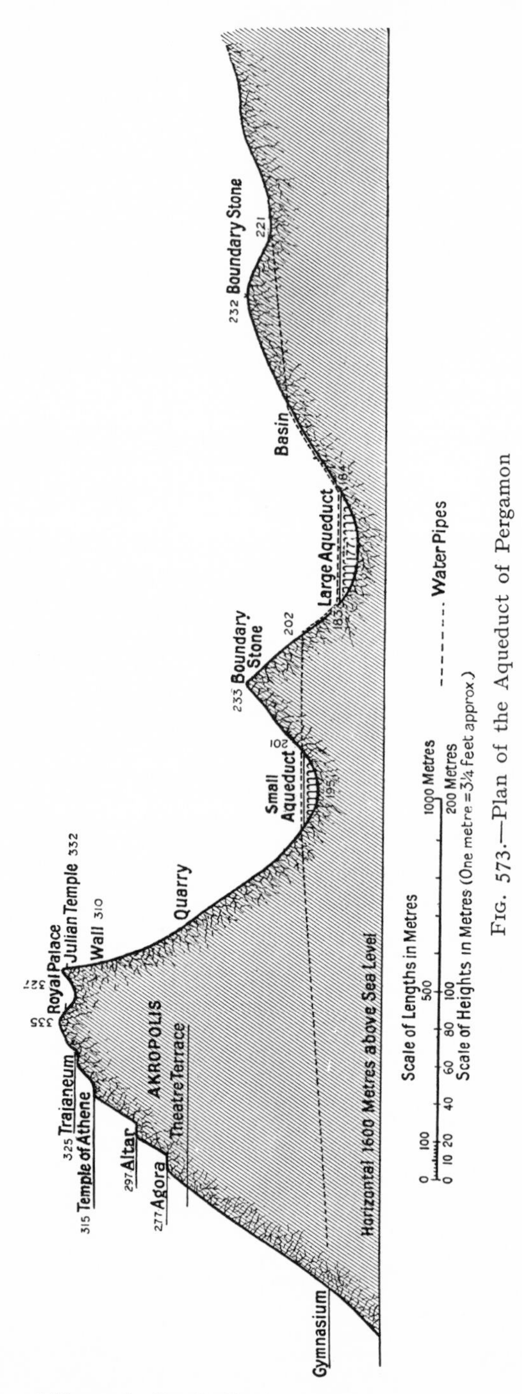

FIG. 573.—Plan of the Aqueduct of Pergamon

Still more remarkable than the aqueduct of Samos is that of Pergamon, presumably constructed about 200 B.C.; for it is a hydraulic aqueduct, whereas that of Samos is based only on the fall of water along a gradient. Difficult technical problems had to be solved in this case. As has been rightly remarked by Gräber, 'the construction of this subterranean aqueduct gives us a conception of the high importance of this ancient town'. The date at which this channel was constructed is not determinable. The water conducted along it had to be raised to a cistern 369 ft. above sea-level. To make this possible, the distributing reservoir (or high-level service tank) had to be placed at a still higher point. According to Giebeler its remains are found at a height of 408 yards on Mount Hagios Georgios. From this point the aqueduct descends to two deep valleys separated by a hilly ridge; these valleys lie 213 and 191 yds. above sea-level, respectively; it then ascends again to the supply station at the higher point. So these two valleys or else the ridges between them had to be overcome with the agency of water-pressure. The maximum

[1] From A. D. Godley's translation (The Loeb Classical Library, Heinemann).

pressure in the aqueduct therefore amounted to a column of water 408 − 191 = 217 yds. high, that is, about 20 atmospheres (Fig. 573).

Gräber, who first assumed that lead pipes were used, later conjectured that the pipes were made of 'brass', that is, of copper or bronze—a surmise to which various objections of an historical and also metallurgical kind may be raised. Dörpfeld, in a letter to the author, considers that a wooden pipe is not improbable. The author is inclined to share this opinion, as wooden pipes can withstand great pressures, were widely used in antiquity, are easily made, and can be joined and rendered watertight without difficulty. Nevertheless it is not out of the question that clay pipes were used, at least in the town. Such clay pipes have been found in the main street that leads upwards from the Eumenian encircling wall. Further clay pipes were found in use as a means of communication to the bathroom of the upper gymnasium. They lay in a rock channel and their height reached midway up the wall. From here the water was conducted in metallic pipes to above the baths. As the Romans later built a second aqueduct in Pergamon, although only for the lower town, it may appear doubtful whether this pipe was not first put in by them. These pipes have never been tested to see whether they are able to withstand the pressure supposed to prevail there—so far as they lie in the upper gymnasium. Presumably they all lay in the perforated stones (Fig. 574) that stand on their edges at distances of about 4 ft. from each other in a trench. These stones are 4 to 5 ft. long, 24 to 27 in. wide, 8 to 10 in.

Fig. 574.—Perforated Stones of the Aqueduct of Pergamon

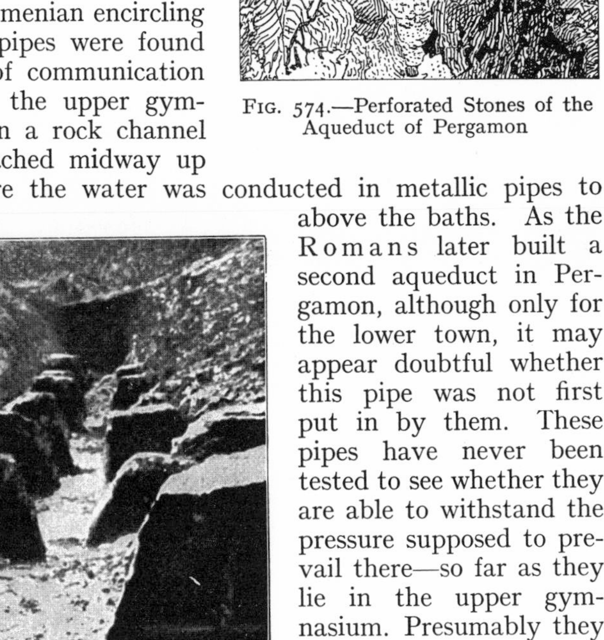

Fig. 575.—Remains of the Aqueduct of Pergamon

thick, and have a hole in the centre. In their present state the upper rim is often broken away. The hole is one foot in diameter. In the later Roman aqueduct such perforated stones 24 to 33 ft. long and with holes $9\frac{1}{2}$ in. in diameter were used. They used to lie on the aqueducts by which the Romans bridged over the above-

FIG. 576.—Remains of the Reservoir of the ancient Aqueduct of Pergamon

mentioned depressions 213 and 191 yds. above sea-level. The Roman pipes circumvent the ridge between the two aqueducts, whereas the Greek pipes lead over it. In the same way the Roman pipes wind their way round a second hill 259 yds. above sea-level—a sign that the pressure was too low to overcome these heights, over which the Greek

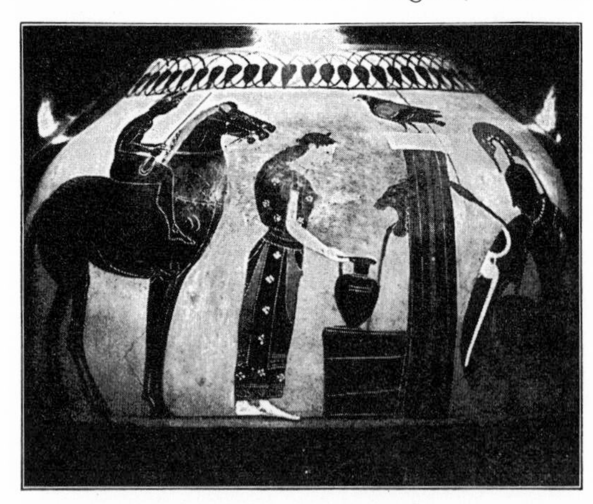

FIG. 577.—Greek Well

A pump only in appearance; the lance of the warrior in the rear causes this illusion. The well is of the same construction as the Roman well depicted in Fig. 594. Vase painting. Berlin, Altes Museum, Antiquarium

pipes led with ease in consequence of their higher pressure. In all, the Romans built five great aqueducts at Pergamon, of which several are remarkable for their length; one conducts water from a distance of 35 miles, whereas another conducts water from Soma, a distance of 21 miles (Figs. 573–576).

The high-pressure water-system of Pergamon is not the only one in antiquity, and certainly not in Greece, for there are others in Patara, Methymna and so forth.

WATER-SUPPLY AMONG THE ROMANS

Roman aqueducts were also often based on the pressure system, although it was avoided wherever possible owing to the difficulty of constructing them and keeping them watertight. Where a single sloping

Fig. 578.—Wells behind houses in the Civilian Settlement on the Saalburg

Fig. 579.—Well with Woodwork and Roof (reconstruction) in the Camp at Saalburg

conduit was sufficient, it was adopted. Among other pressure aqueducts constructed by the Romans there is that at Alatri near Rome. Wherever the Romans took footing, one of their first cares was to provide for a good

Fig. 580.—Well with Wall-frame and Roof (reconstruction) in the Camp at Saalburg

water-supply. They were well aware of the advantages of spring-water. When this was not available they followed the advice of Vegetius (*de re milit.* IV, 10), '*si natura (fontes) non praestat, effodiendi sunt putei aquarumque haustus funibus extrahendi*' (if nature supplies no springs, wells must be dug out and the water must be drawn up by means of ropes). This rule explains why, for example, the whole water-supply of the Saalburg is provided by draw-wells; it shows us the fondness of Romans for using water from every available source. In the civilian settlements situated in front of the camp there are innumerable draw-wells (Fig. 578). Behind every house—indeed, behind almost every building—we find one, and there are others also in the interior of the camp (Figs. 579, 580). So far 12 wells have been excavated in the camp, and 78 outside, that is 90 altogether, dating from different periods. The older wells were lined with woodwork; later this was succeeded by masonry which was about breast-high (Figs. 578 and 580). In most cases, it seems, the wells were protected from dirt by a roof supported on wooden pillars, to which the pulley and bucket were attached. Perhaps there was another cover immediately over the rim of the well. Further, other springs outside the camp had been tapped, from which the water was conducted by wooden pipes to the supply centres in the neighbourhood, where it could be drawn for use as required. These wooden tubes were made by means of long cylindrical borers and connected together by metal rings. In various Roman camps in Germany (Wiesbaden, Hofheim, Heddernheim, Saalburg) iron rings 4 in. in diameter have been found with a collar in the middle such as are still used nowadays at the joints of wooden water-pipes.

The construction of wells encountered difficulties sometimes because water was not always found where it was required. For this reason Vitruvius (VIII, 1) gives the following rules for finding water:

'Before sunrise, lie down flat in the place where the search is to be made, and placing the chin on the earth and supporting it there, take a look out over the country. In this way the sight will not range higher than it ought, the chin being immovable, but will range over a definitely limited height on the same level through the country. Then dig in places where vapours are seen curling and rising up into the air. This sign cannot show itself in a dry spot. . . .

'The kinds of soil described above may be known by their vegetation, such as slender rushes, wild willows, alders, agnus castus trees, reeds, ivy, and other plants of the same sort that cannot spring up of themselves without moisture. But they are also accustomed to grow in depressions which, being lower than the rest of the country, receive water from the rains and the surrounding fields during the winter, and keep it for a comparatively long time on account of their holding power. These must not be trusted, but the search must be made in districts and soils, yet not in depressions, where those significant plants are found growing not from seed, but springing up naturally of themselves.

'If the indications mentioned appear in such places, the following test should be applied. Dig out a place not less than three feet square and five feet deep, and put into it about sunset a bronze or leaden bowl or basin, whichever is at hand. Smear the inside with oil, lay it upside down, and cover the top of the excavation with reeds or green boughs, throwing earth upon them. Next day uncover it, and if there are drops and drippings in the vessel, the place will contain water.

'Again, if a vessel made of unbaked clay be put in the hole, and covered in the same way, it will be wet when uncovered, and already beginning to go to pieces from dampness, if the place contains water. If a fleece of wool is placed in the excavation, and water can be wrung out of it on the following day, it will show that the place has a supply. Further, if a lamp be trimmed, filled with oil, lighted, and put in that place and covered up, and if on the next day it is not burnt out, but still contains some remains of oil and wick, and is itself found to be damp, it will indicate that the place contains water; for all heat attracts moisture. Again, if a fire is made in that place, and if the ground, when thoroughly warmed and burned, sends up a misty vapour from its surface, the place will contain water.'

The above rules show that the Romans had developed a special technique for discovering water. With the exception of pressure-mains, which, as already mentioned, were avoided wherever possible, all other details of water-supply reached an unusually high standard among the Romans of the ancient Empire. This development is not surprising when we consider the partiality of the Romans to water, of which they made prodigal use. The ancient Roman aqueducts daily supplied about one million cubic metres of water, that is, about 120 gallons of water per head of the population. Even nowadays Rome still holds first place in the

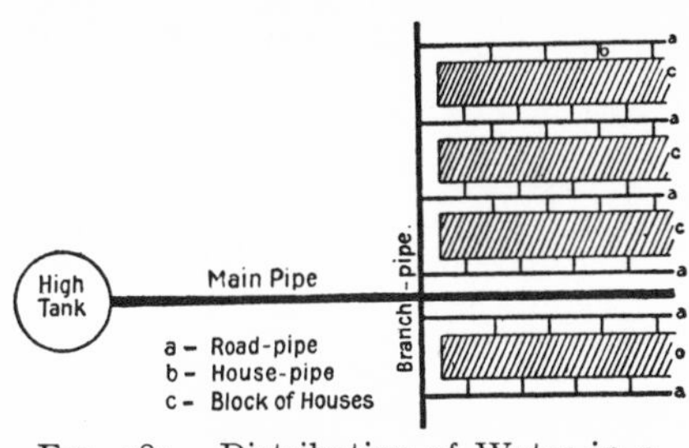

FIG. 581.—Distribution of Water in a Modern Town

The main pipe conducts the water from the elevated container to the town, where it is distributed by subsidiary pipes of different orders of importance among the streets and the houses

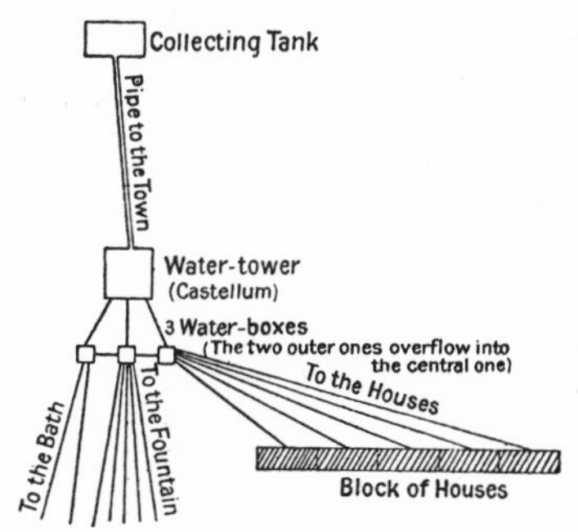

FIG. 582.—Distribution of Water in an Ancient Town

matter of water-supply, a fact which it owes not least to the existence of the ancient Roman aqueducts. Nowhere else in the world is there such a superabundance of water, nowhere are there so many wells, fountains, water-jets, etc. Although a large proportion of these fountains was designed by artists of the Renaissance and Rococo periods, the foundation of all this beauty, the vast quantity of water available, is due to ancient Rome, which provided this lavish supply, and had so vast a wealth of fountains, *jets d'eau,* baths and other such means of spending it. And every provincial Roman town was a miniature Rome. So that wherever Roman civilization has penetrated, we find the remains of their highly developed water-systems—above all, the characteristic aqueducts, which are of such imposing size.

Like other ancient systems, those of the Roman had no main-pipe leading from the principal reservoir to the town ; rather, the water flowed from the source partly along conduits which were often of considerable length and partly over aqueducts to the water-tower (*castellum*) which represents our main reservoir (Figs. 581 and 582). The interior of the water-tower was usually divided into four compartments, namely, into the tank proper and three subsidiary tanks connected with the main tank by pipes. One of these smaller tanks served to supply the baths with which it communicated. The second subsidiary tank supplied the private houses, while the third received the overflow from the first two, which was conducted into the public fountains and water-jets.

The second tank, which supplied the private houses, was not connected with them by a main pipe and branch pipes. Instead, the water was first led into a sort of minor water-tower situated near the houses to be supplied. From this tower it flowed into a cistern, from which it was finally conducted to the individual houses. In the case of more extensive systems this method was of course correspondingly repeated: the aqueduct supplied not one but several main water-towers. From the latter it was again passed on to several private cisterns in various parts of the town, and so forth. The chief disadvantage of this system is that it necessitates the use of very long pipe-lines; for a special subsidiary pipe must be laid from the minor water-towers to each house, and these minor towers have each again to be connected with the main tower. Consequently much of the water runs away unused, and the amount of water required for the system is very much greater than is effectively used; further, it is difficult to control the working. Nevertheless modern Rome has retained many of its water-systems (Aqua Marcia) in this ancient form.

To provide the towns with the necessary water, the Romans spared no effort. At the beginning they, like other peoples, constructed their water-systems underground. Later, however, in Rome as well as in other places, they fetched their water from such great distances that difficulties opposed themselves to the underground construction of the pipes. Moreover, our way of overcoming differences of level by means of water-pressure was avoided by them as much as possible. They preferred to have recourse to the most costly and most laborious artificial constructions in the form of tunnels and aqueducts. In this way the surroundings of many ancient Roman towns, above all of Rome itself, assumed the characteristic appearance due to the presence of these aqueducts. The Campagna, the wide plain surrounding Rome, is traversed in all directions by the gigantic arches of these aqueducts, of which some still nowadays conduct water from distant hills as in ancient times. The Aqua Marcia, which is the third of the fourteen water-systems constructed in the course of time for supplying Rome, connects the capital city with the source 33 miles away. The total length of the system amounts to no less than 57 miles, and there are nearly 7 miles of aqueducts. As the sources are situated 1,056 ft. above sea-level, whereas Rome is only 180 ft., the course could have been made much shorter in view of the gradient of 876 ft. in 33 miles. Instead of doing this, however, the Romans followed all the irregularities of the ground and even passed round hills and spurs, so that the actual length of pipe became extended to the extraordinary distance of 57 miles. The Aqua Julia, which was built in the year 43 B.C., is 14½ miles long, of which there are 7 miles of aqueducts. The Aqua Claudia, which was constructed by the Emperors Claudius and Trajan, consists of two aqueducts which coincide over great lengths. Their total length amounts to no less than 97½ miles, of which 54 miles belong to the so-called 'Anio Novus' and 43½ to the 'Aqua Claudia' proper. Many of the other water-systems of Rome are of considerable length, as also those of the Roman provinces. For example, the aqueduct from the Eifel to Cologne is nearly 50 miles long.

The aqueducts are high arches, usually narrow, which follow in close succession; above them is the channel along which the water passes.

The arch and the channel are of masonry. The older aqueducts in the vicinity of Rome are in general built of large slabs. The openings of the arches are lined with wedge-shaped stones and often supported once more on the inside by brickwork, which leans against the side-pillars. The bricks lie horizontally in the sides and radially in the arch, where there are often three or four superposed concentric layers. Later, to reduce the cost of construction, large slabs were given up in favour of smaller stones. There are, however, no general rules embodied in the building of aqueducts. We may say that each of the many constructions of this kind still extant exhibits individual characteristics, mostly conditioned by the nature of the building material available in the vicinity. Particularly ambitious examples are the aqueducts with two or three vertically superposed channels; they are often of considerable height. These artificial

FIG. 583.—The Campagna near Rome, with the remains of ancient Roman aqueducts

constructions naturally added enormously to the total cost of building these water-systems. In spite of the cheapness of labour at that time a foot of running water, according to calculations by Belgrand, in the case of the two aqueducts of the Aqua Claudia, cost about 27 shillings, a very high figure, if we consider the small cross-section.

The channel along which the water flowed has cross-sections of very different form in the different aqueducts. Except in isolated cases it is covered over with masonry to prevent dirt getting into the water and also to avoid the sun's heat. In some cases there are channels superposed vertically (Fig. 584). For example, at the Porta Maggiore of to-day at Rome there are still over and adjacent to the entrance huge structures through which the channels of no less than five water-systems pass: they are, from below upwards, Marcia, Tepula (now in the wall), Julia (in the wall and in the gateway), Claudia, Anio Novus (only above the entrance).

Compared with the aqueducts the tunnel constructions are of small account. After what has been said above about the tunnels of Siloah and Samos there is little to be said about them from the technical point of view. A few details are given in Fig. 585. On the other hand, it is noteworthy that the Romans clarified their water by allowing impurities to settle. The water from the sources carried along with it dirt, slime and other heavy substances, which partly deposited themselves in the channels but which were removed, when present to an excessive degree, by means of settling-ponds. These ponds (*piscinae* = fish-ponds) were great containers, constructed of masonry, into which the water ran and was allowed to stand for a while before being drawn off for use. Sometimes, as in the case of the *piscina mirabilis* (Fig. 586), they served the double purpose of storing and clarifying the water simultaneously. Many *piscinae* consisted of two superposed containers. The water ran into the lower one and passed up through an aperture in the partition into the upper container, whence it was drawn off (Figs. 587–589).

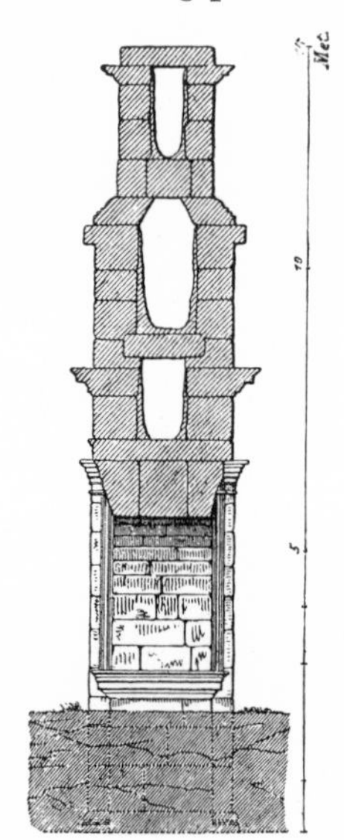

FIG. 584.—Section through a part of the Aqua Marcia, showing three superposed channels

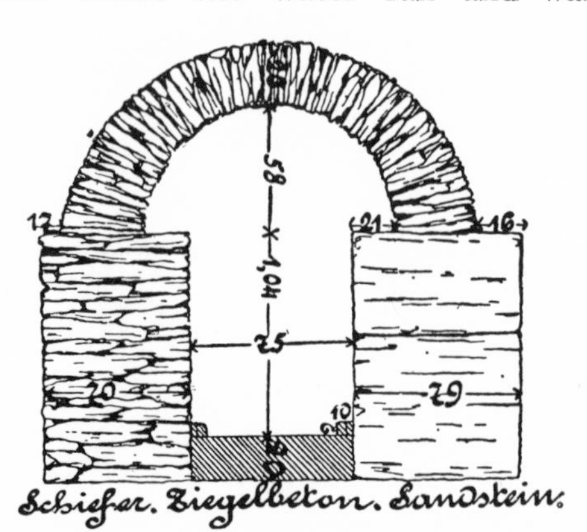

FIG. 585.—Tunnel, part of the Water-system of Trèves

The channel consists of a floor, two side-walls, and an arch. The floor has in general three strata: one of slate, one of concrete (with gravel), and one of brick-mortar as a covering. The side-walls are composed of various materials. The floor and the walls have been smoothed with the greatest care. The channel runs along hilly slopes; gorges are bridged over by means of aqueducts

Within the towns the water was conducted in subterranean channels. It is noteworthy that in the ancient Roman water-systems a sort of pressure-reducer occurs, which, in places where there was a steep gradient and consequently a high pressure in the channel, reduced the pressure to within practical limits. Such a device has been found, for example, at Pompeii. It consisted of two pillars with an open container at the same level. The water was conducted up a pipe in the one pillar into the container and then passed on through the other. Its pressure was then only that due to the height of the pillar and the width of the second pipe. The pressure due to the original gradient was thus eliminated.

To conduct the water further to the wells and houses pipes of clay or lead were used. Stone pipes are also found, but they are rare. The lead tubes were simply made from sheet-lead, bent round a core. They are all oval or drop-shaped in cross-section, and are soldered with lead at the seam. They were also joined together by being soldered with lead, the end of one pipe being widened by means of a tool resembling a mandril (Fig. 590). The end of the next pipe was thrust into this funnel-shaped opening and the gap between the two ends was filled with lead or soldered. Belgrand has made some experiments to test the durability of the lead seams of Roman water-pipes. He made pipes having a thickness of wall

FIG. 586.—Interior view of the Piscina Mirabilis at Baiae

just over a quarter of an inch. He found that at a pressure of three atmospheres they tended to become circular in cross-section; at eight atmospheres they became perfectly circular, and at eighteen atmospheres they burst, but the seams remained intact. Thus the seams resisted pressure better than the lead itself. Fieber has proved that in place of pure lead a solder containing small quantities of tin was also used to connect these pipes (see also p. 46).

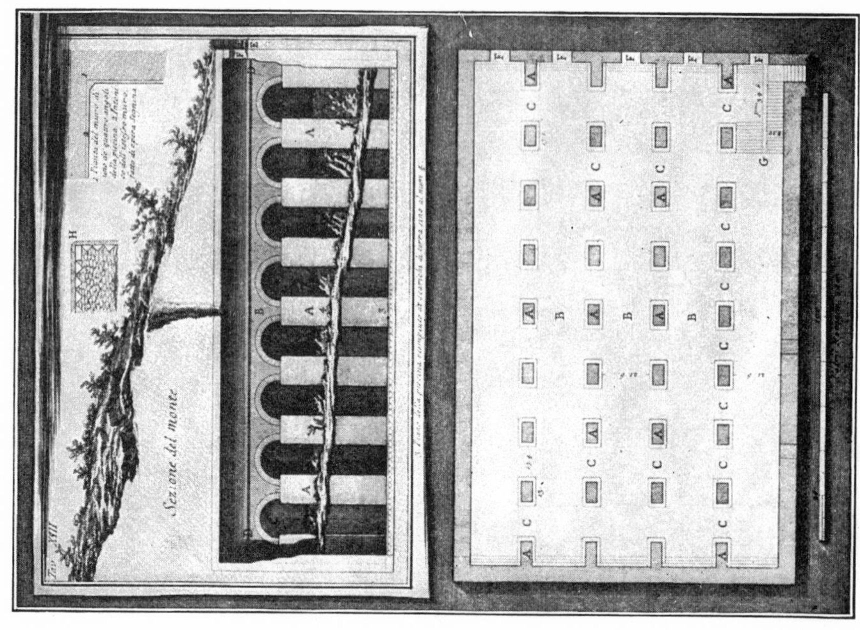

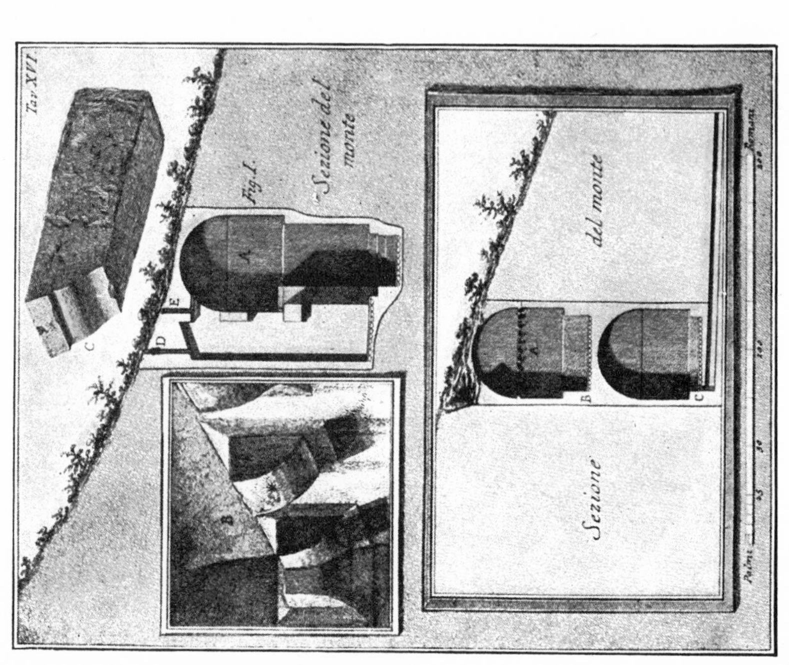

FIGS. 587, 588.—*Piscina* at Castel Gandolfo (see Figs. 587–589)

Vitruvius (VIII, 6, 10) considers clay pipes preferable to lead pipes, as

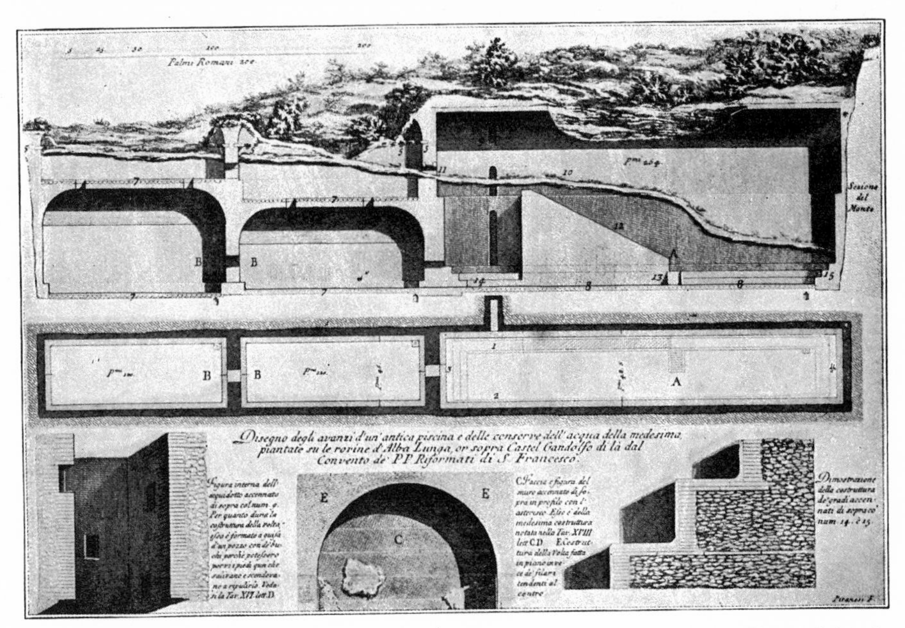

FIG. 589.—Vertical section through the two-storied Piscina at Castel Gandolfo, and details of the same

The piscina is built into the hill and consists of a number of containers partly supported by pillars, some of which stand in pairs one above another or are subdivided into two parts by channels

they can be more easily replaced and also because less wholesome water is supplied by the leaden pipes. Lead produces white-lead, and so, in his opinion, cannot itself be healthy, for lead-casters always look ill. Further, the

FIG. 590.—Lead Water-pipes

The pipe had originally an oval or drop-shaped cross-section, like the pipe on the right, but water-pressure has made them circular. Observe the short pieces of pipe and the consequent numerous joins. From the 'House of Livia', Rome

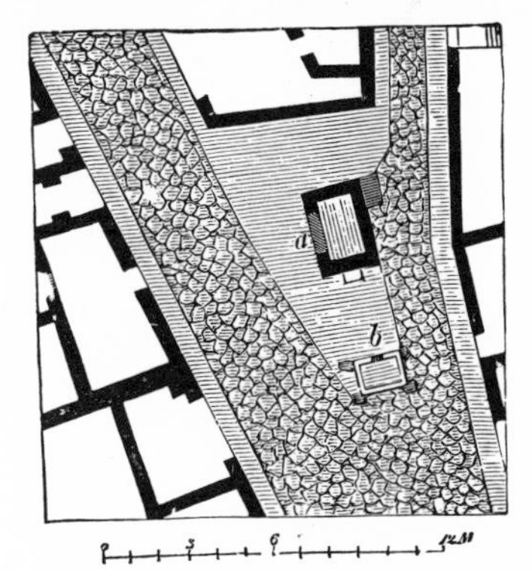

FIG. 591.—Fountain with Water-tower in Pompeii (ground-plan)

a, Water-tower; *b*, well

water from clay pipes certainly tasted better, for even at banquets it was drunk not out of silver or metal goblets but out of earthenware vessels. In an exhaustive study, in which reference is made to a work of Helwes, Kobert has recently shown that cases of poisoning due to lead water-pipes have occurred even in modern times and that Vitruvius' opinion must therefore be deemed correct. Nowadays lead pipes occur only in houses, whereas in antiquity they were used in the streets, so that the water remained in contact with them much longer.

In the streets water was drawn from the public fountains, in the houses either also from fountains that were constantly running or from tapping-cocks. The street-fountains often had a special little water-tower in their immediate vicinity (Figs. 591 and 592). The water flows first into the tower and then into the fountain. The simpler fountains consisted of a small massive pillar with a central cavity through which the water-pipe ascended (Fig. 594). The pipe ended in an exit which was usually orna-

FIG. 592.—Fountain with Water-tower at Pompeii (perspective view)

mented with some figure. Below it was a basin (Fig. 592) made of hewn stones connected by brackets. At the front edge of this basin there is an overflow gap through which the excess water runs off. Besides this general type of fountains there are many others which, however, present no new technical features.

The water used in the houses had to be paid for. The mouth of the pipe was therefore often closed by means of a stopcock or tap (Figs. 594, 596), so that the amount of water used could be regulated to prevent waste. The water used was paid for in Rome in terms of a definite unit, the 'Quinarius'. The quinarius (called after the silver coin of the same name) corresponded to the quantity of water that flowed per unit of time through a vertical pipe slightly less than 1 ft. long and about $1\frac{1}{5}$ in. wide, when there was a column of water at rest 30 ft. 1 in. above its inlet. In 24 hours this yielded a quantity of water amounting to, roughly, 92 gallons. Various specimens of taps have been preserved, also some that

FIG. 593.—Fountain in the interior of a house (Mosaic Fountain) at Pompeii

could cut off part of the water-system. Fig. 596 shows a tap from the Palace of Tiberius on the island of Capri. It is clear that the part *b*

FIG. 594.—System of Lead Pipes that may be closed by means of a tap, in a house in Pompeii

FIG. 595.—Section of a Fountain in Pompeii

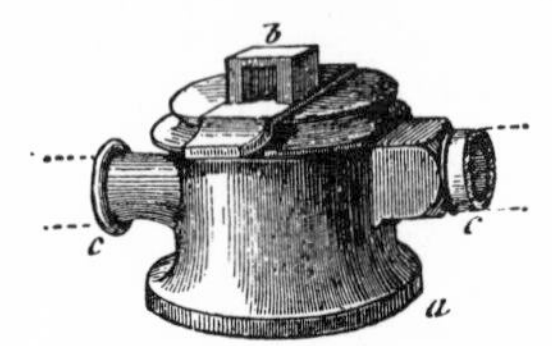

FIG. 596.—Water-tap from the Palace of Tiberius, Capri
(By turning *b* in *a* the pipe *c* is opened)
Museo Nazionale, Naples

turned in *a* and so opened or closed the pipe *c* according to its position.

DRAINS AND SEWERS

THE distribution of drains in antiquity in general differed little from that of the present day; the large towns were mostly well provided with drainage systems, whereas no provision at all was made in the case of small towns. In any case, the number of drainage-systems was apparently smaller than now in proportion to the number of cities. The hygienic value of drainage was probably taken less into account than considerations of comfort. The larger a town was, the more difficult and the more laborious it became to remove refuse and sewage waters which accumulated in great quantity. For this reason—and probably not for sanitary reasons—drains were built for removing all this matter from the town mechanically and with as little effort as possible.

DRAINAGE SYSTEMS IN THE NEAR EAST

The construction and position of these drains indicate that they were primarily used to allow dirty water to flow away. In the course of time they seem to have been used for removing refuse of every kind. Such drains are found in almost all the larger ancient cities. In Babylon Layard found a well-developed system of drains which, like that of other Mesopotamian towns, such as Nimrod, consisted of a main channel and subsidiary channels. The subsidiary drains extended to below the houses and received the sewage to be removed. The construction of the channels involved some noteworthy technical features; for example, they were vaulted (Figs. 597 and 598). The vaulting was not merely simulated by the gradually increasing projection of the higher layers of stone, but was true vaulting produced by a proper setting of the stones, which were partly wedge-shaped as usual in the case of true vaulting-stones. The general construction of these vaults, in particular that of Nimrod, leaves no doubt that pointed arches were used as scaffoldings. Another noteworthy feature is the steep gradient at which the sewage flowed into the main drain; this indicates that it was felt desirable to remove refuse as rapidly as possible. The subsidiary drain joins the main drain at about a third of its height, sloping fairly steeply downwards; it is connected by a vertical shaft with the building to be drained, in this case the South-east Palace of Nimrod. The subsidiary drain was made of burnt brick and covered with plate-tiles. The vertical shaft was closed at the top by a large plate with a hole in the middle, into which the dirty water was poured. As this hole is smaller than the bore of the drain, it seems justifiable to assume that a pipe have may led into it. At

Nimrod brick pipes have actually been found which served to connect the building with the network of drains.

The drain constructions of other Mesopotamian towns were carried out in a similar way.

The drains of Jerusalem are worthy of special mention because they were partly constructed in rock and also because it was known that the sink-waste carried along in it could be put to good use for agricultural and horticultural purposes. The drain-system of Jerusalem was not built all at the same time but was developed at various intervals from ancient Jewish times to the period of Roman domination. The oldest drains were at any rate constructed before the time of King David, that is, before about 1055 B.C. When King David built his fort Zion and made Jerusalem the centre of his kingdom he probably had the ancient drain-system considerably extended. We are indebted to Schick for some detailed investigations into this system; he makes the following statements:

FIG. 597.—Drain under the North-west Palace of Nimrod

FIG. 598.—Drain under the South-east Palace of Nimrod

'Between the hollows, rocks and stone-houses there were lanes in the form of wide channels or gutters, which had been hewn in the rock or, where there was no rock, constructed of masonry. These drains conducted all the rain and waste water to the edge of the rock. In general these lanes were narrow and crooked, but the chief lane which came down from the north from Millo was somewhat more spacious and also less crooked than the short side-lanes that branched off from it to the left and right. The exits of these drains at the edge of the rock naturally lay lower than the lanes and the houses. Joab entered Jerusalem by way of these water-channels, that is through the exits of the gutters in the lanes and of the sewers, so that David could enter into possession of the town without shedding blood.'

In Jerusalem waste water and sewage seem to have been removed by separate channels; the truth of this conjecture appears fairly well established, since drain-pipes have been discovered which were undoubtedly used only for conducting away waters used in ritual lustrations in the Temple. The Temple was provided with a special water-system which supplied the copious quantities of water necessary for the ceremonials. It also had its own drains, as is proved by many traces that have been left. As other similar drains have been found, the view that in Jerusalem the waste and sewage waters had separate outlets seems justified. The reason is obvious. Nowadays a simple device at the exits of waste-pipes and sewage-pipes (the 'elbow-joint') prevents odours from the latter from penetrating into the interior of the house. Water must always remain in this elbow-joint, which serves to cut off the rooms of the house from the sewer drains: moreover, latrines are specially ventilated. These devices were not known at that time and therefore other methods were adopted for excluding unpleasant odours from living-rooms and above all the holy Temple. Hence the method, which was laborious and costly, of building a double system of drains, which incidentally proves that the Jews recognized among other sanitary facts the importance of keeping drains away from living apartments.

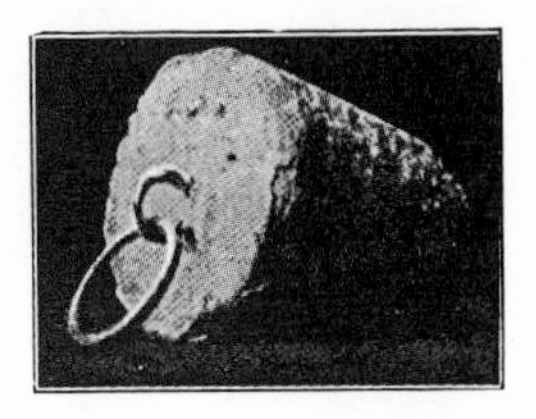

Fig. 599.—Lead Plug for closing the rain-water drain in the Temple of the Dead of Sahura

A further fact seems to have been made use of in Jerusalem, namely the value of sink-matter. A large container into which a drain leads and also ponds that are in communication with drainage systems prove that

Fig. 600.—Embedded Copper Pipe for running off rain-water in King Sahura's Temple of the Dead

the substances suspended in the drain-waters were allowed to settle and were then used as manure. The water that was drawn off still contained a sufficient quantity of such substances and therefore served to water gardens.

The Egyptians also knew how to build drainage systems. The fact that as early as the year 2500 B.C. they conducted away the water resulting from ritual lustrations is proved by Borchardt's excavations at King Sahura's mortuary temple at Abusir, which was built about that time. Besides constructions for draining off rain-water there were here discovered in five different places in the walls traces of limestone basins, provided with metal fittings, which served as sinks. The exit was closed by a lead plug nearly an inch long carrying a loop (Fig. 599). This plug was attached to a chain by means of a bronze ring which passed through the loop. Connected to the bottom of the basins were copper pipes which united and conducted the used water, or the accumulated rain-water, into the valley below (Figs. 600 and 601). The total length of the pipe-system was over 1,330 ft. One piece of the piping is still fully intact. It con-

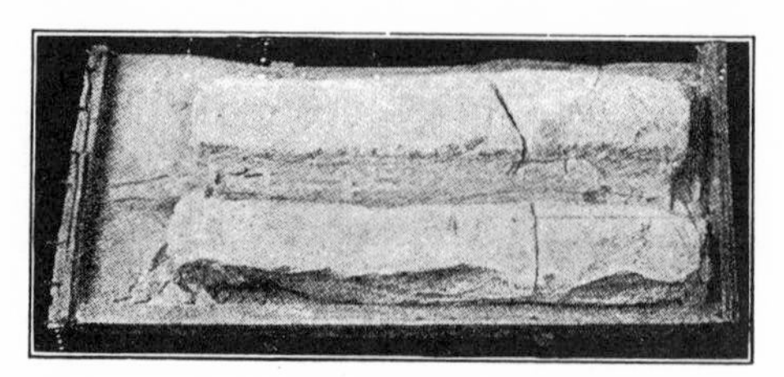

FIG. 601.—Part of the Groove containing the Rain-pipe in King Sahura's Mortuary Temple

sists of beaten copper and has a diameter of 1·9 in. and a thickness of about $\frac{1}{16}$ in. It was simply bent together, being neither soldered nor riveted. The longitudinal seam had been closed by merely placing one of the edges over the other and hammering them together. The pipe lay in a groove cut out of a stone and was fixed in it by means of a mortar composed of 45·54 per cent. of gypsum and 41·36 per cent. of calcium carbonate.

DRAINS AND SEWERS AMONG THE GREEKS

The drain constructions of the Greeks reached a high state of perfection in very early times. Even the Palace of Knossos had privies with water-

FIG. 602.—Public place of retirement with Water-flushing in Timgad

flushing: they are, indeed, not uncommon in Greek antiquity nor, later, among the Romans. They are also found in many houses in Thera, where they are not only flushed with water but are also provided with marble basins which serve for washing the hands. In Pergamon there are public places of retirement that were under the control of the building-police : in Ephesus these places were in fact splendidly fitted up during the imperial age. It may be mentioned here that Roman towns also had these public institutions, some being provided with water-drainage : it is probable that these provisions, like so many others, were taken over from Greek civilization. At the time of Diocletian (A.D. 284–305) Rome had no less than 144 public lavatories, a great proportion of which were probably provided with flushing-pans. There is an example of them at the Forum Civile in Pompeii. It consists of two parts, an ante-room and a main room. Three sides of the latter are provided with conveniences that lie above a drain that runs round the bottom of the sides. Water entered the drain through an opening in the rear left corner and flowed out at the corresponding corner on the other side. A similar building with a drain running all round the bottom was discovered by Michaelis in the great thermae at Pompeii. There is a particularly fine example at Timgad (Fig. 602) ; there are others at Puteoli. When the latter were excavated in 1850 they were thought to constitute a temple, as it did not strike the archaeologists of that time, unaccustomed to such luxurious arrangements, that they might belong to the sanitary requirements of a reasonably civilized people. The details of the water-drainage of these outbuildings in antiquity differed greatly of course from those of to-day. There was no compressor, nor were the repositories of a particular shape ; on the other hand, they resembled in many ways the forms of these conveniences at their first appearance in our own civilization. The flushing was done either directly from the water-mains or, usually, still more simply : the accommodation was situated directly above a natural or artificial stream of water or a drain, which rapidly swept away all refuse.

FIG. 603.—Shower-bath, according to a Greek Vase-painting

Berlin, Altes Museum, Antiquarium

Among the Greeks the baths also communicated directly with the drainage system. In the excavations at Pergamon a bathroom has been laid bare in the upper gymnasium, which was probably last reconstructed in the second century B.C., but probably belonged to an earlier period ; in it the water in use ran through a series of baths (probably seven) in which those bathing stood and allowed the water from mains overhead to flow over them in the manner of our shower-baths (Fig. 603). The water ran out of the last bath on to the earth and thence into a drain.

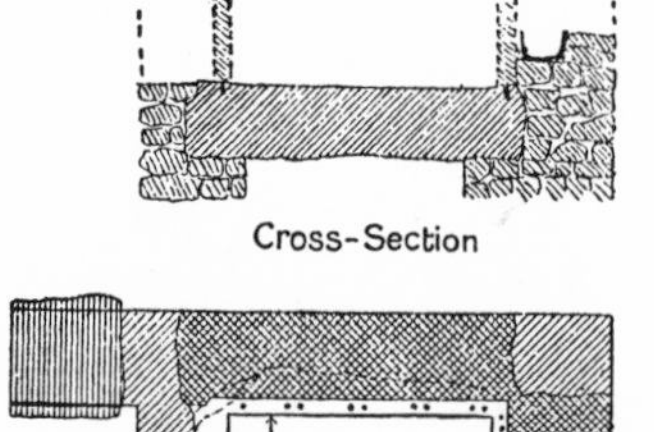

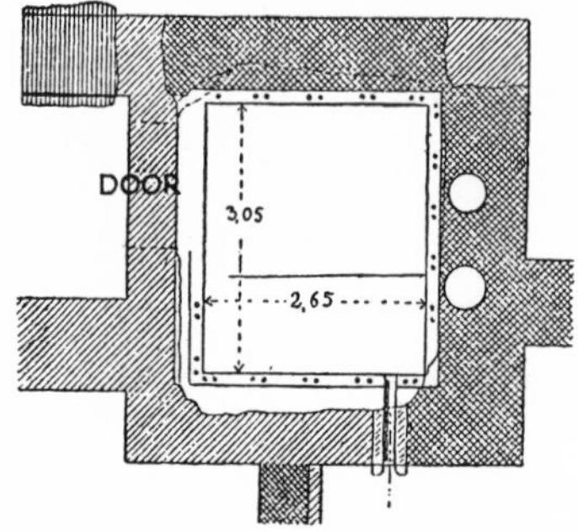

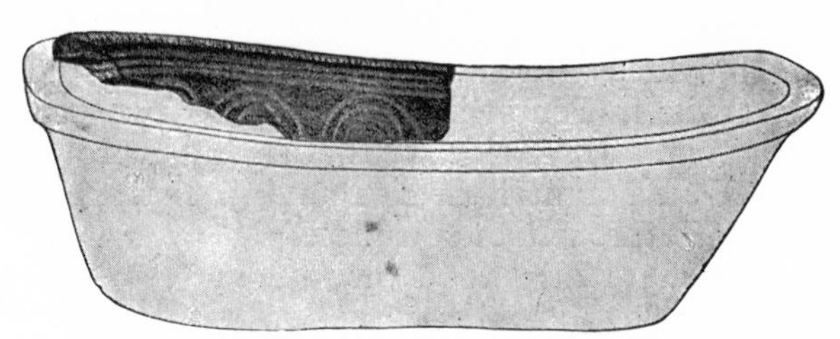

FIGS. 606 and 607.—The Bath at Tiryns
(Above, the handle attached to the outer side)

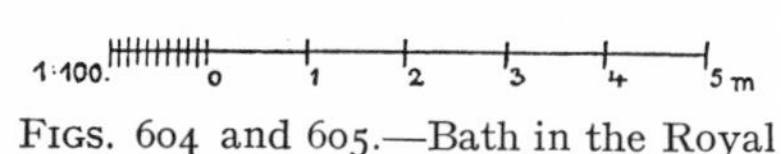

FIGS. 604 and 605.—Bath in the Royal Castle at Tiryns
The bath itself stood in the part of the room nearest the exit-pipe

The drainage-system of Miletus has dimensions such as are not attained 'even in that of a modern city' (according to von Salis). Similarly extensive systems are to be found in Athens, Olympia, Samos, and so forth.

Besides being connected with the water-system and the drains, the earliest bathing-establishments were technically equipped to the fullest extent. For example, the oldest Greek bath known to us, namely, that in the royal castle at Tiryns (Figs. 604 and 605), has a floor which consists of a single stone slab which at the same time serves as the foundation for the walls. The floor is inclined in order to collect the overflow and to conduct it

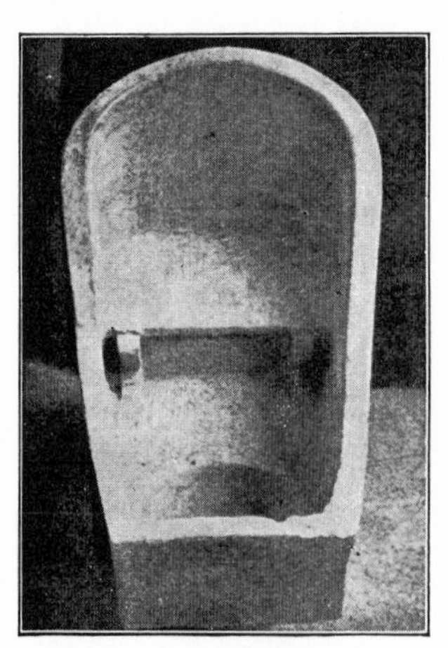

FIG. 608.—Combined Foot- and Hip-bath from Mycenae

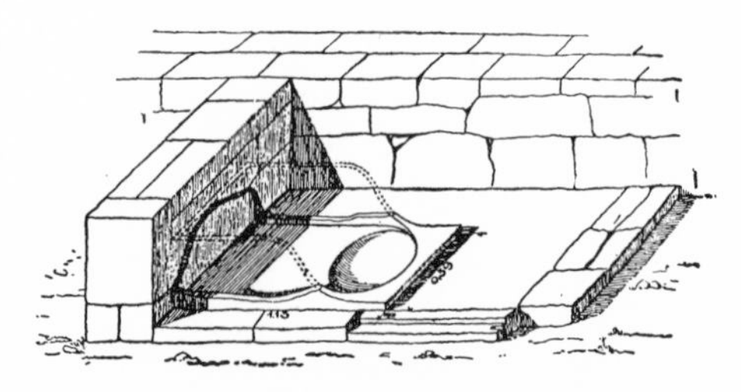

FIG. 609.—Foot-bath from Priene

into a special gutter to the drain. The form of the bath, pieces of which are preserved, is represented in Figs. 606 and 607. It was made of burnt clay and had a handle on the outside to lift it ; in the interior there were ornaments in the shape of wave patterns. Besides these large baths there were also others, for example, foot-baths and hip-baths (Fig. 608). A bath, traces of the floor of which have been found at Priene, seems to have served similar purposes, certainly that of a foot-bath. To judge from the attachments in the side-walls the latter were

Fig. 610.—Lavatory (at the back) and Foot-baths (in the front centre) in the Gymnasium at Priene

perhaps shaped to form a seat or so that a board for sitting upon could be placed across. But perhaps they were additions for hip-baths. A bathing establishment, presumably for a number of baths, has been found in the gymnasium at Priene : it resembles to an extraordinary degree the most modern hygienic baths for workmen (Fig. 610). In many modern factories we find washing conveniences arranged in rows. The principle underlying them is also embodied in the row of baths in the gymnasium at Priene, in which water issuing from the mouths of lions' heads runs into a long trough which has its upper end $2\frac{1}{2}$ ft. above the floor. The water flowed off over the edge of the baths down the inclined floor which conducted it into a gutter ending in the street. In the foreground there are still visible two stone seats, in front of which there are cavities for foot-bathers. The drains in the floor of the Palaestra at Olympia are shown in Fig. 611.

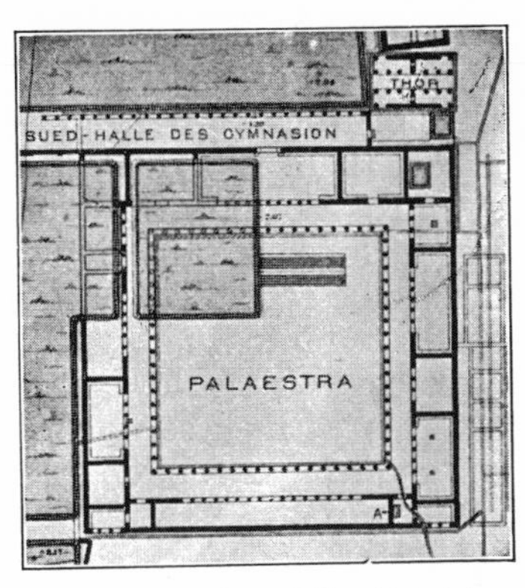

Fig. 611.—Plan of the Palaestra at Olympia

The Athenian drainage is worthy of particular notice because it allows the waste water to escape by a method nowadays called 'the soakage system'. The main drain, consisting partly of false and partly of true vaults, divides, when it has left the town, into a number of smaller channels, so that the waters which had first been collected together again separate into little rivulets. They run along these little drains underground for some distance and thence flow out into the lower-lying plains, where they soak away. It is not known whether plantations were sown after the manner of our irrigation trenches in order to exploit the manures contained in the waters. But as a sort of movable stopper has been found in one of the smaller drains it may be surmised that the city of Athens used its waste waters to good purpose by distributing them among the individual farmers or leaseholders of the properties on the soakage plains. The main Athenian drain was made of ashlar, the branch-drains were of burnt clay. Movable covers allowed the drains to be cleaned. The individual clay pipes were loosely inserted into one another just as is done to-day with drainage pipes. But there are also found in Greek drainage-systems pipes with raised edges so that they can be conveniently fitted into each other. When they were loosely placed together they were fastened by leaden clamps. It has not been possible to ascertain whether a lubricant was used at the points of contact. In Samos the drains were partly hewn in rock.

ROMAN DRAINAGE-SYSTEMS

Among the Roman drainage systems, which in general closely resemble those of the Greeks, the great drain of Rome, the *cloaca maxima,* which is still preserved, deserves special mention. Like most ancient drains, it was probably open originally and only later closed. Perhaps it first served to drain off waste waters, and was only later used for its proper purpose. For, between the Capitoline, the Palatine and the Esquiline Hills of Rome, at a height of 40 ft. above sea-level and 23 ft. above the Tiber, there is a hollow valley which must formerly have been a swamp. To allow this ground to be built upon, it had first to be drained. For this purpose the rivulet flowing from this hollow into the Tiber had first to be regulated, banked up and furnished with lateral drains which conducted into it all the collected waters. Some of these waters will also have come from the Palatine. Later the sewage waters were taken up together with these waters and then, owing to the objectionable odours, the whole construction was covered in. In this way the cloaca maxima was gradually evolved ; according to tradition it was built by the fifth King of Rome, Tarquinius Priscus (616–578 B.C.), but the form in which we now see it probably owes its origin to later (Republican) times.

The dimensions of the cloaca maxima vary greatly. The cross-section increases in proportion as it approaches the Tiber,—a natural result of its origin, as described just above ; more and more drains led into the cloaca along its course, and consequently the mass of water became continually greater. Merckel makes the following further remarks about it. The floor of the cloaca maxima consists of the well-known polygonal lava-stones so much used in antiquity for making pavements : the walls are of great blocks of tufa which lie three to five layers deep. Isolated layers

FIG. 612.—View of a part of the Cloaca Maxima

FIG. 613.—The exit of the Cloaca Maxima into the Tiber
Peperino was used as the building material at the mouth

are of travertine. The blocks are $8\frac{1}{2}$ ft. long, $2\frac{1}{2}$ ft. high and $3\frac{1}{3}$ ft. wide. No layers of mortar were used at the joints; the stones in the interior seem to be held together by iron clamps fixed with lead. The vault is of the barrel-type and was doubtless built over scaffolding; it consists of wedge-shaped stones seven to nine layers thick, but with only three layers at the mouth. The width of the cloaca maxima varies extraordinarily. Some places allow us to observe that they were originally open; at other places the cloaca is covered only with strong stone slabs, which can still be easily raised nowadays, giving a glimpse of the rapidly flowing water below. At other places, again, the vault is made of bricks. In short, everywhere there is evidence that the construction of the cloaca was proceeded with at different times and according to different points of view. This may also be inferred from the shafts, which reach to different heights and vary in manifold ways as regards the construction of their longitudinal sections and their upper apertures.

As in Rome, so in many Roman provincial towns drainage systems were constructed; indeed, sometimes even standing camps, *castra*, were provided with them. At Saalburg a system of drains has been found which apparently served to drain the soil, to receive the waste-waters and perhaps also to remove the sewage. Whether the last purpose was intended has not been proved, as the site of the latrines has not yet been discovered. The waters from the Saalburg flowed through large and small drains which were partly lined with wood, partly with masonry; the steep gradient of the ground was used to advantage and the waters flowed into acute-angled trenches situated in front of the walls of the stronghold. Thence it flowed northwards into the open. Many of these trenches still serve a useful purpose nowadays in conducting away the water that collects in the camp during heavy rains and so keeping the interior of the fortification dry.

IRRIGATION AND DRAINAGE

IRRIGATION and drainage are intimately related technical subjects, as both depend on the use of open or closed trenches, and on the exploitation of the contour of the country. The constructions are all so simple and so much resemble those of to-day in principle, that there is not much call for comment. What excites our wonder is less the technical execution than the magnitude of some of these tasks, which have achieved world-wide renown, such as the draining of the Campagna by the Romans.

The earliest drain-constructions of which we have knowledge date back to about 1900 B.C., before the reign of the Babylonian King Khammurabi. As explained by Merckel, they served to keep dry the objects deposited in the burial-mound of Ur. This was done by the simple expedient of inserting clay pipes, having little holes at the top, into the swampy ground. The swamp-water ran through these holes into the pipes and thus flowed away. Naturally the network of pipes was constructed with the pipes slanting downwards and at points where there was a gradient, until finally a main-pipe received all the water and conducted it away. The system was laid out so efficiently that complete drainage resulted. The fact that the contents of the mound have remained preserved till the present day is chiefly due to this excellently devised system of drainage. Similar constructions were also found in several places in Babylon and Assyria. They also played a part in regulating the flow of rivers. Mighty walls were built which cut off from the rivers Euphrates and Tigris the lands to be laid dry, so that the waters from those rivers should not cause inundations. Drain constructions were then built, in which either clay pipes were used or else open gutters, through which the water flowed away. In this way it was made possible to make wide stretches of land available for cultivation.

Irrigation and drainage became particularly developed in Egypt, which was rightly called a 'gift of the Nile'. The Nile rises during the months from June to October and inundates the land. In doing so it deposits a bluish-grey slime, a sort of mud, which constitutes the fruitful arable soil. As far as this mud reaches there is growth and prosperity; where it ends the desert begins. Now, the rise and fall of the Nile is by no means regular. In the years in which the rise was small the crops failed and famine ensued. This fact made it imperative to regulate the inundations of the Nile. This was accomplished with the help of canals and great basins into which the waters of the Nile were conducted at the periods of high-water. In this way excessive inundation was avoided and, further, all parts of the country were certain to receive water. In what way the system of canals and water-basins was distributed in detail can no longer be ascertained exactly. At any rate it depended on exact measurements of the height of the Nile, for which purpose measuring posts (nilometers) were erected; they were kept in buildings to which only priests had access. The true level of the Nile was kept secret, as certain taxes were raised, the amount of which was determined by the priests according to its actual or alleged height. The mythical Lake Moeris is also supposed to have been a great irrigating and draining basin. Herodotus gives a description of it which has, however, been shown to be very untrustworthy. Whether it was a natural lake of enormous extent that later dried up or, as others assume, an artificial basin of gigantic dimensions, will probably never be clearly established. Oechelhäuser even assumes that Lake Moeris was no lake at all and that one must decide in favour of certain recent investigators who regard it merely as a piece of arable land reclaimed from the swampy Fayum in the Delta of the Nile and protected from inundation by means of dykes. The riddle of Moeris has been invested with much fancy, but none of the suggestions seems likely to bring us nearer to the truth.

We are better informed about the mighty drainage-works that laid dry the lake-bed of Kopais in Boeotia. Merckel has shown, however, in a detailed discussion that this basin is still a fruitful subject of research. Strabo writes that the rising waters of this lake led to the destruction of several towns including Athenai,[1] Arne, Midea and Eleusis.[1] The ancient Orchomenos also met its doom here. Strabo points out that the lake had no outlet except the subterranean connections into which the Kephissos entered. The mouths of these entrances into the lake, the so-called suction-holes, often became blocked up through earthquakes or by alluvium. Alexander the Great had them opened up and cleaned, a task which was carried out by the engineer Krates. Later, artificial galleries were driven into the rock, so that effective drainage was ensured.

Similar galleries were used by the Romans in one of their oldest drainage-works, that for laying dry the Alban Lake, which was constructed in the year 396 B.C. To Etruscan prisoners of war fell the task of mining a tunnel through the rock, through which the waters of the lake flowed away. Although this was an immense labour it calls for no comment in technical respects. We know from earlier parts of the present book that by the use of an enormous amount of man-power feats could be accomplished that still leave us astonished. It may be recalled that time was no object; we discussed in detail the processes of mining and working rocks in the section on 'Mining'. Other similar tasks were effectually carried out in the same way, such as the lowering of the level of Lake Velinus in the land of the Sabines in the year 289 B.C. These enterprises were not always successful. Under the Emperor Claudius thirty thousand slaves worked for eleven years to pierce a tunnel nearly eight and a half miles long through rock, the purpose of which was to drain Lake Fucinus. The failure of the scheme was due to mistakes in calculating the differences of height and other details.

[1] Local towns, not to be confused with their better-known namesakes in Attica. —*Trans.*

More success attended the efforts to drain the Campagna, the Pontine marshes and other localities. The Campagna and the Pontine marshes, which nowadays appear as deserted territory, were once flourishing and fruitful lands—particularly the part of the Campagna nearer Rome—where wealthy Romans had their villas and gardens. In the Campagna the waters flowing down towards the sea accumulate and form swamps. The Pontine marshes originate in the same way. The Romans had constructed a well-organized network of drains which laid dry all this marshy country so that it became habitable and could be cultivated. The draining was carried out by means of open trenches or dykes and also with the help of pipes. Only after the downfall of Rome did neglect lead to the formation of new swamps. Malaria followed in their wake, the country became depopulated and has remained so to this day. It is being proposed at the present time to carry out draining operations again to win back the soil. Similar drainage works were carried out wherever Roman influence and Roman civilization made itself felt. But, as in the Campagna, when the Romans withdrew, these works were also neglected and their blessings likewise vanished.

ROADS AND BRIDGES

GENERAL REMARKS

THE roads of antiquity may in general be brought under one of two headings : either they served as a means of communication between neighbouring places that carried on an active trade with each other, or they had been constructed for strategic reasons. The purpose of the latter was to make it possible for the army to reach the frontier in quick marches so as to ward off invaders or to advance into neighbouring territory. The state of the roads was no less different than their purpose. The ordinary roads, built for traffic and trade, were in general in a bad state : often they were mere foot-tracks or foot-worn paths without foundation of any sort and without means for draining off the water ; and nothing or only what was absolutely necessary was done to preserve them. Military roads were different. They were laid down with the greatest care and with high technical skill ; moreover, they were kept in an excellent state of repair. Special officials, often in great number, were entrusted with their supervision. The idea according to which all roads were built, ordinary and military, was founded on the simple axiom that the straight line is the shortest distance between two points. So far as the conditions of the country do not require curves and corners ancient roads in general run in absolutely straight lines.

ROADS OF THE EAST

Comparatively little is known to us of the roads of Mesopotamian peoples. Only very few traces of them have been found, and they can give us no idea of their appearance, their condition, or of how they were made. Layard has found remains of a road leading to Nineveh which was paved with stones. But the remains were insufficient to allow conclusions to be drawn about the method of road-building prevalent in those parts.

In Egypt it was not necessary to construct high-roads, for the Nile, then as now, formed the best and most convenient trade route. Nevertheless there were isolated roads from the Nile valley to the East as well as to the West, which connected the chief trade centres with more distant places. For the most part, however, they seem to have been simple caravan tracks that in the course of time developed of themselves into roads. Later the roads received a facing of stone. The roads which passed along the edge of the desert were protected from it by walls. Whether these walls were intended to prevent the roads being covered up by the desert sand or whether they were to protect the caravans from the attacks of desert tribes has not been definitely established. Rameses II had a road tunnelled in rock along the coast of Syria, probably the only example of this type of road-construction made by the Egyptians. Most Egyptian roads were made in later times—after the Roman conquest—and hence are to be regarded as Roman roads. They are constructed in accordance with the technical principles found serviceable by the Romans in constructing their own roads.

GREEK ROADS

We are better informed about Greek roads than about those of the peoples just mentioned. As in so many of the applied arts of the Greeks, so in road-building we clearly discern Phoenician influence.[1] It is even probable that the first Greek roads were actually constructed by the Phoenicians, who thus connected their coastal towns in Greece with the interior of the country in order to transport valuable products from them to their ships. The products brought to the coast were mostly wood, copper, ore and so forth, which were either used for building ships and for constructing wharves or were loaded up on the ships. These most ancient of Phoenician roads were very simple. Tracks were cut through woods, irregularities of the ground were smoothed out, and where swampy soil was encountered near the coast, as often happened, causeways were erected over which the roads passed. When, later, Greek civilization became more and more dissociated from Phoenician influence and when Greece entered upon her golden age, a new and original form of road-building arose. A particular feature of Greek life was the deciding element for the development of this method in Greece. Not only were ordinary traffic roads and military roads required, as in the case of other peoples, but festival routes were also needed that led to the holy places and temples of the gods. Some of these holy places were reverenced by the whole people. At certain seasons or on certain days there were festive processions, to take part in which people came from afar. To allow the procession to pass by undisturbed, roads had to be laid down and provision had to be made for allowing the costly ceremonial carriages to pass along without suffering harm. This was achieved by cutting parallel tracks in the road, the distance between them being equal to the width between the wheels. These tracks in old roads constructed for processions are still preserved nowadays to a considerable number. The distance between the tracks varies, the depth of the surface of the track amounts to nearly 3 in. We have here in a certain sense the earliest form of tram- or of rail-transport, and a type of road-structure that has not yet become obsolete. As an example we may quote a high-road between Heringsdorf and Swinemünde on the Baltic in which tracks have also been laid,—in this case on iron supports; ordinary country carts travel along on them. Corresponding to the average number of encounters of vehicles on these single tracks a number of loops were made such as we still find on narrow mountain tracks. The contour of the country was followed just

[1] An obsolete theory.—*Trans.*

as in the earlier stages of railroad building ; the rail-track passed round all bends and curves, around all hills and obstacles, instead of cutting through them, as is now done. That is why many of the railway lines in Germany, as elsewhere, have such an extraordinary number of curves. In the same way the Greeks were not able to carry out artificial constructions on a large scale ; they made their tracks follow all the unevennesses of the ground while keeping straight wherever possible, and so their roads were very circuitous. In this way distances were considerably lengthened. They knew, however, how to remove rocks, if they were not too massive, or to level them, how to build good causeways, how to give their roads lasting surfaces by paving them, how to give them an artistic finish by setting up tombstones, herms, fountains and so forth along the sides. There are, however, no exceptional features in the road-construction of the Greeks.

ROMAN ROADS

Striking improvements manifest themselves when we come to consider Roman roads. They represent the highest stage of development in road-making. The Romans were compelled to have good roads, as it was only by constructing and preserving them that the Roman Empire could exist and endure. Rome's extensive trade made greater demands on the laying-down of the network of roads than was the case with other peoples. It was necessary to be ready at any moment to transfer soldiers—sometimes mighty armies—to frontiers that were often far distant. So Roman rule spread and the system of roads developed simultaneously. A special class of craftsman, the road-builder, came into being ; numerous workmen were enlisted into the service of building and maintaining roads. At first it was the legions themselves who did this, since work had to be found for them, too much leisure tending to produce dissatisfaction and mutiny. Further, slaves and conquered people had to lend their aid when a military road was to be built. These vassal peoples were well aware of the value of roads for upholding Roman rule ; they knew that they could be permanently freed from the Roman yoke only when the roads had been destroyed. When the Roman Empire fell to pieces, this was, therefore, the first act of many peoples in order to hinder armies from advancing anew. Nevertheless numerous old Roman roads have been preserved to the present day—the best proof of their excellent construction and the high stage of development reached in Roman road-building.

There was, indeed, ample scope for development in the course of centuries. The total length of the roads built by the Romans is estimated at over 47,000 miles, a distance approximately equal to twice the circumference of the earth. The roads constituted a network of lines resembling those of our modern railways : the shortest route was aimed at, no matter what obstacles were in the way. Rocks were cleared away, tunnels were dug through hills, embankments were thrown up, swamps were drained, and the road itself was built as if to last for ever. Matschoso says expressively that Roman roads resembled walls that had been laid on their sides.

This advanced technique of road-building started from simple beginnings. In the Roman empire, as elsewhere, simple connecting ways were first made, which were gradually improved until finally a smooth highroad resulted. But even the original simple roads seem to have been constructed with a view to their lasting for ever. Even nowadays we find, for example, in the Grand-Duchy of Oldenburg, ancient Roman timber-roads, that is, roads made only of logs or planks, which have outlasted centuries. The survey-sheet No. 1734 of the Royal Prussian Topographic Survey of 1898 had one of the routes marked 'Roman timber-road' (*Bohlweg*). The planks consist partly of oak and partly of fir-wood, and are mostly shaped. They have the form of boards with wedge-shaped cross-section (Fig. 614). The planks lay either close to each other

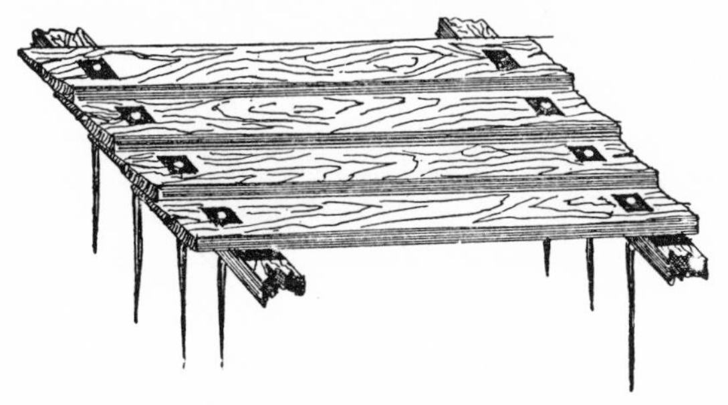

FIG. 614.—Diagrammatic representation of a Roman log-road

or overlapped a little, so that the thin edge of each plank was under the thick edge of the next. In soft swampy ground longitudinal beams were fixed under the planks. Each plank had a triangular or rectangular hole at each end through which a plug was inserted in order to keep the structure rigid. The unevennesses that resulted from the wedge-shape of the planks was filled in with sand or earth. Böcker has given a detailed description of a timber-path of this type. He says:

> 'In the timber-road one plank projects a little beyond the next like the tiles on a roof. The planks have been shaped by an axe and are fastened by longitudinal beams and plugs. The whole work has been done very carefully. The planks consist mostly of oak, whereas the plugs are made also of birch, fir and alder. The white rind of the birch is still recognizable. The planks are 10 feet long, 9 inches wide, and over 3 inches thick. At a distance of 9 inches from each end there is a square hole over 1½ square inches in area, through which a plug has been inserted to fasten the plank more firmly into the soft soil of the moor. The longest plug is 4½ feet long, 1¾ inches thick at the top, ⅘ inch thick at the bottom. Most of the plugs are 2 to 3 feet long: some carry a head 2¾ inches across and 4 inches long. The plugs have apparently been sharpened with a few cuts, those of oak are somewhat rectangular. The planks are cracked on one side, and this cracked side faces upwards.'

At a spot about ten minutes from the above timber-road many separate pieces of wood have been found, and Böcker has succeeded in establishing that there is at this point a second timber-road which runs approximately parallel to the first and also has the direction north-west to south-east.

The timber-roads here described are mentioned by Tacitus who writes in his *Annals* (I, 61) that Germanicus had sent his lieutenant Caecina in advance 'in order to reconnoitre the hidden depths of the wood and to build bridges and dams over swampy and treacherous ground'. But later (I, 63) he writes:

'After he (Germanicus) had led his army to the River Ems, he brought the legions back by means of the fleet just as he had brought them thither. Part of the cavalry received the order to proceed to the Rhine along the shores of the North Sea. Caecina, who led his own detachment, was warned, although he was returning by a well-known route, to cross over the Long Bridges (*pontes longi*) as rapidly

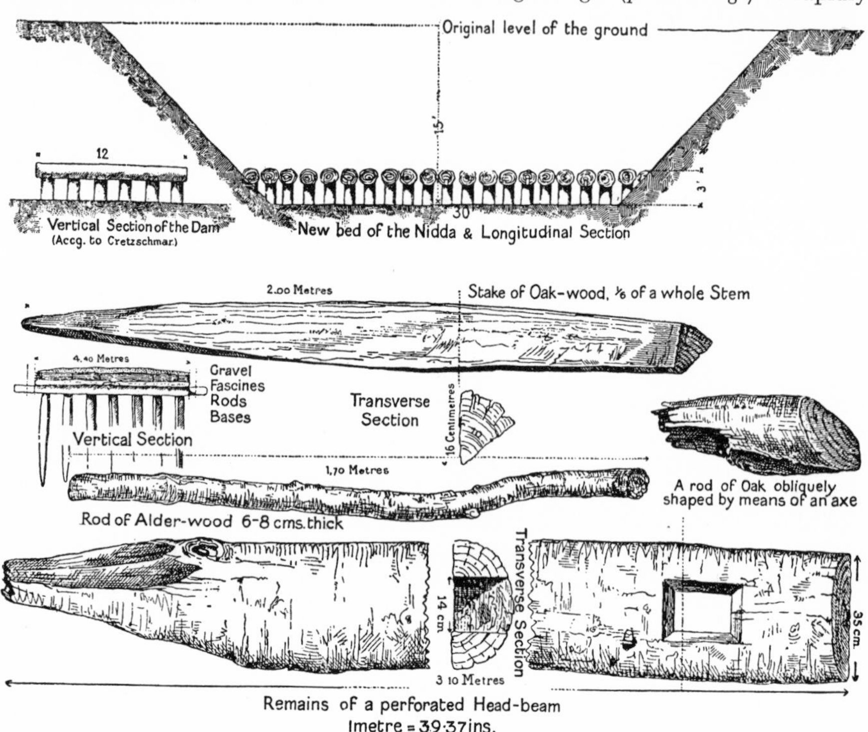

FIG. 615.—Roman Road supported on stakes, at Rödelheim

as possible. This is a narrow path through extensive swamps which had once been raised (*aggeratus*) by L. Domitius. The rest was slimy, viscous, clinging mud or else cut up with streams; round about were gradually ascending woods, which Arminius held in occupation at the time, as he had forestalled the army, heavily laden with baggage and arms, by means of shorter routes and forced marches. Caecina meditated how he could repair the bridges worn with age and at the same time ward off the enemy. He determined to pitch camp on the spot (where the swamp began over which the Long Bridges led), in order that one part of the army could resume the work (of restoring the bridges), and the other could take up the battle.'

A derived form of timber-road is that constructed on stakes; it consists of the above kind of timber-road mounted on stakes or joist-frames and often having a covering of pavement. An example of such raised roads was found at Rödelheim (Fig. 615); it was 13 ft. wide and was made of oak stems about 7 ft. high, which had been rammed into the loamy soil or the underlying layer of gravel. All the stakes had been split longitudinally from the solid logs, many stems having been split six times (as shown in the figure). The stakes were extraordinarily close together, their head-ends stood at the same height over the length and breadth of the road. Stems with fissures along the middle were placed over these

Fig. 616.—Section of a Roman High-road (*Via Appia*)
Deutsches Museum, Munich

ends, the convex surfaces being directed upwards. Our figure shows complete stems which were supposed to have been found during a first excavation undertaken by Cretsschmar and also with the stakes themselves, but later researches did not confirm this result. These 'head-beams' were sometimes longer than the breadth of the road. The longer pieces had rectangular holes in the parts projecting beyond the road; the purpose of these holes has not yet been determined (see Fig. 615). Perhaps

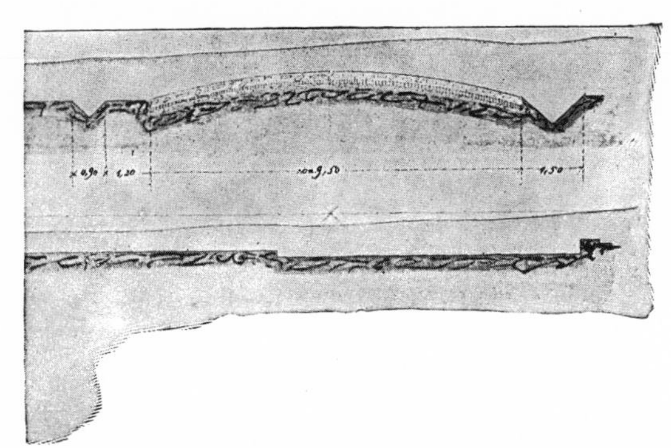

Figs. 617 and 618.—Section through Roman Roads at Heddernheim

they supported a railing, perhaps stakes were passed through them into the ground below to prevent the road from slipping sideways, as would appear possible under the pressure of heavy traffic. The depressions between the head-beams were filled out with billets of alder wood. Fascines were placed over this structure and on them gravel, which formed the face of the road.

We are probably not wrong in assuming that these timber-roads, laid down as late as in the period of the Roman Empire, are one of the oldest forms of Roman road-construction : for in the vicinity of Rome there were numerous swamps that had to be traversed. Until better methods were devised, the timber roads were probably also laid down there.

FIG. 619.—Section through the Bedding of an ancient Roman Road
Deutsches Museum, Munich

Later, a better road was constructed, starting from Rome and passing in particular through the Pontine marshes, which led in a straight line to Cumae ; this is the ' via Domitiana ', of which the poet Statius (45–96 B.C.)

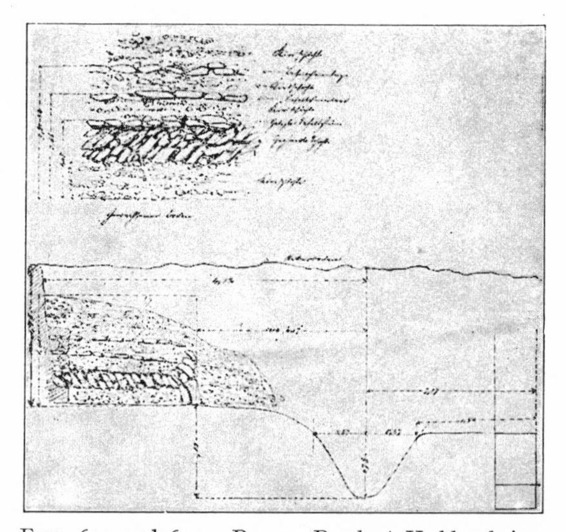

FIGS. 620 and 621.—Roman Road at Heddernheim
Sequence of the layers from below upwards : ground-soil, layer of fragments, deposited basalt stones, layer of grave, layer of basalt, layer of gravel, basalt, gravel

gives a detailed description (*Silvae,* IV, 3, 40). According to his account two parallel furrows (*sulci*) were first dug, which marked the limits of the road and were also to receive and conduct away the water that drained

FIG. 623.—Part of the Via Appia

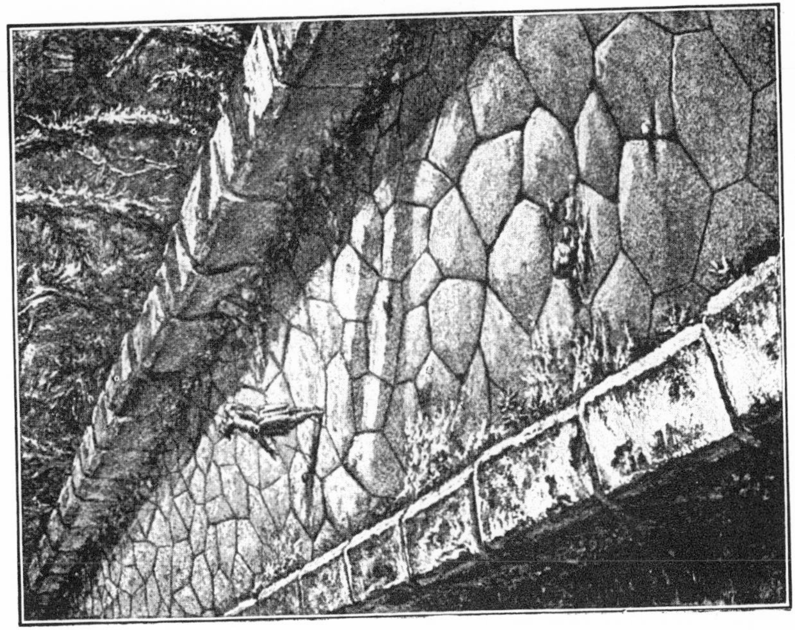

FIG. 622.—Part of the Via Appia

off it. The earth between the two trenches was next removed so that a wide trench resulted, which was to receive the bedding. A row of large kerb-stones (*umbones*) was placed along the sides of this trench to mark its boundary and to keep in the bedding. To fix them firmly in marshy ground strong wooden stakes were rammed in at their sides. The bedding was then covered with large flag-stones over which further layers of stone were placed. Care was taken to make the road convex upwards. The actual surface consisted of a layer of smaller stones which was stamped

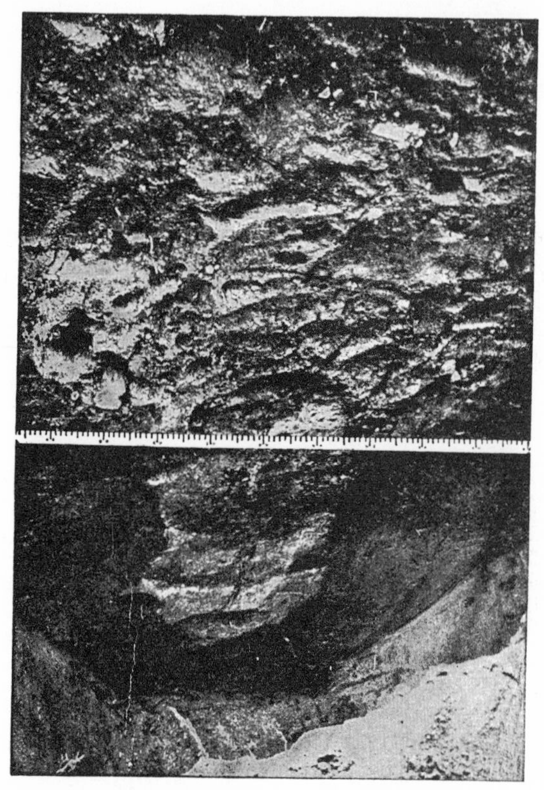

Fig. 624.—Soak-away Channel below a Roman Road at Heddernheim

down and filled in with sand or gravel. In this way a smooth surface was obtained from which, in consequence of the convexity, the rain-water could drain off on either side into the trenches or gutters.

Almost all Roman roads are found to have been constructed in this way. They all have trenches, convex surfaces and kerb-stones (Figs. 616 to 618). The bedding consists of various layers of stones decreasing in size from below upwards (Figs. 619–621). In isolated instances we find departures from this rule due to the nature of the surroundings or for some specific purpose. Thus, some roads have in place of the layer of stone a layer of mortar mixed with large broken stones (Fig. 619), others have a layer of earth that has been stamped down. In some, again (Rheims), the lower layer of large stones has been laid down dry, whereas in others we find hydraulic mortar to have been used.

Nor is the quality of the surface always the same. In general it consits of small stones stamped down and mixed with sand. In many cases, however, the roads are paved, different kinds of material being used for

FIGS. 625 and 626.—Roman Mile-posts
Provincial Museum of Trèves

this purpose. We find ordinary paving-stones with not even the top surface smoothed (for example, at Septimer) and we also find well-paved roads constructed with the utmost care (Via Appia). (See Figs. 622 and 623.) In addition some roads have particularly artistic draining devices; there is one at Heddernheim which has a deep longitudinal channel under the road-metal, which serves as a soak-away for rain-water, together with the two side-gutters. It was dug out while the road was under construction, covered with logs and then with road-metal, consisting of gravel with or without a substratum of coarser stones from river-beds. The water, besides running off the convex surface into the side-channels, also soaked through the gravel into this underground channel (Fig. 624).

The width of the roads varied greatly. Whereas the Via Iulia and some others were only $6\frac{1}{2}$ ft. wide, the Via Appia, as well as the Roman road to the Saalburg and many others, was 14 ft. wide.

Fig. 627.—Roman Milestones at the top of the Julian Pass (Switzerland), 7,627 ft. high, which used to flank the ancient Roman road laid down by Augustus

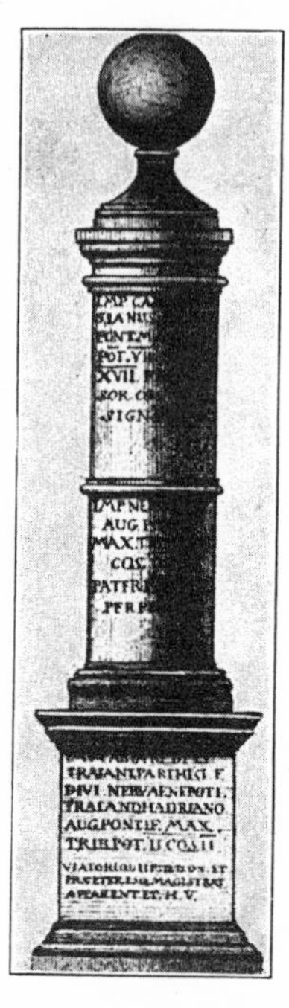

Fig. 628.—Reconstructed Roman Milestone

Again, others were 23 ft. wide, and even more. Many roads, however, had not even the whole of their surface paved. In particular, the Alpine roads were often paved over a strip only 5 ft. wide, whereas the road itself had a width of nearly 7 ft., and in some places even 10 ft.

The roads also varied greatly in their aspect. Many were quite plain, others exhibited important decorative features, in particular, those that started from the great towns. The latter had sculptured sepulchral monuments for miles along the road on both sides. Frequently these high-roads had footpaths running alongside which were often raised and separated from the road proper by a low kerb of stones. Besides this, stones were laid down to make it easier to mount horses and to load and unload beasts of burden. Often there were seats. There were always milestones, mostly in the form of round columns which stated the distance exactly and also other facts such as the name of the emperor under whose direction the road was built (Figs. 622 and 623, and Figs. 625 to 628).

TUNNELS AND CUTTINGS

In building roads it was often found necessary to make a passage through rocks. The Romans were undaunted by this task and so we find numerous Roman roads consisting in part of cuttings and tunnels, for example that at the Iron Gate (*Eiserner Tor*) which runs along the Danube and was built by Tiberius. It was completed as late as A.D. 103 by Trajan. The tunnelling was carried out by means of the processes already treated in the section on 'Mining'. It has been widely thought that the Romans had at their disposal special means for this work and that these means were generally known in antiquity and used by other peoples. Livy in Book 21, Chapter 37 of his Roman History mentions, as if the process itself were common knowledge, that Hannibal used 'fire and vinegar' in his famous crossing of the Alps in the year 218 B.C. to remove the rocks which blocked his path. This passage in Livy has often been commented on, but never fully explained. Philologists and chemists have sought to discover what this 'vinegar' (*acetum*) of Hannibal may have been. Whereas some read '*aceta*', which they interpret as a kind of ice-pick, others take it to be a blowpipe, and others, again, regard it as having been just ordinary vinegar. In particular, Hermann Schelenz, a recognized authority on the history of the natural sciences, has adduced many proofs that vinegar was actually used, which was even at that time prepared in great quantities, particularly in viticultural districts. At the Science Congress in Vienna in 1913 the present author took up a stand against this view and showed by chemical calculations that to dissolve a comparatively small quantity of rock consisting of limestone such immense quantities of vinegar would have been required that its transport by the means then at the disposal of the ancients was quite out of the question. He further showed that the dissolving of limestone even in blocks of comparatively small size would have delayed the army to a quite fantastic extent. But Hannibal took only fifteen days to cross the Alps. Lastly, evidence was furnished to show that this method of dissolving the stone appears impossible for geological reasons. We do not know the exact route followed by Hannibal. Here again there is wide divergence of opinion. But savants are unanimous that only the Eastern Alps or certain parts of the Eastern Central Alps can come into question. The possible roads, then, led exclusively through regions belonging to the gneiss or schistose Alps, in which lime-formations rarely occur. Moreover the soft limestone could be decidedly more easily removed with the tools then available than the hard gneiss which does not dissolve at all in vinegar; this in itself makes the use of vinegar seem highly improbable. But since the Carthaginians were presumably not acquainted with this difference between gneiss and limestone, and since, as already mentioned, limestone occurs in only small traces along the whole route, the first attempts at using vinegar as a solvent were most probably made on gneiss, if they were made at all. The failure of their endeavours must have taught them that it was impossible to dissolve the rock with vinegar, even with the assistance of heat. On chemical, physical, technical and geological grounds, then, we conclude that Hannibal cannot have used vinegar, and so the passage under consideration in Livy seems still to be unexplained.

E. O. von Lippmann remarks that

'The process mentioned in this passage in Livy and also by many other ancient writers refers only to the superstition that vinegar has a particularly " cold nature " and that therefore when vinegar is poured instead of water on to stone heated by igniting a pile of wood over it the meeting of these two extremes would produce a quite extraordinary effect. The superstitious belief in the great " cold " and the resulting immense " power " of vinegar was universally prevalent in antiquity; as has been mentioned elsewhere by the author the military commander Metellus is credited with having " dissolved " a brick tower in the course of a night by means of vinegar! This superstition is still met with. In Switzerland the author has met Italian workmen who in constructing a pathway over the rocks sprinkled vinegar (out of a glass bottle) besides water on the heated stone " *perchè è molto più freddo* " (because it is much colder), and they called this a trade secret.

'That there can be no question of stone being actually " dissolved " is immediately clear from chemical calculation. According to the equation

$$CaCO_3 + 2C_2H_4O_2 = (C_4H_6O_4).Ca + CO_2 + H_2O$$

100 parts by weight of limestone require 120 parts of pure acetic acid or 2,400 parts of vinegar of 5 per cent. strength.' Thus, to dissolve only one ton of limestone Hannibal would have had to transport more than twenty-four tons of vinegar up over the difficult tracks of the Western Alps.

BRIDGES

A particularly important part of a road is that represented by a bridge. The development of bridges was, however, not possible until communications had left the rudimentary stage. It is likely that when a stream had to be crossed fords were first sought, around which settlements formed in many cases; sometimes, indeed, a ford was the origin of a town. Besides fords, ferries and eventually bridges were used for crossing a river. Whether the most ancient bridges were boat-bridges, as has been conjectured, must be left an open question. It does not seem probable; it is more natural for the bridge to have developed from a tree-trunk laid across a narrow part of a stream. If a broader part had to be bridged over, it was natural to place so many tree-stems end to end as were necessary to connect the two banks. The junctions could be effected more easily by erecting supports on the bank or at shallow points in the stream in the shape of stakes or rocks. This is probably the simplest explanation of the origin of bridges, and it does not presuppose the idea of boat-bridges, maintained by many writers.

It is true that boat-bridges came into use very early. Thus Herodotus (VII, 25 *et seq.*) writes of the bridge thrown by the Persian King Xerxes over the Strymon [1]:

'Thus did Xerxes accomplish this work; and for the bridges he charged the Phoenicians and Egyptians with the making of ropes of papyrus and white flax, and storing of provision for his army, that neither it nor the beasts of burden in the march to Hellas should starve.'

---

[1] Now called Struma.

Further (VII, 36), he tells of another boat-bridge and gives the following details of its construction:

'New masters of their craft set about making the bridges. The manner of their doing it was as I will show. That they might lighten the strain of the cables, they laid fifty-oared ships and triremes alongside of each other, three hundred and sixty to bear the bridge that was nearest to the Euxine sea, and three hundred and fourteen to bear the other; all lay obliquely to the line of the Pontus and parallel with the current of the Hellespont. Having so laid the ships alongside they let down very great anchors, both from the end of the ship nearest the Pontus to hold fast against the winds blowing from within that sea, and from the other end, towards the west and the Aegean, to hold against the west and south winds. Moreover they left for passage an opening in the line of fifty-oared ships and triremes, that so he that would might be able to voyage to the Pontus, or out of it. Having so done, they stretched the cables from the land, twisting them taut with wooden windlasses; and they did not as before keep the two kinds apart, but assigned for each bridge two cables of flax and four of papyrus. All these were of the same thickness and fair appearance, but the flaxen were heavier in their proportion, a cubit thereof weighing a talent.[1] When the strait was thus bridged, they sawed balks of wood to a length equal to the breadth of the floating supports, and laid them in order on taut cables, and having set them alongside they then made them fast. This done, they heaped brushwood on to the bridge, and when this was all laid in order they heaped earth on it and stamped it down; then they made a fence on either side, lest the beasts of burden and horses should be affrighted by the sight of the sea below them.'

Boat-bridges were much favoured by the ancients and occurred frequently even in late Roman times when the building of good and lasting bridges had long been mastered. Boat-bridges were particularly suitable for military purposes: they were the quickest to construct and the easiest to demolish. For this reason certain sections of the army always transported the necessary material for building such bridges. The iron implements and hooks for holding together the planks were often prepared for use beforehand.

Of the military bridges and, indeed, of all bridges constructed at short notice, that built by Caesar for his first crossing of the Rhine has achieved especially great renown.

It has frequently been reconstructed in recent times, and there are numerous models of it extant. Caesar's description of how it was built is so clear that a technically trained reader has no difficulty in following it accurately. The bridge is particularly noteworthy because it apparently had no predecessor; Caesar himself calls it 'new'. He writes (*De bello Gallico*, IV, 16–19):

'For the reasons above mentioned Caesar had decided to cross the Rhine; but he deemed it scarcely safe, and ruled it unworthy of his own and the Romans' dignity, to cross in boats. And so, although he was confronted with the greatest difficulty in making a bridge, by reason of the breadth, the rapidity, and the depth of the river, he still thought that he must make that effort, or else not take his army across. He proceeded to construct a bridge on the following plan. He caused pairs of balks eighteen inches thick, sharpened a little way from the base and measured to suit the depth of the river, to be coupled together at an interval of two feet. These he lowered into the river by means of rafts, and set fast, and

[1] About 80 lbs.

drove home by rammers; not, like piles, straight up and down, but leaning forward at a uniform slope, so that they inclined in the direction of the stream. Opposite to these, again, were planted two balks coupled in the same fashion, at a distance of forty feet from base to base of each pair, slanted against the force and onrush of the stream. These pairs of balks had two-foot transoms let into them atop, filling the interval at which they were coupled, and were kept apart by a pair of braces on the outer side at each end. So, as they were held apart and contrariwise clamped together, the stability of the structure was so great and its character such that, the greater the force and thrust of the water, the tighter were the balks held in lock. These trestles were interconnected by timber laid over at right angles, and floored with long poles and wattle-work. And further, piles were driven in aslant on the side facing down stream, thrust out below like a buttress and close joined with the whole structure, so as to take the force of the stream; and others likewise at a little distance above the bridge, so that if trunks of trees, or vessels, were launched by the natives to break down the structure, these fenders might lessen the force of such shocks, and prevent them from damaging the bridge.

'The whole work was completed in ten days from that on which the collecting of timber began, and the army was taken across.'[1]

In the following remarks we follow Cohausen in general but not in all details. In his careful investigations he has rightly insisted that we must regard Caesar's Rhine bridge as a so-called trestle-bridge (*pont de chevalets*), the trestles of which (Fig. 629) consist of two pairs of legs, each pair being joined together in parallel (*cd, cd*), and a capping-piece (H). Legs and capping-piece were made from cleft logs felled in the vicinity and were bound together *in situ*: the legs were pointed and were thrust into the bed of the river by means of blows. The bridge was held together by the method adopted for attaching the trestles; this consisted in each capping-piece being connected to its successor by means of balks or stretches. Further, the legs were shored against the impact of the water. Thus, if we take the above remarks as our basis, the Rhine bridge consisted of the following parts (Fig. 630): the legs *cd*, which are pointed at *d*, the capping-pieces *gh* which rest on the beams *i* and *k*, the clamps at *ghik*, which connect the legs and capping-pieces, the shores or props *d* and *k* which are submerged, and the devices *op* and *mn* (counter-props) that make the bridge safe from obstacles floating down the stream and are intended to give additional rigidity. Higher up the stream we have to picture stakes that have been rammed in, that is a sort of open frame weir, which broke the force of the current.

Doubtless pontoons were used to build the bridge; from them the stakes were sunk through the water into the river-bed, and the capping piece was next laid across and fastened. Whether the stakes were rammed down by means of hammers or with the help of rams (elementary pile-drivers) erected on the pontoons is not mentioned by Caesar. To keep the direction right guiding ropes were probably stretched from bank to bank which, assisted by anchor-ropes leading obliquely to the banks and to fixed points in the river, perhaps served to prevent the pontoons from moving during the work.

[1] From the translation by H. J. Edwards in the Loeb Classical Library (Heinemann). The reader is referred to page 201 of his translation, facing which is a useful sketch and explanatory notes.—H. L. B.

The site of the bridge has not yet been clearly established. It was probably between Andernach and Coblence. At any rate great credit is due to the technical genius of Caesar and his builders for successfully constructing this bridge in the strongly flowing Rhine.

In contrast with these bridges, built only as temporary structures, permanent bridges played a very important part in antiquity; they

FIG. 629.—Trestle-bridge set up on land as a model of Caesar's Rhine Bridge

are met with even in ancient Babylon, where probably the oldest bridge of technical importance—that over the Euphrates—was constructed. It connected the two halves of the ancient city of Babylon, and is supposed to have been built by Nebuchadnezzar. The river is 1,000 yds. wide at that point. More than 100 stone piers were erected in it, on

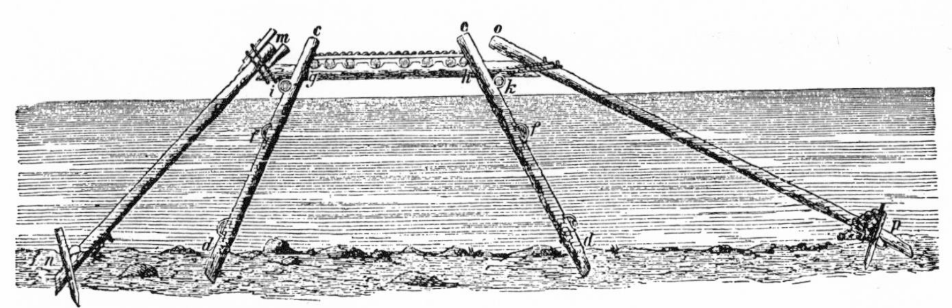

FIG. 630.—Caesar's Rhine Bridge (one section). The direction of the stream is *mn*→*op*

which the platform of the bridge was placed: this platform, 30 ft. wide, was made of beams cut from the palm-tree and was roofed. Although this bridge seems a notable work, there are several technical weaknesses. In the first place a simple calculation shows that the space between successive stone piers, whose width is unknown, was only very small, perhaps 17–20 ft. These narrow gaps and the large number of piers represent a great hindrance to the flow of the river, and bring about blockages and even inundations at high water. Moreover, the method of building in the river itself seems not to have been known; rather the river was diverted during the construction of the bridge. The piers had the sides turned up stream pointed so that the water broke easily on them: they were blunt at the other side. Later, bridge-construction was improved, probably also in Mesopotamia, by adopting arched openings (Fig. 631). In the sections on 'Water-supply', 'Drainage', 'Building', we have dealt fully with arches and their construction, so that we may dispense with further remarks here. The methods involved in building arches and vaults in the case of bridges in no wise differ from that used for aqueducts and channels. The periods of development likewise correspond with the stage of progress of vault-construction. It will therefore be sufficient if we make special reference only to particularly remarkable bridges of antiquity; the method of arching, the corbelling, the use of scaffolding, and other details may be obtained from the above-mentioned sections.

FIG. 631.—Mesopotamian arched Bridge
(Built in the manner of a vault.) Ancient bridge over the Tigris at Diezîreh

Of the ancient Greek bridges there are comparatively very few remnants left and these give us no idea of what stage of progress the Greeks had reached in the building of their best bridges. On the other hand, the Romans showed themselves to be masters in this art. At first they used wooden bridges. The oldest Roman bridge, the '*pons sublicius*', built in the year 625 B.C., was of wood, and is supposed to have been loosely jointed, as has been asserted by various investigators, because the use of iron was prohibited by religious prescriptions at that time. Later these rules were no longer closely observed, and bridges were built in great number with planks fastened by iron clamps.

The old wooden bridges, however, soon gave place to stone bridges, which were constructed in accordance with the rules set out earlier in the text. The arch was built up over a scaffolding, the stones were

FIG. 632.—Ancient Roman Bridge with high ramp and high arch (Ponte Salario). Built A.D. 569

FIG. 633.—Ancient Roman Bridge with arches of different shapes and steep ramp (Ponte Lucano)

connected together by iron clamps fastened in by means of molten lead in the manner already described in detail above. The mortars, when used, either consisted of mixtures of lava with lime-mortar or else hydraulic mortar was used. The town of Amalfi at the entrance of the valley of Molini has an old bridge that dates back probably to the fifth century A.D.; in it natural pozzolona was used as a cement. The bridge is still extant and has lasted through nearly 1,500 years in spite of the absence of iron clamps. Its span is 23 ft., its width 5 ft., and its height above the river-bed about 10 ft. It is evident that the Romans used in their bridge-construction all the means practised in the other branches of building.

Ancient Roman bridges often exhibit astonishingly high vaulted

FIG. 634.—Pons Aelius (the present-day Ponte Sant' Angelo in Rome). Built about A.D. 136

arches, which artificially raised the roadway. Consequently ramps were necessary to lead up to them. If we enquire into the reason for this peculiar construction we again recognize that the Romans did not know how to span over large distances; the piers therefore considerably narrowed the free passage of the stream, so that at high water a considerable rise in level had to be expected. What was taken in width had to be made up in height in order to prevent dangerous accumulation of water. Consequently the bridge was built as high as possible, and the openings of the arches were also extended upwards as far as possible. (Figs. 632–636).

A particularly noteworthy and famous bridge is that built by the Emperor Trajan in the year A.D.104 across the Danube beyond the Iron Gate. Unfortunately the details of its construction have been lost, but from data given by Dio Cassius we may infer that it consisted of 20 stone piers. Its height is supposed to have been 167 ft., its width 67 ft. The distance between the piers was 190 ft., and they were connected by arches. The height seems improbable at first sight, but less so when we consider that the platform of the bridge was probably of wood. The picture on Trajan's Column in Rome allows us to recognize that only the piers were of stone. From these piers a supporting framework projected, between which arches were spanned, which, to all appearances,

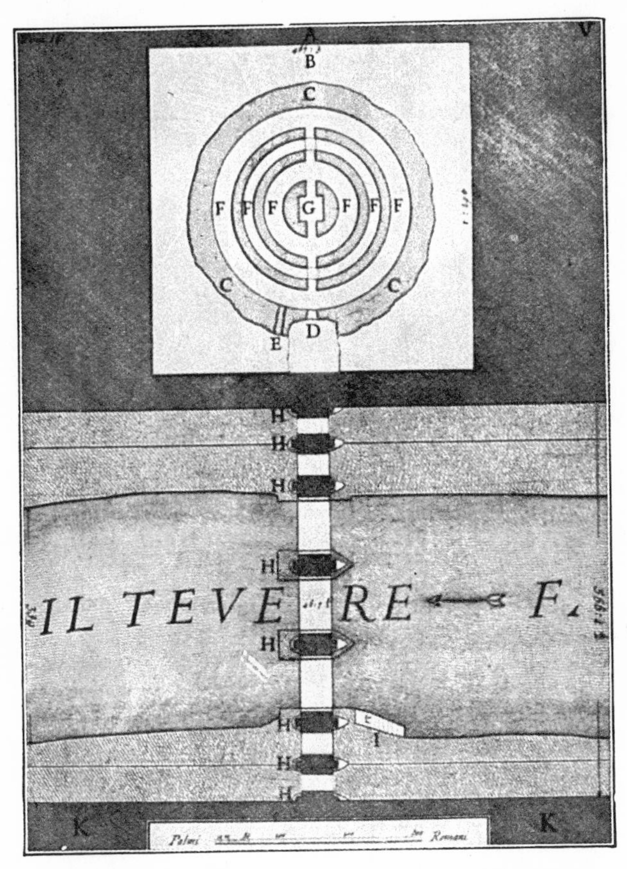

FIG. 635.—The Foundations of the Ponte Sant' Angelo

Piranesi gives two piers in the river and two complete and one half-pier on each bank; doubts have recently arisen whether the foundation was constructed in this way at the time the bridge was first built, but no essential divergence from Piranesi's data is involved; the question raised is whether there were only two piers and therefore two arches on the bank on which the Castel Sant' Angelo stands. In 1688 it was adorned with ten colossal statues of angels, designed by Bernini. In the years 1892–1894, when the flow of the Tiber was being regulated, the bridge was remodelled: at present only the three middle arches are of ancient Roman origin. The top part of the ground-plan represents the Castel Sant' Angelo, the tomb of the Roman Emperor Hadrian (*moles Hadriani*), in which all the Emperors from Hadrian down to Caracalla were interred. The rising path F leads to the tomb G

were also made of wooden beams. The actual platform of the bridge rested on these arches and consequently was supported by the framework let into the pillars. The bridge was provided with a railing.

Another feature is the way in which the stone piers are fixed in the middle of the Danube. This mighty stream could not be deflected from its course. Coffer-dams were therefore fixed in the stream; nothing

FIG. 636.—The Isola Tiberina (Tiber Island) at Rome with the two bridges (Pons Cestius on the left and Pons Fabricius on the right)

A feature of the Pons Fabricius is the way in which the weight on the pier has been relieved by means of an aperture above the foundation

FIG. 637.—Model of the Roman bridge (one arch right across the river) at Mainz

Museum of Antiquities of the town of Mainz

FIG. 638.—Model of a Piling-grating with ballasting and parts of the masonry of a pier of the Roman Rhine-bridge at Mainz. Museum of Antiquities of Mainz

The model shows the high foundation of the pier. It is not established how the piling-grating was erected in the swiftly flowing Rhine. (See the remarks in the text about the bridge thrown by the Emperor Trajan over the Danube)

is known of their construction. At any rate it is clear that the Romans used such means, a fact that is confirmed by the details of other of their bridge-constructions.

It is probable that such coffer-dams were also used in building the bridge at Mainz in the swift current of the Rhine. Otherwise we cannot

FIG. 639.—Roman Medal, made of lead

In the foreground on the right: the Rhine bridge at Mainz. Found in the Saône at Lyons, preserved in the Bibliothèque nationale in Paris. Diameter 3–3½ in.

explain how the piling-grating and stone foundations can have been constructed. In the Rhine-bridge (Figs. 637 and 638) the wooden framework rising from the stone pillars which supported the platform of the bridge was probably built in a similar way to that adopted for Trajan's bridge over the Danube, as represented on the Trajan Column in Rome.

FIG. 640.—The Bridge at Trèves in its modern form

Whether piling-gratings were used in the bridge over the Danube is not known, but certain finds render it probable. An ancient Roman design on a lead medal (Fig. 639) allows us to recognize some details of the Roman bridge at Mainz, in particular the arch, piers, foundations, railing, and so forth. The upper structure exhibits features that lead us to infer that its architecture was of wood (compare Fig. 637).

The Roman Moselle Bridge at Trèves (Figs. 640 and 641) is well preserved; in its original form it probably dates back to the time of the Emperor Constantine the Great, A.D. 274–337. Of the eight piers only seven are still visible, the eighth being covered by alluvial soil that has been thrown up. And of these seven only five are of Roman origin, as can easily be recognized by their dark colour (the material being basalt lava). The other two (shown with lighter shading in Fig. 641), were destroyed by the French in 1689 and then restored. The distance between the piers is 67 ft. Projections from their upper parts suggest that the original upper structure was likewise of wood, but it is possible that they also served to hold the scaffolding for erecting the arches.

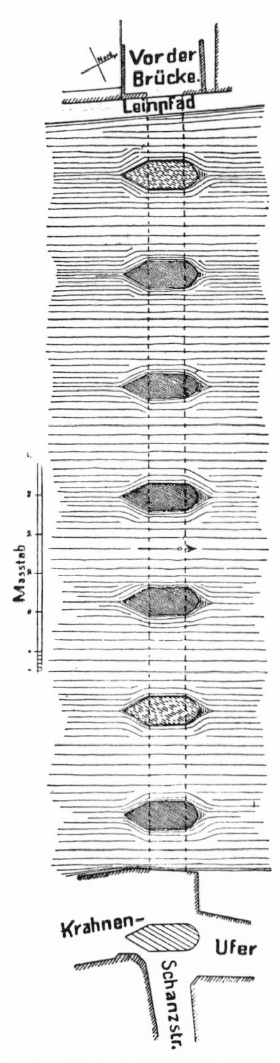

FIG. 641.—Ground-plan of the Bridge at Trèves

SHIPS AND SHIP-BUILDING

THE OLDEST FORMS OF SHIPS: SHIPS OF THE EAST

ALTHOUGH there are no facts to support the assumption, ships are supposed to have their origin in floating tree-stems. According to another legend a small crustacean, the nautilus, is the prototype of the most ancient ships. Such evidence is too meagre to allow inferences to be drawn about the earliest forms of ships. We find such forms, indeed, in a fairly advanced stage of development among the Mesopotamian peoples as well as among the Egyptians. Several finds dating back to prehistoric times, such as dug-out canoes, allow us to recognize isolated steps of the earlier development, but they

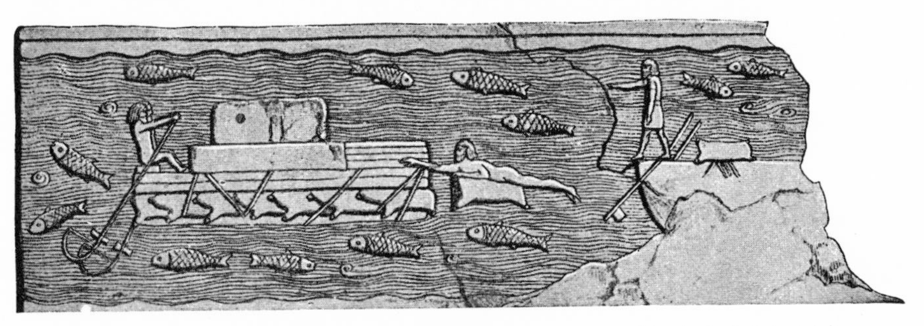

FIG. 642.—Assyrian Kelek and (behind) a man on a Float (inflated skin)

On the right there is also a float on the boat (circular ?), to which strings are apparently attached; perhaps they served to tie the man to the float as is nowadays done with our swimming-belts. Relief from Nineveh

are not sufficient to give us a connected picture. The Mesopotamian means of travelling over water allow us to differentiate accurately between two fundamental forms: one resembling a raft, the other a boat. The raft type is exemplified in the 'kelek' which is still in use nowadays, and which is shown in ancient Assyrian representations, for example on a relief-tablet preserved in the British Museum (Fig. 642). According to the researches of Lehmann-Haupt the kelek is probably still made in just the same way as formerly. Inflated sheep-skins, so-called 'burdjuks', are fixed under a frame which in the case of small keleks consists of willow rods and other flexible material (Fig. 643). A platform of boards is placed on these. Straw, reeds or moss is spread over the top; this completes the construction of the vessel, which carries persons or freight. For large transports keleks are made which are often composed of as many as 2,300 such inflated sheep-skins. The carrying power is very great, as was once tested by the great strategist von Moltke in his travels. The kelek has the further advantage of carrying its passengers safely through rapids such as occur in mountain streams of unequal depth and varying speed, although there is a great deal of swirling and churning of the waters and the passengers do not escape a good wetting. The individual burdjuk, as the above-mentioned Assyrian and also

FIG. 643.—Making Keleks from 'Burdjuks'

Babylonian representations of the ninth century B.C. show, was further used as a float for individual persons. For this purpose the sheep-skin was sewn together and tied under the body. A mouthpiece appears to have been supplied to allow escaped air to be replaced while swimming

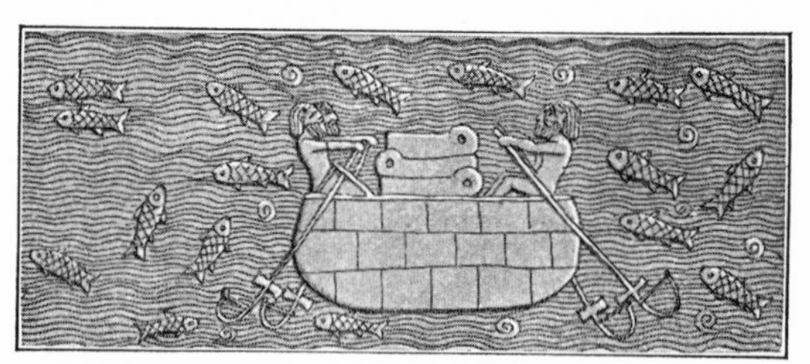

FIG. 644.—Circular Assyrian Boat. Relief from Nineveh

(Fig. 642 and 645). This Mesopotamian float is a forerunner of the cork swimming-belt, which was early known to the Romans. In the year 390 B.C. Camillus sent a messenger to the Capitol, who swam the Tiber on a cork float.

Besides keleks the Assyrians, however, also had circular ships whose body consisted of animal skins stretched over a wooden frame or a net-work of reeds. These circular ships were used for transport as well as purposes of war (Figs. 644 and 645). On them, for example, Shalmanasser

III (782–772 B.C.) fought against the natives of the shores of Lake Urmia. Herodotus pronounces these circular ships to be the greatest wonder that he encountered in the Land of Two Rivers, and his accurate description leaves no doubt that his knowledge of them was first-hand. He writes (I, 194):

'I will now show what seems to me to be the most marvellous thing in the country, next to the city itself. Their boats which ply on the river and go to Babylon are all of skins, and round. They make these in Armenia, higher up the stream than Assyria. First they cut frames of willow, then they stretch hides over these for a covering, making as it were a hold; they neither broaden the stern nor narrow the prow, but the boat is round like a shield. They then fill it with reeds and send it floating down the river with a cargo; and it is for the most part palm-wood casks of wine that they carry down. Two men standing upright steer the boat, each with a paddle, one drawing it to him, the other thrusting it from him. These boats are of all sizes, some small, some very great; the greatest of

FIG. 645.—Circular Assyrian Vessels, somewhat elongated, used as war-ships

The boat is propelled by means of oars and also towed (by the two men in front): it is provided with a steering device. Above in the middle is a man with a float. Relief in the Palace of Sanherib at Nineveh, dating from the seventh or the end of the eighth century B.C.

them are even of five talents burden.[1] There is a live ass in each boat, or more than one in the larger. So when they have floated down to Babylon and disposed of their cargo, they sell the framework of the boat and all the reeds; the hides are set on the backs of asses, which are then driven back to Armenia, for it is not by any means possible to go up stream by water, by reason of the swiftness of the current; it is for this reason that they make their boats of hides and not of wood. When they have driven their asses back into Armenia they make more boats in the same way'.[2]

The Phoenicians also navigated their waterways in circular boats; to them[3] falls the credit of having first undertaken long sea-trips. As early as 3000 B.C. they are supposed to have founded the fishing-town Sidon, which was dependent on shipping owing to its geographical position. Its population increased so rapidly that in the year 2760 B.C. its inhabitants founded the daughter-town Tyre; this was in turn followed by the town Gades in 1160 B.C., which is our modern Cadiz—a proof of the

[1] The Attic talent = about 58 lbs. avoirdupois; the Aeginetan = about 82.
[2] From A. D. Godley's translation, The Loeb Classical Library, Heinemann.
[3] Rather to the Cretan Minoans—*Trans.*

great distances covered by their ships at even that remote period. From Gades the Phoenician ships sailed to the coasts of the North Sea and the Baltic to fetch tin and amber. The ships originally used by the Phoenicians were probably the round ships met with in the ancient Assyrian representations. They were also on that account called γαῦλοι (*gauli*), a term derived from the milk-pail which had a similar shape and bore the same name. The *gauli* of the Phoenicians first probably served as freighters, but later also as war-ships. It is very probable that as war-vessels they were first provided with the spur used for ramming which is mentioned about the year 700 B.C.; the spur was then adopted by the Greeks, who first used it in the naval battle at Alalia (in Corsica) in 536 B.C. Perhaps the Phoenician *gauli* were also the first ships to carry a sail. Their sailing device was of a characteristic construction inasmuch as it consisted of a fixed beam, that is, not a yard that could be lowered. This beam was attached horizontally to the mast and the main-sail was tied to it. The boom, to which the lower end of the sail is now ordinarily attached, was missing. On both sides of the stern there was a steering-oar. In proportion as the sea-voyages of the Phoenicians became longer the size of the ships, the number of the oarsmen and the dimensions of the tackle increased. We shall see below that some of these peculiarities of Phoenician ships are met with again in those of other peoples, in particular in those of the Egyptians and Greeks. We are reminded of the Greek legend about the civilization that was spread abroad by Cadmus of Phoenicia: while he was wandering in Europe to find the sister stolen by Zeus, he founded a number of Greek towns which he provided with the comforts of Phoenician civilization.

THE SHIPS OF THE EGYPTIANS

The Egyptians carried on their trade chiefly by land. Their shipping was restricted to the Nile, but perhaps also extended to the Red Sea. Isolated voyages, such as the expedition of Queen Hatshepsut in 1650 B.C., in which five ships set out for the land of Punt, which is probably somewhere on the coast of Somaliland, are to be regarded as unusual enterprises. In spite of this limited range of their shipping the Egyptians learned much in the construction and equipment of ships from the Phoenicians. Moreover, they adapted their ships, which plied on the busy waterway of the Nile, to the most varied needs, so that very different types of ships, from the pleasure-yacht and the ship of mourning to the heavy ship of commerce, came into being, of which many drawings give us detailed information.

Herodotus (II, 96) gives us an account of the manner in which Egyptian ships were built:

'The boats in which they carry cargo are made of the acacia, which is in form most like to the lotus of Cyrene, and its sap is gum. Of this tree they cut logs of two cubits length and lay them like courses of bricks, and build the boat by making these two-cubit logs fast to long and close-set stakes; and having so built they set cross-beams athwart and on the logs. They use no ribs. They caulk the seams within with byblus. These boats cannot move upstream unless a brisk breeze continue; they are towed from the bank; but downstream they are thus managed: they have a raft made of tamarisk wood, fastened together with matting of reeds, and a pierced stone of about two talents' weight; the raft is let go to float down ahead of the boat, made fast to it by a rope, and the stone is made fast also by a rope to the after part of the boat. So, driven by the current, the raft floats swiftly and tows the "baris" (which is the name given to these boats), and the stone dragging behind on the river bottom keeps the boat's course straight. There are many of these boats; some are of many thousand talents' burden.'[1]

This account of Herodotus seems in general to be correct, but it may be doubted whether the estimate he gives of the carrying power of ancient Egyptian freighters is not too high. Since a 'talent' corresponds to about 58 lbs. these ships are credited with carrying many tons of cargo. If we consider the modern ships on the Nile, and also the ancient pictures, it does not seem probable that ancient Egyptian ships were capable of carrying such loads. Besides this, the method of ship-construction described by Herodotus does not seem to have been the only method practised by the Egyptians. Smaller boats such as were used for catching fish were made in the simplest way by binding together lotus-stems—as is shown on reliefs that have been preserved, in particular one in the Berlin Museum. From mural paintings we further learn that the papyrus was also used for making these boats, the stems being bound together by strings of papyrus. Pliny's assertion (VI, 82) that these papyrus boats traversed the ocean as far as the island Taprobane (now Ceylon) is probably due to an error which arose from the fact that Egyptian sails were sometimes made of papyrus; but this was rare. Only isolated representations of Nile boats, as in a mural painting at Kom el Ahmar, lead us to conjecture that the sail is of papyrus, and that it consists of separate sheets arranged so that they can be folded together or reefed. Usually, Egyptian sails were made of linen or other material. They were in many cases painted, and they formed an important article of commerce which the Phoenicians in particular bought in great quantities. 'Fine linen with broidered work from Egypt was that which thou spreadest forth to be thy sail,' we read in Ezekiel xxvii. 7. Egyptian sails were also constructed from mats made of palm-leaves. We see all the details of their construction in mural paintings in Thebes and Beni-Hasan, but nothing is to be added to what has already been said in the section on the production of textiles. For the rest, Herodotus' account of the building of ancient Egyptian ships may be supplemented by the remark that large cargo vessels were built of wooden planks in the way still practised to-day; the planks were produced by sawing and were fastened with nails (Fig. 646).

The sailing vessels had either one or two oars at the stern which served as rudders. They rested on poles or were fastened to them by strings so that they could be easily moved. They often reposed in a deep groove cut in the stern. On the rudder and also on the sides an eye was usually painted (Fig. 648); the symbolic meaning of this is well known—it is to ward off ill-luck (see also the remarks attached to Fig. 654). The single mast originally used was later succeeded by a double mast.

[1] A. D. Godley's translation, Loeb Classical Library, Heinemann.

The form of Egyptian ships varied widely according to their purpose, and likewise the names given to them by ancient writers. The larger

FIG. 646.—Building a Ship in Egypt

The body of the ship is supported at both ends by props. On the left is an overseer. The workmen are using (from right to left) an adze, a smoothing implement (?), a hatchet, chisel, and wooden mallet

boats, no matter whether they were pleasure-vessels or vessels for procuring market wares, all had cabins. But we also find cabins in the smaller boats, which were towed. In some freighters the cabins were large enough to be used as stables for transporting animals. A special device which we frequently meet with in antique vessels is a rope that is stretched from the bow to the stern over the whole length of the boat, even over the cabins; its purpose was to prevent the boat breaking in the middle. (Figs. 650 and 651, see also p. 493.) This rope relieves the strain on the keel.

FIG. 647.—Types of Egyptian Ships

Fisherman's simple Nile-boat in a lotus thicket. Limestone relief on the doorpost of a grave. Berlin Museum, Egyptian section

Sails were of use on the Nile only when the winds were favourable. When the sails were not required, it was found convenient to unstep the mast (Fig. 649). Pictures from Eileithyia show us that many Egyptian ships were therefore equipped with dismountable masts. At the

FIG. 648.—Types of Egyptian Ships: Funerary Barge (painted)

In the middle is a baldachino supported by six wooden posts; below, a couch. The four sons of Osiris are crouching at the corners; at the feet of the dead person we see Isis, at the head Nephthis. On the side of the vessel is the protective 'eye' and also on the two steering-oars resting against the vertical posts. The form of the ship corresponds exactly with that of Fig. 646. Berlin Museum, Egyptian Section

lower end of a mast depicted in the mural painting of a grave at Eileithyia we can discern a wheel which was formerly often interpreted as a device

FIG. 649.—Types of Egyptian Ships. Galley with one sailing-mast (from Gurnah)

The sides and the single steering-oar are painted; the oar is fastened to a high post (stern-post) and is moved by a handle which comes down vertically (tiller). The mast is dismounted; the yard has had the two parts of which it consists folded and tied to the mast. Berlin Museum, Egyptian Section

for stepping and unstepping the mast. Detailed investigation has, however, shown that it belongs to a chariot that is loaded up on the

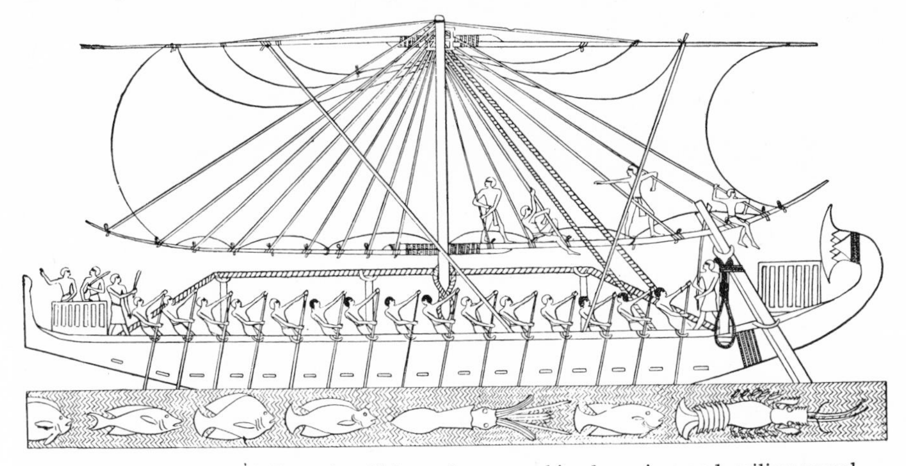

FIG. 650.—Types of Egyptian Ships: large combined rowing and sailing vessel

A cable has been stretched over the whole length of the ship and is also coiled round the mast. The yard is in two parts, joined at the mast, and is supported by long oblique poles, which apparently rest on the starboard and port gunwales; parts of the rope-work suggest that they can be hauled up or down. Composite beam. Oarsmen standing and 'pulling'. Oars in rings. At the bow a sort of 'bridge' and overseers or commanders with scourges. At the stern a second (empty) bridge, steering-oar attached to the stern-post, and steersman holding a tiller coming down vertically from the rudder. Behind him is a great loop of rope for fastening the rudder or attaching the ship to the mooring-place (Fig. 651 makes the latter suggestion seem improbable, as we see this loop still hanging down although the ships are certainly moored)

roof of the cabin. The horses which are to pull the chariot have also been placed aboard. The sails seem always to have been rectangular.

Whether lateen sails, that is, sails of triangular shape, were used in ancient Egypt seems doubtful. When very wide sails were used the yards were

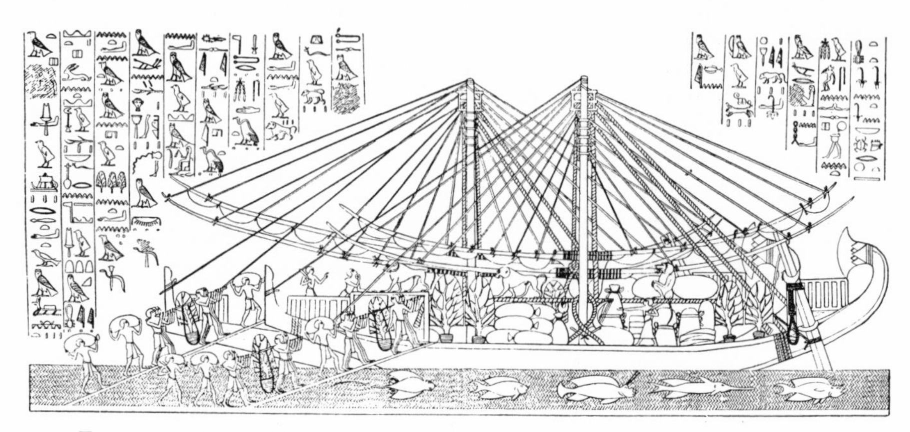

FIG. 651.—Types of Egyptian Ships: two large cargo vessels being loaded
The sails have been completely removed, the spars let down; below them are loops of rope on which the sailors can stand when manning the sails. The remaining details are as in Fig. 650

united at the mast by having the ends of their two halves tied together by ropes (Figs. 650 and 651). At the bottom edge of the sail was a main-

FIG. 652.—Ring-rowlocks on Egyptian ships; Oarsmen standing
Fragment of a limestone relief in Derel Bahrî. Height 8 in., width 8½ in. (One of the men has been painted on flat, instead of being worked in relief.) Berlin Museum, Egyptian Section

boom (Figs. 650 and 651). In many ships the yards could be hauled up and down. The oars or sweeps of Egyptian ships had a long round shaft to which the flat oval or circular blade was attached (Fig. 649). They were held in position either by dowels (pin-rowlocks) or by rings attached to the gunwale of the boat, which at the same time served as fulcra for the oars (Fig. 652). The oarsmen either stood, kneeled, or sat on low rowing-seats (Fig. 649) or benches. The boat itself was either propelled forwards by the oars in the ordinary way or 'pulled' by jerks in the direction facing the oarsmen. The number of oarsmen was often very great. It is noteworthy that at the bow there is nearly always one man armed with a stick who apparently has command. Sometimes a special platform, that is, a 'bridge', has been erected for him (Fig. 650). There were, of course, special constructions in the case of war-ships, of which a great number were built by some Egyptian kings, for example, by Ramses the Great (1392–1326 B.C.). In his reign the Red Sea Fleet consisted of 400 vessels which could accommodate thousands of warriors and which are alleged to have cruised as far as India, while the Mediterranean Fleet reached Phoenicia. According to the pictures handed down to us the ancient Egyptian war-ship had a high forecastle on which the bowmen stood. There was a similar sterncastle aft, for the steersman as well as for further bowmen. The oarsmen were protected from enemy missiles by a special bulwark. A fighting-top was attached to the mast, from which slingers could sling stones down on the enemy.

Whether anchors were known to the Egyptians is doubtful. From a representation of a cargo-ship discovered in the Royal Tombs at Thebes we can recognize that the cargo-ships were moored by means of ropes coiled round hooks. Such hooks seem to have been set up in great numbers at mooring-places, just as nowadays we have rings available at wharves for attaching ships.

GREEK AND ROMAN SHIPS: THE 'MEDITERRANEAN' SHIP

Greek ship-building [1] developed, as already mentioned, from that of the Phoenicians. For this reason Greek ships reveal many characteristics found in Phoenician ships. Owing to the intimate trade relations between the Greeks and the Romans it was inevitable that Roman ships should likewise exhibit features that are to be traced back to Phoenician origin. Thus in Mediterranean countries there is a fairly uniform type of ship, which became further standardized by the simple and uniform character of the materials, tools, and conditions of working.

The ships were built in a special yard in which woodwork was erected as a substructure, like the modern 'slip' (ὁλκός). The ship was put together on this slip. To allow the vessel to run down, the slip was made on a slant and built longer than was necessary to take the keel of the ship. Whether there was a dock with the slips seems doubtful. In general the ships to be repaired were not docked. But since they were usually drawn up on land and run into sheds when not in use, they were probably also repaired in these sheds; so we may regard them in a sense as docks. To lay up the mammoth vessel 'Alexandreia', built

[1] Cf. the chapter on 'Ships', p. 567, of *A Companion to Greek Studies*, Whibley (Cambridge University Press).

264 B.C. (see below), a sort of dry-dock is supposed to have been constructed, a basin which could be shut off from the sea by a dam. The ship was brought in and the basin was pumped out. The ship, no doubt laterally supported, was thus placed in dry dock. It was found necessary to keep the ships under cover in sheds because, with few exceptions, they had no full-decks ; moreover, their outer sides were as a rule unprotected. The copper-sheathing nowadays used was unknown at that time. A sheathing of lead plates was nailed on only in isolated cases, as in the case of the 'Alexandreia'. Consequently, when the vessel was at sea, thick crusts soon formed on the outside and marine worms settled on it. Rain-water collected inside and had to be bailed or pumped out. The wood soon rotted on account of the moisture. All these factors made it advisable not to leave the ships in water but to drag them out and place them under shelter. Sheds for this purpose seem to have been in use even in Homer's time ; at least, the Phaiakian ships are laid up at some kind of slip or landing-stage (ἐπίστιον, *Od.* vi, 265). The wharves were also constructed with a view to reducing the effect of moisture as much as possible. Vitruvius (V, 12, 7) directs that the wharves should lie towards the north, because in the southern position the wood would be much more likely to rot on account of the warmth, which gives rise to worms and other harmful influences ; in view of the risk of fire, as little wood as possible was to be used in making the buildings in which ship-building took place.

The chief work at these wharves fell to the shipwrights, but rope-makers, sail-makers, painters, smiths, leather-workers were also actively engaged. The most varied kinds of woods served as raw material for ship-construction : they were used unseasoned as well as very dry. Unseasoned wood was taken for the curved parts of the ship, that is for the ribs and planks ; dry wood was used wherever the individual parts had to be glued together. For the body and the keel the silver-fir, the pine-tree, the evergreen oak, and the black acacia were used. The inner parts and the cat-heads were made of ash-wood. The planks were cut from the linden-tree and the red beech, which, as Theophrastus remarks (*H. pl.* V, 4, 4), has the valuable property of not rotting in water. Masts and yards were made from the pine, whereas wood from the olive-trees and Italian pines was preferred for the oars. In addition to these results of research into the materials used in ship-construction we are indebted to Blümner for further details of the activities of the shipwrights.

Their tools resembled those now in use. They manipulated the broad-axe as well as the double-axe and worked with a set-square, plumb-line and cords for fixing directions. Their appliances also included the drill and the plane. Nails served to hold together the parts of the ship ; they were made of iron or bronze ; wedges, screws, pegs, strings, and glue were also used. A vivid description of the work involved in building a ship is given by Homer in the *Odyssey* (V, 243 *et seq.*) :

'But when she had shewn him where the tall trees grew, Calypso, the beautiful goddess, returned homewards, but he fell to cutting timbers, and his work went forward apace. Twenty trees in all did he fell, and trimmed them with the axe; then he cunningly smoothed them all and made them straight to the line. Meanwhile Calypso, the beautiful goddess, brought him augers; and he bored all the pieces and fitted them to one another, and with pegs and morticings did he hammer it together. Wide as a man well-skilled in carpentry marks out the curve of the hull of a freight-ship, broad of beam, even so wide did Odysseus make his raft. And he set up the deck-beams, bolting them to the close-set ribs, and laboured on; and he finished the raft with long gunwales. In it he set a mast and a yard-arm fitted to it, and furthermore made him a steering-oar, wherewith to steer. Then he fenced in the whole from stem to stern with willow withes to be a defence against the wave, and strewed much brush thereon. Meanwhile Calypso, the beautiful goddess, brought him cloth to make him a sail, and he fashioned that too with skill. And he made fast in the raft braces and halyards and sheets, and then with levers forced it down into the bright sea.'[1]

THE CONSTRUCTION AND EQUIPMENT OF SHIPS AMONG THE GREEKS AND ROMANS

The construction of the ship began with the laying down of the keel (ἡ τρόπις), which was a four-edged beam. In the case of mercantile vessels it was made of pine; on the other hand, in war-vessels, which had to resist more violent shocks, it was made of oak (Theophrastus, *H. pl.* V, 8). But even the keel of oak did not suffice for all purposes, since the ships were constantly being drawn on land at night and dragged in and out of the sheds, to and from the water. Further, the ships often ran ashore in shallow coastal waters. It was therefore found necessary to give the keel a special protection, particularly when the boat was being launched for the first time. A strong log was for this purpose nailed to the keel and formed a second or false keel. The keel was slightly bent upwards at each end. The stern-posts were connected with it and sloped obliquely upwards, the bows projecting fairly steeply in a forward direction. Consequently the fore-part of the ship became acute-angled. The stem was not always straight, but sometimes assumed a curve. As a rule it was composed of two pieces, partly to give it more strength and partly to accentuate the curve, the upper part being called the ship's beak (ὁ στόλος). The beak ended in a pointed piece of wood projecting forwards, namely the stem-head, which in the case of war-vessels also served as a ramming-beam with which the enemy ships were rammed. As the stem had also to withstand severe buffetings, and as in the case of merchant-vessels, too, it had to take all the impacts against wharfs, rocks and so forth, it was constructed so as to offer as much resistance as possible. This was achieved not only by rebating the different parts together and nailing them, but also by wrapping metal bands around them. Inside, at its lower part, pressure was exerted by a beam, the inner stem, which was pressed outwards by a special plank, the knee, which consolidated the whole stem. The stern was formed in a similar way and was likewise provided with a knee. In Homer's time both stem and stern were given a horn-like shape, the upper parts, which formed the horns, being bent

[1] Translation from the Loeb Classical Library, Heinemann.

outwards in opposite directions. Consequently the ship looked double-tailed (ἀμφιέλισσα) from the side. Later, the ' stolos ', that is, the uppermost part of the stem, was formed in the shape of a swan's neck or a hook ; and still later this neck was curved backwards and ended in a knob or in a volute. The stern-post is always curved towards the inner side of the ship and there ends in a sort of fan which is made of a number of boards (Fig. 653 and 654). This fan-part of the stern, the ἄφλαστον,

FIG. 653.—Form of a Greek Ship

The stern ends in a fan-shaped device : under the curved stem with its high deck there are the two ramming-beams and below them the spur (see later in the text)
After a Cercyrean coin

FIG. 654.—Form of a Roman Ship

Very high stern, under the roof-like shelter of which the steersman sits. Under the low stem the ramming-beams and below them a spur, in which there is an ' eye ' : the significance of this eye is not clear. By some it is regarded as an ornament, by others as a hole for admitting an anchor chain. Nor is it known whether the ships had one or two eyes. Probably there were two, as in the case of Chinese Junks, and the meaning was probably the same. The Chinese say, ' If it has no eyes it cannot see where it is going.' (For the true interpretation of the eye see page 477.)
After a Roman coin in the British Museum

was never a vane, as has often been asserted ; for then it would have had to turn with the wind, that is, if the ship were being rowed against the wind it would have set itself towards the stern. But the pictures show the fan always pointed towards the fore-end of the ship. In place of the fan another ornamentation of the stern was the ' goose-head ' (Fig. 656 and 661), which, however, sometimes had the form of a swan's neck, as for example in the accompanying two pictures. The fact that it is always the stern and never the stem is proved by the steering-oar, and also by the boat in tow (Fig. 656). We are indebted to the researches of Breusing, Luebeck and Assmann, not only for important discoveries about the technique and terminology of ship-construction, on which the foregoing remarks are based, but also for other details which we shall make use of in the sequel.

Starting out from the keel are the curved U-shaped ribs of the ship, which determine its size and shape. The curvature of the ribs is effected by combining together several pieces either by means of bolts or nails. Further, they are tarred to prevent rotting. With the help of notches corresponding to the width of the keel, they fit closely on to it. The notches prevent a lateral displacement of the ribs. To prevent a displacement backwards or forwards the kelson (δευτέρα τρόπις) is fixed over them ; this is a long piece of timber running parallel with the keel and having grooves that fit over the ribs and hold them fast. Thus the ribs are held clamped between the keel and the kelson, which themselves, however, do not touch. Between them there are gaps through which the water that collects in the bottom of the ship can run to either side. In consequence of this arrangement a ship that has a heavy list can easily be bailed out, as the water is then more accessible.

The skeleton formed by the keel and the ribs is next covered by planking which is simply nailed on in a horizontal position. The lowest planks have to be let into the keel; the heads of individual rows of planks, the 'strakes', have to be fixed into the stem and stern. For this purpose the keel, stem and stern are provided with corresponding rabbets. The planks lie close together. This method of arranging the planking seems, according to the above-quoted passage of Herodotus (II, 96), not to have been followed in Egyptian ships, where the planks overlapped in the manner of roof-tiles. On the highest strake there was superposed a strong beam which also lay over the frame-head or else a particularly strong plank. Holes were bored into it, in which the thole-pins (the thowls) were fixed, against which the oars pushed or to which they were loosely attached by means of leather loops; the thole-pins serving as supporting-points. Pictures on ancient Greek vases, for example, one in the British Museum, and also other pictures, show that the strong beam just mentioned, which formed the proper edge of the vessel, carried a sort of ladder. These 'ladders' have received varying interpretations: whereas Rear-Admiral Glatzel regards them as gang-planks to facilitate landing when the ship is moored to the land, others assume that the gaps in the ladders were used for thrusting through the oars, so that they performed the function of the thole-pin. This view seems more justified, although one may object that the pictures mentioned do not clearly show whether there is not a thole-pin *behind* the ladder which does not show simply because it is not sufficiently prominent in the picture or relief—for example, on that of the Acropolis at Athens (Fig. 655). Nevertheless, we must take into consideration that the ancients were not accustomed to moving the oar between two thole-pins placed close together. Only *one* thole-pin was used, against which it pressed and to which it was held by means of the leather thong. To strengthen the planking still stronger planks were nailed on the inside and outside of the ship; they were narrower and were added in both a vertical and a horizontal position so that they formed a sort of grating in which the ship's body proper lay.

The planks could not be fastened sufficiently closely together to prevent water entering. Special means had therefore to be adopted to make their joints watertight. Tow was mostly used for this purpose; it was placed on the joints and stuffed in with the help of a blunt chisel and a wooden hammer. Molten pitch or a mixture of pitch and wax was next poured into the joint; sometimes pure wax alone was used. Lastly the whole outside of the ship was painted over with tar obtained from the charcoal pile or from special tar-works (cf. p. 249). In isolated instances, as has already been mentioned, the wooden sides of the ships were further protected by having lead sheathing nailed over the outside, a lining of tarred canvas being interposed.

In addition to these elaborations on the outside of the ship, further additions were made in the interior. Above the keel, in the space nowadays called the 'bilge', water collected. To prevent this water from interfering with people's movements in the ship, the bilge was covered over with a layer of loose boards, which could easily be lifted off when the bilge-water was to be bailed out. Ballast in the form of stones, sandbags and so forth were also stowed in the bilge. The water was bailed out by means of buckets and, in smaller ships, was simply thrown overboard; in larger ships a ladder was probably leaned against the inner side of the edge, so that people standing on the ladder could pass the

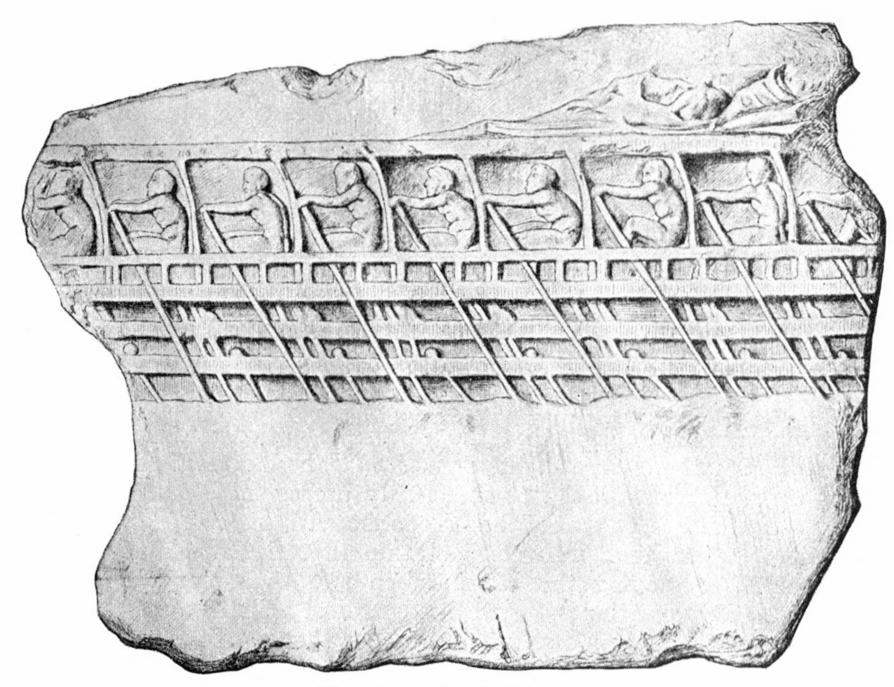

FIG. 655.—Greek Trireme

Three rows of oars (vertically one above another) are recognizable; in the highest row we see the 'ladder' and perhaps thole-pins, but in the lower rows the technical details are not quite clear; nor can we understand why the handles of the two lower rows of oars are covered by transverse beams. Relief from the Acropolis

buckets up and down. From certain passages (Aristophanes, *Lysistrata*, 722) it may be inferred that pulleys were also used for drawing up the filled buckets. Archimedes' screw is also alleged to have been used for removing the water from ships. Water was prevented from entering into ships carrying valuable cargo by having another complete lining of planks on the inside.

In early times probably only merchant vessels had decks in the modern sense, that is, decks that covered the whole interior; for in such vessels it was necessary to protect the cargo from the vagaries of the weather. Other ships had only half a deck or were left quite uncovered. The ships of Homer's time had a fore-deck and an after-deck, the space amidships being left uncovered (*Odyssey*, XII, 229, and XIII, 74). The deck rested on beams called deck-beams, which ran transversely across the ship from the heads of the ribs on one side to the other. It was not, as in our ships, an unbroken plane surface, but was always lower in the middle; the purpose of this was to bring the oarsmen nearer the water and to provide a higher structure fore and aft or on both sides. These two elevations, the 'forecastle' at the front and the quarter-deck aft, changed their aspect greatly in the course of time. At one time they had a protective planking, in particular the forecastle; at other times the quarter-deck, especially in Roman ships, carried a structure which served as the captain's cabin (Fig. 656). This cabin consisted

FIG. 656.—The After Part of a Roman sailing-vessel. (Mosaic picture out of Casa quirinale of Claudio Claudiano)

The after-peak ends in the 'goose-head' (see page 484). On the after-deck there is a defence. A passage-way runs round the upper deck. Behind the goose-head is the 'captain's cabin'. In the body of the ship we see several decks superposed; at the side is a steering-oar. The sail is provided with rings and reefing-points (see page 491) and has been partly reefed. The boat in tow is also worthy of note. On the left is a lighthouse. Capitoline Museum, Rome

of a framework of wooden beams and wooden hoops covered with cloth. In many cases we find a passage-way on one of these decks (Fig. 656, and on the left of Fig. 661). Sometimes again we find war-machines of very different kinds, particularly onagers, on the forecastle. Draw-bridges were built up on it which gave access to enemy ships at close quarters, and, above all, the 'dolphin' was placed here. This was a heavy iron or lead block which was allowed to fall on the enemy ship for the purpose of shattering it. We also find on the forecastle the capstan and the contrivances for raising and lowering the mast.

As already mentioned, except in the case of the trading vessels, in which there was a complete deck, the space amidships between the fore-castle and the quarter-deck was at first left open. It was occupied by the oarsmen, and in the case of war-ships by the soldiers. To give the soldiers a better stand in the battle running planks were fixed on the inside, which rested on supporting beams. The oarsmen sat between these planks, that is, nearer the centre-line. Later, a middle-deck evolved from the running-planks, but in the case of the war-ship the centre still remained open. Although the open space became smaller and smaller the war-ship was never built with a complete deck. There were good reasons for this: firstly, provision had to be made for dismantling the mast, which was a hindrance in battle; ships were propelled only by oars and never by means of the sails during actual conflict. Secondly, a favourite method of attack was to steer straight for the enemy, and to pass sufficiently closely to break their oars. To avoid sacrificing one's own oars and to counter a similar manœuvre on the part of the enemy it was necessary to have a free space in the centre of the ship which would enable the oars to be drawn in quickly and placed on end.

Below the foredeck and the quarter-deck were recesses which served partly for storing ropes but partly also as sleeping-compartments; they must certainly have been very narrow and uncomfortable. The tank containing the drinking-water was also kept here. In the larger ships a bulwark ran between the fore- and after-deck, and prevented water from splashing into the interior. In the case of war-ships this bulwark also served as a defence. Whereas it was usually made of boards nailed on a ladder-like framework of beams, these boards, in the war-vessels, were further specially covered with skins or cloth, or were lined with shields—all devices for arresting and catching enemy arrows. Below the partition there were probably also oval-shaped holes leading downwards to the outside through which water that had accumulated on the deck could run out; these are the scuppers.

A special construction added to war-ships was the spur (*ἔμβολος* or *ἔμβολον*, *rostrum*), a very effective weapon if we bear in mind the mode of construction of the ships. A skilful use of it decided many a naval engagement. Its importance found expression in ordinary life in many ways; for example, in Rome the orator's tribune was ornamented with beaks of enemy ships, namely the above-mentioned spurs; they were also added to monuments. The spur was a powerful projection composed mostly of several timbers, usually with a triple point added, and fixed in front of the bows. It has already been stated that it was derived from the Phoenicians. At first it was situated below the water-line so that it struck the enemy ship at a point through which water could penetrate into the interior. It was placed higher and higher in the course of time, and later it was always constructed to lie above the water. The reason is probably that the ramming has to be executed with great force. Since the resistance of the air is less than that of water, the spur when it was attached below the water-line could not attain the speed necessary for an effective blow. Consequently the power of percussion was increased by having the spur above the water-line. (The draught of most war-ships was not much more than 3 ft.) In spite of this, the splintered wood and beams would produce a leak that would extend below the water-line. In addition to the spur the war-ship had a second weapon, the battering-ram (Figs. 653, 654, 657), the end of which was often shaped in the form of an animal's head, and was of wood. Whereas the spur aimed at the parts of the main body of the enemy ship which lay just above the water-line, the battering-ram was directed at the higher parts, that is, against the sides of the vessel, the bulwarks, the upper works and so forth. But it also had a further purpose. The spur was intended solely to make a leak in the enemy vessel. If it penetrated far, it could not easily be pulled out, and, under some circumstances, the ship using it would herself be drawn under. The battering-ram therefore acted as a brake when the spur had entered far enough, and stopped the forward motion ; it was then possible to row backwards quickly, away from the vicinity of the rammed ship.

The oars also underwent many changes in the course of time. At the beginning, the blade was wide and flat, but ended in a point. Sometimes it was ornamental in form and resembled a shovel. Later the blade lost this aspect and instead became long and narrow. Everything of importance about the connection between the oar and the thole-pin has been said above. The actual rowing was done exactly as nowadays ; in boats men used two oars simultaneously ; the larger oar of the bigger vessel was worked by one man, who applied his two hands to it. Whether very large oars were manipulated by several oarsmen at each is still an unanswered question. In the so-called 'polyeres' (many-banked boats) in which there were several rows of oarsmen, specially strong planking was built up, on the sides of the ship, in which special apertures (we would call them 'rowing-ports') were made ; through them the oars were thrust. To prevent water entering through these ports into the interior of the ship, animal skins were stretched over them, having a slit through which the blade of the oar was pushed. As the blade was wider than the handle the slit would always leave a little gap. We know from several accounts that water often enough actually did penetrate into the interior through these slits (Appian, *De rebus Syriac.* 27). The oarsmen sat behind one another on seats, about which we know practically nothing. What we do know, namely that the seats were covered with sheep-skins, is of no technical importance. We have only the definite knowledge that the oarsmen of the Greeks and Romans rowed with their faces towards the after part of the ship, that is, they worked the oars by pulling the handles towards themselves. They were sometimes exercised on land in rowing by means of models specially constructed for the purpose and made of beams. In the ships they rowed to the word of a commander, and often to the notes of a flute, which were intended to make them more efficient.

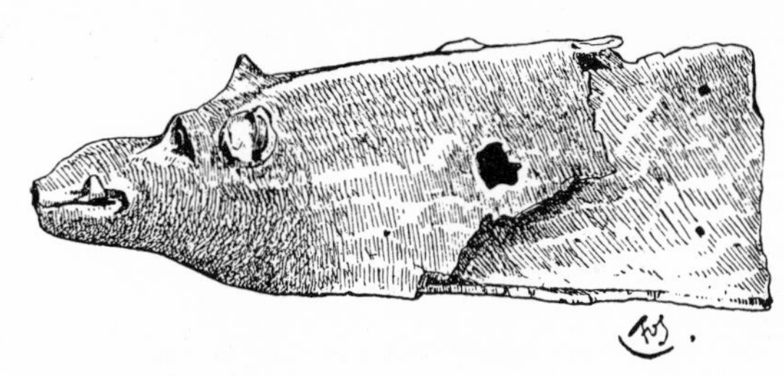

FIG. 657—Battering-ram of a Roman War-ship

In the case of river-ships the oars in some cases also seem to have been used by pushing the handle away from the body, so that the oarsman could see where he was going. Some pictures allow us to draw this conclusion, for example Fig. 658, which represents a wine-transport on the Moselle. This ship is narrow and pointed at the stern, has high sides and is provided with a passage-way. The steersman sits aft.

The rudder was no more than an oar and was distinguished only by its greater length and the greater width of the blade. The smaller ships had a steering-oar inserted between two thowls, or resting on an incision in the middle of the stern. But the steering-oar could also be held in the water on either side of the stern, a method of steering small boats which is still practised to-day. Possibly the mysterious 'seven-foot thwart' mentioned in Homer (*Iliad*, XV, 728) was intended to make it easier for the steersman to move over from one side to the other for this purpose.[1] In larger ships this moving about and the transposing of the rudder from one side to the other was avoided by having two steering-

FIG. 658.—Rowing-ship on a River (Wine-transport on the Moselle)
Relief. Provincial Museum, Trèves

oars that rested in an incision in the gunnel or the bulwark or passed through apertures in the ship's sides (Fig. 600). At their upper ends they had, just as nowadays, a horizontal handle, a 'tiller'. The two steering-oars were manipulated separately and acted independently of each other. In a calm sea one man was probably sufficient to serve them; in a moving sea two would certainly be necessary, who would have to work in perfect harmony, each using two hands for his rudder. When one man alone did the steering the unused steering-oar was probably simply lifted out and hung on to the ship by a ring on its handle until it was required again. It seems improbable that the tillers were connected by a strap which was pulled in the one direction or the other, as required, by a man sitting in front of it, and so serving both steering-oars. For such a strap would allow the tillers only to be drawn inwards and not outwards (on account of their being at the sides). Many ships had a steering-oar fore and aft so that one could progress in either direction

[1] Unlikely, for it seems to have been forward of the after-deck.—*Trans.*

without turning the boat round. Such ships, which could move in either direction, appear also to have been common among the Germans; at any rate Tacitus (*Germ.* 44) reports of the Suiones:

> 'The style of their ships differs in this respect, that there is a prow at each end, with a beak ready to be driven forwards; they neither work it with sails, nor add oars in banks to the side: the gearing of the oars is detached as on certain rivers, and reversible as occasion demands, for movement in either direction.' [1]

Schuchardt has inferred from pictures of ships of the later bronze age that a bush (willow-branch or birch) appears to have been used in place of a sail, as is still done by various primitive races of the present day.

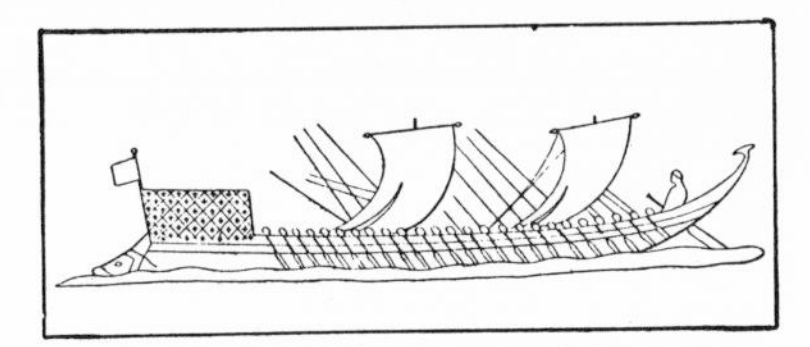

FIG. 659.—Two-masted Vessel

Two-masted pentecoster (fifty-oared vessel) which was propelled by means of oars and sails. At the after-peak the 'fan'. Two equally high masts with one yard each. A flag at the bow

The sailing equipment of Greek and Roman ships was extremely simple. Usually the ships had only one mast, which was made of fir-wood in Homer's time, but there were also some with two masts (more than two is very unlikely), as shown in Fig. 659. The mast rested on the keel in a framework of beams, called the 'mast-box', into which the heel of the mast was stepped. The mast was thickest at the level of the gunnel (Figs. 660 and 661), for experience had taught navigators that when the full pressure of the wind was exerted on the sails the mast broke most easily at this point. Parallel uprights ran closely along both sides of the mast, between which it moved in such a way that it could be conveniently brought into a horizontal position, being lowered towards the after end of the vessel. When it was restored to its vertical position hoops were placed round it and the beams to hold it in position. This contrivance, which is still used in our river-ships, was very simple and convenient for laying down even a comparatively tall mast, as its centre of gravity could be suitably chosen to reduce the work to a minimum. Athwart the ship above the collar of the mast there was a cross-beam with a semicircular portion cut out at the centre. This gap in the cross-beam, the 'middle thwart', received the mast, which leaned against the beam and so was better able to withstand the pressure of the wind. At the top of the mast were two stays

FIG. 660.—A small Roman Ship

On the after-peak we see the fan (see p. 484); a mast provided with wooden steps for climbing, shown in its lowered position. Two steering-oars. After a bas-relief in the cathedral of Salerno.

[1] Hutton's translation in Loeb Classical Library. Hutton comments: 'Apparently like the lumbermen's "caravels" sometimes seen in the backwoods of Canada.'

attached to the port and starboard bows; a third stay served to connect it to the stern. In general the masts were low; the term 'high mast' is therefore only used in a relative sense. Composite masts were not known. To climb up the mast the stays just mentioned were used (Fig. 661) or wooden blocks nailed like steps along the mast (Fig. 660). It has not been definitely established whether rope-ladders were used, as has been asserted by some writers. A wooden block was fixed to the top of the mast (the 'mast-head') which carried the pulleys required for hoisting up the yards (Fig. 661). On larger ships and war-ships there was also a place of vantage encircled by a breastwork for a lookout or soldier at the mast-head, that is, a sort of fighting-top. Above the mast-head a flagstaff projected which carried the pennant.

FIG. 661.—Roman Sailing-vessel flying a flag

On the after-peak the 'goose-head'. Aft is a quarter-deck. Apparently there are several decks. On the left is a stern-gallery and a lower middle space (see page 488). Composite yard that can be turned. Mast tapers towards the top. A flag at the top. Sails partly brailed and consisting of pieces stitched together. The crew is seen climbing up the ropes

The yards were also mostly made of fir-wood, which, as Pliny remarks (XVI, 39), was particularly appropriate on account of its lightness. They were thickest in the middle and tapered somewhat at the ends. They were often made of two pieces overlapping at the mast and tied together (Fig. 661). The mast never carried more than one (single or composite) yard, from which the rectangular sail, made of canvas, was suspended. The yard was connected with the mast by means of a loop which encircled the mast and through which little balls were threaded to allow the yard to slide up and down the mast easily. The position of the yards could be altered by special ropes, braces and sheets, and adjusted to the prevailing direction of the wind (Fig. 662). The sail was provided with rings on its front surface, through which ropes ran (Fig. 656). The sail area was reduced by pulling these ropes, and thus differed from our method. Luebeck has aptly compared this ancient method of brailing, instead of reefing, with the pulling up of a window-blind (Fig. 661). Many ships, in particular war-ships, had besides the main-mast a second mast in front of it, that is, a fore-mast which more nearly resembled our modern bowsprit and was inclined towards the front ; it carried a sail which, like that of the main-mast, was usually rectangular. It seems very probable that the fore-mast was also used as a derrick when the ship was unloading in harbour. The sails were often made of several pieces stitched together (Fig. 661). To make them more capable of withstanding the wind-pressure, special strips, presumably of canvas, were sewn on. This makes them appear divided into squares and rectangles. Moreover they often had a covering of paint. To give the crew a foothold when attending to the yards foot-ropes (or 'horses') were attached to the latter, such as we still make use of in our vessels (see Fig. 651, p. 480).

Like the Egyptian ships, so the Roman and Greek ships often had a strong cable which ran round the ship from stem to stern ; it was called *ὑπόζωμα* (hypozoma), and its purpose long remained hidden and formed

FIG. 662.—Greek Sailing-vessel with steering gear and 'braced yards'

The yard is provided with braces (the five ropes or sheets that run down from the top left side to the right), to allow it to be set in the direction of the wind. Attic vase of the end of the sixth century B.C. Vase Collection of Würzburg University

the subject of much discussion. We are inclined to agree with Breusing who regards it as a precaution against the keel breaking, a danger which occurred in ancient vessels, especially war-vessels, because they were often made over-long in comparison with their width, in order that the number of oarsmen would be as great as possible.[1] The 'hypozoma' was fixed on only when the ship was to be launched.

Another important part of the ship's equipment was the anchor (*ἄγκυρα, ancora*), which however appears to have been used only seldom in the harbours. The ships were fastened in a manner still practised in many fishing-harbours (for example, in Scheveningen) ; the fore- or after-peak was drawn close up to the jetty, and the ship was made fast by ropes attached to rings fixed in the wall of the jetty. On the fore- or after-peak of many ships of antiquity there was often a high wooden or stone post about which the mooring-rope was probably coiled when the ship was in port. In this way many ships could be moored in even a small harbour. Connection between the land and the ship was made by means of gang-planks (Fig. 660), which were perhaps laid on the ladders mentioned by Glatzel (see p. 485).

[1] Rather, to prevent the timbers from starting when the ram was used.—*Trans.*

For anchors the ancients originally used heavy stones (εὐναί, called 'senchilsteine' by the Germans, that is, sinking-stones) or pyramidal basket-work filled with stones. Until the year 700 B.C., the metal anchor seems to have been unknown, and, indeed, seems never to have been used in Egypt at all. About 650 B.C. there were anchors on the ships of the Phoenicians and Greeks, which already had the later hook-form, but were made of wood. They were weighted by pieces of iron or lead or stones (Fig. 663). From data given by various writers we may assume their weight to be about 8 cwt., of which only 60 to 80 lbs. were due to the wooden anchor.

FIG. 663.—Primitive wooden Anchor weighted by a stone (a constructed copy)

Museum für Meereskunde, Berlin

Later the anchors were made less heavy. The anchors of the Attic triremes weighed a little over 44 lbs. Between 600 B.C. and 550 B.C. the first anchors entirely of metal made their appearance and had the familiar form of modern anchors (Figs. 664–6). Like the ancient wooden anchors they already exhibit the anchor-stock, a rod at right angles to the plane of the arms, which makes the arms lie in such a position that their ends dig themselves in more deeply when the anchor cable is pulled. The anchor-stock of the first metal anchors is of wood; the anchors themselves have sometimes one, sometimes two arms. Further, there were also 'bower-anchors', that is, anchors resembling in form an inverted open umbrella, such as are still often used nowadays for anchoring light-ships

FIGS. 664–666.—Forms of Greek Anchors. (Pictures on Roman coins)

It is noteworthy that the ancient anchors already show the anchor-stock (transverse piece) which makes the anchor fall in a position that made it sink in further when pulled. Representations without anchor-stock, which also exist, are probably pictures of land-anchors that are thrown on to the shore

and buoys. The inside of these bower-anchors was filled with stones and sand-bags to increase their weight (Fig. 664). Even about the year 500 B.C. anchor-buoys were used consisting of a network of ropes (σαϱγάνη) shaped like a basket and filled with pieces of cork; their purpose was to enable the anchor to be recovered if the cable snapped. The anchor was thrown into the sea from the fore-part of the ship. To prevent damaging the ship's side it was suspended from a beam that projected beyond the side. In some cases it was also thrown into the water from aft. The anchors were attached to strong cables ; iron anchor-chains are first mentioned by Caesar (*De bello Gallico*, iii, 13, 3), who reports that the Veneti used them.

THE 'TRIREME' PROBLEM

According to the number of banks of oars that a ship carried it was called moneres, bireme (dieres), trireme, tetreres, quinquereme, polyeres, etc. (Figs. 655 and 667). The way in which the oarsmen in these polyremes and, in particular, in the triremes were arranged has long been a subject of controversy, ever since de Baïf first raised the point in 1536 ; indeed, enough literature has appeared about the subject to fill whole libraries. The question of the distribution of oars is designated by the term 'trireme problem'—although it by no means refers to triremes alone—simply because ancient writers distinguish three sets of oarsmen in such triremes, namely the 'thranites' (upper bank), the 'zygites' (middle bank) and 'thalamites' (lower bank). In this extensive literature to which philologists, scientists and naval experts have contributed, we find extremely different views represented, and many different ways of seating the oarsmen in the triremes and polyeres are depicted. Of the more recent theories concerning the polyeres we quote only that of Assmann (according to Luebeck's interpretation) :

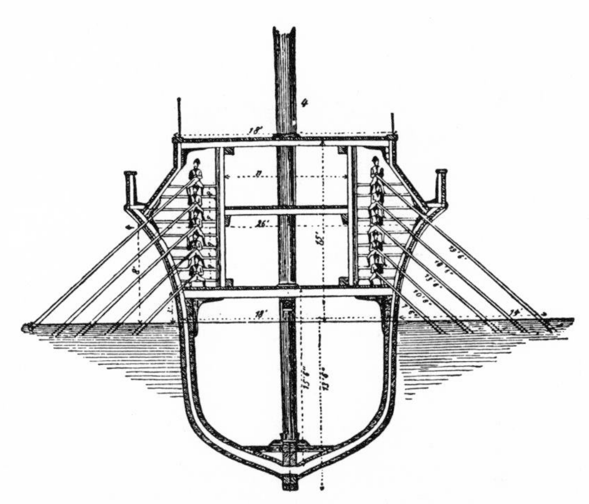

FIG. 667.—Penteres or quinquereme

> 'Since in the case of ships with more than three banks of oars we still read only of thranites, zygites and thalamites, Assmann makes the highly probable inference that the body of oarsmen in the polyeres were always based on the grouping-system of thalamites, zygites and thranites, being repeated by superposition, the rowers of each group sitting not only above and in front of each other but also in echelon towards the middle of the ship, in order to avoid being too high and to prevent the ship becoming top-heavy.'

Weber considers that the attempts to solve the trireme problem have been unsuccessful on account of the misinterpretation of two words : 'because it has not been recognized that ἄνω and κάτω used in the nautical sense do not signify above and below but fore and aft, and that the ancients in perhaps a thousand cases talk of rows of oarsmen and *not* of tiers of oars.' After careful reflection he comes to the conclusion that 'as the water exerts an upthrust on every blade of oar the lowest blades in the case of tiers of oars would be thrown among the higher blades if there were any appreciable swell. But if an oar remains in the water for any time or is drawn back in it the progress of the boat is retarded. At any rate the highest oars would have to be raised sufficiently high to allow the lowest oars also to be drawn back above the water, but in the case of a swell this would mean that the blades would rise higher than the handles, an absurd waste of force and time. Further, this is a labour that could be performed neither by one man with an oar 17 feet long nor by three men with oars 53 feet long. Rather this effort of rowing corresponds with the numbers given by the ancients to the numbers in the rows, namely in the sense that three rows of oarsmen belonged to a trireme-oar of an average length of 17 feet and that forty rows of oarsmen belonged to the tessaraconters-oar, of which the average length was 53 feet (see Fig. 668).

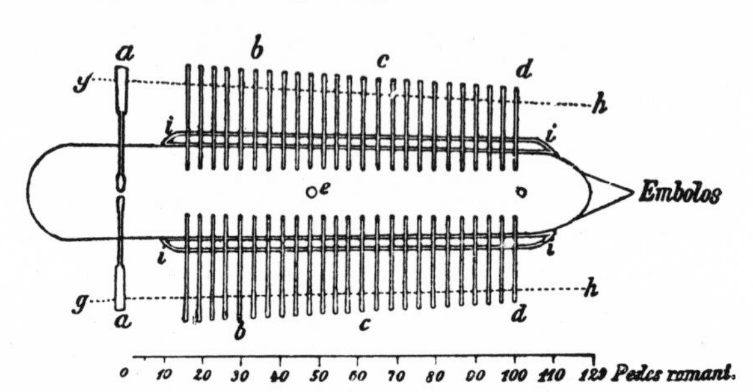

FIG. 668.—Trireme with oars raised out of the water; when lowered the oars all dip in together at the water-line *gh*

a, Pedalion, steering-oar; *b*, thranite oarsman; *c*, zygite oarsman; *d*, thalamite oarsman; *e*, main mast

'Thus it is impossible to propel ships ordinarily unless their oars are in a line in the water; but when the distance between the oars is only a little over three feet it is necessary to have the fulcrum of the oar alternately high and low and to arrange the seating of the oarsmen with padding (not wood) in order to avoid their being knocked or crushed. If then an oar is let go it moves along in its plane and never hits the head of the next oarsman nor does it strike his feet, which are encased in padding.'

Recently the trireme problem has again been exhaustively studied, this time by Busley. He comes to the conclusion that it is certainly possible for three banks of oars of different lengths to keep rhythm. But a necessary condition is that the ratio of the length of the handle to the whole oar must be the same in each case, all oars must touch the water at the same moment and must be drawn through the water with the same speed. As the oarsmen with the shortest oars describe the smallest arc, they must make a slight pause in order to get into time with the others again. Thus the thalamites would have to sit with their oars raised out of the water long enough for the oars of the thranites to come parallel with their own. They would then have to swing forward and remain in the extreme forward position until the thranites had also swung full out; both sets of oars would then be plunged in simultaneously to commence the next stroke. If the length of the oars of the zygites were intermediate between that of the thranites and the thalamites, they would also have to remain still for a moment during each stroke, but not so long as the thalamites. The pause depends on the relative lengths of the oars. It required long training to have a trireme crew, rowing with oars of different lengths, sufficiently practised to execute ramming manœuvres. Busley, however, conjectures that the oars of the thranites and zygites were equally long, although the blades of the thranites may have been broader. It was therefore easy for them to keep in rhythm. The thalamites required special practice to fit in with them. These investigations of Busley, whose essential results are as given above, probably give the clue to the mystery of the trireme.

SIZE AND SPEED OF ANCIENT SHIPS

The size of ancient ships was in general not great. If we reckon their carrying power in tons in accordance with present-day custom we find that the large merchant-vessels could take a cargo of about 52 tons. In general we may assume that ships of over 100 tons were exceptional. Among the exceptions there are, it is true, some of considerable size which were mostly built for a special purpose. Thus the ship built by Caligula and described by Pliny (XVI, 40), which transported the obelisk that stands in front of the Vatican from Egypt to Rome, had, according to Assmann's calculations, a cargo capacity of 2,500 tons. The three-master 'Alexandreia' which Hiero of Syracuse commanded to be built was too large for all the harbours of Italy and Sicily, so that Hiero found himself obliged to present it to Ptolemy Philadelphus, King of Egypt. This ship was able to load up 60,000 bushels of corn, 10,000 earthenware vessels full of salted fish, and a very large quantity of other provisions. It had 60 rooms and halls, a kitchen, garden, gymnasium, library, bathroom and so forth. From these data Graser calculates that this ship, for which the harbour of Alexandria alone was available as an anchorage, had a carrying capacity of 4,200 tons. From the point of view of modern ship-construction it is therefore still to be reckoned among the smaller vessels. The number of oarsmen varied widely in accordance with the size of a ship: a ship with a single bank of oars (*moneres*) had up to 50 oarsmen; the triremes at the time of Demosthenes had on either side 31 thranites, 27 zygites and 27 thalamites; in the case of a few large ships, such as the *tessarakonteres* (40 banks of oars) of Hiero of Syracuse, the number rose to 4,000. The side of this vessel, the 'Alexandreia,' had a length of over 414 ft., along which 40 rows of 50 oarsmen sat.

It is also possible to make fair calculations of the speed of ancient ships. Herodotus (IX, 86) relates that during the long days a ship traversed 70,000 fathoms by day, and 60,000 by night. A sailing vessel that had been on the water for 9 days and 8 nights would have travelled 11,100 stadia in this time; this corresponds to 1,300 stadia in 24 hours. We thus arrive at an average velocity of 6 miles per hour, but we must bear in mind that the length of the stadium is not quite certain. The road (itinerary) stadium amounted to 240 paces = 175 yds. (according to Eratosthenes, about 200 B.C.), whereas the Olympic stadium was 214 yds. and the Roman stadium 206 yds. From distances given by Strabo and Ptolemy Dörpfeld calculates the length of the stadium as 185 yds. From data given by Xenophon (*Anabasis*, XI, 4, 2) we actually get for the average velocity of a trireme a value of 9½ knots. Fleets of ships of course travelled more slowly; they covered only about 2⅓ miles in an hour. According to Weber we may take the average speed as nearly 5 knots.

Busley in his detailed study and calculations of the speed of triremes starts from the number of strokes that could be executed per minute and from the fractions of time taken for dipping, pulling and recovering. Taking into account the weight of the triremes he assumes 20 strokes per minute. On the basis of these calculations and other arguments he comes to the following conclusions:

> 'The result of the velocity of triremes as obtained in different ways seems to indicate that the oarsmen alone achieved a mean velocity of 4 knots. With the additional help of sails an average speed of 5 knots could be maintained with a favourable wind, that is from aft, provided the sea was not running too high, but this was regarded as a particularly good rate of travel. A classical instance of this is afforded by the voyage of the triremes which, in 405 B.C., after the naval battle of Aegos Potami, which decided the Peloponnesian war, brought the news of the defeat to Athens. This voyage was regarded as exceedingly rapid; the triremes ran along at about 5 knots. More than 6 knots could be attained for only a very short space of time with all forces strained to the utmost, for example, during a ramming manœuvre in a naval engagement.'

NAVIGATION

IN spite of the considerable amount of sea-traffic at many stages of ancient history the art and science of navigation were but little developed. Navigation was restricted to the coasts, and only the Phoenicians ventured to travel on the open sea. The Romans, in particular, had a fear of the high seas, and although they had to maintain great fleets for their trade and for war purposes they never became efficient mariners. Just as little courage was shown in travelling at night as in leaving the vicinity of the coast. Mariners rowed or sailed along the coast only by day—short cuts, however, across bays that stretched far inland were not avoided—at night the ships were drawn up on land. Although the Mediterranean, the chief field of activity of ancient shipping, is to be classed among the less stormy seas, the ancients dreaded to set out on voyages in certain months when storms were to be feared. Hesiod states in his calendar that there are two periods that are favourable to sea-travel:

> 'In the middle of August,' he says in effect, 'when the hot summer is reaching its close, the weather is good at sea and there is no danger for ship or crew, unless Poseidon or Zeus happened to wish to destroy someone. For at this time the air is clear and the sea is quiet. But one must hasten to return and must not remain away till the time of grape-gathering, for south-west winds soon come with rain and heavy seas. The other time for travel is in the Spring. When the leaves on the young shoots of the fig-tree are as long as a crow's foot the sea is navigable. In Autumn when one sees the Pleiades set before Orion in the morning sky, all winds are stormy and no vessel dare be entrusted to the water—rather, they must be drawn on land and covered in order that the moist winds do not spoil them. And the stopper must be removed to allow the rain-water to run out and to prevent the wood from rotting.'

This 'stopper' refers to a plug inserted in a hole in the bottom or next to the keel in the smaller craft of antiquity. Its removal allowed any contained water to run out when the vessel was on land.

Despite this apprehensiveness towards sea-travel which prevailed among all the ancients, several bold enterprises were embarked upon. As early as three thousand years B.C. the Egyptians passed through the Red Sea to the land of Punt, which lay in Southern Arabia or on the Somali coast; and about 600 B.C., by command of the Pharaoh Necho II, Phoenician navigators seem to have travelled from the East Coast of Egypt all round Africa. In the third year after their departure they returned via the Pillars of Hercules, that is, the Straits of Gibraltar. Even at that early time Necho II wished to have the canal constructed, which was realized much later in the building of the Suez Canal in the nineteenth century, and which was to establish a water connection between the Mediterranean and the Red Sea. To what extent this plan was suggested by the circumnavigation of Africa cannot be ascertained, but Herodotus' account of this bold sea-voyage shows that in this, too, the Phoenicians remained true to their habits on such distant travels : they landed at some place or other, cultivated the ground, sowed seed, and then waited for the harvest. When they had collected the harvest and stocked their ships with it, they set sail again. But neither these isolated instances of courage and enterprise, nor the fact that crossings were made from Italy to Africa and from Syracuse to Malta and on to Crete, can alter the fact that among the ancients navigation was in general restricted to coastal voyages and was regarded as a precarious undertaking requiring many precautions.

As a result of this circumstance few provisions were taken on board, and the ships remained comparatively small. For land was touched every night or harbours entered, places of refuge which were immediately sought when a storm threatened. Here food could be found ; one could cook, eat and sleep, so that neither provisions nor comfortable quarters for the crew were required on the ship. At first man-power was used to pull the ships in to the shore, later the windlass invented by Archimedes was used ; this device also served to let newly-built ships off the slip into the sea. Archimedes is supposed to have invented the windlass used when the giant ship 'Alexandreia' of King Hiero of Syracuse had to be launched. How far ships were often dragged may be seen from the fact that, according to the accounts of Strabo (VIII, 6, 4) and of Pomponius Mela (II, 3), a double slip (*δίολκος*), that is, a slide, was constructed at the isthmus of Corinth over which ships could be dragged from the Aegean into the Ionian Sea, the isthmus being nearly 4 miles across and 263 ft. high.

In voyaging along the coast much care was exercised. In unknown waters pilots were called into action ; shallows and rocks were marked with warning signals. The seaman made ample use of sounding-leads so as to recognize danger-spots in time. Fleets of several ships in strange waters travelled in line, the first taking soundings, warning the rest and, where necessary, making the course visible by means of maritime signals. Pilots were also used for running the ships into the harbours. It has already been mentioned in the section on 'Lighting' that numerous watch-fires and lighthouses served as signals and warning-signs to the seaman at nightfall.

Good landing-places were denoted by landmarks. An example of such landmarks has been preserved for us in the form of a column of rectangular cross-section, namely the so-called Iliad Tablet of Lesches ; this is a relief dating from the time of the first Roman Emperors and representing the destruction of Troy according to the 'Little Iliad' of Lesches (about 672 B.C.). This column was formerly thought to be a lighthouse (Fig. 669), but Geitel has given conclusive proofs that it is a landmark.

As now, so at that time there were handbooks for navigators, the most excellent example of which is the *Σταδιασμὸς ἤτοι περίπλους τῆς μεγάλης θαλάσσης*, that is, 'The Stadium-traveller, or a Trip round the

Mediterranean '. It contains in detail all the information that a navigator of that time would wish to know. In spite of all these data the book gives no real ' sailing directions ', nor were these necessary, as no definite course was steered over the sea ; navigators hugged the coast. As

FIG. 669.—Landmark denoting a Landing-place
On the right is a ship drawn up on the shore

examples of the form in which the information was given we give the following quotations :

' Coming from seawards you see low land in front of which lie small islands. On approaching more closely you see the town on the coast, a white sand-dune and the shore. The whole town also has a white appearance. It has no harbour, but you will lie to safely at Hermaion. For the rest, the town is called Leptis. . . .

' From Gaphara to Amaraia is 40 stadia.[1] The breakwater offers a sheltered position. Drinking-water is available. Tilled ground is seen near the river. The river is called Oinoladon. . . .

' From Thapsos to Little Leptis is 170 stadia. It is a small town. Banks rise up out of the water there, and it is difficult to put in to the town. . . .

' From this promontory you see the town Adrymeton at a distance of 40 stadia. There is no harbour. . . .'

When voyages across the sea were actually undertaken, it was very difficult to find one's bearings. According to Breusing the navigators neither had a means of measuring distances nor were they acquainted with the compass, which would have enabled them to keep on a definite course. Consequently one was compelled to take direction by the sun and stars, which failed as soon as the sky became clouded. The direction of the waves probably gave some indication of the course of the vessel, but this would also be of no avail after a short while. All these circumstances justify the apprehensive attitude of the ancients towards travelling on the high seas. As one could keep only approximately to the intended course, the point of the coast aimed at was never accurately gauged ; rather, a point was struck in its vicinity. Soundings had then to be taken, if the appearance of the coast-line was no guide, so as to discover one's whereabouts from the nature of the shallows. The sounding-lead was hollowed out at the bottom ; the cavity was filled with tallow, to which parts of the sea-bottom adhered. The direction in which land lay was also tested by setting birds free. Conditions were gradually improved when seamen learned to observe the sea- and air-currents, and in particular to exploit the trade-winds, to draw sea-maps, and finally to determine the length of shadows at different places and for different times of the year by means of the ' gnomon ', the pointer of the sun-dial. The numbers obtained with the gnomon were set out

[1] A stadium is about 202 yds. Cf. p. 497.

in tables; an example of these tables is given by Pliny (VI, 33). Thus if a ship was equipped with a gnomon it could determine its latitude roughly from the length of the shadow, the date and the tables.

On account of the limitations imposed by the imperfect nautical instruments in use at that time all the measurements were necessarily more or less wrong. Thus the gnomon did not allow the length of the shadows to be determined to a sufficient degree of accuracy. Its adjustment was faulty and difficult on ships. How could it be precisely set at sea? It was probably only in later times set parallel to the earth's axis. But even that could be done only with difficulty on ships. The clepsydra (see p. 226) was likewise an instrument that would work with little accuracy on the high seas. Whether the speed of the ship and the drift were taken adequately into account when soundings were in progress appears doubtful. The contrivance given by Vitruvius (Book X, 9) for measuring the speed of ships, which depends on the number of revolutions of a partly immersed paddle-wheel, is probably to be regarded rather as an ingenious toy than as serving a useful purpose for shipping. Vitruvius does not take into account that the construction of taximeters and hodometers for land use has to be modified under sea-conditions, where disturbing factors such as the impact of the waves against the paddles, the swell of the sea, drift effects and so forth comes into action. Nevertheless it cannot be denied that the ancient peoples, in spite of their faulty methods and instruments, achieved remarkable results in finding their bearings at sea, for in most of their travels they seem finally to have reached their objective.

HARBOURS

WHEN modern seamen encounter stormy weather, they avoid the coast and steer for the open sea ; the ancients, however, regarded harbours as the only safe refuge for their ships, for even ships that were drawn up on the shore were exposed to the danger of storms and high waves. The harbours were therefore constructed with great care, special attention being given to finding a good anchorage and also as much security as possible from enemy attacks. When these advantages could not be united artificial constructions were made to serve one or other of these purposes more effectively. Preference was given to the bays which formed natural harbours. To protect the harbour from invasion it was usually included in the scheme of fortifications. Another important factor in deciding the site for a harbour was its proximity to sources of drinking-water. Merckel, who has made a special study of harbours, refers to the following peculiarities of various ancient harbours.

The Phoenicians were masters of harbour construction ; their coast-towns Sidon and Tyre both had large harbours. Sidon is situated on a triangular point of land ; long reefs and islands stretch to the north and south of it. These islands were permanently connected with the reefs by means of walls, and the whole was rendered secure by moles and fortifications. Two harbours were created in this way. Tyre was situated on an island which was connected with the mainland by means of a mole, and harbours were also made by using stretches of the curved shore-line.

Even some of the oldest Greek harbours had artificial moles consisting of double walls. The gaps between the mighty stones of these double walls were filled in with pieces of rock. There are still remains of such moles preserved which allow us to recognize that they were fortified ; for example, the harbour of Methone [1] (Figs. 670–674). The moles were often of considerable height. The mole of the harbour of Samos, constructed in the reign of Polykrates (540–523 B.C.), was no less than 117 ft. high. One mole of the harbour at Rhodes was 1,500 ft. long.

The harbours of the Romans were also excellently equipped. Among them the harbour of Rome, situated on the mouth of the Tiber at Ostia, assumed great importance. Originally the coast itself formed a landing-place ; the ships anchored anywhere indiscriminately along the coast until in the course of time a portion was marked off by two columns. Increasing trade and the occurrence of many shipwrecks at the unprotected landing-beach called for the construction of a harbour ; this harbour was enlarged by degrees until finally the Emperor Trajan (about

[1] The modern Modon.—*Trans.*

A.D. 53–117) extended it on a gigantic scale and made a model harbour of it (Fig. 675). The inner harbour of Ostia was hexagonal in form; its water-surface amounted to about 60 acres, its depth was 20 ft.; the wharves stretched along a front of nearly $1\frac{1}{4}$ miles. To make this harbour over 80 million cubic ft. of earth had to be removed, and about 20 million cubic ft. of masonry had to be erected—a stupendous task. The sheds used extended over a length of almost a mile. The harbour was splendidly equipped also in other ways, such as by works of art and triumphal arches.

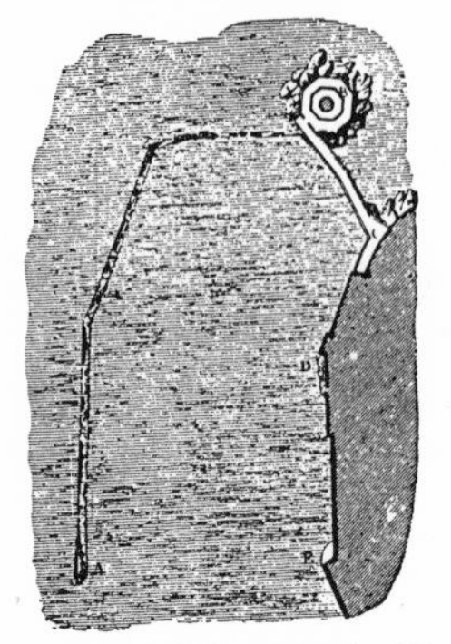

FIG. 670.—Plan of the Harbour of Methone

AB, Ancient Greek mole; B, fort (of recent origin); C, town-gate; D, remains of an ancient Greek wall fortification

FIG. 671.—The ancient Greek mole of Methone, seen from the end of the mole A (in Fig. 670), and view of the fort B indicated in Fig. 670 (in the middle at the back) and the town (on the right). In the town-wall (directly above the highest point of the boat in the picture) we see remains of the old fort-wall (D in Fig. 670 and Fig. 674)

FIG. 672.—The Head of the Greek Mole of Methone

FIG. 673.—The Head of the Mole of Methone seen from above. The surrounding wall is filled in with pieces of rock

FIG. 674.—Remains of the ancient Greek Fort-wall of Methone (D in Fig. 670)

No less a task was the construction of the naval port at Cape Misenum, which, indeed, under Nero (A.D. 54–68), was to have been connected by a canal with Rome—an intention, however, which was never carried out. On the other hand, a mighty reservoir (233 by 86 ft.) was built above this harbour, from which the fleet could obtain its water-supply; this was the *piscina mirabilis* (see Fig. 586), which was hewn out of the hill-

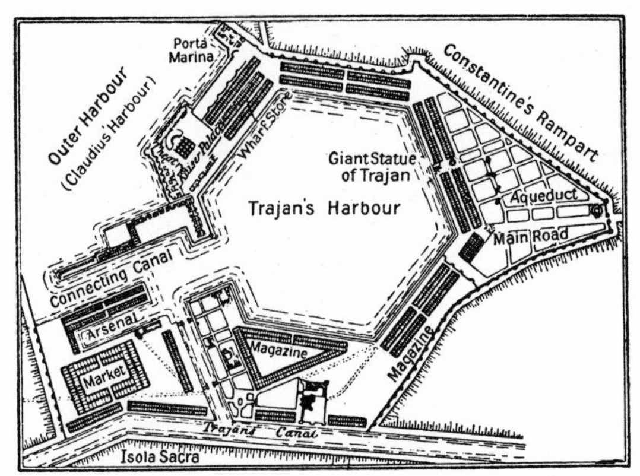

FIG. 675.—Plan of Trajan's Harbour at Ostia

side and still exists in an excellent state of preservation. It has a vaulted roof borne by 48 massive pillars. Besides this marvellous construction the war-harbour at Cape Misenum has an immense mole, some blocks of

FIG. 676.—The Nike of Samothrace standing on the prow of a ship
This gigantic goddess of victory was erected about 300 B.C. by Demetrios Poliorketes to celebrate a victory at sea

which, made from the local tufa, reach a height of 27 ft. The mole was 2,700 ft. long.

To carry out these constructions in water effectively it was necessary to have water-proof mortars. These mortars were not, however, always applied. Sometimes the blocks were merely piled one above another; in other cases, as at Cape Misenum, a form of hydraulic cement made from pozzolana, sands and small stones was used. Further, a water-tight mortar was produced from pure lime and oil. A sort of coffer-dam was also known for working in water. It was made by erecting walls that enclosed a rectangular space. The water was then removed from this space, and was replaced by stones or masonry. The foundations of some moles were made by throwing an immense number of stones and great quantities of rubble into the sea until a solid bank was formed on which the mole proper could be erected. In many cases rivulets with steep gradients were deflected into the harbours to clear them of rubbish by washing it out to sea. The entrance to the harbour was made as narrow as possible so as to facilitate its defence. Entrances 323 ft. wide, such as that of the war-harbour of Zea at Athens (Fig. 355, p. 271), were rare. Usually the entrance was further protected by fortifications and arranged so that it could be closed by means of chains, cross-beams or gates. Well-equipped harbours such as that of Ostia were abundantly provided with cranes, windlasses and other devices for unloading.

INDEX OF AUTHORITIES

ANCIENT AND MODERN, QUOTED OR MENTIONED IN THE TEXT

INDEX OF SUBJECTS

See also Contents, p. xi, and List of Illustrations, p. xvii